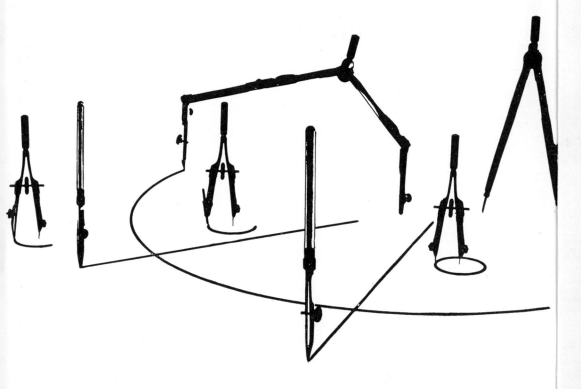

Sixth edition revised and enlarged by CARL L. SVENSEN

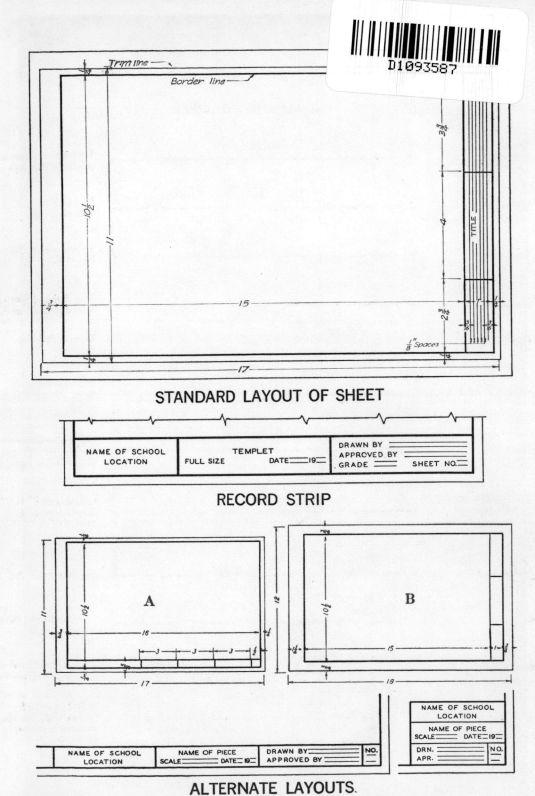

STANDARD LAYOUT OF SHEET

RECORD STRIP

NAME OF SCHOOL LOCATION	TEMPLET FULL SIZE DATE 19	DRAWN BY APPROVED BY GRADE SHEET NO.

A

B

NAME OF SCHOOL LOCATION	NAME OF PIECE SCALE DATE 19	DRAWN BY APPROVED BY	NO.

NAME OF SCHOOL LOCATION		
NAME OF PIECE		
SCALE DATE 19		
DRN. APR.		NO.

ALTERNATE LAYOUTS.

Mechanical Drawing

Mechanical Drawing

a text with problem layouts

THOMAS E. FRENCH

CARL L. SVENSEN

WEBSTER DIVISION, McGRAW-HILL BOOK COMPANY
St. Louis   New York   San Francisco   Dallas   Toronto   London

TEXT-FILMS: Listed below are six filmstrips and eight motion pictures, seven of them with follow-up filmstrips for review and discussion. These films have been produced with the assistance of the author of this text, Carl L. Svensen. The chapter with which each film is correlated is indicated after the film title. These motion pictures and filmstrips may be purchased from the Text-Film Department of the McGraw-Hill Book Company, Inc.

The Language of Drawing (Motion picture) Correlated with Chapter 1

Scales: Flat and Triangular (Filmstrip) *Compasses and Bow Instruments* (Filmstrip) Correlated with Chapter 2

Freehand Lettering and Figures for Working Drawings (Filmstrip) Correlated with Chapter 3

Shape Description, Parts I and II (Motion picture and filmstrip) Correlated with Chapter 5

Sections (Motion picture and filmstrip) Correlated with Chapter 8

Auxiliary Views, Parts I and II (Motion picture and filmstrip) Correlated with Chapter 9

Size Description (Motion picture and filmstrip) Correlated with Chapter 10

Shop Procedure (Motion picture and filmstrip) Not directly correlated with any specific chapter, but may be used to advantage with Chapter 13

Isometric Drawing (Color filmstrip) Correlated with Chapter 14

Developments (Color filmstrip) *Intersections* (Color filmstrip) Correlated with Chapter 20

MECHANICAL DRAWING

Library of Congress Catalog Card Number: 57–6389

x

22297

Preface

This, the Sixth Edition of *Mechanical Drawing* is extensively revised and completely rewritten. The author has made many changes that should help both the instructor and the student. It contains much new material including new chapters on "Reading and Making Drawings" and "Electrical Drafting." The chapter on "Architectural Drawing" treats the subject more completely than that in the Fifth Edition and contains excellent examples of contemporary houses. The introductory chapter is entirely new and well illustrated; it gives the student an over-all graphic view of mechanical drawing and its uses.

There are nearly a thousand illustrations in the volume. Many old ones have been replaced, and about two hundred are new. Other new features are a "Glossary of Shop Terms," a selected "Bibliography," six new tables in the Appendix, and a "Correlated List of Visual Aids."

At the ends of Chaps. 2 to 23 instructors and students will find graded lists for the selection of the problems in Chap. 24. These are suggestions which will help the teacher organize his course and assign problems according to the individual student's ability. About 135 of the 536 problems in Chap. 24 are new.

This edition conforms with the best standards of readability. The text has been checked for difficult passages. Paragraphs and sentences have been shortened and simplified where possible. New words are usually defined when they are first used. In this book the student is offered the opportunity to acquire a basic vocabulary in mechanical drawing.

The illustrations of the Sixth Edition are larger and easier to read and understand than those of earlier editions. The use of the new double-column format makes possible a closer placement of the illustrations to their text references.

Eight sound movies with seven follow-up filmstrips, and six separate filmstrips help to make this book a more effective teaching tool. These films, available from the McGraw-Hill Text-Film Department, are correlated with the text. Teachers desiring to use separate problem books are referred to *Problems in Mechanical Drawing, First Course* and *Second Course* by Levens and Edstrom.

The authors wrote the first edition of *Mechanical Drawing* to help students learn to visualize in three dimensions, to develop and strengthen their technical imagination, to think precisely, to read and write the language of the industries, and to gain experience in making working drawings according to modern commercial practice. These continue to be the objectives of the Sixth Edition.

All the above changes and additions conform with present industrial practice and the best teaching methods of today's progressive instructors. Since teachers suggested the improvements, this edition reflects more than ever the benefit of actual use.

Acknowledgment is given to the authors' friends, the teachers, for their professional assistance. Their advice has made it possible for the author to continue to meet their needs and those of their students. Appreciation is here expressed to all who have contributed in any way to this or previous editions. In connection with the Sixth Edition, the author is especially grateful for the active interest and valuable assistance of the following persons: Frank C. Panuska, David B. Krutzel, Russell G. Helms, Myer S. Markowitz, Herbert W. Yankee, B. Leighton Wellman, Ralph S. Paffenbarger, Thomas L. Moore, Val H. Aurit, Marlene Clifford, and W. E. Street.

As in the past, teachers' comments and suggestions will always be welcome and appreciated.

CARL L. SVENSEN

Contents

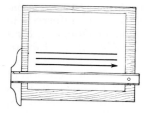

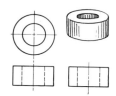

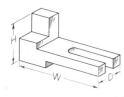

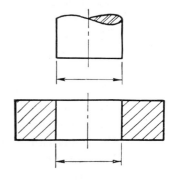

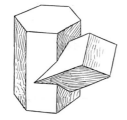

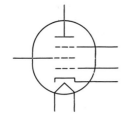

The motion picture *The Language of Drawing* has been prepared to correlate with this chapter.

1 The language of drawing

1·1 The language of industry. By putting mechanical drawings to many uses, industry functions smoothly and supplies us with the goods we need. In doing this, industry has steadily raised our standard of living (Figs. 1-1, 1-2). People who grow up and work in twentieth-century America find life better and their jobs easier because of mechanical drawing.

The machines that make our automobiles (Fig. 1-3) start out as mechanical sketches on an engineer's pad of sketch paper. The automobiles, too, are drawn up first in the manufacturers' drafting rooms. These drawings tell the people in the factories how to produce the cars. Jet airplanes, television sets,

Fig. 1-1 An American jet transport, the Boeing 707. Aircraft designers and draftsmen drew the plans for this plane long before it was manufactured. (*Boeing Airplane Company*)

Fig. 1-2 The Santa Fe Railway Super Chief train has many thousand different parts. For every part a drawing is made. It would be almost impossible to build the train without these drawings.

motorboats, telephones, refrigerators, and many other things that we use every day originate on the drafting board. Machines provide us with food and clothing—machines that inventors or engineers first describe in mechanical drawings. Civil engineers design our highways, bridges, tunnels, and airports. Electronic engineers design our radio and television sets. Architects draw plans for the buildings where we work, for our schools, and for our homes. Mechanical drawing plays a part in the life of everyone.

1·2 A pictorial language. Even in ancient times, men drew pictures to show others what they had in mind. Only drawings give the directions that are easy for builders to follow.

Some of the earliest builders made crude sketches on clay tablets that still exist. It is probable that they also made detailed plans of their buildings on parchment or papyrus, but we have not found any fragments of such drawings. The people of Mesopotamia used drafting materials as early as 2200 B.C. A statue of one of their kings, Gudea (Fig. 1-4), shows him with a drawing of a building on his lap.

Ancient Egyptian stone masons made plans for the pyramids and other buildings on papyrus, slabs of limestone (Fig. 1-5), and sometimes wood. They may have used large wooden T-squares, 8 or 10 ft long, to draw the lines on the ground for the first layer of big stone blocks. Sailors of ancient Greece and Rome made rough maps of the world

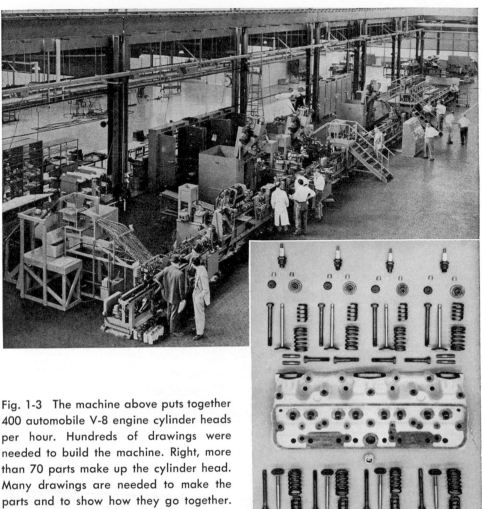

Fig. 1-3 The machine above puts together 400 automobile V-8 engine cylinder heads per hour. Hundreds of drawings were needed to build the machine. Right, more than 70 parts make up the cylinder head. Many drawings are needed to make the parts and to show how they go together. (*Oldsmobile Division, General Motors Corporation*)

they knew. Perhaps the Romans made the best mechanical drawings of ancient times when they drew pictures and plans for their buildings, aqueducts (Fig. 1-6), and forts.

For centuries men struggled with the problem of drawing solid objects on flat surfaces. It was difficult to show accurately the dimensions of length, width, and height on drawings of two dimensions. Progress was slow until Leonardo da Vinci, an Italian genius of the fifteenth century (1452–1519), made a study of drawing and painting. His sketches were easy to understand (Figs. 1-7, 1-8), and for several years he taught others his methods. After his death other Europeans continued da Vinci's studies, but his teachings were not published until 1651. Among these scholars were mathematicians who explored dif-

(*Text continued on page 6.*)

THE LANGUAGE OF DRAWING   3

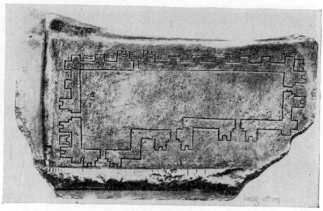

Fig. 1-4 Gudea, left, and the drawing on his lap, above. (*From Ernest de Sarzec, Découvertes en Chaldee, 1891*)

Fig. 1-5 Below, the plan on limestone of the tomb of an Egyptian king. (*From Clark and Engelbach, Ancient Egyptian Masonry*)

Fig. 1-6 Engineers of ancient Rome knew the importance of making drawings. The Pont du Gard, near Nîmes, France, is a good example of the aqueducts they built. (*From T. Schreiber, Atlas of Classical Antiquities, 1895*)

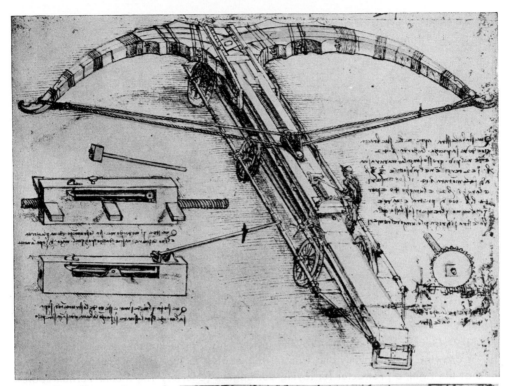

Fig. 1-7 Above, Leonardo da Vinci's sketch of a giant crossbow. Notice the two suggestions showing the tripping action of the crossbow. Da Vinci often wrote his comments from right to left as a mirror image of ordinary writing. In this way he kept many of his ideas as private as possible. (*Courtesy Lieb Museum*)

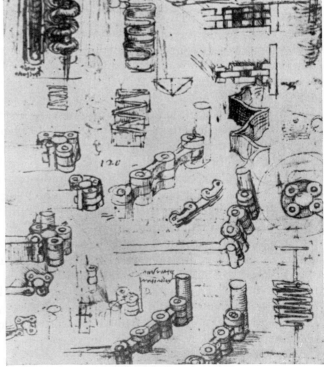

Fig. 1-8 Right, Leonardo da Vinci's sketch of a sprocket chain. Notice the many different views. (*Courtesy Lieb Museum*)

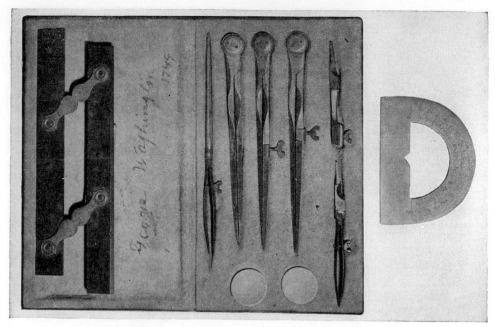

Fig. 1-9 George Washington's drawing instruments. At the left are parallel rulers, useful in drawing parallel lines and transferring angles; in the middle, dividers and pens; and at the right, a protractor for laying out angles. (*Courtesy The Mount Vernon Ladies' Association, Mount Vernon, Virginia*)

ferent ways to show exact measurements on their drawings. Gradually they found how to draw more accurate pictures of the things they wanted to make. Gaspard Monge (1746–1818), a Frenchman of Napoleon's time, discovered the principles from which the system we use today has been developed. For some time his methods were considered a military secret.

Americans can take pride in the wide use they make of this pictorial language and in the advances they contribute to the art. George Washington and his officers used drawing instruments (Fig. 1-9). In Figs. 1-10 and 1-11, we can see the plans that Thomas Jefferson made for Monticello, his beautiful home in Virginia. At the United States Military Academy, where every cadet learns to

express his ideas of roads, bridges, machines, buildings, military operations, and so on in a pictorial way, another French scholar, Claude Crozet, taught Monge's projection methods of drawing for the first time in this country. American teachers and engineers added to Crozet's work and further developed this pictorial language. West Point graduates, among whom were the first trained engineers of our country, have often contributed to our technical progress. They have drawn pictures and plans for some of our railroads, bridges, public buildings, lighthouses (Fig. 1-12), canals, and atomic energy plants.

We usually find it difficult, and in most cases impossible, to describe in words the appearance of the things we

(*Text continued on page 10.*)

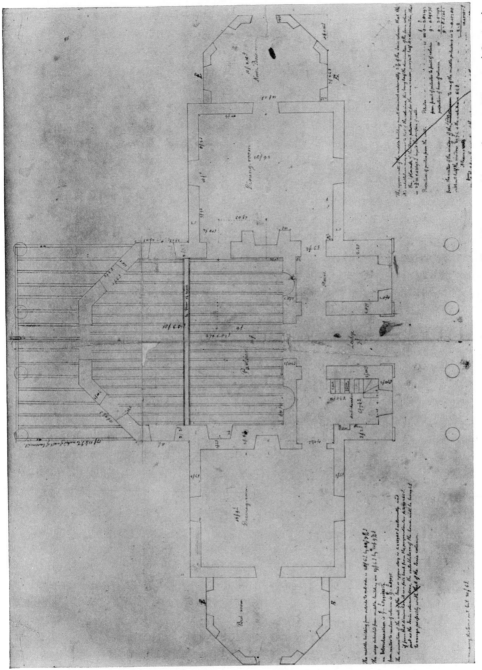

Fig. 1-10   Thomas Jefferson's plan for the first story of his home, Monticello. (Courtesy *Massachusetts Historical Society*)

Fig. 1-11 An early drawing for Monticello by Thomas Jefferson. (Courtesy Massachusetts *Historical Society*)

Fig. 1-12 Minot's Ledge lighthouse in Boston Bay was designed by West Point graduates. (*Courtesy U.S. Military Academy*)

Fig. 1-13 An X HR$_2$S (Sikorsky S-56) transport helicopter of the U.S. Marine Corps. This photograph shows only the outside details.

Fig. 1-14 A perspective drawing of a bridge. Notice how it gives the effect of distance.

want to make or build. Since words fail to give a complete or accurate description, we use pictorial sketches, drawings, diagrams, and photographs. Today there is hardly a newspaper, magazine, catalogue, or book without them.

1·3 A precise language. Photographs (Fig. 1-13) are often used today to show what an object looks like. We also use perspective drawings (Fig. 1-14) to show an object as it appears to our eyes. However, such drawings and photographs do not show the exact shape and size of all the details of an object. A photograph or a perspective drawing does not show the inside parts or the exact way in which the pieces fit together. We need another kind of drawing to show this information.

Mechanical drawings that are known as *projection drawings* give exact details with accurate measurements. They provide the builder or manufacturer with the exact description that he needs to build what the designer has in mind (Fig. 1-15). Projection drawings are more widely used than any other type of drawing. To make such a drawing (Fig. 1-16), we view and draw an object from different sides. We draw its shape and the outline of its parts. We use different types of lines according to definite rules. We make the lines exact lengths (or proportional lengths), and we add measurements to show their true lengths. In this way we project each view of the object onto our drawing paper.

We study mechanical drawing and the rules of projection drawing so that we can not only make accurate mechanical drawings of our own but also

Fig. 1-15 To inspect this casting, the inspector checks its measurements with the dimensions called for on the drawing. If the drawing is not well done and easy to read, many costly errors will be made.

understand the mechanical drawings of others. In Chaps. 2 through 10 of this book are most of the rules for the precise language of mechanical drawing. By applying these rules and making good projection drawings, we can show other people exactly what we want to make or build.

1·4 A universal language. Because a projection drawing gives a precise picture of the article to be made, it means the same thing to everyone. Drawings that are made correctly can be used not only in this country, but also with few changes in countries where people speak a different language. In this country many different workmen read and use the same drawing.

By following carefully the rules of projection drawing, different kinds of industry have developed special sym-

bols that are useful in their daily work. Chapters 11 through 23 of this book tell how to make the drawings for machinists, aircraft workers, sheet-metal workers, electricians, electronics technicians, carpenters, and other workmen.

Since mechanical drawing is the language of industry, there is often a demand for draftsmen who can make good projection drawings. Manufacturers and builders need good draftsmen to make the drawings for their workmen.

Learning mechanical drawing is much more than simply learning to draw. It is learning to use a new and useful language. This precise, universal language is important to anyone who expects to work in the manufacturing or construction industry or who wishes to become a professional engineer. In many lines of work, we may be more

THE LANGUAGE OF DRAWING **11**

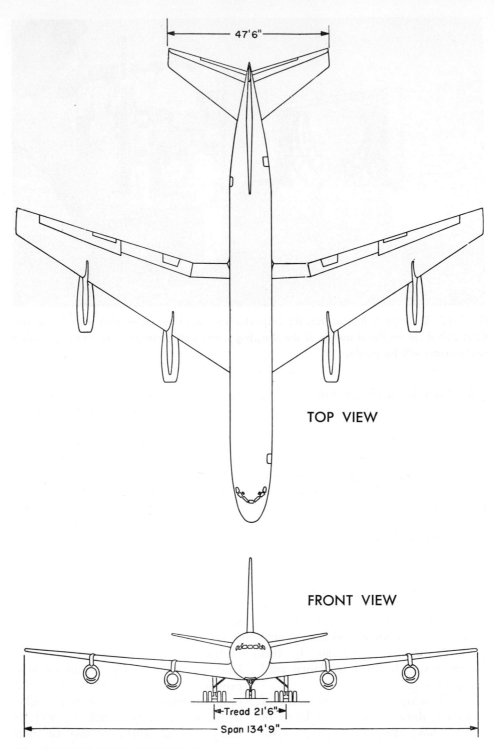

47'6"

TOP VIEW

FRONT VIEW

Tread 21'6"

Span 134'9"

12 MECHANICAL DRAWING

valuable employees if we can make good drawings. But it is even more important that we be able to read drawings. A drawing is made once but may be read many times, since many more people have to read drawings than make them. The best way to learn to read them is to learn to make them.

Fig. 1-16 On page 12 and below are the views of a simple projection drawing. Notice the difference between these views and the photograph above. The front, top, and side views of this jet transport show accurately its outline and over-all dimensions. (*Douglas Aircraft Company, Inc.*)

DC-8 Dimensions

SIDE VIEW

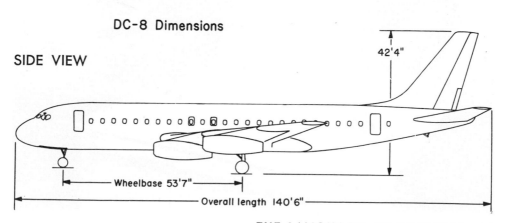

42'4"

Wheelbase 53'7"

Overall length 140'6"

Fig. 1-17 Drawings are put to many uses. This scale model of a factory is built over a plan for the building and grounds. (*Factory Management and Maintenance*)

Fig. 1-18 Drafting machines of various kinds are often used in industry. The operator of this machine has made a map by tracing an aerial photograph. (*Wild Heerbrugg Instruments, Inc.*)

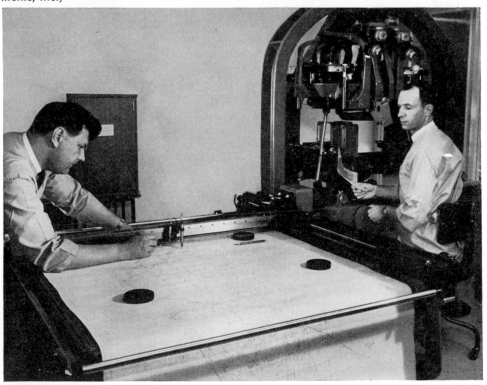

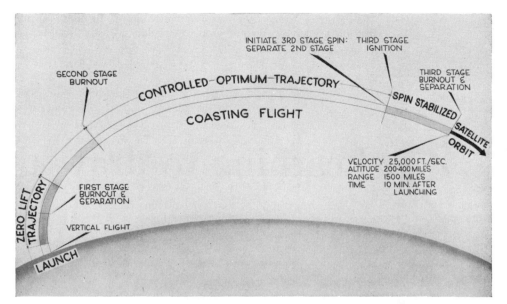

INITIATE 3RD STAGE SPIN: THIRD STAGE
SEPARATE 2ND STAGE   IGNITION

SECOND STAGE
BURNOUT

CONTROLLED—OPTIMUM—TRAJECTORY

THIRD STAGE
BURNOUT &
SEPARATION

COASTING FLIGHT

SPIN STABILIZED

SATELLITE

ORBIT

ZERO LIFT TRAJECTORY

FIRST STAGE
BURNOUT &
SEPARATION

VELOCITY 25,000 FT./SEC.
ALTITUDE 200-400 MILES
RANGE   1500 MILES
TIME   10 MIN. AFTER
          LAUNCHING

VERTICAL FLIGHT

LAUNCH

Fig. 1-19 Above, drafts-
men sometimes work on
advanced scientific developments. A commercial
draftsman made this draw-
ing. It is the flight path
planned for a rocket de-
signed to launch a man-
made satellite.

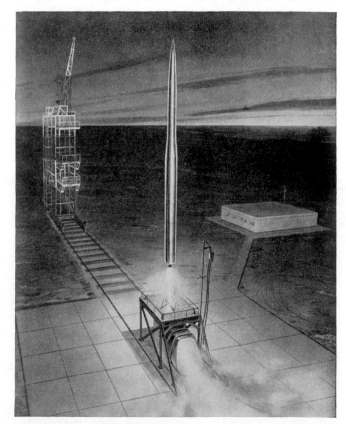

Fig. 1-20 Right, an art-
ist's idea of the launch-
ing of a satellite-carrying
rocket.

THE LANGUAGE OF DRAWING **15**

The filmstrips *Scales: Flat and Triangular* and *Compasses and Bow Instruments* have been prepared to correlate with this chapter.

2 Learning to draw

2·1 The drafting room. Engineering work of all kinds starts in the drafting room (Fig. 2-1). Here the designs are worked out and the necessary drawings are made and checked. Chapter 1 explained why drawing is really a language and why drawing is used in all industrial work. Sometimes designers or engineers first make freehand sketches; but for engineering work where accuracy is necessary, drawings are made with instruments. In learning to read and write this language, we must learn what tools and instruments to use and how to use them skillfully, accurately, and quickly.

Fig. 2-1 Partial view of the engineering department of Chance Vought Aircraft, Inc., Dallas, Texas.

2·2 Attaching the paper. Mechanical drawings are made on a wide variety of papers, either white or tinted (cream or pale green, and so forth). In many drafting rooms, drawings are made directly in pencil on high-grade paper known as *vellum* or on tracing paper or tracing cloth that will allow light to pass through. When paper or tracing cloth of this type is used, copies can be made by blueprinting or other methods (Arts. 11·13 to 11·15). On a soft pine drawing board, the paper may be held in place by drafting tape, thumbtacks, or staples. On a composition or other hard-surfaced board, drafting tape is used.

To fasten the paper (Fig. 2-2), place it on the drawing board with the left edge an inch or so away from the left edge of the board. Left-handed students will work from the right edge. The lower edge of the paper should be placed about four inches up from the bottom of the board, or as much more as will provide a comfortable working position. Then line up the paper with the T-square blade as shown in Space 1. Holding the paper in position, move the T-square down as in Space 2, keeping the head of the T-square against the edge of the board. Then fasten each corner with drafting tape (Space 2), staples, or thumbtacks. If you use thumbtacks, be sure to push them in until the heads are in contact with the paper. Sheets of drawing paper not larger than 12″ × 18″ may be held in place by fastening the two upper corners.

2·3 American Standard trimmed sizes of drawing paper. Two series of sizes are commonly used. One is based upon the 8½″ × 11″ size letter paper. Multi-

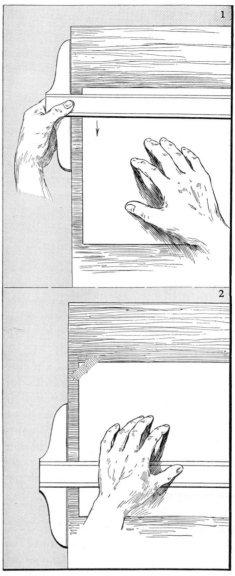

Fig. 2-2 Adjusting and fastening the paper.

ples of this size give standard dimensions as follows: A, 8½″ × 11″; B, 11″ × 17″; C, 17″ × 22″; D, 22″ × 34″; E, 34″ × 44″. Another series is based upon a sheet 9″ × 12″ and multiples of this size as: 9″ × 12″; 12″ × 18″; 18″ × 24″; 24″ × 36″; 36″ × 48″.

2·4 Drawing pencils are made with uniformly graded leads, designated by degrees as follows:

6B (softest and blackest)	H (medium hard)
	2H (hard)
5B (extremely soft)	3H (hard, plus)
4B (extra soft)	4H (very hard)
3B (very soft)	5H (extra hard)
2B (soft, plus)	6H (extra hard, plus)
B (soft)	
HB (medium soft)	7H (extremely hard)
F (intermediate between soft and hard)	8H (extremely hard, plus)
	9H (hardest)

The right grade to use will depend upon the surface of the paper and the kind of line required for blackness and width. For laying out the views on fairly hard-surfaced drawing paper, the usual grades of pencil are 4H, 5H, or 6H. For finished views or for drawing on tracing paper or tracing cloth for reproduction, the H or 2H pencil is much used. Softer pencils are used for sketching, lettering, arrowheads, surface-treatment symbols, figures, border lines, and so forth (HB, F, H, 2H), according to the result desired on the paper being used.

2·5 Sharpening the pencil (Fig. 2-3). Sharpen the pencil by cutting away the wood, *on the plain end*, at a long slope. Be careful not to cut the lead, but expose it for about one-fourth inch or more as at A in Space 1. Mechanical sharpeners (which give points as shown at B in Space 1) with a draftsman's special cutter are in quite general use. After the wood has been cut away, shape the lead to a long conical point by rubbing it back and forth on a sandpaper pad as at C in Space 2 or

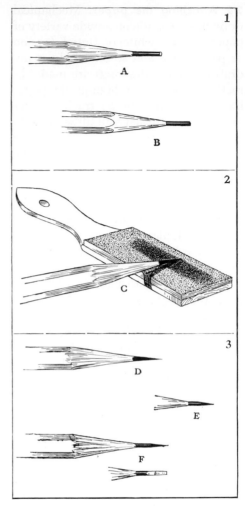

Fig. 2-3 Sharpening the pencil.

on a fine file, rotating it slowly in the fingers to form the point (Space 3 at D and E). Keep the sandpaper pad or file at hand so that the point can be kept sharp by frequent rubbing. Some draftsmen prefer a flat or chisel point (Space 3 at F), especially for drawings with a large number of long straight lines.

Pencil lines must be both clean and clear, and dark enough to bring out the views. You can avoid using too much pressure and grooving the paper if you use the proper grade of lead. Develop the habit of rotating the pencil between the thumb and forefinger as the line is being drawn. This will help you keep a uniform line and will keep the point from wearing down unevenly. Mechanical pencils with threaded or slip chucks for desired grades of leads are also widely used by draftsmen. The leads must be shaped to the desired points in the usual manner with a file or sandpaper pad.

Never sharpen a pencil over the drawing board. Wipe the lead with a cloth to remove the fine dust from the point. Care in such matters will do much to keep drawings clean and bright.

2·6 Erasers and erasing shields. Soft rubber, pink pearl rubber, or artgum is used for cleaning soiled places or light pencil marks from drawings. Ruby or emerald pencil erasers are best for most purposes for removing either pencil or ink marks. Ink erasers contain a grit and have to be used with extreme care, if used at all, to avoid injuring the surface of the paper or cloth. Electric erasing machines are in common use in engineering offices.

Metal or plastic erasing shields have openings of various sizes and shapes and are convenient for protecting lines which are not to be erased.

2·7 Horizontal lines (Fig. 2-4, Space 1) are drawn with the upper edge of the T-square blade as a guide. Hold the head of the T-square against the left edge of the board with the left hand[1] and move it to the desired position.

[1] Left-handed persons reverse this rule by placing the head of the T-square against the right edge of the board.

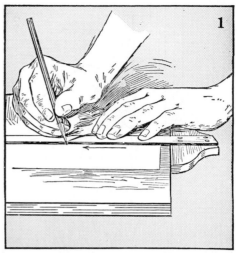

Fig. 2-4 Space 1. Drawing horizonal lines.

The pencil should be held about an inch from the point and inclined slightly in the direction in which the line is being drawn. A plane through the pencil lead and the line being drawn should make a right angle (or slightly more) with the surface of the guide. This will keep the point of the lead away from the corner between the guiding edge and the paper so that the draftsman can see where the line is being drawn. Care must be taken to keep the line parallel to the guiding edge.

2·8 Vertical lines (Fig. 2-4, Space 2) are drawn by a triangle in combination with the T-square. Hold the head of the T-square against the left edge of the board and move it to a position below the start of the vertical line. Then place a triangle against the T-square blade and slide it along to the desired position. Always keep the vertical edge of the triangle toward the left[2] and

[2] Left-handed persons reverse this rule by keeping the vertical edge of the triangle toward the right, and the head of the T-square against the right edge of the board.

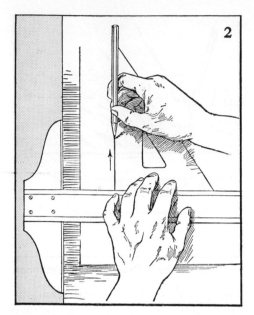

Fig. 2-4 Space 2. Drawing vertical lines.

draw upward. Incline the pencil in the direction in which the line is being drawn and keep the point from the corner between the guiding edge and the paper.

2·9 Inclined lines. The 45° triangle (Fig. 2-5) has two angles of 45° and one of 90°. Slanted or inclined lines at 45° are drawn with the triangle, held against the T-square blade, as shown for three positions at A, B, and C. Note that the lines drawn at A and B are at right angles to each other and so are the two lines drawn at C.

The 30°–60° triangle (Fig. 2-6) has angles of 30°, 60°, and 90°. Inclined lines of 30° and 60° are drawn with the triangle held against the T-square blade. Several positions are shown in Figs. 2-6 and 2-7. Note that lines drawn with the triangles in the first and last positions in Fig. 2-6 are at right angles to each other as are the lines drawn

with the triangles in the second and third positions. Also, lines drawn with the triangle in positions A or B of Fig. 2-7 are at right angles to each other. When both positions of the triangle in Fig. 2-7 are used, lines may be drawn at 30° with each other as at C.

2·10 Inclined lines at angles varying by 15° may be drawn by using the 45° and the 30°–60° triangles in combination with the T-square. The methods of obtaining different angles are shown in Fig. 2-8. In Space 15 the lines have been drawn for all the positions, and all the angles are 15°. By using the arrangements of Spaces 2 and 13, or Spaces 6 and 9, two angles of 30° and two angles of 150° may be obtained. Try different combinations of triangles until you are familiar with the various arrangements.

2·11 Parallel lines. Parallel horizontal lines can be drawn with the T-square, whereas parallel vertical lines can be drawn by using a triangle in combination with the T-square. Parallel lines at regular angles may be drawn with the triangles as suggested in Fig. 2-8. Parallel lines in any position may be drawn by using a triangle in combination with the T-square (or another triangle) as shown in the steps of Fig. 2-9, or they may be drawn directly with a drafting machine (Fig. 2-12).

2·12 To draw a line parallel to a given line (Fig. 2-9, Space 1). Place a triangle against the T-square blade (Fig. 2-9, Space 2) and move them together until one edge of the triangle matches the given line (Space 3). Holding the T-square firmly, slide the triangle along

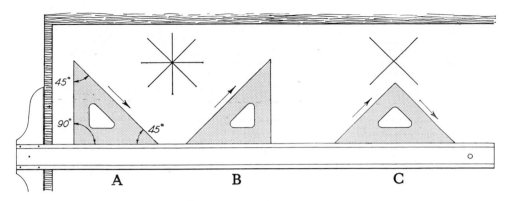

Fig. 2-5 The 45° triangle.

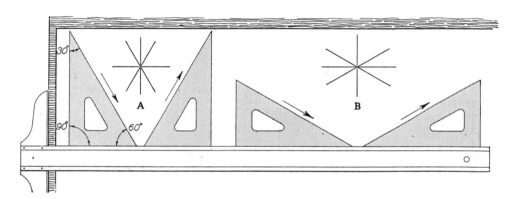

Fig. 2-6 The 30°–60° triangle.

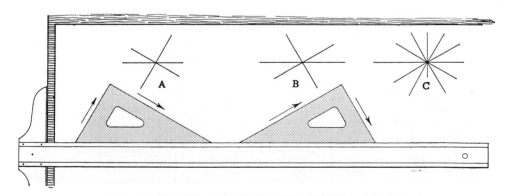

Fig. 2-7 The 30°–60° triangle.

Fig. 2-8 Drawing lines with the T-square and triangles.

the blade until the desired position is reached. Then draw the parallel line (Space 4). In Fig. 2-9 the hypotenuse of the 45° triangle is used to draw the parallel line, but other edges or the 30°–60° triangle may be used.

2·13 Perpendicular lines may be drawn in many positions with triangles as suggested in Fig. 2-8. For example, the following combined positions may be drawn: Spaces 2 and 9; Spaces 3 and 10; Spaces 4 and 11; Spaces 5 and 12; Spaces 6 and 13.

Perpendicular lines in any position may be drawn using a triangle in combination with the T-square (or another triangle) as shown in the steps of Figs. 2-10 and 2-11, or they may be drawn directly with a drafting machine (Fig. 2-12).

2·14 To draw a line perpendicular to a given line (Fig. 2-10, Space 1). Place a triangle with one edge against the T-square blade (or another triangle) and move them together until one edge of the triangle matches the given line (Space 2). Holding the T-square firmly, slide the triangle along the blade until the desired position is reached. Then draw the perpendicular line along the other exposed edge of the triangle (Space 3). The 30°–60° triangle is shown, but the 45° triangle may be used (Space 4).

Another method is shown in Fig. 2-11. Place a triangle against the T-square blade with the hypotenuse matching the given line (Space 2). Turn the triangle about its right-angled corner (Space 3) until it is in the position of Space 4, move to the desired position, and draw the perpendicular line.

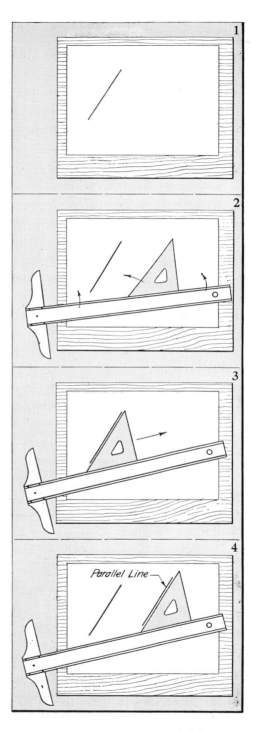

Fig. 2-9 Drawing a parallel line.

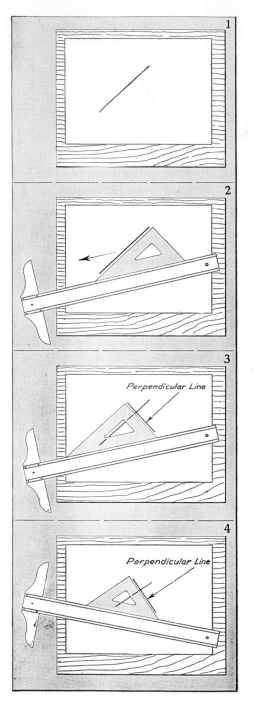

Fig. 2-10 Drawing a perpendicular line. First method.

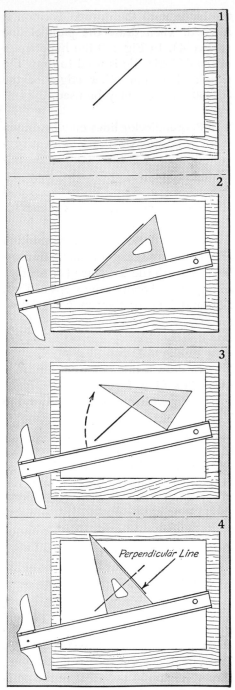

Fig. 2-11 Drawing a perpendicular line. Second method.

24 MECHANICAL DRAWING

Fig. 2-12 This drafting machine is one type used to save time. (*Universal Drafting Machine Corporation*)

2·15 Drafting machines. It is estimated that over 60 percent of the industrial drafting departments now use drafting machines. Figures 2-1 and 2-12 show drafting machines being used. Many school drafting departments teach drawing with drafting machines.

A drafting machine is a device composed of a parallel motion arm and an adjustable protractor head to which a pair of scales is attached. The scales are ordinarily at right angles. The arm allows the scales to be moved to any place on the drawing and parallel to the starting position.

Drafting machines combine the functions of the T-square, triangles, scales, and protractor. Lines can be drawn the exact lengths in the required places and at any angles by moving the scale ruling edge to the desired positions. This results in greater speed with less effort in making drawings. A complete understanding of the possibilities, efficient use, and care of the drafting machine will reveal its value.[3]

2·16 Parallel-ruling straightedges (Fig. 2-13) are used by many draftsmen, especially when the draftsmen are working on large boards and when the straightedge is to be held in a vertical or nearly vertical position. A guide cord, clamped to the ends of the straightedge, runs through a series of pulleys on the back of the board so that the straightedge may be moved up and down in parallel positions.

[3] *Drafting Machine Practice* is an inexpensive but comprehensive source of information. It is published by Universal Drafting Machine Corporation, Cleveland, Ohio.

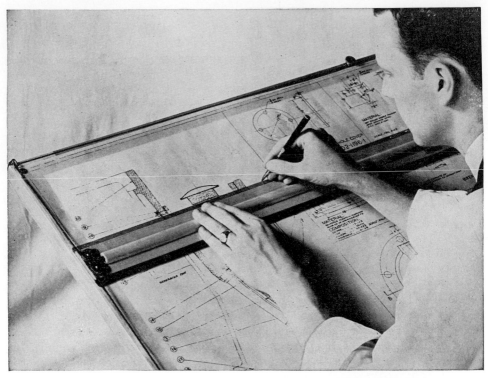

Fig. 2-13 Parallel-ruling straightedge. (*Eugene Dietzgen Company*)

2·17 Scales. All measurements of lengths or distances on a drawing are made with the *scale*. Scales are made with different divisions for different purposes. There are three commonly used scales.

2·18 The mechanical engineer's scale (Fig. 2-14) has inches and fractions of an inch divided to represent inches. The usual divisions are:

Full size, 1 in. divided to read in 32nds
Half size, $\frac{1}{2}$ in. divided to read in 16ths
Quarter size, $\frac{1}{4}$ in. divided to read in 8ths
Eighth size, $\frac{1}{8}$ in. divided to read in 4ths

These scales are used for drawing parts of machines or where larger reductions are not required.

2·19 The architect's scale (Fig. 2-15) is divided into proportional feet and inches. The usual scales are:

Full size, $12'' = 1'-0''$
$\frac{1}{4}$ size, $3'' = 1'-0''$
$\frac{1}{8}$ size, $1\frac{1}{2}'' = 1'-0''$
$\frac{1}{12}$ size, $1'' = 1'-0''$
$\frac{1}{16}$ size, $\frac{3}{4}'' = 1'-0''$
$\frac{1}{24}$ size, $\frac{1}{2}'' = 1'-0''$
$\frac{1}{32}$ size, $\frac{3}{8}'' = 1'-0''$
$\frac{1}{48}$ size, $\frac{1}{4}'' = 1'-0''$
$\frac{1}{64}$ size, $\frac{3}{16}'' = 1'-0''$
$\frac{1}{96}$ size, $\frac{1}{8}'' = 1'-0''$
$\frac{1}{128}$ size, $\frac{3}{32}'' = 1'-0''$

These scales are used in drawing buildings and in making many mechanical, electrical, and other engineering drawings. Sometimes they are also called mechanical engineer's scales.

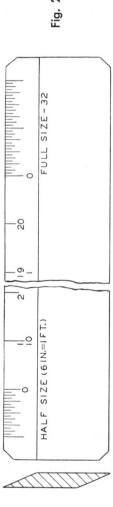

Fig. 2-14 Mechanical engineer's scale.

FULL SIZE - 32

HALF SIZE (6 IN.=1 FT.)

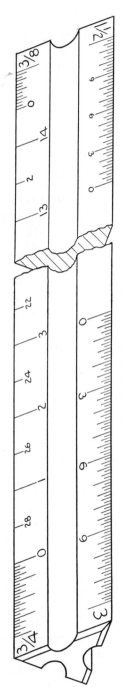

Fig. 2-15 Architect's scale.

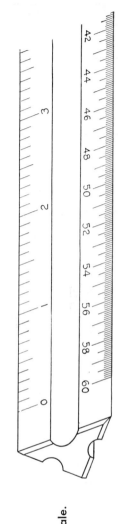

Fig. 2-16 Civil engineer's scale.

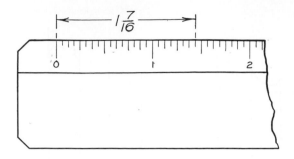

Fig. 2-17 Making a measurement ($1\frac{7}{16}$").

2·20 The civil engineer's scale (Fig. 2-16) has inches divided into decimals. The usual divisions are:

10 parts to the inch
20 parts to the inch
30 parts to the inch
40 parts to the inch
50 parts to the inch
60 parts to the inch
70 parts to the inch

With this scale one inch may be used to represent feet, rods, miles, and so forth, or to represent quantities and time or other units on graphical charts. The divisions may represent single units or multiples of 10, 100, and so forth. Thus the 20 parts to inch scale may represent 20, 200, or 2000 units. This scale is especially useful to civil engineers who design and build roads and other public works projects.

2·21 The triangular scale is used a great deal in schools and in some drafting offices because it contains a variety of scales on a single stick. Many draftsmen prefer flat scales, especially when frequent changes of scale are not required.

The symbol ′ is used for feet and ″ for inches. Thus three feet four and one-half inches is written 3′–4½″.

When all dimensions are in inches, the symbol is usually omitted.

2·22 Full-size drawings. When the object is not too large for the paper, it may be drawn full size using the inches and fractions scale. To lay off a full-size distance (Fig. 2-17), put the scale down on the paper along the line to be measured. Make a short dash on the paper opposite the zero on the scale and another short dash opposite the division representing the desired distance. Do not make a dot or punch the paper.

2·23 Drawing to scale. If the object is large or has little detail, it may be drawn in a *reduced proportion*. The first reduction is to the scale of 6″ = 1′–0″, commonly called *half size*. To measure a distance at this scale, use the full-size scale on the architect's (or other full-size) scale and consider each half inch as representing one inch, each quarter inch as representing one-half inch, and so forth. Thus the 12″ scale becomes a 24″ scale.

EXAMPLE: To lay off 3⅝″, start at zero and count three *half inches*, and five-eighths of the next half inch as shown in Fig. 2-18. Do not divide the dimensions by two but *think full size*.

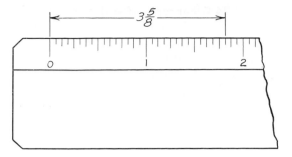

Fig. 2-18 Measuring to half size.

This will save time and avoid mistakes. If the regular mechanical engineer's scale is used (Fig. 2-14), the scale of ½″ = 1″ may be used to make direct measurements.

If smaller views are required, the next reduction that may be used is the scale of 3″ = 1′–0″, often called *quarter size*. Find this scale on the architect's scale and examine it. The actual length of three inches becomes one foot, divided into 12 parts, each representing one inch, and these are further divided into eighths. Learn to think of the 12 parts as representing real inches.

EXAMPLE: To lay off the distance of 1′–0½″ (Fig. 2-19). Notice the position of the zero mark, placed so that inches are measured in one direction from it and feet in the other direction as shown in the figure.

If the regular mechanical engineer's scale is used (Fig. 2-14), the scale of ¼″ = 1″ may be used.

For other reductions the scales mentioned in connection with Figs. 2-14 and 2-15 are used.

For small parts, enlarged scales may be used, such as 24″ = 1′–0″ for double-size views. Very small parts may be drawn four or eight times size or for some purposes 10, 20, or more times full size.

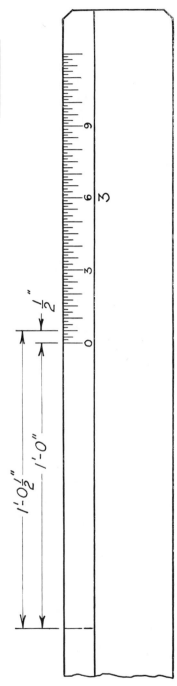

Fig. 2-19 Reading the scale.

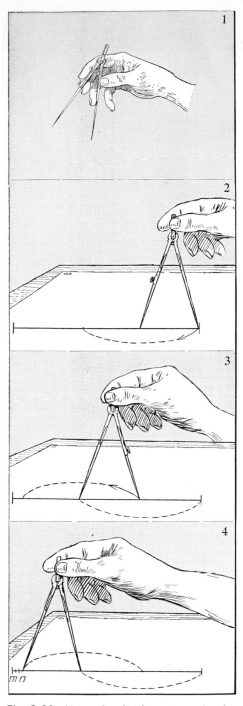

Fig. 2-20 Using the dividers. Once the distance is set, take care not to change it.

2·24 Other types of scales are made for decimal dimensioning in inches with inches divided into fiftieths to be read in hundredths. For the metric systems there are scales with centimeter and millimeter divisions.[4] Still another type of scale is the flat scale. Flat scales are made with the graduations for all scales of the triangular scale. They are also made for $4'' = 1'-0''$ and $2'' = 1'-0''$, but these are seldom used.

2·25 Scale indication. The scale to which the views are made should be given on the drawing, either in the title or, if several parts are drawn to different scales, near the views.

EXAMPLES

Mechanical Engineer's Scale
Full Size or $1'' = 1''$
Half Size or $\frac{1}{2}'' = 1''$
Architect's Scale
$6'' = 1'-0''$
$3'' = 1'-0''$
$1\frac{1}{2}'' = 1'-0''$
Civil Engineer's Scale
$1'' = 100$ feet
$1'' = 200$ miles

For some purposes a graphic scale is placed on the map or drawing.

EXAMPLE

SCALE OF FEET

100   0   100   200

2·26 The dividers. Dividing lines and transferring distances is done with the dividers or the bow dividers. The dividers are held in the right hand and adjusted (see Space 1, Fig. 2-20).

To divide a line into three equal parts, adjust the points of the dividers

[4] Metric: 10 millimeters = 1 centimeter; 100 centimeters = 1 meter; 1 meter = 39.37 inches.

until they appear to be about one-third the length of the line and place one point on one end of the line and the other point on the line (Space 2). Turn the dividers about the point that rests on the line as in Space 3, then in the alternate direction as in Space 4. If the last point falls short of the end of the line, increase the distance between the points of the dividers by an amount estimated to be about one-third the distance *mn* and start at the beginning of the line again. Several trials may be necessary. If the last point overruns the end of the line, decrease the distance between the points by one-third the extra distance.

For four, five, or more spaces, proceed as described except that the correction will be one-fourth, one-fifth, and so forth, of the overrun or underrun. An arc or the circumference of a circle (see page 546) is divided in the same way by using the distance between the points of the dividers as a chord. The small knurled screw on one of the legs is used to regulate a hairspring to make small adjustments in the distance between the points.

2·27 To divide a line into any number of equal parts using the scale. If the length of the line is not easily divisible, the scale may be used as shown in stages in Fig. 2-21. Line *AB* is to be divided into nine equal parts. Draw a perpendicular line through one end of *AB*, as line *AC* (Space 2). Apply the scale so that nine divisions of the scale are included between point *B* and line *AC* (in this case nine half inches) and mark the divisions (Space 3). Vertical lines through the marks will divide *AB* into nine equal parts (Space 4). The geometrical method upon which Fig.

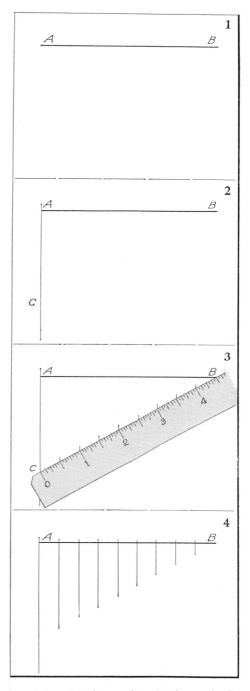

Fig. 2-21 Dividing a line (scale method).

2-21 has been based is given in Art. 4·6.

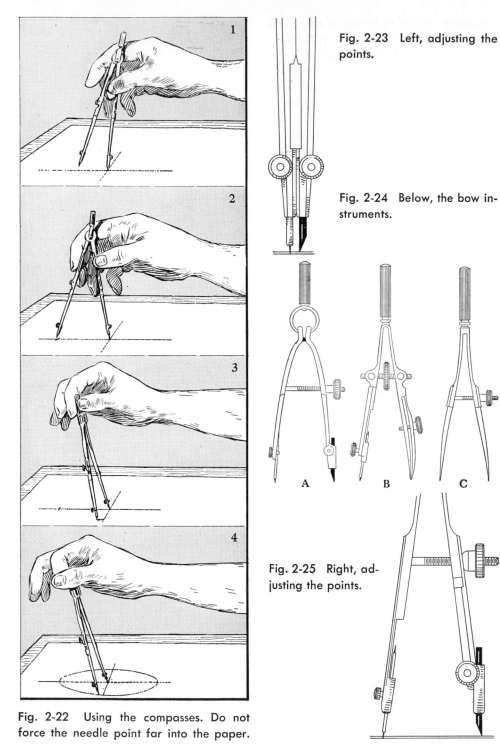

Fig. 2-23 Left, adjusting the points.

Fig. 2-24 Below, the bow instruments.

A   B   C

Fig. 2-25 Right, adjusting the points.

Fig. 2-22 Using the compasses. Do not force the needle point far into the paper.

2·28 The compasses. Views on drawings are composed of straight lines and curved lines. Most of the curved lines are circles or parts of circles (arcs). When the radius is about 1 in. or larger, the large compasses are used (Fig. 2-22). The regular compasses are about 6 in. in height. The legs may be left straight for radii under 2 in. when the pencil point is used. For radii of 2 in. or more, the legs should be adjusted perpendicular to the paper.

2·29 Using the compasses. Before circles are drawn, the lead should be sharpened as shown in Fig. 2-23. Then the shouldered end of the needle point should be adjusted until the point is just a *very little* beyond the lead point.

The compasses are used entirely with the right hand (see Fig. 2-22). They are opened by pinching them between the thumb and second finger (Space 1) and set to the proper radius by placing the needle point at the center and adjusting the pencil leg with the first and second fingers (Space 2). When the radius is set, raise the fingers to the handle (Space 3) and revolve the compasses by twirling the handle between the thumb and finger. Start the arc near the lower side and revolve clockwise (Space 4), inclining the compasses slightly in the direction of the line. Do not force the needle point way into the paper. Long radii are obtained by using a lengthening bar in the compasses to extend the pencil leg. For extra long radii, beam compasses are used (Art. 2·33). Using the compasses with the pen point for inking is described in Art. 11·6, Fig. 11-7.

2·30 A set of bow instruments (Fig. 2-24) consists of the bow pencil A, the

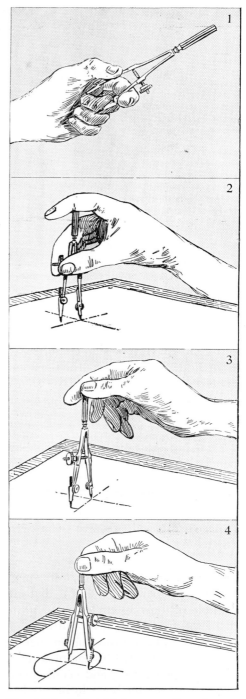

Fig. 2-26 Using the bow pencil to draw a small circle or arc.

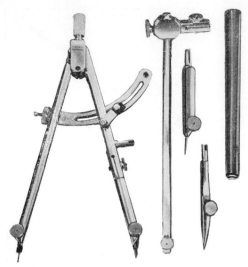

Fig. 2-27 Giant bows. (*Gramercy Import Company, Inc.*)

bow pen B, and the bow dividers C. They may be any one of the three patterns shown: ring bow A, center screw B, or side screw C. Before the bow pencil is used, the lead should be sharpened and the needle point adjusted as shown in Fig. 2-25.

2·31 Using the bow pencil. The bow pencil (Fig. 2-26) is used to draw small circles and arcs. Set the radius as in Space 2. Start the circle near the lower part of the vertical center line (Space 3) and revolve clockwise (Space 4).

2·32 Large bow instruments, 6-in. (master or giant bows, Fig. 2-27), that are capable of drawing circles up to 10 in. diameter are finding favor with draftsmen. They provide the convenience of using one instrument instead of several. Pen legs, pencil legs, and needle-point legs permit master bows to be used in place of the small bows, the regular compasses, and the dividers. Large bow instruments provide a means of

securely holding any desired radius, or the distance between the points.

2·33 Beam compasses (Fig. 2-28) are used for drawing arcs or circles with large radii. They consist of a bar (beam) upon which movable holders for a pencil part and a needle part may be positioned along the bar and fixed at any desired distance apart. The pencil part is interchangeable with a pen part. The pencil point may be replaced with a needle point in order to use the beam compasses as dividers or to set off long distances. The usual bar is about 13 in. long, but a coupling may be used to add an extra length of 7 in. to permit drawing circles up to 38 in. diameter. Longer bars may be used to provide up to 100 in. radius if needed.

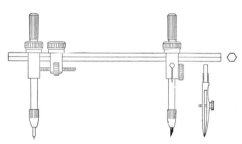

Fig. 2-28 Beam compasses.

2·34 Curves are drawn with the irregular or French curve. These are made in many different forms, a few of which are shown in Fig. 2-29. To use a curve (Fig. 2-30), fit it by trial against a part of the line to be drawn, then shift it to match the next portion, and so forth. In general, each new position should fit at least three points on the part just drawn. It is necessary to notice if the radius is increasing or decreasing and to place the curve accordingly. Do not try to draw too much of the line with one position of the curve.

Fig. 2-30 Using the irregular curve.→

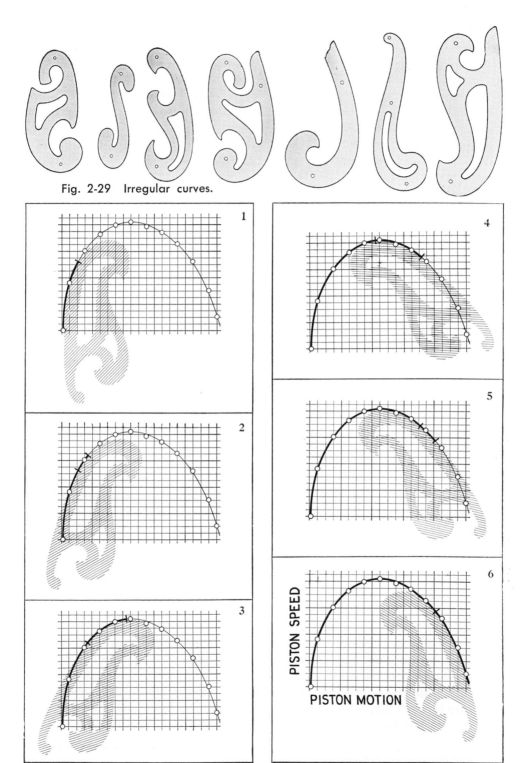

Fig. 2-29 Irregular curves.

2·35 Templates save the draftsman a great deal of time. They are made of sheet Celluloid or plastic, with openings for shapes which are often used on drawings so that the outline may be traced. Templates are made in sets for circles and other curves. Separate templates may be obtained with the usual scales for many sets of standard graphical symbols. By using them, draftsmen can draw quickly such items as boltheads, nuts, electrical symbols, architectural symbols, plumbing symbols, outlines of machine tools, and many other outlines. The use of these symbols will be discussed in later chapters.

2·36 Problem suggestions. Group A, page 361. Three lists are presented. List 1 includes basic problems that in general are more elementary than those in Lists 2 and 3. All, or a selection from List 1, may be used according to the time available and the purpose of the course. Some instructors may prefer the type of problems in Alternate List 1. Additional assignments may be made from List 2. For a more complete course with older or advanced students, selections should be made from all three lists, starting with Probs. A·1, A·4, A·5, A·6, A·10, and A·12.

LIST 1   Problems A·1, A·6, A·10, A·21
  ALTERNATE LIST 1 Problems A·13 to A·21 inclusive

LIST 2   Problems A·3, A·7, A·22, A·23

LIST 3   Problems A·4, A·8, A·9, A·12, A·24

Additional problems may be selected from Chap. 24.

AMERICAN STANDARDS

A standard is defined as a model or example which has been set by authority, custom, or general consent. Simple examples are the letters on page 37 and the tables in the Appendix. Many standards are created through the American Standards Association, which is supported entirely by private enterprise.

The American Standards Association, Incorporated, has among its members trade associations, technical societies, professional groups, and consumer organizations. Through the work of 2000 standing committees, the cooperating agencies create, develop, and revise American Standards.

The ASA provides standards that are nationally accepted and used. It avoids duplication and works over conflicting standards that have been proposed. The ASA provides standards for uniform sizes, specifications, and names used in the design, production, and marketing of many goods and services.

American Standards are widely used by industry and commerce, and by city, state, and Federal government agencies. Manufacturers use them to lower production costs, to eliminate misunderstandings, and to operate more efficiently. Consumer groups use them to measure quality. Government agencies use them as a protection to the public in buying items.

Draftsmen and engineers should know the American Standards for the industry in which they work. Over 1600 standards have been approved by the American Standards Association, Inc., 70 East 48th Street, New York 17, N.Y.

The filmstrip *Freehand Lettering and Figures for Working Drawings* has been prepared to correlate with this chapter.

3 Lettering

3·1 Lettering. The complete description of any machine or structure requires the use of the *graphical language* to describe shapes and of the written language to tell sizes, methods of making, kinds of material, and other informa-tion. The written language used on drawings is always in the form of *lettering*, not handwriting. Simple free-hand lettering, perfectly legible and quickly made, is an important part of modern engineering drawings.

Fig. 3-1 American Standard letters. (*Extracted from American Drafting Standards Manual, Y14.2-1957, with the permission of The American Society of Mechanical Engineers*)

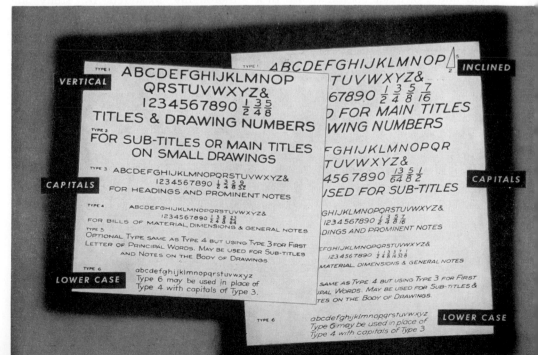

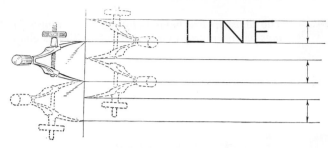

Fig. 3-2 Spacing guidelines.

3·2 Various styles of lettering, each of which is appropriate for a particular purpose, are used in display lettering and printing. The standard form of letter used on working drawings is the style known as *single-stroke commercial gothic.* It is appropriate because it is easy to read and easy to hand-letter. Lettering consists of *capital* letters and *lower case,* small, letters. There are two kinds of capital and lower-case letters, *vertical* and *inclined* (Fig. 3-1). Some companies use vertical letters exclusively; some use inclined letters exclusively; others use vertical letters for titles and inclined letters for dimensions and notes, or other combinations. In a similar way, some schools adopt vertical lettering as a standard and some adopt inclined lettering. The draftsman accepting a position with a company

must be able to use the standard of that company. In learning both styles, it is better to take up vertical lettering first. The single-stroke letters presented in this chapter are in agreement with the forms presented in the American Standard *Drawings and Drafting Room Practice.* The Standard recommends widths of strokes and heights of letters for certain purposes. For regular dimensions and notes, dimensions and capitals are made ⅛ in. high.

The ability to letter well and rapidly can be gained only by constant and careful practice. The forms and proportions of each of the letters must be thoroughly mastered by study and practice. Frequent, short practice periods lead to a mastery of the skill. The letters must then be combined into uniformly written, easily read words.

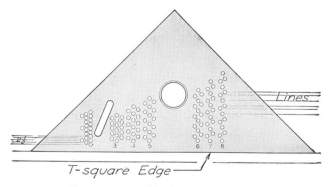

Fig. 3-3 Braddock-Rowe triangle.

3·3 Guidelines ruled lightly with a sharp pencil should always be drawn for both the top and bottom of each line of letters. The clear distance between lines of letters varies from ½ to 1½ times the height of the capitals. Figure 3-2 illustrates one method of spacing guidelines when several lines of letters are to be made. Mark the height of the letters on the first line, set the dividers to the distance you want to leave between base lines, and step off the required number of lines. With the same setting, step down again from the top point, or guideline.

The Braddock-Rowe triangle (Fig. 3-3) and the Ames lettering instrument (Fig. 3-4) are timesaving and useful devices for ruling guidelines. Lines are ruled by inserting a sharp pencil point in the holes of either of these devices and moving it back and forth guided by the T-square edge. The different spacing of groups of holes provides for different sizes of letters, either capital or lower-case. The numbers give the heights of capital letters in thirty-seconds of an inch. Thus No. 4 is ⅛ in. between the top and bottom of the group of three holes.

3·4 Lettering practice with the pencil and the pen should precede the lettering of words and sentences. Particular attention should be given to numbers and fractions because these form a very important part of every working drawing. The instructions given in Arts. 3·7 to 3·12 apply to both pencil and pen lettering.

3·5 Pencil lettering. The order of strokes and the proportions of the letters should be learned by practicing with the pencil before trying to use

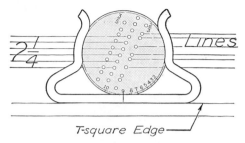

Fig. 3-4 Ames lettering instrument.

pen and ink. Since more and more commercial drafting rooms are using pencil tracings, every qualified draftsman should be able to do good pencil lettering. Use an HB, F, or H pencil that gives a firm opaque line on the paper being used. (*Opaque* means **not reflecting or passing light.** Therefore, the drawing will make good copies. See Arts. 11·13 to 11·15.) Cut away the wood and sharpen the lead to a long conical point (Fig. 3-5 at A). Learn to use an even pressure and to turn the pencil in the fingers after every few strokes to get uniform lines. Hold the pencil just firmly enough to control the strokes.

3·6 Pen lettering. The term *single stroke* means **the width of the stem of the letter is the width of the stroke of the** pen. A pen for single-stroke lettering must, therefore, make the required width of line in any direction without pressure enough to spread the two halves of the pen point (the nibs). For large letters (¼ in. high) Esterbrook's 802 and Hunt's 512, which are ball-pointed pens, are among the most desirable. For ordinary dimensions and notes, both Esterbrook's 819 and Gillott's 404 are satisfactory. (Do not use a ruling pen for lettering.) The pen should be held in the position shown in Fig. 3-5 at B. The strokes are drawn

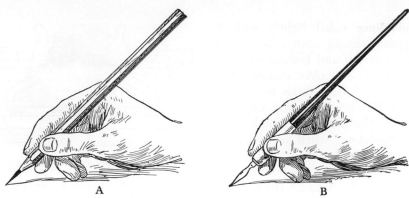

Fig. 3-5 Position of pencil and pen for lettering.

with a steady even motion of the fingers and a slight uniform pressure, not enough to spread the nibs.

3·7 Single-stroke vertical capitals. An alphabet of vertical capitals and the vertical numerals are shown in Fig. 3-6. Each letter is shown in a square so that the proportions of its width to height may be easily learned. Observe that the T, Z, X, A, O, and Q fill the square, whereas the H, L, E, N, and so forth, are narrower and the M and W are wider than their height.

In learning to letter, the first step is to study the shapes and proportions of the individual letters and the order in which the strokes are made. The arrows and numbers on the letters give the order and direction of the strokes. Vertical strokes are always made downward. Horizontal strokes are made from left to right. Some forms of the ampersand, or character to represent "and," are shown in Fig. 3-7 at B, C, and D, with the construction at A for type B.

3·8 Numerals require special attention and practice. Notice the variations from those used in ordinary figuring, especially the 2, 4, 6, and 9 (Fig. 3-6).

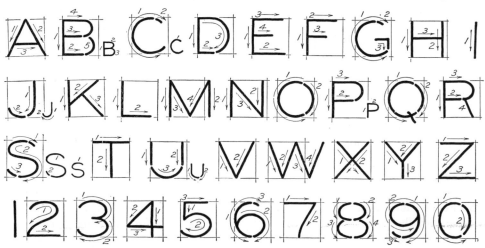

Fig. 3-6 Single-stroke vertical capitals and numerals.

40 MECHANICAL DRAWING

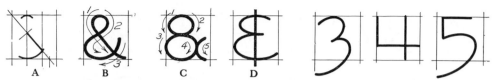

A	B	C	D

Fig. 3-7 Ampersands.

Fig. 3-8 Alternate numerals.

Other forms for the 3, 4, and 5, shown in Fig. 3-8, are used in the aircraft and other industries, as well as for government contracts.

3·9 Fractions (Fig. 3-9) are always made with a horizontal division line. Fraction numbers are about two-thirds the height of whole numbers, and a clear space is left above and below the division line.

3·11 Single-stroke inclined capitals. An alphabet of inclined capitals and numerals with the order and direction of strokes is given in Fig. 3-12. There are two things to watch: (1) Keep a uniform slope and (2) make the correct shape on the curves of the rounded letters.

Inclined direction lines should be drawn by one of the methods illustrated in Fig. 3-13. At A a slope of 2 to

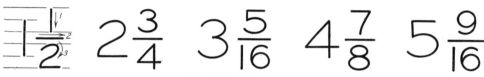

Fig. 3-9 Fractions.

3·10 Single-stroke vertical lower-case letters (Fig. 3-10) are usually made with the *bodies* two-thirds the height of the capitals. The *ascenders* (b, d, f, and so forth) extend up to the *cap line*

5 is set by marking two units on a horizontal line and five units on a vertical line and then using the T-square and triangle. A lettering triangle (with an angle of about 67½°) is shown at

Fig. 3-10 Single-stroke vertical lower-case letters.

(Fig. 3-11), and the *descenders* (g, j, p, and so forth) drop the same distance below (Fig. 3-11). Vertical lower-case letters are based on the combination of circles and straight lines. The monogram in Fig. 3-11 contains 18 of the 26 letters.

Fig. 3-11.

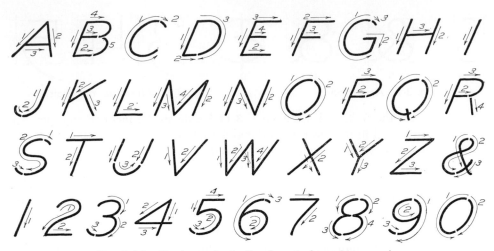

Fig. 3-12 Single-stroke inclined capitals and numerals.

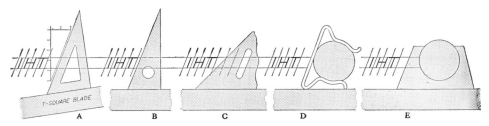

Fig. 3-13 Direction lines.

Fig. 3-14.    Fig. 3-15.

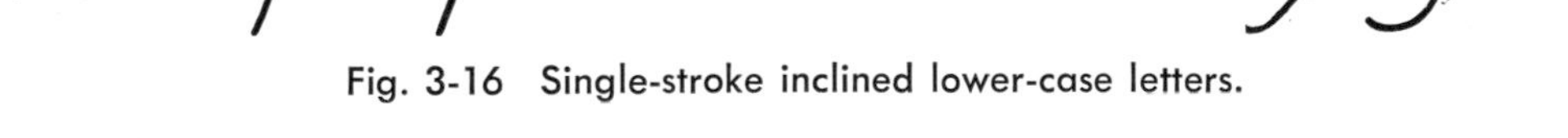

Fig. 3-16 Single-stroke inclined lower-case letters.

THUS   NOT THUS

Fig. 3-17.   Fig. 3-18.

B, the use of the slot in the Braddock-Rowe triangle is shown at C, and the use of the Ames instrument is shown at D. The form taken by the rounded letters when inclined is illustrated in Fig. 3-14, which shows that the curves are sharp in the upper right-hand and lower left-hand corners and flattened in the other two corners. Note the horizontal direction of the crossbar of the letter H in Fig. 3-15. Also, note that the lines of A, V, and W make equal angles on each side of an inclined center line.

3·12 Single-stroke inclined lower-case letters are shown in Fig. 3-16. This style of lettering, sometimes called the *Reinhardt letter,* is in general use for notes on drawings because it is very legible and effective and can be made very rapidly. The bodies are two-thirds the height of the capitals, with the ascenders extending to the cap line and the descenders dropping the same distance below the base line.

For study, the letters may be divided into four groups:

Group I: i j k l t v w x y z
Group II: a b d f g p q
Group III: h m n r u y
Group IV: c e o s

Group I contains the straight-line letters. Keep the slope uniform by following direction lines penciled lightly on the sheet. Be particularly careful about the slant of the angle letters v, w, x,

and y and have their sides make equal angles with the sloping center line.

The letters of Group II are made up of both a partial ellipse whose major axis slants 45° and a straight line (Fig. 3-17). The "hook" letters of Group III are made with part of the same ellipse. The letters of Group IV are made with the same shape of ellipse as the capitals (Fig. 3-18).

3·13 Composition. Composition in lettering means the arrangement and spacing of words and lines with letters of appropriate style and size. After the shapes of the separate letters have been mastered, all practice work should be with words and sentences. The keynote of success is *uniformity.* Uniform height is obtained by having each letter meet the top and bottom guidelines; uniform weight by making all strokes of the same thickness; uniform direction by drawing and following direction lines either vertical or inclined; uniform shade by careful spacing.

Letters in words are not placed at equal distances from each other but are spaced so that the areas of white spaces included between the letters are about equal. In this way they appear to be spaced uniformly. Thus two adjacent letters with straight sides would be spaced much farther apart than two curved letters. Note the variation in spacing in the word "lettering" in Fig. 3-19. In general, keep letters fairly close together.

LETTERING COMPOSITION
INVOLVES THE SPACING OF LETTERS WORDS AND LINES AND THE CHOICE OF APPROPRIATE STYLES AND SIZES

Fig. 3-19 An example of spacing.

PENCILED PENCILED

Fig. 3-20 Extended letters. Compressed letters.

In spacing words, the clear distance between them should not be more than the height of the letters, or they may be spaced by allowing room for the letter O between them. Many variations in letters are possible, such as extending or compressing them (Fig. 3-20). In such cases all the letters of an alphabet must be extended or compressed in proportion.

For the contents and composition of titles, see Art. 11·11.

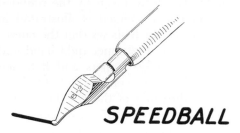

SPEEDBALL

Fig. 3-21 Speedball pen.

ABCDEFGHI JKLMNOPQR STUVWXYZ&

Fig. 3-22 Commercial gothic alphabet.

3·14 Wide-stroke letters. The usual lettering on working drawings has been described in the preceding articles. Larger sizes of letters may be made in single strokes with special lettering pens, such as the Speedball pen shown in Fig. 3-21, or with other wide-stroke pens, such as the Drawlet, Payzant, Leroy, Edco, and Wrico. These pens are made in different sizes to give a variety of widths of strokes.

3·15 Commercial gothic alphabet. An alphabet of this type is shown in Fig. 3-22. It may be drawn either freehand or, if rather large, with instruments

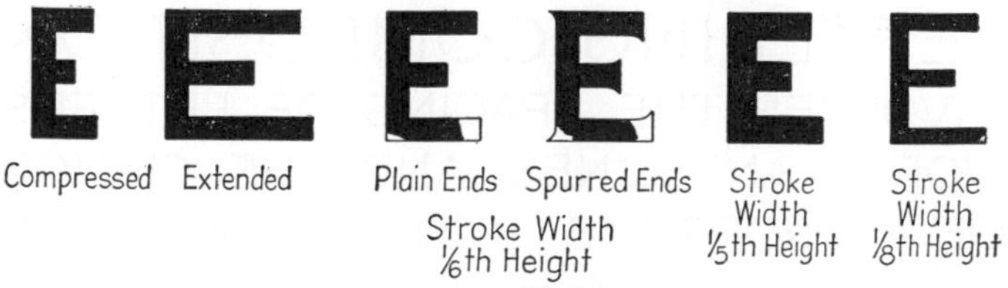

E E E E E E

Compressed   Extended   Plain Ends   Spurred Ends   Stroke Width ⅕th Height   Stroke Width ⅛th Height
Stroke Width ⅙th Height

Fig. 3-23 Variations.

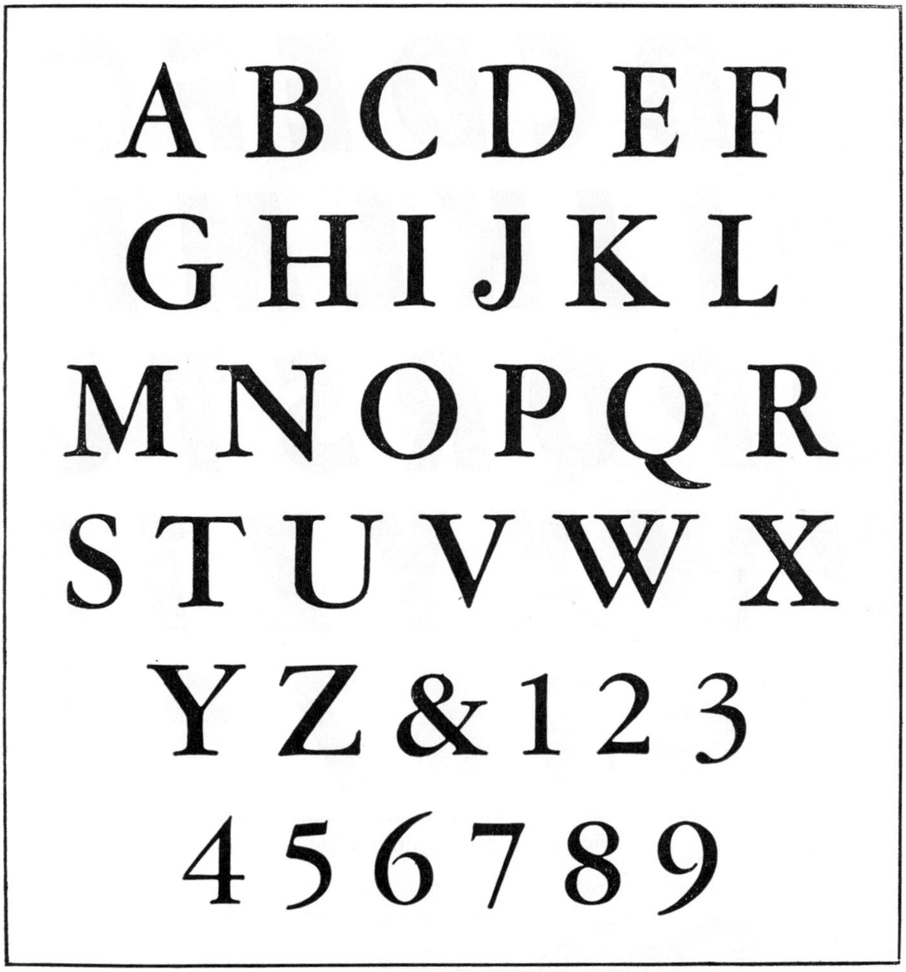

```
A B C D E F
G H I J K L
M N O P Q R
S T U V W X
Y Z & 1 2 3
4 5 6 7 8 9
```

Fig. 3-24 Roman alphabet.

and filled in with a brush. For some purposes the letters may be left in outline as shown for V, W, and X in Fig. 3-22. Commercial gothic letters may be compressed or extended and may have either plain or spur ends (Fig. 3-23). Width of stroke may be from one-eighth to one-fifth the height of the letters.

When commercial gothic letters are drawn with the round-point pens mentioned in Art. 3·14, the ends of the letters may be left rounded as formed by the pen or they may be squared or spurred with a fine-point pen.

3·16 Poster letters. Legibility at a distance is the first requirement for poster letters. Rather wide strokes should be considered. The alphabets shown in Figs. 3-24 and 3-25 indicate two kinds of letters that are suitable for posters. Other letters, both vertical and inclined, will be observed on good posters and in books devoted to lettering.[1]

[1] *The Art of Lettering* by Carl Lars Svensen, 2d ed., D. Van Nostrand Company, Inc., Princeton, N.J. *Learning to Letter* by Paul Carlyle, Guy Oring, and Herbert S. Richland, McGraw-Hill Book Company, Inc., New York.

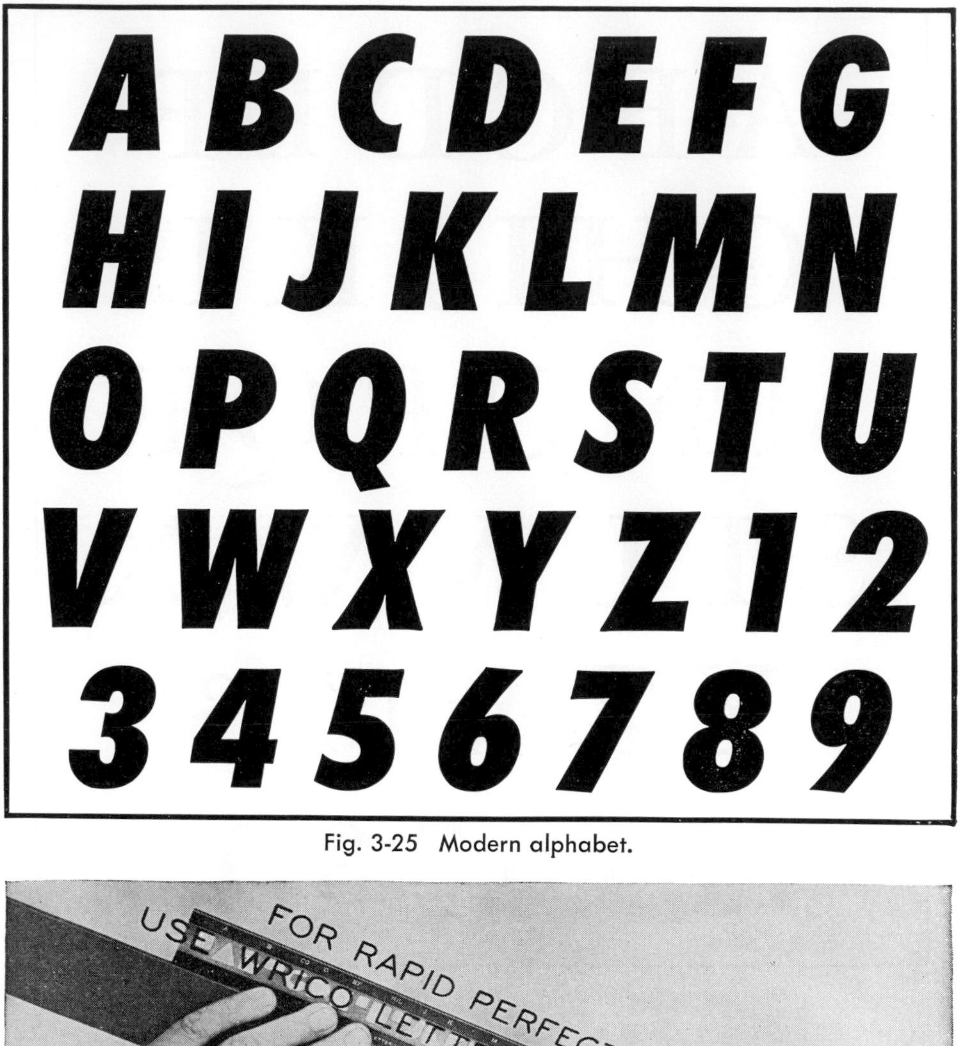

ABCDEFG
HIJKLMN
OPQRSTU
VWXYZ12
3456789

Fig. 3-25 Modern alphabet.

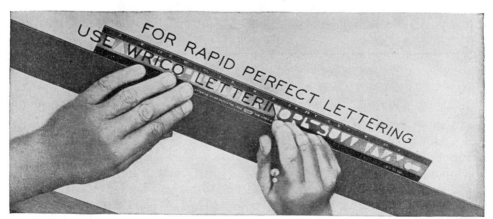

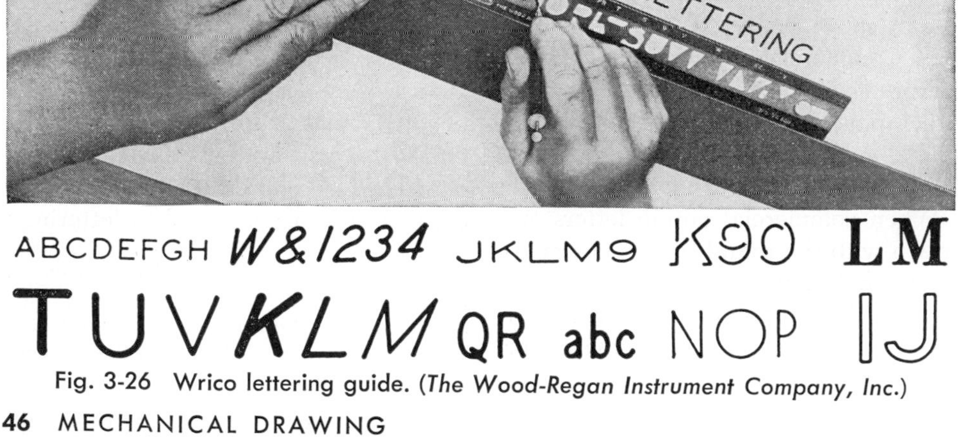

FOR RAPID PERFECT LETTERING
USE WRICO LETTERING
ABCDEFGH W&1234 JKLM9 K90 LM
TUVKLM QR abc NOP IJ

Fig. 3-26 Wrico lettering guide. (*The Wood-Regan Instrument Company, Inc.*)

Fig. 3-27 Wrico Universal scriber lettering guide. (*The Wood-Regan Instrument Company, Inc.*)

3·17 Roman alphabets. Figure 21-3 shows a Roman alphabet derived from Old Roman letters. A single-stroke letter based upon the Roman alphabet (Fig. 21-4) is used on many architectural drawings and is also effective as a poster letter when made with a wide-stroke pen.

sizes ranging from 0.09 to 0.5 inches high or larger. Different sizes of pen points are used to obtain different widths of strokes. Guides and templates are also made for many of the symbols used on drawings, such as welding symbols, architectural symbols, electrical symbols, and other forms and char-

Fig. 3-28 Some variations obtained from the same Wrico scriber guide.

3·18 Lettering devices and guides. Draftsmen use such instruments to produce uniform lettering in standard

acters. Well-known guides include Wrico, Wricoprint, Wrico scriber, and Leroy.

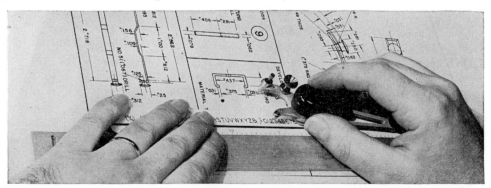

Fig. 3-29 Leroy scriber lettering guide. (*Kueffel & Esser Co.*)

Wrico guides (Fig. 3-26) consist of strips of plastic with openings shaped like the parts of all letters and numbers. Letters are formed by moving a special pen in contact with the sides of the openings. Some kinds of letters, about full size, are shown in the illustration.

Wrico scriber guides (Fig. 3-27) consist of plastic strips or templates with grooves to form letters. A tracer point moved in the grooves forms the letters with the pen. Adjustments can be made on the scriber to get several sizes and kinds of letters from a single guide (Fig. 3-28).

Leroy lettering guides (Fig. 3-29) consist of plastic templates with grooves to guide a tracer point for the scriber to form the letters.

Guides for different sizes and kinds of letters can be obtained for any of the lettering devices. Different sizes of points are made for the special pens so that fine lines can be used for small letters and wider lines for larger letters. When scribers are used, they may be adjusted to get vertical or slant lettering of several sizes from a single guide.

One of the principal advantages of lettering guides is in maintaining uniform lettering, especially where there are a number of draftsmen. Another important use is for lettering titles, note headings, and numbers on drawings and reports.

The Vari-Typer, a typewriter designed for use with interchangeable type faces, can be used to type on tracing cloth or paper up to twelve feet in width. A special ribbon is used to give clear letters on tracing cloth.

3·19 Problem suggestions. Group B, page 374. Lettering is best taught in short, unhurried periods. Problems B·1 to B·8 are for vertical lettering. Problems B·9 to B·16 are for inclined lettering. As an alternate, lettering exercise books[2] are suggested. They are convenient and save time as guidelines are already ruled. If time permits, Prob. B·17 should be assigned and kept as a cover sheet for the drawings made in the course.

[2] *Lessons in Lettering*, Book I (vertical lettering) and Book II (inclined lettering) by Thomas E. French and William D. Turnbull, McGraw-Hill Book Company, Inc., New York.

4 Geometrical constructions

4·1 Geometrical constructions have important uses in making drawings and in solving problems by diagrams or graphs. The lines forming the views on mechanical drawings can usually be located with the instruments and equipment described in Chap. 2. It is sometimes necessary or convenient, however, to use geometrical constructions. The student should become familiar with the more commonly used constructions explained in this chapter.

4·2 To bisect a straight line. A line may be divided into two equal parts by measuring it with a scale, by trial with the dividers (Arts. 2·26 and 2·27), or geometrically as in Fig. 4-1.

Given line AB, with any radius greater than one-half AB and centers at A and B, draw intersecting arcs. (Intersect means cut across.) A line, CD, drawn through the intersections will be perpendicular to line AB and will divide it into two equal parts.

4·3 To erect a perpendicular to a given line at a point, O, on the line. *First method* (Fig. 4-2): With O as a center

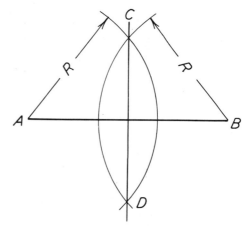

Fig. 4-1 To bisect a line.

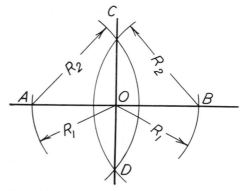

Fig. 4-2 To erect a perpendicular to a line at a point on the line.

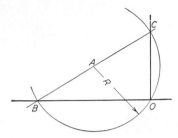

Fig. 4-3 To erect a perpendicular to a line at a point on the line.

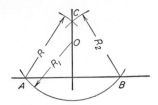

Fig. 4-5 To erect a perpendicular to a line from a point outside of the line.

and any suitable radius, R_1, draw an arc that will intersect the line in two points, A and B. With A and B as centers and any radius, R_2, greater than one-half AB, draw arcs intersecting at C or D. Then lines OC and OD are perpendicular to line AB at O. *Second method* (Fig. 4-3): With point O at or near the end of the line and point A as a center (selected about as shown), draw an arc of a circle with radius AO intersecting the line at B. Draw BA and extend it to intersect the arc at a point, C. Then OC is perpendicular to the given line.

4·4 To erect a perpendicular to a given line from a point, O, outside the line (Figs. 4-4 and 4-5). With O as a center, draw an arc with a radius, R_1, long enough to intersect the line in two points, A and B. With A and B as cen-

ters and a radius, R_2, greater than one-half AB, draw arcs intersecting at C. Then OC is perpendicular to the given line.

4·5 To draw a perpendicular to a line with a triangle and the T-square (Fig. 4-6). A line, CD, may be drawn perpendicular to a given line, AB, through any point on the given line or outside of it as suggested in Fig. 4-6. Refer also to Art. 2·14.

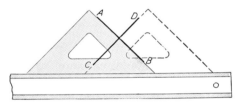

Fig. 4-6 To draw a perpendicular to a line with a triangle and T-square.

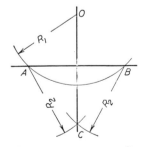

Fig. 4-4 To erect a perpendicular to a line from a point outside of the line.

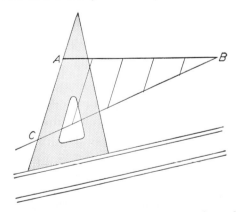

Fig. 4-7 To divide a line into a number of equal parts.

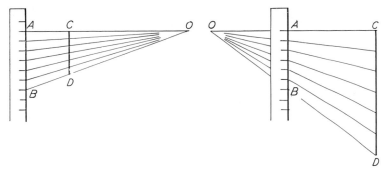

Fig. 4-8 Reducing.   Fig. 4-9 Enlarging.

4·6 To divide a given straight line into any number of equal parts (Fig. 4-7). You can divide a line into any number of equal parts by using the dividers as described in Art. 2·26 or by using the scale as described in Art. 2·27. A geometrical method is shown in Fig. 4-7. To divide the line *AB* into five equal parts, from *B* draw another line at a convenient angle. On it step off five equal spaces of any convenient length. From the last point, *C*, draw *CA*. Through each of the other points on *CB*, draw lines parallel to line *CA*. Line *AB* will then be divided into five equal parts. Use a triangle and T-square to draw the parallel lines (Art. 2·11, Fig. 2-9).

Fig. 4-10 **A protractor and examples of different angles.**

4·7 To reduce or enlarge linear dimensions (Figs. 4-8 and 4-9). A special scale for this purpose may be geometrically made. Its construction is based on the laws of proportional triangles. Draw two parallel lines at a convenient distance apart, one, *AB*, to the given scale and the other, *CD*, to the desired length, either shorter (Fig. 4-8) or longer (Fig. 4-9). Lines through *AC* and *BD* will intersect at point *O*. Draw lines from *O* through each division of the given scale *AB*. These will divide *CD* in proportional spaces to form a new scale to make measurements.

4·8 Angles (Fig. 4-10). The size of an angle is measured in degrees (°), minutes (′), and seconds (″). There are 360° in a circle, 60′ in a degree, and 60″ in a minute. A *right angle* (90°) is

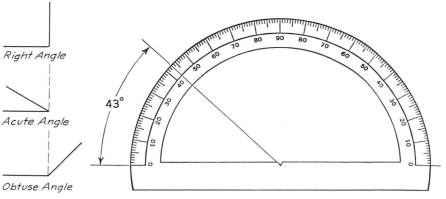

Right Angle

Acute Angle

43°

Obtuse Angle

GEOMETRICAL CONSTRUCTIONS **51**

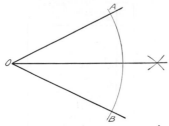

Fig. 4-11 To bisect an angle.

radius equal to chord CD, draw an arc with C' as a center intersecting the first arc at D'. Then angle $D'O'C'$ will be equal to angle AOB.

4·11 Triangles (Figs. 4-13 to 4-17). A *scalene* triangle is one which has no two sides equal. An *equilateral* triangle has three equal sides. An *isosceles* triangle has two equal sides and two equal angles. A *right* triangle has one right angle.

To construct a triangle, given the lengths A, B, and C of the sides (Fig. 4-13), draw one side, as A, in the desired position. With its ends as centers and radii B and C, draw intersecting arcs.

An equilateral triangle (Fig. 4-14) may be constructed by drawing one side in the desired position and drawing intersecting arcs with ends as centers and the length of the side as a radius. Another method is to draw 60° lines from each end of the base with the 30°–60° triangle.

To construct an isosceles triangle (Fig. 4-15), draw the base. With the ends as centers and using one of the equal sides as a radius, draw intersecting arcs.

To construct a right triangle (Fig. 4-16), given two sides A and B, draw one side, as A. At one end of A erect a perpendicular (Art. 4·3, Fig. 4-3) equal to length of side B and join the ends of lines A and B as shown. To construct

measured by one-fourth of a circle. An angle of less than 90° is an *acute angle* and one of more than 90° is an *obtuse angle*. A *protractor* is used in measuring or laying out angles. A semicircular form is shown in the illustration, where an angle of 43° is measured.

In Art. 2·10 (Fig. 2-8) we learned that angles varying by 15° could be constructed with the 45° and 30°–60° triangles. An angle of 90° can be readily bisected with the 45° triangle or trisected with the 30°–60° triangle.

4·9 To bisect an angle (Fig. 4-11). With O as a center and a convenient radius, draw an arc cutting the sides of the angle at A and B. With A and B as centers and any radius greater than one-half AB, draw intersecting arcs. A line through this intersection and point O will bisect the angle.

4·10 To copy an angle (Fig. 4-12). Given angle AOB and line $O'B'$, draw an arc with O as a center and any convenient radius. With O' as a center and the same radius, draw an arc. With a

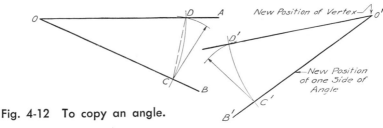

Fig. 4-12 To copy an angle.

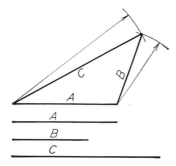

Fig. 4-13   Triangle.

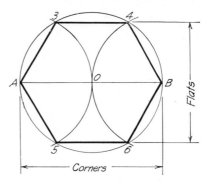

Fig. 4-18   Hexagon.

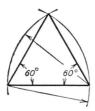

Fig. 4-14   Equilateral triangle.

Fig. 4-15   Isosceles triangle.

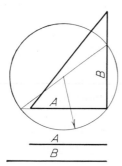

Fig. 4-16   Right triangle.

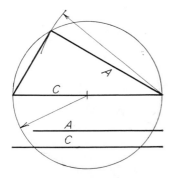

Fig. 4-17   Right triangle.

a right triangle, given one side A and the hypotenuse C (Fig. 4-17), draw a semicircle on C as a diameter. Then with radius A and center at one end of C, draw an arc to intersect the semicircle. Draw lines from the intersection to the ends of C to complete the triangle.

4·12 To draw a regular hexagon, given the distance across corners (AB in Fig. 4-18), draw a circle with AB as a diameter. With A and B as centers and the same radius, draw arcs to intersect the circle. Join the points to complete the hexagon. A hexagon may be constructed directly on line AB without using the compasses. In this method the lines are drawn with the 30°–60° triangle and T-square in the order shown in Fig. 4-19.

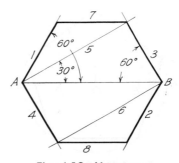

Fig. 4-19   Hexagon.

GEOMETRICAL CONSTRUCTIONS   **53**

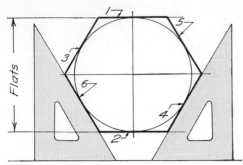

Fig. 4-20 Hexagon.

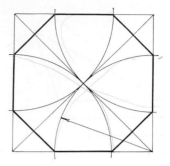

Fig. 4-22 Octagon.

4·13 To draw a regular hexagon, given the distance across flats (Fig. 4-20), draw a circle with a diameter equal to the distance across flats. With the T-square and 30°–60° triangle, draw lines tangent to the circle in the order indicated by the numbers. The hexagonal form of bolthead and nut is used to such a large extent (Chap. 12) that we must know how to draw a regular hexagon.

4·14 To draw a regular pentagon in a circle (Fig. 4-21), draw a diameter AB and a radius OC perpendicular to it. Bisect OB, and with this point, D, as a center and radius DC, draw arc CE. With C as a center and radius CE, draw arc EF. Then CF will be one side of the pentagon. With the same radius as a chord, mark off the remaining points on the circle.

4·15 To draw a regular octagon in a given square (Fig. 4-22), draw the diagonals of the square. With the corners as centers and a radius equal to half a diagonal, draw arcs cutting the sides of the square and connect these points. Another method is to draw a circle with a diameter equal to a side of the enclosing square and draw tangents with the T-square and 45° triangle.

4·16 To draw a circle through any three points not in a straight line (Fig. 4-23). Given the points A, B, and C, draw lines AB and BC. Bisect these lines by the method used in Art. 4·2. Point O, where the bisectors cross, will be the center of the required circle. In the final construction:

$$R = OA = OB = OC$$

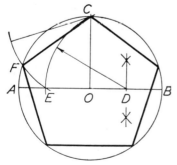

Fig. 4-21 Pentagon.

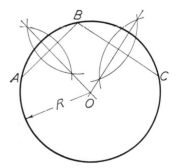

Fig. 4-23 Circle.

4·17 To draw a tangent to a circle at a given point, *T*, on the circle (Fig. 4-24). The draftsman's method is to arrange a triangle in combination with the T-square (or another triangle) so that the hypotenuse passes through the center *O* and the point *T*. Hold the T-square firmly in place, turn the triangle about its square corner, move it until the hypotenuse passes through *T*, and draw the tangent.

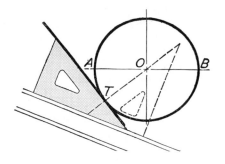

Fig. 4-24   Tangent to a circle.

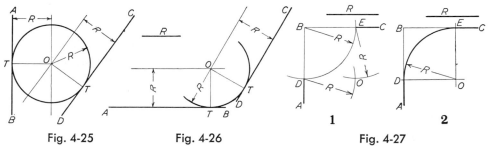

Fig. 4-25   Fig. 4-26   Fig. 4-27

Arc tangent to two lines.

4·18 To draw an arc tangent to two given lines, *AB* and *CD*, with a given radius, *R* (Figs. 4-25 and 4-26). Draw lines parallel to *AB* and *CD* at a distance *R* from them. The intersection of these lines will be the center of the required arc. Locate the points of tangency, *T*, by drawing perpendiculars to the tangent lines through the center of the arc (reverse Fig. 4-24).

When the angle between the lines is a right angle (Fig. 4-27; see *fillets* and *rounds*, Art. 7·9): Round the corner *ABC* (Fig. 4-27 at 1) using an arc with center *B* and radius *R* to cut the given lines at *D* and *E*. With *D* and *E* as centers and radius *R*, draw arcs intersecting at *O*. An arc with center *O* and radius *R* will be tangent to the lines at points *D* and *E* (Fig. 4-27 at 2).

4·19 To draw a reverse or ogee curve (Fig. 4-28). To connect two parallel lines *AB* and *CD* by a smooth curve, draw the straight line *BC*. On this line select a point, *E*, through which the desired curve is to pass. Draw the perpendicular bisectors of *BE* and *CE* (Art. 4·2) and extend them to intersect perpendiculars to *AB* and *CD* drawn from *B* and *C*. Then O_1 and O_2 are centers of arcs (radii O_1E and O_2E) for the required curve. The line of centers O_1O_2 must pass through *E*, the point of tangency.

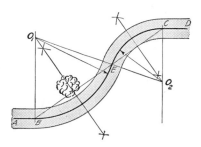

Fig. 4-28   Ogee curve.

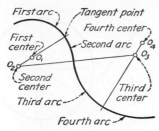

Fig. 4-29 Tangent arcs.

4·20 To approximate a noncircular curve with circle arcs (Fig. 4-29). Find, by trial, the center of an arc that will cover a portion of the curve. Connect the end of the arc with the center. The next center for an arc tangent to the first arc must lie somewhere on this line. Continue the process as shown in Fig. 4-29. Remember that, when two arcs are tangent to each other, the two centers and the point of tangency must lie in a straight line.

4·21 To lay off the approximate length of an arc on a straight line (Fig. 4-30). Given the arc *AB*. At *A* draw the tangent line *AD*. Set the dividers to a small space. Start at *B*, step along the arc to the point nearest *A*, and, without lifting the dividers, step off the same number of spaces on the tangent. Then *AD* is the length of the arc.

4·22 To draw an involute. Assume that a string has been wound around a square (Fig. 4-31) in a counterclockwise direction and that the loose end is at point 4. Start unwinding in a

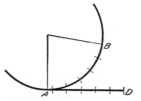

Fig. 4-30 Length of an arc.

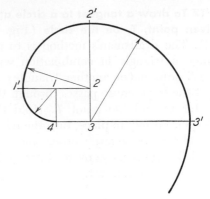

Fig. 4-31 Involute of a square.

clockwise direction, keeping the string taut. In unwinding the string, you will describe an involute of the square. To draw the involute, take a radius 4–1 with center at 1 and draw the arc 4–1′, ending at 1′ on the side 2–1 produced. With radius 2–1′ and center 2, draw arc 1′–2′. Continue in like manner with the corners of the square as centers, increasing each successive radius by the length of a side. In the same way the involute of any polygon may be drawn.

4·23 To draw the involute of a circle (Fig. 4-32), divide the circumference of the circle into a number of equal parts; draw radial lines and tangents at the end of each radial line. Lay off

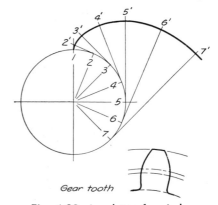

Gear tooth

Fig. 4-32 Involute of a circle.

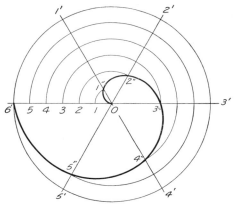

Fig. 4-33 Spiral of Archimedes.

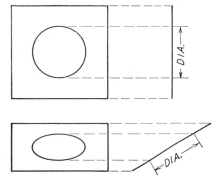

Fig. 4-34 Circle projected as an ellipse.

the *length of the arc* from point 1 to point 2 on the tangent 2–2′ (Art. 4·21). Lay off on each tangent the length of the arc from the point of tangency to point 1. Through the points thus found (2′–3′–4′, and so forth), draw the involute as a smooth curve, using the irregular curve. This is the curve of the involute gear tooth (Art. 19·9).

4·24 To draw a spiral of Archimedes (Fig. 4-33). Draw a circle, divide it into a number of equal parts, and divide a radial line into the same number of equal parts. With O as a center and a radius O–1, draw an arc to radial line O–1′ to locate point 1″. In like manner draw arcs with radii O–2, O–3, and so forth, to radii to locate points 2″, 3″, and so forth, as shown. Draw a spiral of Archimedes as a smooth curve through the points thus located.

4·25 The ellipse. A plane is a flat, level surface. If a circle is parallel to a plane and if every point on the circle is carried over to that plane by straight lines perpendicular (at right angles) to the plane, another circle will be formed on the plane. The second circle is known as the *projection* of the first. Projection means *thrown forward*. If a circle is perpendicular to a plane, its projection will be a straight line. If it is at an angle, its projection will be an *ellipse*. A square card with a circular hole, drawn in different positions, as in Fig. 4-34, illustrates the foregoing statements. An ellipse is defined as a curve generated (formed) by a point moving in a plane so that the sum of its distances from two fixed points, called the *foci*, is a constant (always the same) and is equal to the major axis (or longest diameter).

The two foci are always on the major axis of the ellipse. A line through the center perpendicular to the major axis is called the *minor axis*, or *short diameter*. To find the foci (Fig. 4-35), draw an arc with its center at one end of the minor axis and a radius equal to one-half the major axis. This arc will cut the major axis at the foci F_1 and F_2.

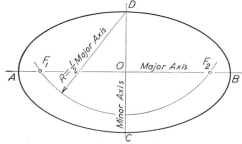

Fig. 4-35 Ellipse.

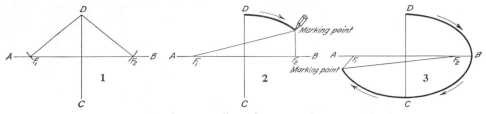

Fig. 4-36 To draw an ellipse by pin and string method.

4·26 To draw an ellipse by the pin-and-string method. Given the major and minor axes AB and CD (Fig. 4-36 at 1), locate the foci F_1 and F_2 as described in Art. 4·25. Drive pins at points F_1, D, and F_2 and tie a cord tightly around the three pins. Then remove the pin D and insert the point of a pencil (or other marking point) in the loop. Keep the cord taut and move the point as indicated at 2 and 3. An ellipse will be described.

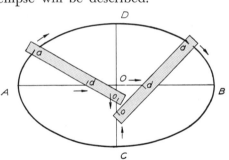

Fig. 4-37 Trammel method.

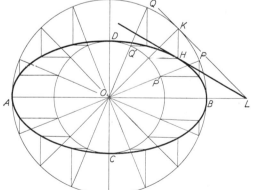

Fig. 4-38 Two-circle method.

58 MECHANICAL DRAWING

4·27 To draw an ellipse by the trammel method (Fig. 4-37). Cut a strip of stiff paper (called a *trammel*) and mark distance ao equal to one-half the major axis and ad equal to one-half the minor axis. Move the strip as indicated by the arrows, keeping point d on the major axis and point o on the minor axis. Point a will locate points on the ellipse. Make light marks at point a for the different positions of the trammel and sketch the curve lightly through the points thus located. Then, using the irregular curve, draw a smooth curve.

4·28 To draw an ellipse by the concentric-circle method (Fig. 4-38). With O as a center, draw circles on the major and minor diameters. Draw a number of radial lines, OP, OQ, and so forth, cutting the large circle at P, Q, and so forth, and the small circle at P', Q', and so forth. A vertical line through P will intersect a horizontal line through

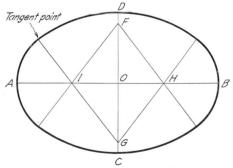

Fig. 4-39 Approximate ellipse.

P' in a point on the ellipse. In like manner perpendicular lines from points on the large circle will intersect horizontal lines through corresponding points on the small circle to form points on the ellipse. Find as many points as necessary and, using the irregular curve, draw a smooth curve through them.

A tangent at any point, H (Fig. 4-38), may be found by drawing a line perpendicular to the main axis from the point until it intersects the outer circle at K. The next step is to draw an auxiliary tangent, KL, that cuts the major axis extended at L. From L the required tangent LH is then drawn.

4·29 Approximate ellipses may be drawn with arcs of circles (Fig. 4-39). When the minor axis is at least two-thirds of the major axis, the four-center approximation shown may be used. Make OF and OG each equal to AB minus CD. Make OH and OI each equal to three-fourths of OF. Draw FH, FI, GH, and GI, extending them as shown. Draw arcs through points D and C with centers at G and F, and through A and B with centers I and H.

Another method is shown in Fig. 4-40. Draw line AD, arc AE with radius OA and center O, and arc EF with center D. Draw line GH, the perpendicular bisector of AF which will locate centers I and H for arcs AT and TD. Lay off $OJ = OI$ and $OK = OH$ to locate centers J and K.

4·30 To draw an arc tangent to two given arcs (Fig. 4-41). Locate center O of the required arc at the intersection of arcs drawn with centers O_1 and O_2 and radii equal to the given radii plus or minus R as shown at A and B.

4·31 Problem suggestions. Group C, page 378. Three lists are presented. Since List 1 includes basic problems, it would be desirable to use all of them in any course which includes geometrical constructions. Additional assignments from Lists 2 and 3 may be made according to the age group of the students, the time available, and the purpose of the course.

LIST 1 Problems C·1, C·3, C·5, C·7, C·11, C·14, C·17, C·22, C·25, C·27, C·28

LIST 2 Problems C·4, C·6, C·8, C·9, C·12, C·15, C·19, C·23, C·26, C·29

LIST 3 Problems C·10, C·13, C·16, C·18, C·21, C·24, C·30, C·31, C·32, C·33, C·34

Additional problems may be selected from Chap. 24.

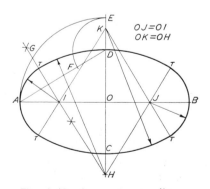

Fig. 4-40 Approximate ellipse.

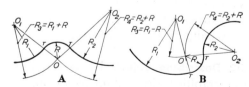

Fig. 4-41 Arc tangent to two arcs.

 The motion pictures and follow-up filmstrips *Shape Description, Parts I* and *II* have been prepared to correlate with this chapter.

5 Theory of shape description

5·1 Mental pictures and their description. There are two things that a designer, inventor, or builder must be able to do: (1) He must be able to visualize or see clearly in his mind's eye what an object looks like without actually having the object, and (2) he must be able to describe it so that others could build it completely from the information given on his drawing. A few lines properly drawn on paper will describe an object more accurately and more clearly than a photograph or a written description. Line drawings must be used because photographs cannot be taken of an object yet to be built. These methods of using lines are based on principles known as the *theory of shape description*. The ability to describe the real shape of an object with lines, and to read and understand such descriptions, requires a thorough knowledge of these principles.

5·2 Describing objects by views. For the graphical description of an object we should have available the paper, pencil, and instruments explained in Chap. 2. On the paper we can make measurements in a single plane only. All objects have dimensions that may be at angles or perpendicular to the paper as well as parallel to it. A picture could be made that would show, just as a photograph would, the general appearance of the object, but it would not show the *exact* forms and relations of the parts of the object. It would show it as it *appears* and not as it really is.

Our problem then is to represent solid objects on a sheet of paper in such a manner as to tell the exact shape. This is done by drawing *views* of the object as seen from different positions and by arranging these views in a systematic manner.

In Space 1 of Fig. 5-1 arrows indicate directions for viewing a rectangular prism. Views in each of these directions are shown and named. In Space 2 a picture of a cylinder is shown together with the three views. Notice that the *top view* shows the true circular shape of the cylinder as seen from above. The

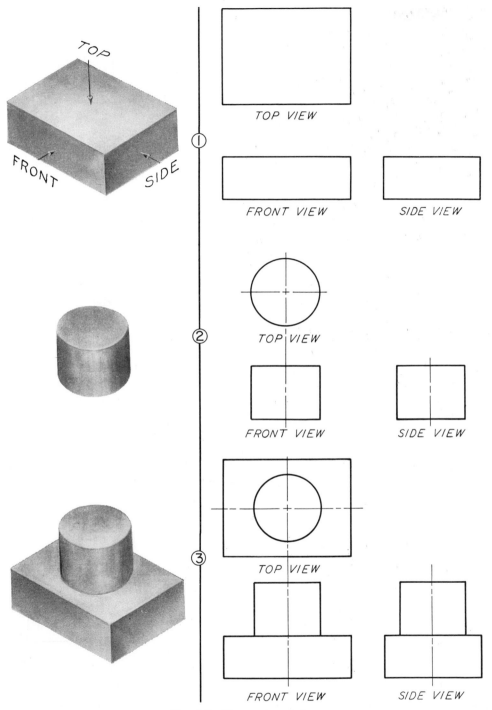

TOP

FRONT   SIDE

① TOP VIEW

FRONT VIEW   SIDE VIEW

② TOP VIEW

FRONT VIEW   SIDE VIEW

③ TOP VIEW

FRONT VIEW   SIDE VIEW

Fig. 5-1 Shape description.

Fig. 5-2   Picture of a slide projector (Society for Visual Education Inc., Chicago, Ill.)

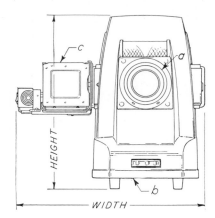

Fig. 5-3   The front view of the projector.

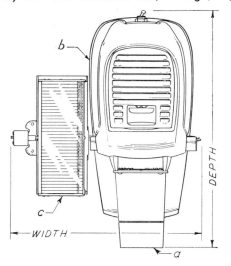

front and *side views* appear as rectangles and are the same size, so the cylinder might be described by two views, the top view to show the shape and the front view to show the diameter and height.

In Space 3 the cylinder has been placed on the prism. Notice how the views from Space 1 and Space 2 combine to form the views in Space 3. Complete views are composed of views of separate parts.

5·3 The relation of views. A picture of a slide projector (Fig. 5-2) shows the

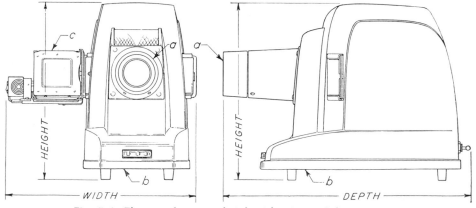

Fig. 5-4   The top, front, and right-side views of the projector.

projector as it ordinarily appears to us, but it does not show the true shapes of the parts. The front of the lens tube appears as an ellipse, although we know it is really circular. This is because the circular end is not in a plane perpendicular to our line of sight. The projector has, in effect, been tilted at an angle in order to show more sides. If we look at the projector from directly in front, we obtain a *view* showing the exact shape of the end of the tube and the outline of the other parts as seen from in front. This is called a *front view* (Fig. 5-3). This view shows the *width*

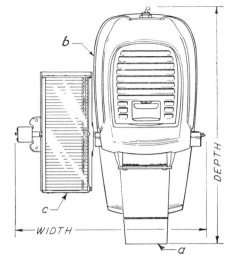

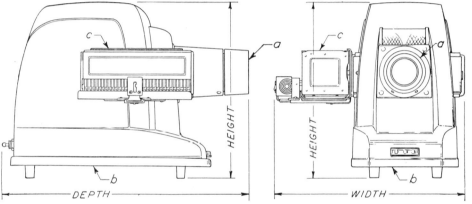

Fig. 5-5 The top, front, and left-side views of the projector.

and *height* of the projector. But this view does not tell us the *depth* (or distance from front to back), so it is necessary to have another view from a position directly above (called a *top view*) or else a view from one side (called a *side view*). In this way either the top view or a side view will show the depth. Often, as in this case, both a top view and a side view, in addition to the front view, are needed to describe the object (Fig. 5-4).

The lens tube is shown as a circle at

a in the front view, but in the top view and side view it is shown as a straight line at *a* (Fig. 5-4). The outline of the base is shown in the top view at *b*, but the bottom of the base is shown as a straight line at *b* in the front and side views.

The three views taken together define the shapes of all the visible parts of the projector and their exact relations to each other.

It is evident that the front and side views are exactly the same height.

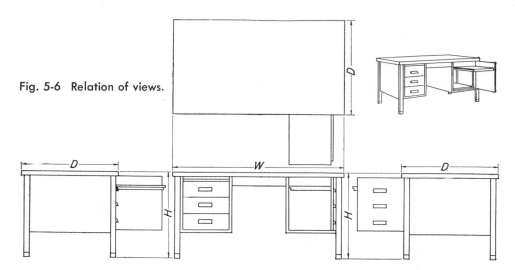

Fig. 5-6 Relation of views.

When drawn, they are placed directly across from each other. The top view is placed directly above the front view and the three views together appear as in Fig. 5-4.

5·4 Left-side view. Sometimes a left-side view will describe an object more clearly than a right-side view and in such cases should be used. Figure 5-5 shows the top, front, and left-side views of the projector. Notice that it shows the slide magazine at *c*, which cannot be seen in the right-side view. For some objects it may be necessary to show both the right- and the left-side views in order to provide a complete description.

Notice the positions of the different views in relation to each other. In Figs. 5-4 and 5-5 it will be observed that the end of the lens tube *a* is toward the front in the top view and that it is toward the front in both the right- and left-side views as shown at *a*.

5·5 Width, depth, and height. As a further explanation of the relation of the three views, study the drawing of the

steel desk shown in Fig. 5-6. Notice that the typewriter shelf is at the right in the top and front views and that it projects toward the front view. Also, notice that it projects toward the front view in both the right-hand and left-hand views. The height, *H*, of the desk shows in the front and side views. The width, *W*, shows in the top and front views. The depth, *D*, shows in the top and side views. Notice the difference between the two side views and the reason for this difference.

5·6 Orthographic projection. The use of different views to describe objects,

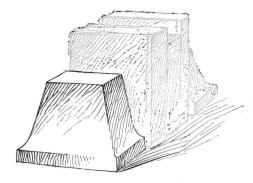

Fig. 5-7 Book end.

as shown in the previous articles, is based upon the principles of *orthographic projection*. This theory must be well understood before complicated or difficult drawings can be made or read.

Ortho- means "straight or at right angles" and -graphic means "written or drawn." Projection comes from two old Latin words, "pro" meaning "forward" and "jacere" meaning "to throw." Thus orthographic projection literally means "thrown forward, drawn at right angles." The following definition has been given: Orthographic projection is the method of representing the exact form of an object in two or more views on planes generally at right angles to each other, by dropping perpendiculars from the object to the planes.

5·7 Planes of projection. Suppose the book end shown in Fig. 5-7 is to be drawn. The draftsman imagines himself to be looking through a transparent plane set up in front of the object (Fig. 5-8). If, from every point of the object, perpendiculars are imagined as extended or projected to the plane, the result on the front of the plane would be the *projection* on that plane, called the *vertical projection*, or *front view*, or in architectural drawing, the *front elevation*. This view will show the true width and height of the object.

Suppose now that a horizontal plane is hinged at right angles to the first plane, with the observer looking through it at the top of the object as in Space 1 of Fig. 5-9. Perpendiculars from the object to this plane will give the *horizontal projection*, or *top view*, or as called in architectural drawing, the *plan*. This view will show the depth of the object from front to back, as

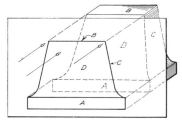

Fig. 5-8 The frontal plane.

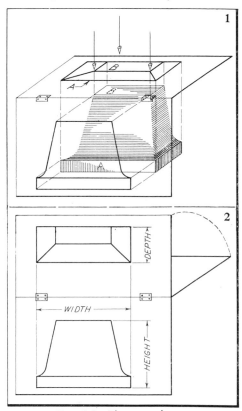

Fig. 5-9 The top plane.

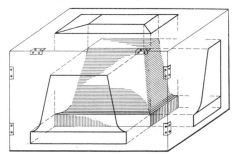

Fig. 5-10 The glass box.

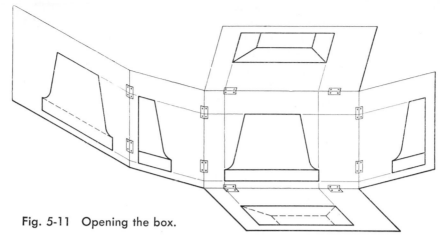

Fig. 5-11 Opening the box.

well as the width already shown on the front view. These two planes represent the drawing paper. If the horizontal plane is imagined as swung up on the hinges until it lies in the extension of the front plane as in Space 2 of Fig. 5-9, the two views will be shown in their correct relationship as they would be drawn on the paper. Together they give the width, W; the depth, D; and the height, H. This explains the reason for the statement made in Art. 5·3 that the top view is always drawn directly over the front view.

5·8 The six planes. The *side view, side elevation,* or *profile projection* is imagined as made on a plane perpendicular to both the front and top planes. Thus the object can be thought of as being inside a glass or transparent box as in Fig. 5-10. The projections on the sides of this box would be the *views,* which we have discussed. When the sides are opened up (Fig. 5-11) into one plane, the views take their relative positions as they would be drawn on the paper (Fig. 5-12). These figures show the views as projected onto all *six planes*

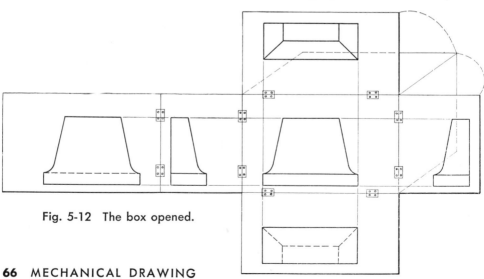

Fig. 5-12 The box opened.

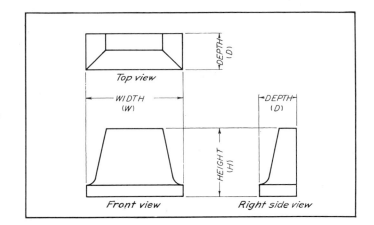

Fig. 5-13 Top, front, and right-side views.

or faces of the box and are arranged according to accepted practice for the six views.

Notice that some views give the same information contained in other views. They may also be, for practical purposes, mirror images of one another. It is unnecessary to show all six views for a working drawing, though an extra view may be desirable in some cases. The top, front, and right-side views as ordinarily drawn are shown in Fig. 5-13. When a left-side view is drawn, it is placed as in Fig. 5-14.

5·9 Studies. As an explanation of how the theory of projection is applied, study the drawings of the objects in the following figures: In Space 1 of Fig. 5-15 each view represents a single surface. In Space 2 the top view shows two surfaces, A, and B, at different levels, and as shown by the front view, surface A is above surface B. In the side view, surfaces C and D are shown, but it is necessary to look at the front view to see which surface is closer to the side plane. In Space 3 surface B is inclined and is shown slightly shortened in the

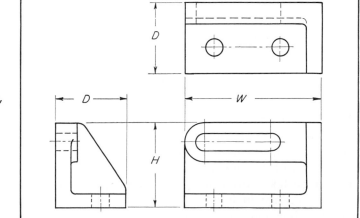

Fig. 5-14 Top, front, and left-side views.

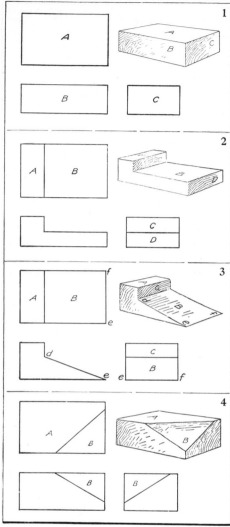

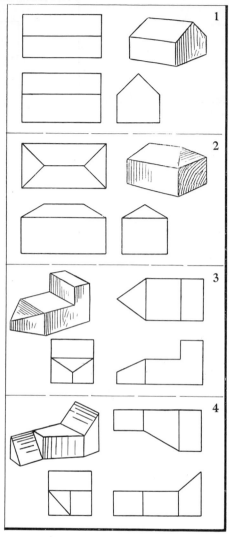

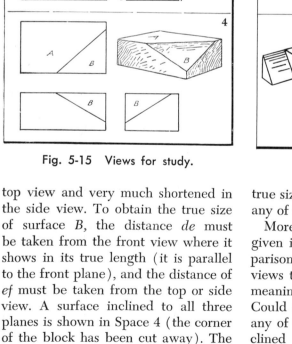

Fig. 5-15 Views for study.

Fig. 5-16 Views for study.

top view and very much shortened in the side view. To obtain the true size of surface *B*, the distance *de* must be taken from the front view where it shows in its true length (it is parallel to the front plane), and the distance of *ef* must be taken from the top or side view. A surface inclined to all three planes is shown in Space 4 (the corner of the block has been cut away). The

true size of surface *B* does not show in any of the views.

More pictures and drawings are given in Fig. 5-16 for study and comparison. Consider the reason for the views that have been selected and the meaning of each line on the views. Could any of the views be omitted for any of the objects? Notice how the inclined surfaces are represented and that the views do not show the true sizes of such surfaces. In Space 1 of Fig. 5-16 the inclined surfaces make angles with the top and front planes but are perpendicular to the side plane. Study and describe the positions of the inclined surfaces in Spaces 2, 3, and 4.

5·10 Hidden lines. Since it is necessary to describe every part of an object, all surfaces must be represented whether they can be seen or not. Parts which cannot be seen in the views are represented by *hidden lines* composed of short dashes (Fig. 5-17). Study the views in Fig. 5-17. Notice that the first dash of a hidden line touches the line at which it starts (Space 1).

If a hidden line is a continuation of a full line, a space is left between the full line and the first dash of the hidden line (Space 2). If hidden lines show corners, the dashes touch at the corners (Space 3). Dashes for hidden arcs start and end at the tangent points (Space 4).

Fig. 5-17 Hidden lines.→

5·11 Center lines (Fig. 11-3 at 4) are used to locate views and dimensions.

Fig. 5-18 Center lines.

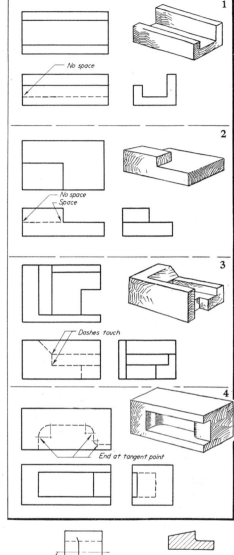

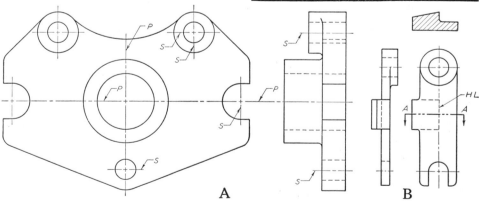

A   B

THEORY OF SHAPE DESCRIPTION 69

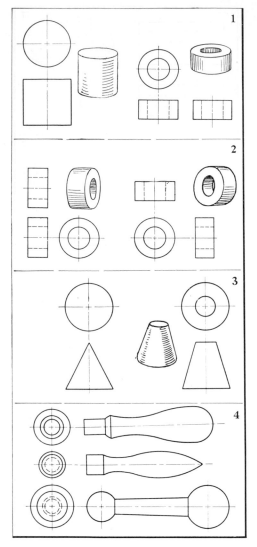

Fig. 5-19 Curved surfaces.

Primary center lines, marked *P* in Fig. 5-18 at *A* are axes of symmetry on symmetrical views, where one part is a mirror image of another part. Secondary center lines, marked *S* in Fig. 5-18, are axes for details of a part or construction. Primary center lines are, therefore, the first lines to be drawn, and the views are worked up from them. Note that center lines represent the axes of cylinders in the side view and that the centers of circles or arcs are located first so that measurements can be made from them to locate the lines on the various views. A hidden line is shown in preference to a center line as *HL* in Fig. 5-18 at *B*.

5·12 Curved surfaces. The fact that some curved surfaces such as cylinders and cones do not show as curves in all views is illustrated in Fig. 5-19 at 1, 2, and 3. A cylinder with its axis (center line) perpendicular to a plane will show as a circle on that plane and as a rectangle on the other two planes. Three views of a cylinder when placed in different positions are shown in Spaces 1 and 2. A cone appears as a circle in one view and as a triangle in the others (Space 3). For a frustum of a cone, one view appears as two circles (Space 3). In the top view the

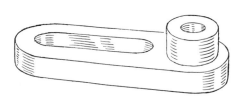

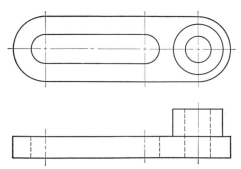

Fig. 5-20 Curved surfaces.

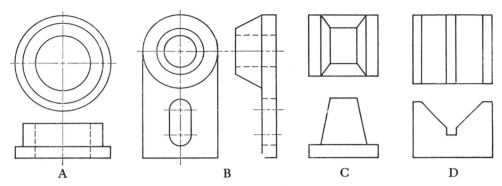

Fig. 5-21 Two-view drawings.

conical surface is represented by the space between the two circles.

Cylinders, cones, and frustums of cones have *single curved surfaces* and are represented by circles in one view and straight lines in the other. The handles in Space 4 have *double curved surfaces* which are represented by curves in both views. The ball handle has spherical ends, and both views of the ends are circles because a sphere appears as a circle when viewed in any direction.

The slotted link of Fig. 5-20 is an example of tangent curved surfaces. Notice how the rounded ends join the sides of the link and how the ends of the slot are tangent to the sides.

5·13 What views to draw. As already mentioned, the six views in Fig. 5-12 are not needed to describe the book end. The three views in Fig. 5-13 are sufficient. The six views explain the theory of making drawings, but it is not necessary to draw them in order to tell which views are needed. The general characteristics of an object will indicate the views required to describe its shape. Three properly selected views will describe most shapes, but sometimes there are features that will be more clearly described by using more views or parts of extra views.

There are some objects that can be described with two views as indicated in Fig. 5-21. When two views are used, they must be the proper ones to describe the shape of the object. Thus in Fig. 5-22 the top and front views at A and B are the same. Since the side views are needed, the front and side views could be used to describe these objects. At C the top view is needed, so the top and front views might be used. At D the front view is needed, so the front and top or front and side views might be used.

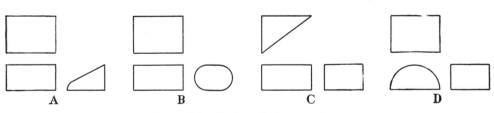

Fig. 5-22 Choice of view studies.

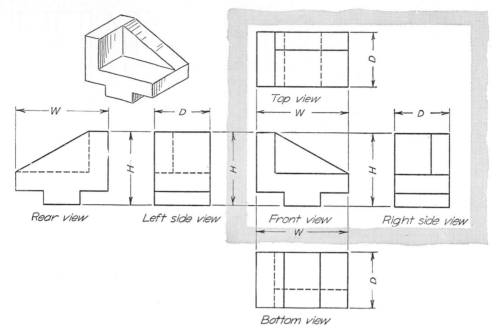

Fig. 5-23   Position of bottom and rear views.

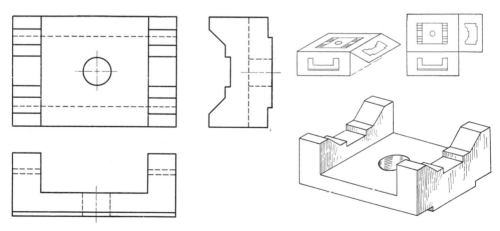

Fig. 5-24   Second position of the side view.

The purpose of the views in all cases is to describe the object, and this should be kept in mind at all times. In general, the views should be drawn to represent the object in the position it occupies in use. This is not always possible. For example, tall objects, such as

vertical shafts, are more readily drawn in a horizontal position. Always consider all possible views and select the ones that will give the clearest and most easily read exact description of the object.

Six views are shown for the object in

Fig. 5-23. Study the picture and the views. It will be evident that the top, front, and right-side views will give the best description of the shape and have the fewest hidden lines.

5·14 Second position of the side view. The proportions of an object or the size of the sheet sometimes makes it desirable to show a side view in the second position or directly across from the top view as in Fig. 5-24. This position is obtained by revolving the side plane about its intersection with the top plane.

Visualization and careful thought about a "mind's eye picture" of an object will help decide which views should be drawn to describe its shape.

5·15 Problem suggestions. Group D, page 381. Many instructors have found it possible to secure better results by assigning only a few problems from List 1, proceeding to sketching in Chap. 6, and then returning to Group D to work the desired number of problems while studying Chap. 7. Three lists are presented. List 1 includes basic problems which are in general more

elementary than Lists 2 and 3. A selection from List 1 should be made according to the time available. Additional or alternate assignments may be made from Lists 2 and 3 according to the age group of the students, the time available, and the purpose of the course. There are sufficient problems listed to provide variation from year to year.

LIST 1 Problems D·1, D·2, D·3, D·4, D·5, D·6, D·7, D·8, D·9, D·10, D·11, D·12, D·13, D·14, D·22, D·25, D·28, D·29, D·30, D·31, D·37, D·39, D·40, D·41, D·43, D·49, D·50, D·52, D·55, D·56, D·61, D·66, D·67, D·68, D·71, D·73, D·74, D·80, D·81, D·84, D·86, D·88, D·96

LIST 2 Problems D·15, D·16, D·18, D·19, D·20, D·21, D·24, D·26, D·27, D·32, D·33, D·34, D·35, D·42, D·44, D·46, D·51, D·54, D·58, D·60, D·62, D·69, D·72, D·76, D·77, D·78, D·79, D·82, D·85, D·87, D·89, D·91, D·92, D·93, D·94, D·95, D·97

LIST 3 Problems D·36, D·38, D·47
Additional or alternate problems may be selected from Chap. 24.

6 Sketching

6·1 Freehand drawing or sketching is a convenient method of shape description that is helpful in the practice of engineering as well as in the study of view drawing. The instructor may prefer to teach freehand sketching before he teaches drawing with instruments. Views can be made more quickly freehand than with the instruments. Such practice develops accuracy of observation, a good sense of proportion, and sureness in the handling of the pencil. The ability to make a good sketch is useful for many purposes, such as (1) sketching different parts from assembly or design drawings in order to draw the details; (2) making partial or complete sketches as an aid in reading drawings, explaining drawings, or working up new ideas; (3) planning changes in existing machines or apparatus; (4) working up new mechanisms; and (5) sketching different arrangements on paper for comparison before making working drawings. Skill in freehand sketching is a "must" for draftsmen, designers, and engineers in present-day industry. Sketching is an important means of communication.

6·2 Sketching equipment includes an F or H pencil sharpened to a long conical point, an eraser, and suitable paper. Plain paper is suggested for beginning practice. Many kinds of squared or graph papers are available that can be used for scale and proportion in making sketches. Other rulings provide for making pictorial sketches and special purposes. Working sketches can be made quickly and conveniently by placing tracing paper over such sketching paper. Measuring tools and other equipment used in making dimensioned sketches from parts of machines or constructions are explained in Arts. 10·24 to 10·26.

6·3 Straight lines (Fig. 6-1). Since views are made up of straight lines and curves, the student should become expert in sketching these elements before starting to sketch views of objects.

Horizontal lines are sketched from left to right as in Space 1 of Fig. 6-1, vertical lines are sketched downward as in Space 2, and inclined lines are sketched in the directions indicated in Spaces 3 and 4.

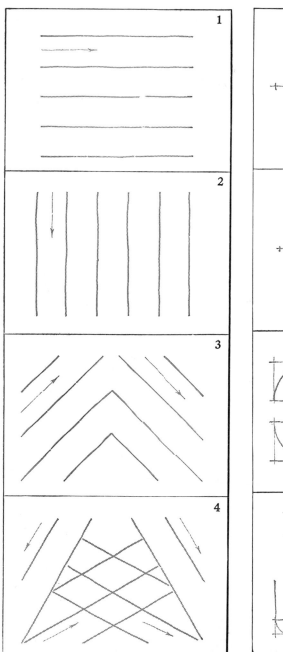

Fig. 6-1 Sketching straight lines.

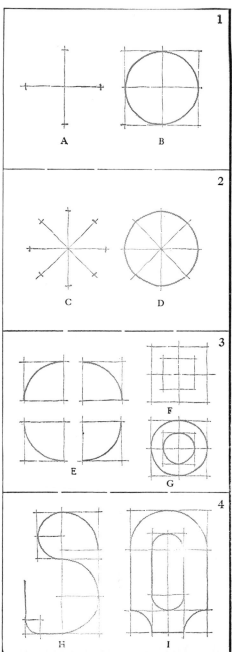

Fig. 6-2 Sketching circles and arcs.

6·4 Circles and arcs are sketched as shown in Fig. 6-2. In Space 1 at *A* and *B*, radii are estimated and marked off on horizontal and vertical center lines to locate a square in which the circle is sketched. In Space 2 at *C* and *D*,

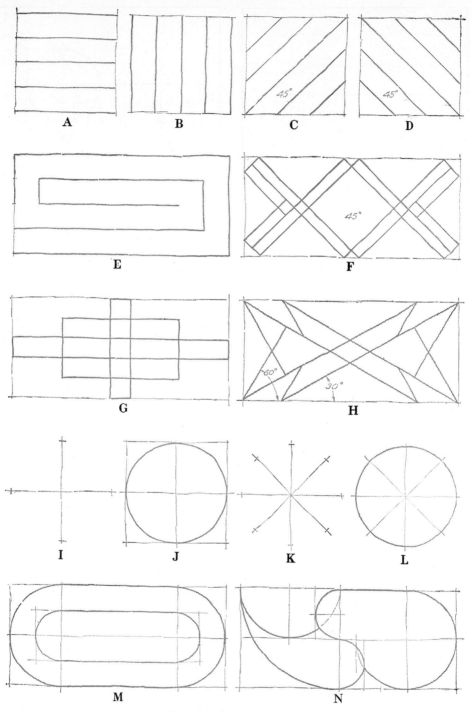

Fig. 6-3 Line exercises.

radii are estimated and marked off on the lines indicated to locate points through which the circle is sketched. Arcs, tangent arcs, and curves are conveniently sketched by blocking in with straight lines as suggested in Spaces 3 and 4.

6·5 Line exercises are presented in Fig. 6-3 for beginning practice. All distances mentioned and angles indicated are to be estimated. Exercises A, B, C, and D may be sketched in 2- or 3-in. squares with parallel lines equally spaced. Exercises E, F, G, and H may be sketched in rectangles 2 by 4¼ in. or 3 by 6⅜ in. Exercises I, J, K, L, M, and N may have a radius of 1 or 1½ in. for the largest circles. Observe the proportions

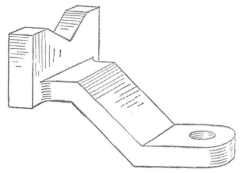

Fig. 6-4 An object to be sketched.

very carefully and locate very light blocking-in lines as accurately as possible by eye.

6·6 A freehand sketch of the V-block (Fig. 6-4) is shown in Fig. 6-5. In Fig. 6-5 the views necessary to describe the

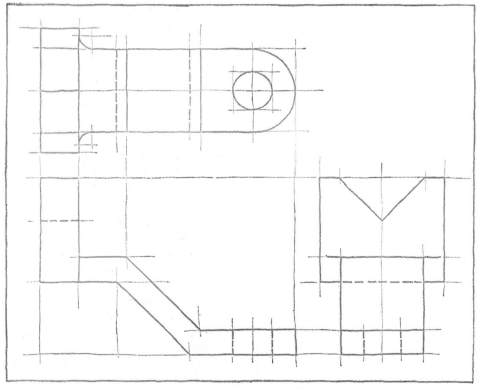

Fig. 6-5 A pencil sketch.

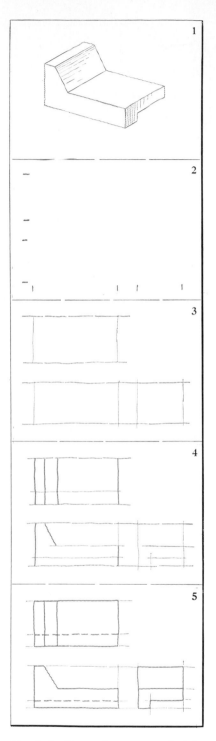

Fig. 6-6 Stages in making a sketch.

shape of the V-block have been sketched freehand. Note how its proportions have been carefully observed on the sketch. Also, note how the blocking-in lines have been sketched in for all the views, so that they are properly located in the available space. Never attempt to sketch one complete view at a time; block them all in and proceed to work up the corresponding details in all the views.

6·7 Making a sketch. Careful practice and systematic methods of work are necessary to develop skill in making sketches.

The stages in making a sketch are shown in Fig. 6-6. Observe the object pictured in Space 1. Select the views necessary to describe it and judge the proportions. Estimate the proportions carefully and mark off distances for the three views as in Space 2. Block in the enclosing rectangles as in Space 3. Locate the details in each of the views and block them in as in Space 4. Finish the sketch by brightening the lines as in Space 5. The preliminary blocking-in lines should be made light so that they will not have to be erased and so that dashes for hidden lines can be drawn over them.

6·8 Orthographic views from pictures (Figs. 6-7 to 6-10). The objects shown are designed to give the student practice in shape description by sketching the views in pencil on plain or squared paper or on the blackboard. Make the sketches large enough to give a clear description of the shape of the object. Consider the proportions of the object and the choice of views needed for a complete description. Block in the views, proceed as described in Art. 6·7, and brighten the result.

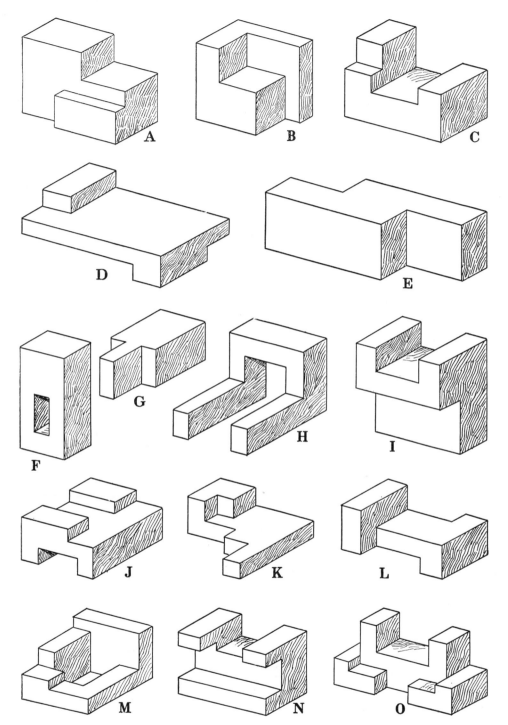

Fig. 6-7 Problems for freehand sketching.

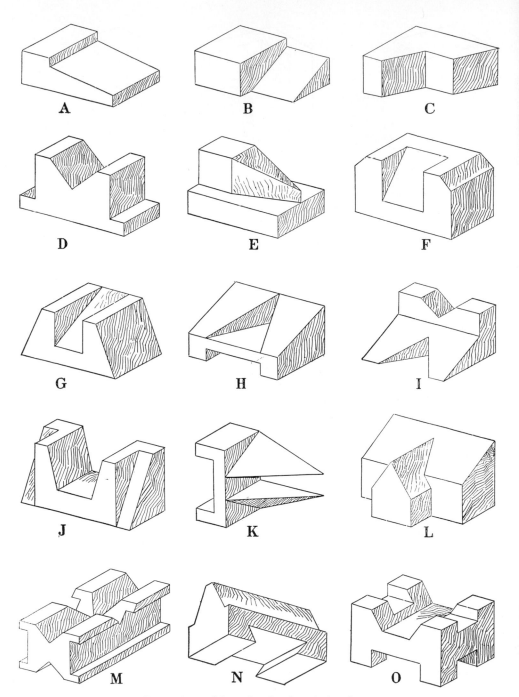

Fig. 6-8 Problems for freehand sketching.

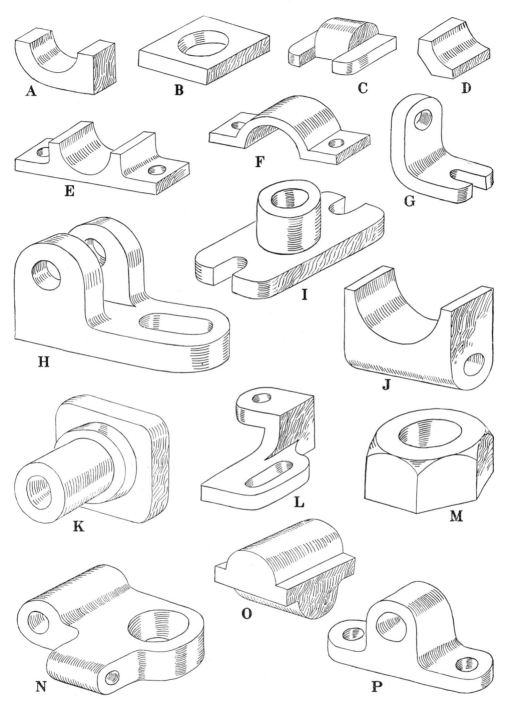

Fig. 6-9 Problems for freehand sketching.

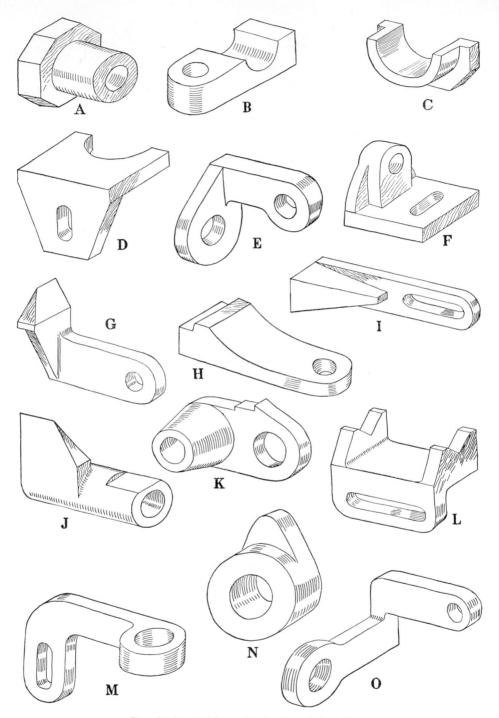

Fig. 6-10 Problems for freehand sketching.

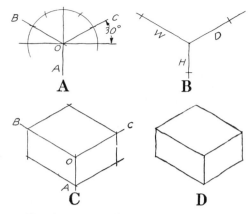

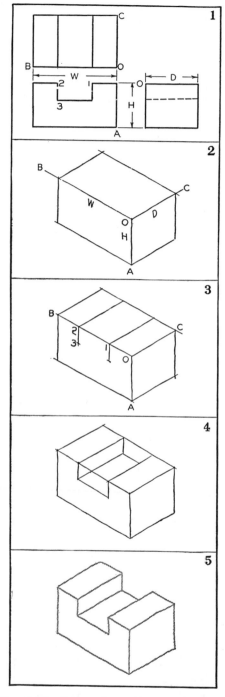

A

B

C

D

Fig. 6-11 Axes for pictorial sketches.

6·9 Pictorial sketches provide a convenient way of reading a drawing or of checking to see if a drawing is understood. While there are several types of pictorial sketches and drawings (see Chap. 14), isometric-type sketches are most often used for this purpose.

An isometric sketch is based on three lines, called *axes,* which are used to show the directions in which distances are laid off for heights (H), widths (W), and depths (D) of an object (Fig. 6-11). The height is shown by a vertical line (OA). The width (OB) and the depth (OC) are shown by lines making 30° with the horizontal. The 30° lines may be located by estimating one-third of a right angle as suggested in the figure.

6·10 To make an isometric sketch of an object, use very light lines which need not be erased when the picture is complete. Follow the steps in Fig. 6-12, where in Space 1 are shown the usual three orthographic views. Sketch the three axes as in Space 2. Note that:

Height (H) = OA
Width (W) = OB
Depth (D) = OC

Fig. 6-12 Stages in making an isometric sketch.

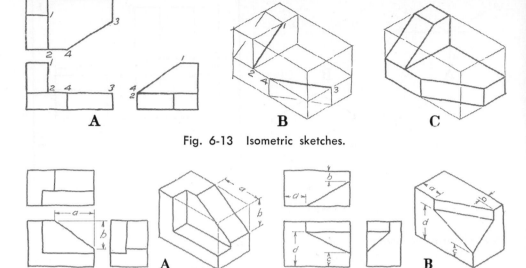

Fig. 6-13 Isometric sketches.

Fig. 6-14 Isometric sketches.

On the three axes lay off the height (*H*), the width (*W*), and the depth (*D*), estimating them from the orthographic views. Block in the enclosing prism. In Space 3 lay off distances 0–1, 1–2, and 2–3 and sketch lines through points 1, 2, and 3 parallel to the axes. These will indicate the part to be cut out as shown in Space 4.

In Space 5 the lines have all been brightened to show the picture of the object.

Any object may be enclosed in a box as suggested in the above method and its dimensions laid off parallel to the axes. Note, however, that the objects in Figs. 6-13 and 6-14 have some lines that are *not parallel* to the axes. In such cases locate the ends of the lines and join them. Sets of lines that are parallel on the object will show as parallel on the sketch, even though they are not parallel to one of the axes.

6·11 Circles and arcs on isometric sketches will appear as ellipses or parts of ellipses. To sketch the isometric view of a circle, first sketch the circumscribing square as in Fig. 6-15. Then sketch an ellipse in it, as shown for the circles

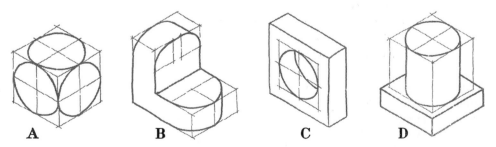

Fig. 6-15 Circles and arcs.

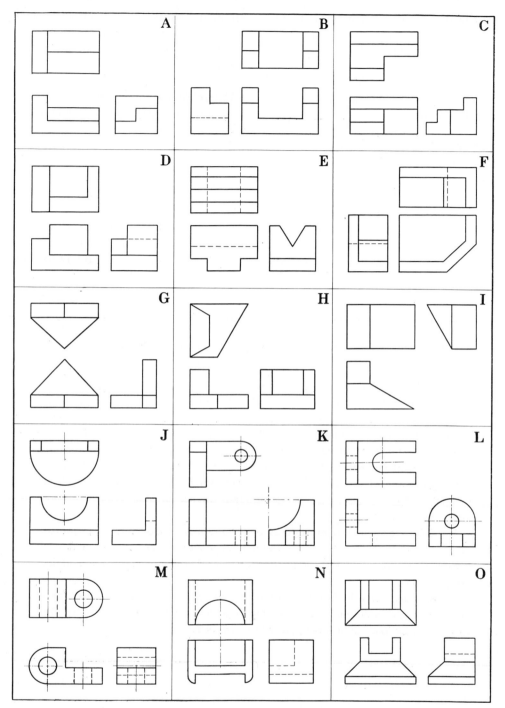

Fig. 6-16 Problems for pictorial sketching.

on three faces of the block at A. The methods of blocking in for arcs and circles are shown at B, C, and D. A study of the objects shown by views and pictures in Figs. 5-15 to 5-17 will be of help in understanding how to sketch pictures.

6·12 Problems in sketching pictures from orthographic views are given in Fig. 6-16. The sketches should be made large enough to show all construction clearly—two or three times the size shown. Block in with light lines and sketch the views in stages as described in Arts. 6·9 to 6·11. Be sure to check the orthographic views to see that all views are complete. In general it is well to sketch the enclosing box or rectangular prism first and then cut away the parts not needed.

6·13 Problem suggestions. A collection of models and parts of machines from which sketches can be made will provide an interesting and valuable method of learning to sketch. Many of the problems in Chap. 24 can be used for sketching practice. View sketches can be assigned from the pictures and pictorial sketches from view drawings (Chap. 14). Selections can also be made from Probs. D·67 and D·73 and from problems in Group N.

ENGINEERING COUNCIL FOR PROFESSIONAL DEVELOPMENT (ECPD)

The ECPD is an organization that improves and promotes the status of engineers. It concerns itself with the professional, technical, educational, and legislative phase of engineers' lives. The following national organizations cooperate in the efforts and activities of the ECPD: American Society of Civil Engineers, American Institute of Mining and Metallurgical Engineers, The American Society of Mechanical Engineers, American Institute of Electrical Engineers, The Engineering Institute of Canada, American Society for Engineering Education, Institute of Chemical Engineers, and the National Council of State Boards of Engineering Examiners.

The ECPD recommends procedures and standards to the national organizations. Its work is carried on through committees concerned with student guidance, engineering curricula, professional education and training, engineering ethics, and publicity.

A great deal of valuable information on the subjects mentioned is available at nominal cost in the publications of the Engineers Council for Professional Development, 29 West 39th Street, New York 18, N.Y.

7 Reading and making drawings

7·1 Reading a drawing consists of studying the views of an object to see what each line means and then deciding from this study how the surfaces that enclose the parts of the object are shaped and exactly where they are located.

In this way a mental picture of the object is obtained—its shape is *visualized*. For working drawings, dimensions must also be given. The principles of dimensioning will be discussed in Chap. 10.

7·2 Translation. When learning to read a drawing, one may start by translating the views of simple objects into words

or words into views. From such a beginning the ability to visualize lines, surfaces, and shapes is developed for constructions which would be very difficult to describe in words. This is the reason why mechanical drawing is used for engineering and architectural work.

Consider the object shown in Fig. 7-1. At A we have a rectangular prism with a hole, at B a frustum of a cone with a hole, and at C the frustum combined with the prism. Note that the picture does not show for certain that the hole goes all the way through. The views at D give an exact description. Try to describe this simple object in words and it will be seen that the com-

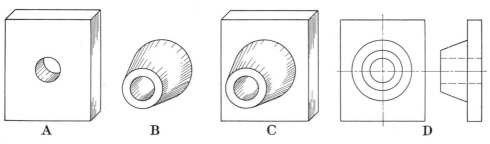

| A | B | C | D |

Fig. 7-1 Translation.

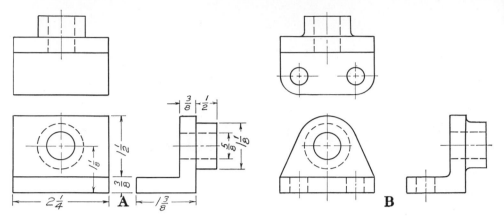

Fig. 7-2 Translation.

binations of lines which make up the views describe it more easily and quickly.

7·3 Views from word description. It is desired to make a bracket bearing. It is composed of a rectangular prism 2¼ in. wide, ⅜ in. high, and 1⅜ in deep. Another prism is placed at the back of, and on, the first prism. It is 2¼ in. wide, 1½ in. high, and ⅜ in. deep. This last prism has a cylinder projecting back from its center. It is 1⅛ in. diameter and ½ in. long. There is a hole ⅝ in. diameter through the cylinder and prism. This very simple object may be translated into views which describe it accurately in much less time as shown at A in Fig. 7-2. If there were bolt holes, rounded edges, corners, and other details such as shown at B, it would take many more words to describe it in writing.

7·4 Projections of distances. We have learned that the height, H, of an object is shown in the front and side views, that the width, W, is shown in the front and top views, and that the depth, D, is shown in the side and top views. This is illustrated for a simple prism in Fig. 7-3 at A and B, and for two other objects at C and D. Thus the height distances are included between parallel horizontal lines, and the width distances are included between parallel vertical lines. Depth distances are included between parallel horizontal lines in the top view

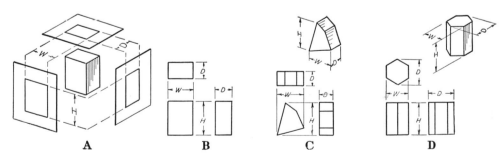

Fig. 7-3 Projections of distances.

and corresponding parallel vertical lines in the side view. These are total distances, but other lesser distances are located in the same way (Fig. 7-4).

7·5 Projections of points. A picture of a notched block is shown at A in Fig. 7-5. To draw three views, lay out the outlines and the notch in the top view as at B. The point a is located in the side view by the distance D, which is taken from the top view. In the front view, point a is located by projecting down from the top view and across from the side view. Other points are located by the same method as shown for point b at C.

7·6 Projections of lines. For straight lines, project the ends of the lines (Fig. 7-6).

1) A straight line parallel to two planes of projection will show its true length when projected to them. Line ab at A shows its true length in the front and top views.

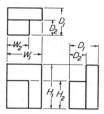

Fig. 7-4 Projections of distances.

2) A straight line perpendicular to a plane of projection will show as a point when projected to that plane. Line ab at A shows as a point in the side view.

3) A straight line inclined to two planes of projection and parallel to the other one will show less than its true length on the planes to which it is inclined and will show its true length on the plane to which it is parallel. Line cd at B shows less than its true length in the top and side views but shows its true length in the front view.

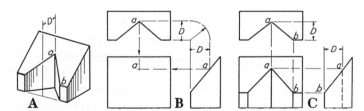

Fig. 7-5 Projections of points.

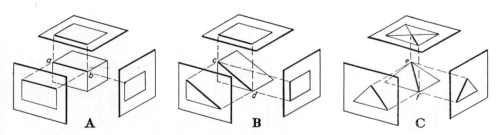

Fig. 7-6 Projections of straight lines.

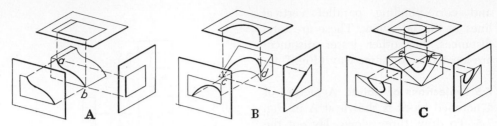

Fig. 7-7 Projections of curved lines.

4) A straight line inclined to all three planes of projection will show less than its true length in all three views, as line *ef* at C.

Curved lines are shown in Fig. 7-7.

1) A curved line in a plane parallel to a plane of projection will show its true shape on that plane. Line *ab* at A is parallel to the frontal plane and shows its true shape in the front view. It shows as a straight line in the top and side views.

2) A curved line in a plane inclined to two planes of projection and perpendicular to the other one will not show its true shape on any of the planes. It will show as a straight line on the plane to which its plane is perpendicular. Line *cd* at B does not show its true shape in the front or top view but shows as a line in the side view.

3) A curved line in a plane inclined to all three planes of projection will not show its true shape on any of them, as line *ef* at C.

7·7 Projections of plane surfaces are obtained by the projections of the lines which define them (Fig. 7-8).

1) A surface parallel to a plane of projection will show its true shape on that plane. Surface 1 at A is parallel to the frontal plane and shows its true shape in the front view.

2) A surface perpendicular to a plane of projection will show as a line on that plane. Surface 1 at A is perpendicular to the horizontal plane and shows as a line in the top view.

3) A surface inclined to a plane of projection will not show its true shape on the plane to which it is inclined. Surface 2 at B is inclined to the frontal and horizontal planes and appears foreshortened in the front and top views. Since surface 2 is perpendicular to the side plane, it shows as a line in the side view.

4) A surface inclined to the three planes of projection will not show its true shape on any of them (surface 3 at C).

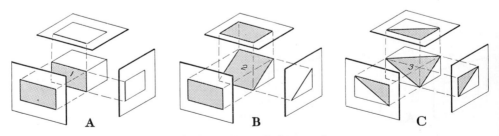

Fig. 7-8 Projections of plane surfaces.

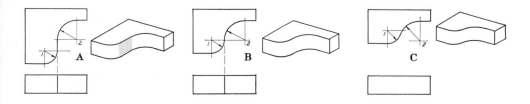

Fig. 7-9 Projections of curved surfaces.

Fig. 7-10 Projections of curved surfaces.

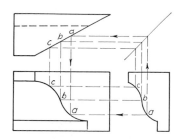

7·8 Projections of curved surfaces. Elementary curved surfaces have been illustrated in Art. 5·11. In Fig. 7-9 cylindrical surfaces form a part of each object. Note the location of the center of the radius in each case. At A there is a flat surface joining the two cylindrical surfaces, so a straight vertical line will show in the front view. At B the centers of the two radii are on a line parallel to the frontal plane. Where the curved surfaces meet there is a limiting line (contour line) for each surface, so a straight vertical line will show in the front view. At C the center of radius 1 is farther back from the frontal plane than the center for radius 2, and there will be no line to project to the front view.

7·9 Projections of lines of curved surfaces are found by projecting a series of points. In Fig. 7-10 the front view of the curved surface is found by taking a convenient number of points on the side view, as *a, b,* and *c,* and locating them in the top view. The next step is to project from the side and top views to locate the points in the front view and then to draw a smooth curve through these points. The front view of a curved line in Fig. 7-11 is also found by projecting from corresponding points in the side and top views.

Fillets and rounds occur on a great many parts. A *fillet* is a filled-in corner (Fig. 7-12 at A, B, and C). A *round* is a rounded-off corner (Fig. 7-12 at D).

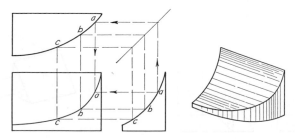

Fig. 7-11 Projections of curved surfaces.

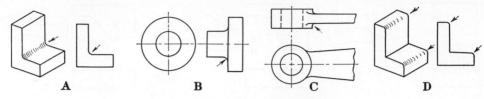

Fig. 7-12   Fillets and rounds.

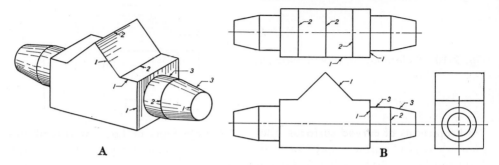

Fig. 7-13   The meaning of lines.

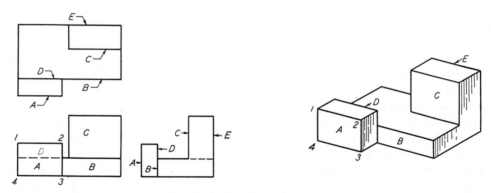

Fig. 7-14   Reading the views.

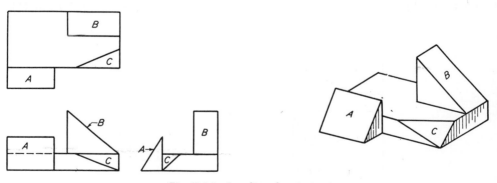

Fig. 7-15   Reading the views.

7·10 The meaning of lines. A line may represent the edge view of a surface, the intersection of two surfaces, or the outline or contour of a surface. In Fig. 7-13 lines numbered 1 represent edge views of surfaces as well as intersections of surfaces. Lines numbered 2 represent intersections of surfaces where shown. Lines numbered 3 represent elements or contour lines. Study each line and see what it means in the views in Fig. 7-13 and on some of the other illustrations.

7·11 Surfaces parallel to the planes of projection. In Fig. 7-14 the surfaces of the object are parallel to the planes of projection. There are three visible surfaces and two hidden surfaces when viewed from in front. Surface A is defined by four lines, 1–2, 2–3, 3–4, and 4–1. Locate these points in each of the three views. It will be seen that surface A is nearest the observer and shows its true shape in the front view. In like manner locate surfaces B and C. Surface B is farther back than surface A and nearer the front than surface C, as shown by the lines which represent them in the side and top views. Locate the two hidden surfaces D and E and sketch their outlines. Find the three visible surfaces and the one hidden surface as represented in the top view. In the side view there are two visible surfaces and two invisible surfaces.

7·12 Surfaces inclined to the planes of projection. In Fig. 7-15 observe the inclined surfaces. Surface A, which is nearest to the front, is inclined to the frontal and horizontal planes. It is perpendicular to the side or profile plane and shows as a line in the side view. Surface B is inclined to the horizontal

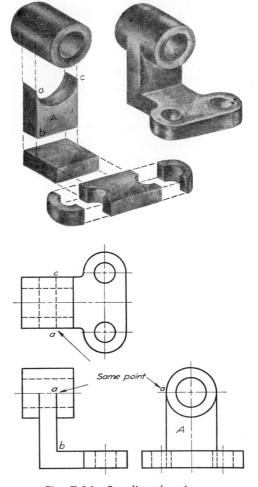

Fig. 7-16 Reading the views.

and side planes. It is perpendicular to the frontal plane and shows as a line on that plane. Surface C is inclined to all three planes. Each surface may be located by placing numbers at the ends of the lines which define it.

7·13 An example for study. The bearing shown in Fig. 7-16 is made up of cylinders, parts of cylinders, and rectangular prisms. There are flat surfaces and curved surfaces that require visible and invisible (hidden) lines. Notice

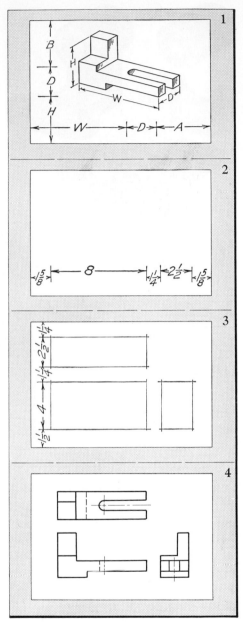

Fig. 7-17 Placing the views.

different parts are described in the views. Study the reason for the visible or hidden lines in each case as well as the necessity for three views in order to give a complete description of the bearing. Considering the three views shown to be the top, front, and right-side views, try to see how the bottom, rear, and left-side views would look. Which lines would be visible and which ones would be hidden? For a casting (see Arts. 13·12 and 13·13) the working drawing would show fillets or rounded-in corners at *b* and between the cylinder and the vertical support (see Fig. 7-12). Fillets are omitted in Fig. 7-16 to simplify the views for study purposes and to show how point *a* in the front view is determined by a tangent point in the right-side view.

7·14 Placing views. The size of the drawing sheet selected should provide for views that will give a clear description of the object. The size suggested for most of the problems in this book is $11'' \times 17''$, with a working space of $10\frac{1}{2}'' \times 15''$. Sheets $12'' \times 18''$ or $11'' \times 17''$ may be used with a working space as specified by the instructor. Figure 7-17 is worked out for a $10\frac{1}{2}'' \times 15''$ working space. The object shown in Space 1 has over-all dimensions of $W = 8''$, $H = 4''$, and $D = 2\frac{1}{2}''$. An easy way of locating the views is to lay off the width ($W = 8''$) and the depth ($D = 2\frac{1}{2}''$) from the left border line as shown in Space 1. The remaining distance, A, will measure $4\frac{1}{2}''$. It is to be divided into three parts to provide a space between the front and side views, a space at the left of the front view, and a space at the right of the side view. If the space between views is

that surface A of the side view is shown by a full line, *ab*, in the front view and by a hidden line, *ac*, in the top view. Compare the three views with the picture and notice how the

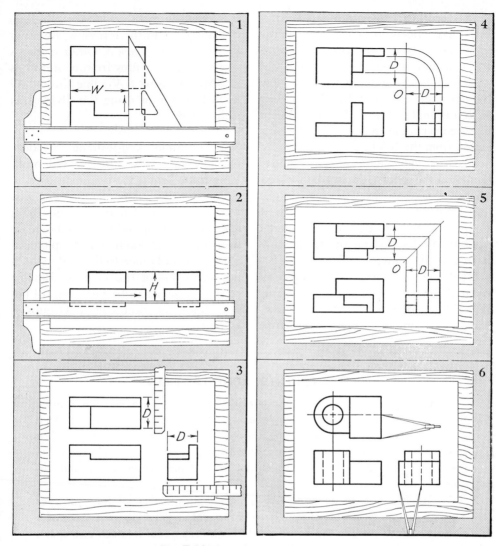

Fig. 7-18 Locating measurements.

made 1¼″, it will leave two spaces of 1⅝″ as shown in Space 2.

Next lay off the height ($H = 4″$) and the depth ($D = 2½″$) upward from the bottom border line as in Space 1. This leaves a distance B of 4″. If 1¼″ is left between views, 2¾″ will be left of the 4″ of which 1½″ can be used below the front view and 1¼″ above the top view.

More space is generally used below the front view because this gives a better appearance. Spaces between and around views depend upon their shapes, the dimensions required, and the size of the sheet.

As draftsmen get more experience, they find it possible to place the views for a drawing by locating a few starting lines without computations.

7·15 Locating measurements. After lines have been drawn to locate the views on the sheet, horizontal or width (*W*) measurements made on the front view can be located on the top view by drawing up from the front view with a triangle (Fig. 7-18, Space 1). In like manner measurements can be projected from the top to the front view.

Vertical or height (*H*) measurements on the front view can be located on the side view by drawing a light line across to the side view with a T-square (Space 2). Measurements can also be located on the front view from the side view.

Depth (*D*) measurements show as vertical distances in the top view and as horizontal distances in the side view. Such measurements can be taken from the top view to the side view, or from the side view to the top view, by using the scale as in Space 3. Other methods include drawing arcs from center *O* as in Space 4, using a 45° line through *O* as in Space 5, or using the dividers as in Space 6.

7·16 Problem suggestions. Models, parts of machines, and selected problems from Group D should be used in connection with this chapter. See List 2 at the end of Chap. 5, page 73. A few prints from industry to be read, described, and sketched in pictorial views will add much to the understanding and value of this chapter. Review of this chapter can be very helpful before doing the problems in Groups J, K, and L.

ENGINEERING REGISTRATION

All states, territories, and the District of Columbia now have laws that require the registration of professional engineers. Engineers are required to obtain a license from the state to practice, as are doctors and lawyers. To obtain such a certificate of registration, it is necessary to present evidence of qualifications to practice. The Model law, upon which the laws of most states are based, requires:

1. Graduation from an approved engineering curriculum of four years or more and a specific record of four years or more of engineering experience of a character satisfactory to the Board (State Registration Board) which also shows that the applicant is competent to practice engineering. A written or a written-and-oral examination may also be required.

OR

2. A specific record of eight or more years of experience in engineering work of a character satisfactory to the Board which shows that the applicant is competent to practice engineering. The applicant must also successfully pass a written or a written-and-oral examination designed to show knowledge and skill approximating that obtained through graduation from an approved engineering course.

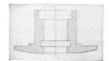

The motion picture and follow-up filmstrip *Sections* have been prepared to correlate with this chapter.

8 Sections

8·1 Sections show hidden details. We have learned how parts of an object that cannot be seen are shown by hidden lines (Art. 5·10) made with short dashes. This method is satisfactory if the object is solid or its interior simple. In drawings which show many inside details, or several pieces together, the hidden lines become confusing or hard to read. In such cases views, called *sections*, may be drawn to show the object as if it were cut apart.

The picture in Fig. 8-1 shows how an electric motor would look if cut

Fig. 8-1 Cutaway view of Tri-Clad electric motor. (See Art. 8·1 for description of numbered parts.) (*General Electric Company*)

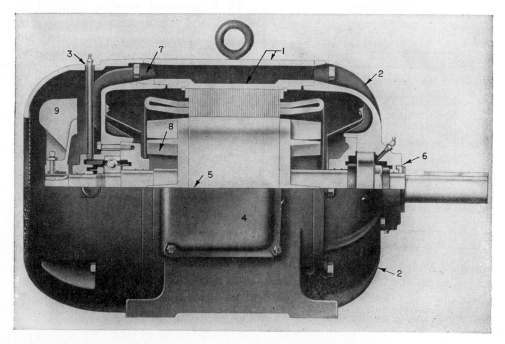

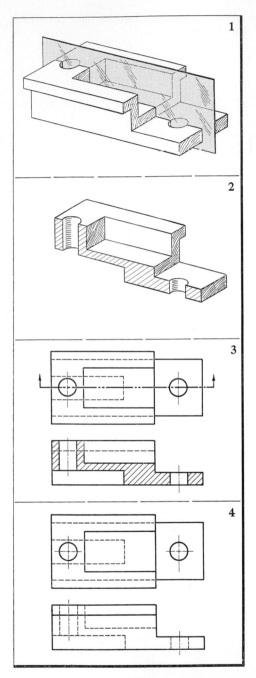

through the center and halfway down, with the cutaway part removed. Compare the upper part of the picture with the lower part. Then imagine how a regular drawing of the motor would look with part of it cut away as in the picture. Think how confusing it would be if one attempted to show all the interior details on an exterior view by using hidden lines. The manufacturer of the motor in Fig. 8-1 has described these details as follows: (1) A cast-iron double-wall frame; (2) ribbed cast-iron end shields; (3) pressure-relief greasing systems; (4) cast-iron conduit box diagonally split for wiring convenience; (5) leads are sealed in a non-shrinking compound at the point where they emerge from frame; (6) rotating labyrinth seal prevents infiltration of grit or liquids; (7) large free-flowing easy-to-clean air passages; (8) modern "ageless" insulation treatment; (9) powerful external fan.

8·2 A sectional view is obtained by supposing the piece to be cut apart by an imaginary cutting plane and the part in front of the plane removed, thus exposing the interior. This is shown in pictorial form in Spaces 1 and 2 of Fig. 8-2. The imaginary cutting plane is shown in Space 1. The appearance of the cut surface, after the front portion has been removed, is shown in Space 2. The sectional view is shown in Space 3. On a drawing the cut surface is represented by section lining with uniformly spaced thin lines generally at 45° (sometimes called *crosshatching*). In the top view the edge of the cutting plane is indicated by a cutting-plane line with the ends turned at 90° and terminated by arrow-

Fig. 8-2 A sectional view is obtained by cutting an object with an imaginary cutting plane, Space 1. Exposed interior, Space 2.

98 MECHANICAL DRAWING

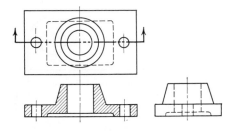

Fig. 8-3 A full section parallel to the frontal plane.

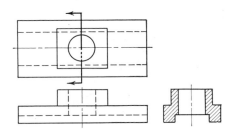

Fig. 8-4 A full section parallel to the profile plane.

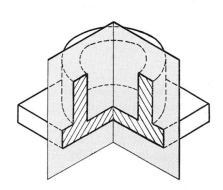

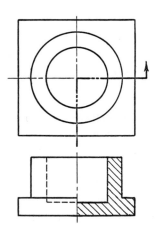

Fig. 8-5 A half section.

heads to show the direction of the view (see alphabet of lines, Fig. 11-2). The part supposed to be cut away is not left out in the top view. Regular full views are shown in Space 4 for comparison.

8·3 A full section is a view of an object as it would appear if cut entirely across the object as in Fig. 8-2, Space 3. The cutting plane may be taken parallel to the frontal plane as in Fig. 8-3, parallel to the profile plane as in Fig. 8-4, parallel to the horizontal plane, or at an angle (see Fig. 9-9).

When it is necessary to identify a section, letters are used at the arrowheads. (Refer to Fig. 16-4, page 217).

8·4 A half section (Fig. 8-5) is a view obtained when the cutting plane extends halfway through the piece. One-half the view is a section and the other half is an outside view. Such views can be used to advantage with symmetrical pieces to show both the interior and exterior in one view. The hidden lines may be left out on both sides unless they are needed for dimensioning. Figure 8-1 is a pictorial half-sectional view.

SECTIONS **99**

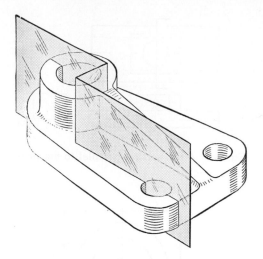

Fig. 8-6   Offset cutting plane.

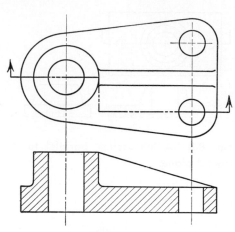

Fig. 8-7   An offset section.

8·5 Offset sections. The cutting plane is usually taken straight through the object, but it may be offset in any part in order to show some detail or to miss some part (Figs. 8-6 and 8-7). Here the offset plane passes through the hole and is in front of the rib. It shows the hole and the rib more clearly than if the section were continued through the center. If the rib were sectioned, it would make the part look heavier.

8·6 To make a sectional view. Think how the object would look if it were actually sawed in two. Draw all lines that are in the plane of the section and all visible lines in back of the plane (Fig. 8-8). Draw only such hidden (invisible) lines as are necessary to describe the shape or for dimensioning.

8·7 Sections of assembled pieces (Fig. 8-9). When two or more pieces are

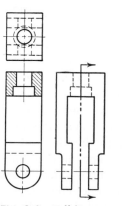

Fig. 8-8   Full lines on a section.

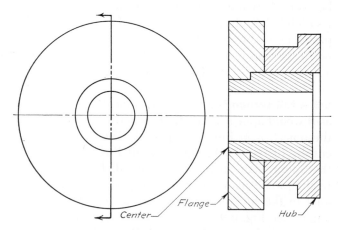

Fig. 8-9   Adjacent pieces in section.

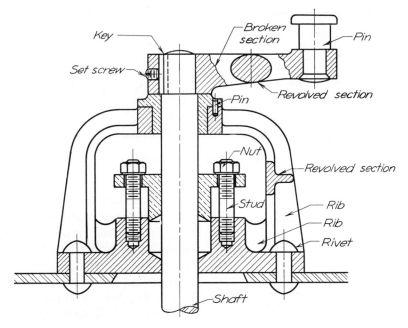

Fig. 8-10   Bolts, shafts, and so forth, on sectional views.

shown together, they are sectioned with lines drawn in different directions. However, any separate piece must have the section lines in the same direction wherever it appears as a cut surface. Section lines at 30° or 60°, and closer or farther apart, may be used when it is necessary to distinguish between a number of adjacent parts.

8·8 Section lining. The spacing between section lines should give the effect of an even tint. This requires uniform spacing of the lines. For most purposes the distance between lines can be about ³⁄₃₂ in., spaced by eye. For small areas use closer spacing (¹⁄₁₆ in.). For large areas use wider spacing (⅛ in.).

Sometimes different materials are indicated by varying the kinds of section lining. The symbols to use when this is done are shown in Fig. 11-9. Ordi-

narily it is better to use the regular section lining and specify the material by a note.

8·9 Special sections. When shafts, bolts, nuts, screws, keys, and similar parts occur in the plane of a section, they are not cut through but are left in full as indicated in Fig. 8-10. The purpose of a sectional view is to show interior details clearly. Therefore, when parts have no interior details, they are best shown in full. Broken sections can be used to show certain interior features. Revolved sections provide a convenient means of showing the shape of a rib or arm at right angles to the view. Note the method of showing the break at the lower end of the shaft to indicate that it is cylindrical. Ribs are not sectioned because to do so would make the part appear heavier and because

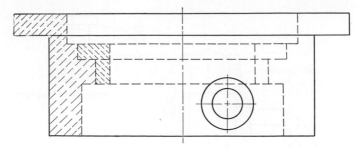

Fig. 8-11   A phantom section.

ribs have no interior detail to be shown.

The hidden or phantom section (Fig. 8-11) is used when it is desired to show on the same view the interior and exterior of a part that is not completely symmetrical. Note that the circular boss in Fig. 8-11 is on only one side of the piece. A half section could not be used in this case.

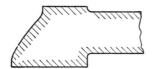

Fig. 8-12   A blacked-in section.

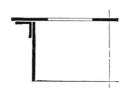

Fig. 8-13   An outline section.

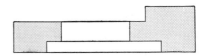

Fig. 8-14   A shaded section.

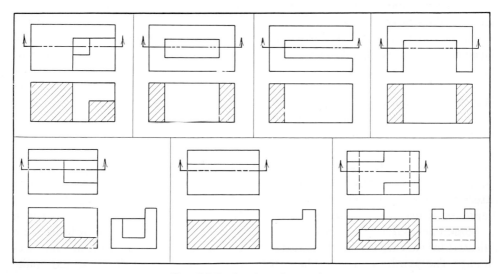

Fig. 8-15   Sections for study.

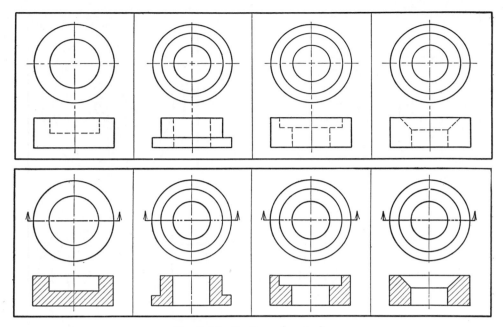

Fig. 8-16 Sections for study.

When the sectioned area is very small, as for thin plates, sheets, and structural shapes, blacked-in sections may be used as in Fig. 8-12. Note the white space between the parts.

A timesaving method of indicating a large sectioned area is to use outline sectioning as shown in Fig. 8-13. This method is often used on design drawings, with the section lines drawn freehand. Still another method is to gray the sectioned area with a pencil or to rub pencil dust over the area (Fig. 8-14).

8·10 Sectional-view problems. Study each piece shown in Figs. 8-15 and 8-16 until the reason for each sectional view is understood. Then redraw by freehand the objects shown in Figs. 8-17 to 8-20, changing one of the views of each to a full section as indicated by the cutting plane. The surfaces that are

cut should have light, uniformly spaced section lines, drawn at approximately 45°. Draw the views large enough so that they can be easily read, perhaps about four times the size shown in the book (estimated).

8·11 Problem suggestions. Group E, page 403. Two lists are presented. List 1 includes basic problems and in general more elementary problems than List 2. Selections should be made according to the purpose of the course. List 2 may be used for additional or alternate assignments, or selections may be used in more advanced groups.

LIST 1   Problems E·1, E·2, E·5, E·8, E·9, E·12, E·14, E·16, E·18

LIST 2   Problems E·3, E·4, E·6, E·7, E·10, E·11, E·13, E·19, E·20, E·21

Additional or alternate problems may be selected from Chap. 24.

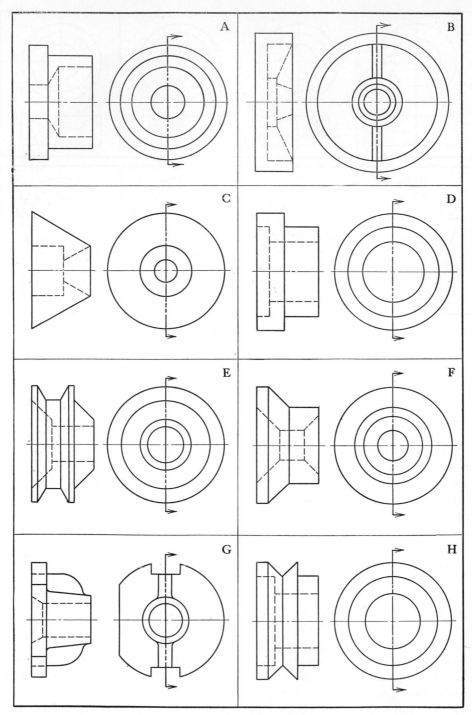

Fig. 8-17 Sectional-view problems.

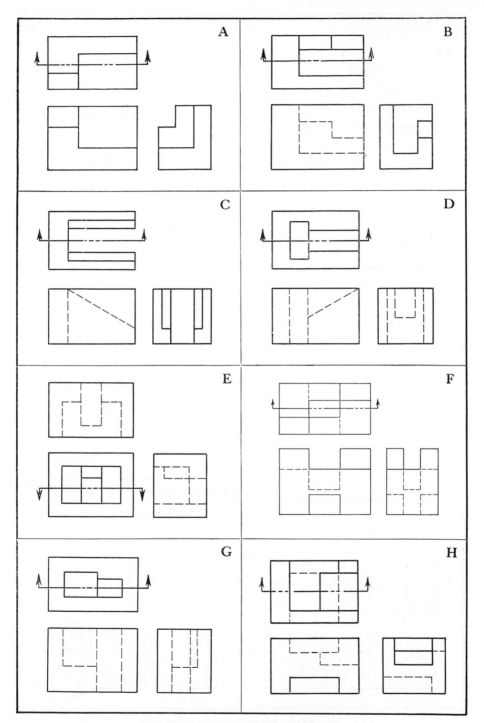

Fig. 8-18 Sectional-view problems.

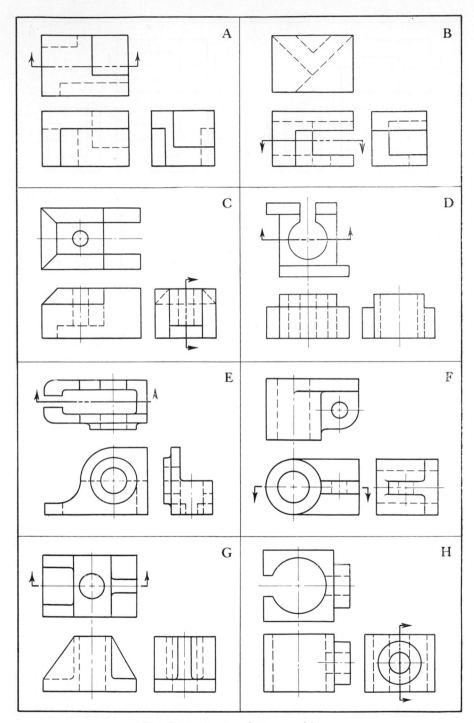

Fig. 8-19 Sectional-view problems.

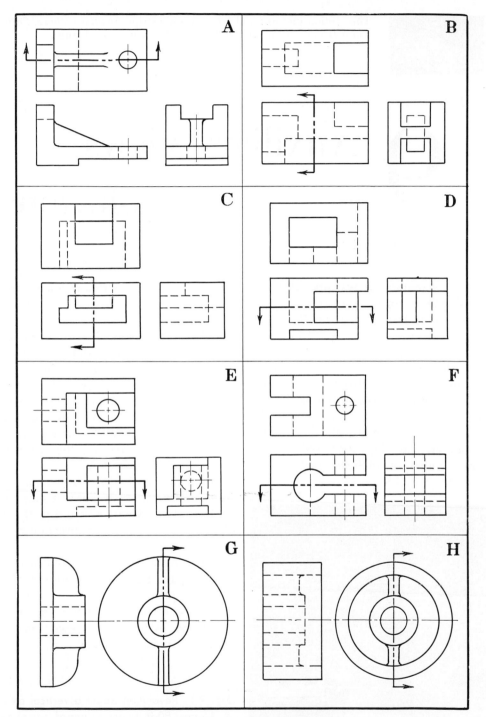

Fig. 8-20 Sectional-view problems.

The motion pictures and follow-up filmstrips *Auxiliary Views, Parts I* and *II* have been prepared to correlate with this chapter.

9 Auxiliary views and revolutions

9·1 Explanatory views projected on other planes. In the previous chapters views have been drawn on the three regular planes with the object in a normal (regular) position. The three regular planes are the top or horizontal plane, the front or frontal plane, and the side or profile plane. In this chapter we shall learn how to draw views of objects that have been revolved or turned about an axis (Fig. 9-1) and how to draw views of inclined surfaces on planes at an angle with a regular plane (Figs. 9-3 to 9-11).

9·2 Auxiliary views. The usual views of an object do not show the true shapes of slanting surfaces (Fig. 9-2 at A). However, a view on a plane parallel to the slanting surface will show the true shape as at B. This together with the side view and a bottom view of the base will give a better description than the views at A.

An *auxiliary view* is a projection on an *auxiliary plane* parallel to a slanting surface. It is a view looking directly at the slanting surface in a direction perpendicular to it.

Observe the anchor pictured in Fig. 9-3 in Space 1 and the position of the auxiliary plane in Space 2. In Space 3 the shape of the anchor is completely described by the two views, one of which is an auxiliary view.

Fig. 9-1 Revolution about a vertical axis. A 15-ton, 80-ft boom shipyard traveling crane. (*McKiernan-Terry Corporation*)

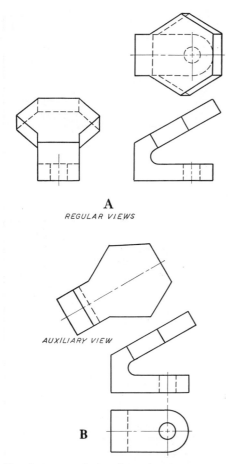

A
REGULAR VIEWS

AUXILIARY VIEW

B

Fig. 9-2 Regular and auxiliary views compared.

Auxiliary views are important for describing the shapes of inclined features, especially when they have an irregular outline. They are also necessary for dimensioning such features.

9·3 The relation of the auxiliary view to the usual views is illustrated by the simple block in Fig. 9-4. The three regular views are shown in Space 1, the side view being obtained by looking in the direction of arrow I. The face A does not show in its true shape in any view. If we locate a plane parallel to

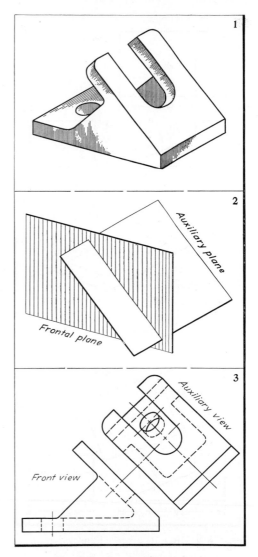

Fig. 9-3 An auxiliary view.

face A, as in Space 2, and look in the direction of arrow II, perpendicular to face A, we obtain an auxiliary view on the auxiliary plane that will show the true size and shape of face A. Such an auxiliary view made on an auxiliary plane and revolved into the plane of the paper is shown in Space 3. The true size and shape of any inclined surface

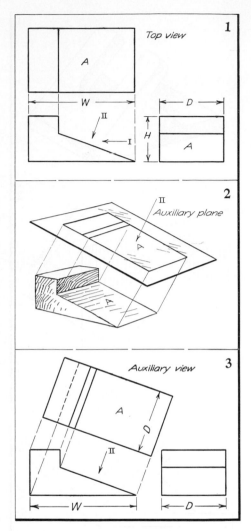

Fig. 9-4 Relation of auxiliary view to other views.

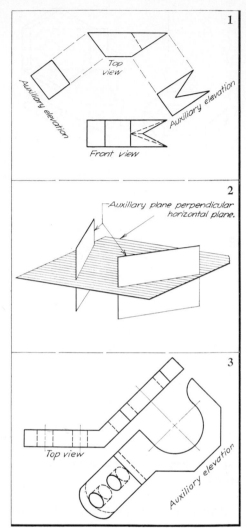

Fig. 9-5 Auxiliary elevations—on planes perpendicular to horizontal plane.

may be shown in a similar way as described in Arts. 9·2 to 9·6.

9·4 Kinds of auxiliary views. Auxiliary views may be classified according to the positions of the planes upon which they are drawn.

Elevation auxiliary views are made on planes that are perpendicular to the

horizontal plane (Fig. 9-5). The positions of the auxiliary planes for the auxiliary elevations of Space 1 are pictured in Space 2. An auxiliary elevation of an angular hook is shown in Space 3.

Left- or right-auxiliary views are auxiliary views made on planes that are perpendicular to the frontal plane (Fig. 9-6). The positions of the auxiliary

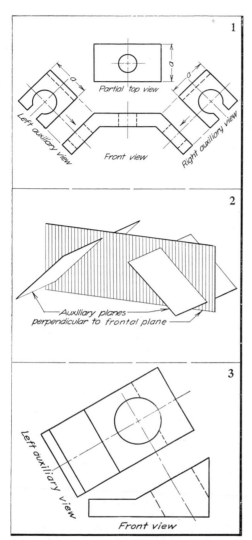

Fig. 9-6 Left- and right-auxiliary views—on planes perpendicular to frontal plane.

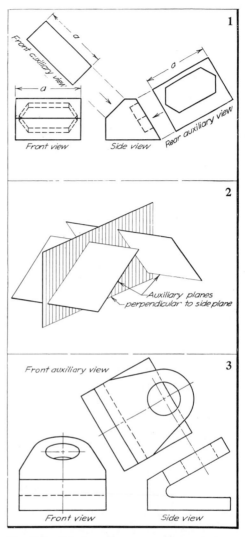

Fig. 9-7 Front- and rear-auxiliary views—on planes perpendicular to side plane.

planes for the left- and right-auxiliary views of Space 1 are pictured in Space 2. A left-auxiliary view is shown in Space 3.

Front- and rear-auxiliary views are auxiliary views made on planes that are perpendicular to the side or profile plane (Fig. 9-7). The positions of the auxiliary planes for the front- and rear-

auxiliary views of Space 1 are pictured in Space 2. A front-auxiliary view of a special angle is shown in Space 3.

9·5 Practical auxiliary views. When working drawings for practical use are being made, the object can often be described by partial views. Notice that the casting in Fig. 9-8 is drawn with a

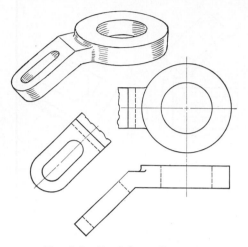

Fig. 9-8 Partial auxiliary view.

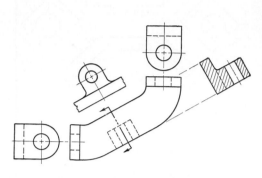

Fig. 9-9 Auxiliary section.

partial auxiliary view and a partial top view. Another practical use of auxiliary views is the auxiliary section (Fig. 9-9).

9·6 To draw an auxiliary view (Fig. 9-10). For a symmetrical object a center line is used to represent the edge of a center plane. Thus for the hexagonal

prism (Fig. 9-10), draw a center-plane line for the auxiliary view parallel to the inclined face at any convenient distance from it and draw a horizontal center-plane line through the top view. Draw projecting lines perpendicular to the inclined face from each point. On each of these lines locate the auxiliary

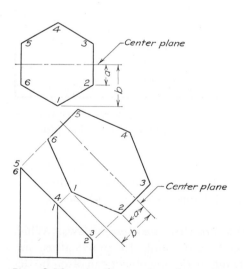

Fig. 9-10 Auxiliary view from center plane.

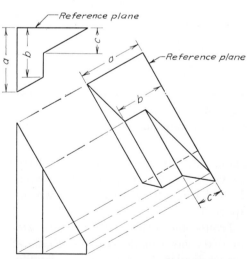

Fig. 9-11 Auxiliary view from reference plane.

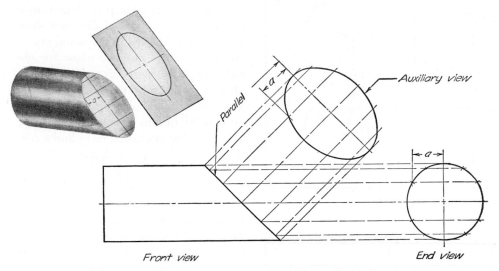

Fig. 9-12 Auxiliary view of cut face of cylinder.

view of the point projected by measuring the distance of the point from the center-plane line on the top view and marking off this distance from the center-plane line of the auxiliary view. Distances a and b are toward the front of the object as shown in the top view and, therefore, are measured toward the front in the auxiliary view. Since the figure is symmetrical, the same distances would be measured on the other side of the line, and the auxiliary view of the inclined face would be completed by joining the numbered points. In Fig. 9-10 only the inclined face has been drawn, but the entire object would be projected in the same way.

Reference-plane lines are used for the solution of unsymmetrical objects. Thus for an unsymmetrical object, such as Fig. 9-11, a reference-plane line is used. This line is placed for convenience in taking measurements. In this case the reference-plane line is placed at the back of the object so that all measurements are laid off toward the front view.

Auxiliary views of curved outlines are obtained by locating a number of points on the curves. This is illustrated by the auxiliary view of the inclined surface of a cylinder (Fig. 9-12). In this case the vertical center line (representing a center plane) of the end view, which shows the end of the cylinder, is a line from which measurements are made and transferred to the auxiliary view. Select a convenient number of points on the front view of the inclined surface. Then draw perpendiculars from them to the auxiliary center line. Project the same points to the side view. Measure the distance from the center line to each point and lay off this distance on each side of the center line of the auxiliary view.

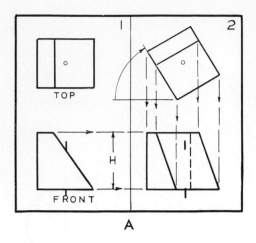

A

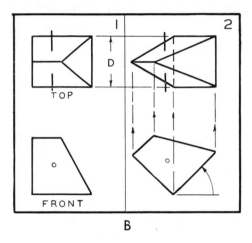

B

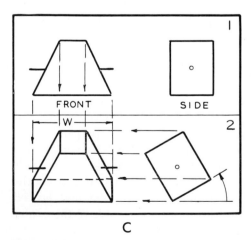

C

9·7 Revolutions. Ordinarily drawings are made for objects placed in simple positions where most of the lines show in their true lengths in the usual views. However, views may be made for objects tipped about an edge, resting upon a corner, or revolved about an axis. Sometimes a revolved view is needed to obtain or check the space necessary for operation or to find a particular true length or shape.

An *axis of revolution* may be taken perpendicular to the horizontal, frontal, or side planes. In Fig. 9-13 at A, the usual views are shown in Space 1. The views after revolution about an axis perpendicular to the horizontal plane are shown in Space 2. In Fig. 9-13 at B, usual views are shown in Space 1, and views after revolution about an axis perpendicular to the frontal plane are shown in Space 2. In Fig. 9-13 at C, usual views are shown in Space 1, and views after revolution about an axis perpendicular to the side plane are shown in Space 2. Revolution may be clockwise (to the right) as in Fig. 9-13 at A or counterclockwise (to the left) as at B. At C, the object has been revolved counterclockwise (to the left) or forward.

9·8 The rule of revolution may be stated in two parts:

1) The view perpendicular to the axis of revolution is unchanged except in position (Fig. 9-13). This is true because the axis is perpendicular to the plane on which it is projected.

2) Distances parallel to the axis of revolution are unchanged. This is true because they are parallel to the plane or

Fig. 9-13 Revolutions.

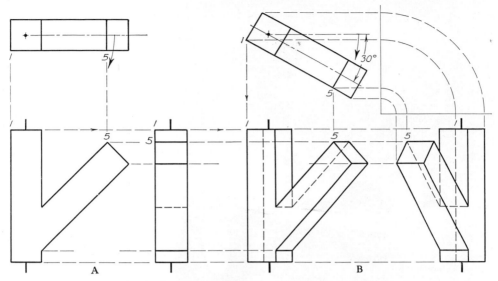

Fig. 9-14 Revolution about a vertical axis—clockwise.

planes on which they are projected. In Fig. 9-13 at A the *H*-distances are parallel to the frontal and side planes. At B the *D*-distances are parallel to the side and horizontal planes. At C the *W*-distances are parallel to the frontal and horizontal planes.

9·9 Vertical axis of revolution. Figure 9-14 shows the method of drawing an object revolved about a vertical axis. Given the three views, as at A, it is required to draw the views after the piece has been revolved clockwise through 30° about a vertical axis. First draw the top view in its new position B. Since the axis is vertical, the height has not been changed; so a horizontal projecting line may be drawn from point 1 of the front view in A and a vertical pro-

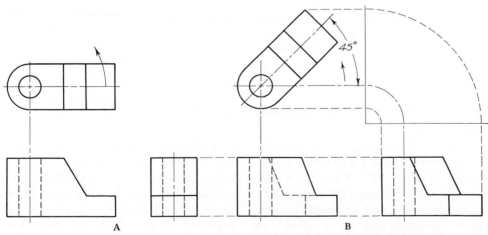

Fig. 9-15 Revolution about a vertical axis—counterclockwise.

Fig. 9-16 Revolution about a horizontal axis. Concrete mixer. (*The Jaeger Machine Company*)

jecting line from the top view in B. The intersection of the two lines just drawn will locate the position of point 1 in the new front view. Proceed in the same way for each point and join the points to complete the view. The side view is obtained from the front and top views in the usual manner. The object shown in Fig. 9-15 is revolved counterclockwise through 45°.

9·10 Revolution about a horizontal axis is illustrated in Fig. 9-16. The method of drawing the views of an object revolved about a horizontal axis is shown in Fig. 9-17. First draw the views in the usual way. Then revolve to a new position about an imaginary axis taken perpendicular to a plane of projection.

At A in Fig. 9-17 we have two views of an object in a natural position. Suppose a hole is drilled through from the front and a shaft inserted as shown. The object might be revolved about the shaft or axis into a new position as at B. It will be observed that the front view of B is the same as the front view of A, except that its position has been changed. The top view of B is obtained by projecting up from the new front view and across from the top view of A.

9·11 Practical revolved views. When working drawings for practical use are being made, objects often can be described better by drawing one of the views, or part of a view, in a revolved position. In Fig. 9-18 the top view shows the angle made by the right-

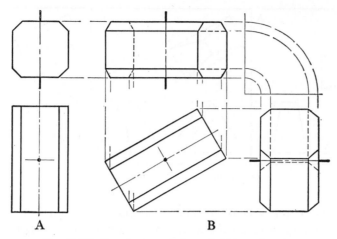

Fig. 9-17 Revolution about a horizontal axis.

hand part, and the front view shows the true shape, in a revolved position. In Fig. 9-19 the angles are shown in the front view, and the true shapes, together with the total length when the parts have been revolved, are shown in the top view.

9·12 Successive revolutions. After an object has been revolved about an axis perpendicular to a plane, it may be revolved about an axis perpendicular to another plane. This is double, or successive, revolution and is illustrated in Fig. 9-20. The piece shown at A has been revolved about a vertical axis

through 30° at B. From this position it has been revolved about an axis perpendicular to the vertical plane through 45° at C.

9·13 Direction of revolution. An object may be revolved to the right or to the left about an axis perpendicular to either the horizontal or the vertical plane. An object may be revolved forward or backward about an axis perpendicular to the side plane. In this case the side view would be the unchanged view, and the widths of the front and top views would be the unchanged distances.

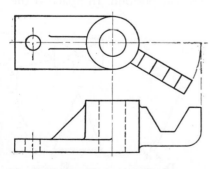

Fig. 9-18 Revolution applied—vertical axis.

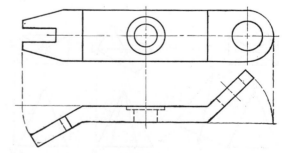

Fig. 9-19 Revolution applied—horizontal axis.

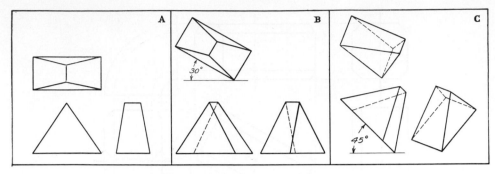

Fig. 9-20 Successive revolution.

9·14 To find the true length of a line.
Since an auxiliary view of an inclined
surface shows its true size and shape, it
may be used to find the true length of a
line as in Fig. 9-21 at A. Line OA does
not show its true length in the top or
front view because it is inclined to the
planes of projection. But line OA shows
its true length in the auxiliary view as
it is parallel to the auxiliary plane.

If the pyramid is revolved as in Fig.
9-21 at B, so that the top view of line
OA is horizontal, the front view of OA
will then show its true length because
the line is then parallel to the frontal
plane.

Instead of revolving the whole pyramid, just the line OA may be revolved
until it is parallel to one of the planes
of projection. In Fig. 9-21 at C and D

the line has been revolved until its top
view is horizontal at OA'. The point A'
can then be projected to the front view
where OA' will be the true length.

Revolution may, of course, be such
as to make the line parallel to any one
of the three planes. Its projection on
the plane to which it is parallel will
show its true length. In Fig. 9-21 at E
the line has been revolved parallel to
the horizontal plane, and the true
length is shown at OA' in the top view.

**9·15 True shape of an inclined plane
by double revolution.** A surface will
show in its true shape when it is parallel to a plane. In Fig. 9-22 the surface
1–2–3–4 of the object pictured in Space
D is inclined to all three of the normal
planes. In Space A the object is drawn
in its normal position. In Space B the

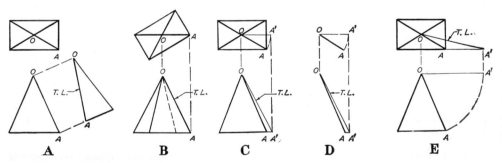

Fig. 9-21 Finding the true length of a line.

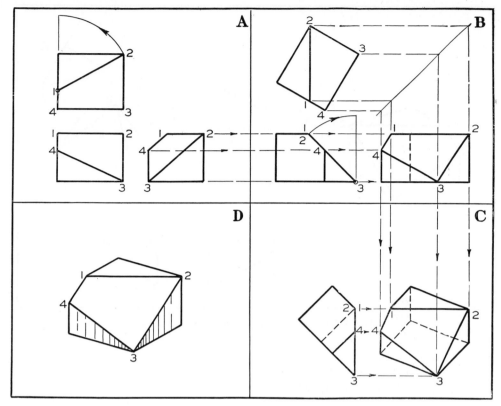

Fig. 9-22 True shape by revolution.

object has been revolved about a vertical axis until the inclined surface is perpendicular to the frontal plane. In Space C the object has been revolved from the position of Space B until the surface 1–2–3–4 is parallel to the profile plane and shows its true shape.

9·16 True shape of an inclined plane surface by oblique or double auxiliary views. Such views are made on a plane parallel to a surface which is inclined to all three of the normal planes. Surface 1–2–3–4 in Fig. 9-23 is inclined to the three normal planes. At A an auxiliary view has been drawn on a plane perpendicular to the inclined surface. At B an auxiliary view has been drawn

from the view at A on a plane parallel to the surface 1–2–3–4. The true shape of the surface is shown at B.

9·17 Problem suggestions. Group F, page 411. Group G, page 420. Two lists are presented. List 1 includes basic problems which in general are more elementary problems than List 2. Selections should be made according to the purpose of the course. List 2 may be used for additional or alternate assignments or may be used for more advanced students.

LIST 1 Problems F·1, F·2, F·4, F·6, F·8, F·10, F·12, F·17, F·19, F·21, G·1, G·2, G·5

(Problem List continued on next page.)

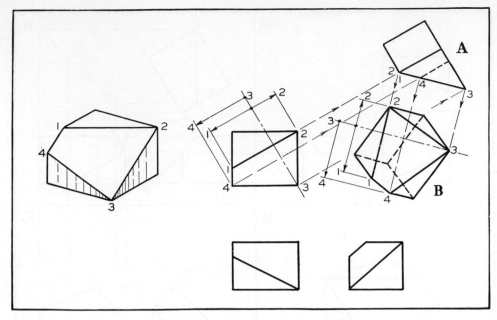

Fig. 9-23 True shape by double auxiliary.

LIST 2 Problems F·5, F·7, F·9, F·11, G·9, G·10, G·11
F·13, F·14, F·15, F·16, F·18, Additional or alternate problems may
F·20, F·22, F·23, F·24, G·3, G·6, be selected from Chap. 24.

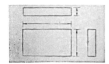

The motion picture and follow-up filmstrip *Size Description* have been prepared to correlate with this chapter.

10 Principles of size description

10·1 Size. We have learned that the two things to be told about an object are its shape and its size. In the previous chapters we studied the methods of showing the shape. When information about the size is added to the shape de-

Fig. 10-1 Size accuracy. Hoke gage blocks are square. A stack of them pressed together stands solidly on a surface plate. Tie rods through the center holes bind the stack rigidly if desired. Here a complicated magnesium casting is being scribed easily and exactly. Precision gage blocks are the basic master standards of measurement which establish the inch as a definite value. Accuracy here is measured in millionths of an inch. The measuring faces of the blocks are guaranteed flat and parallel in all sizes within four millionths of an inch per inch of length. Blocks are used in stacks to make up any desired dimension. (*Pratt & Whitney Company, Penn-Texas Corporation*)

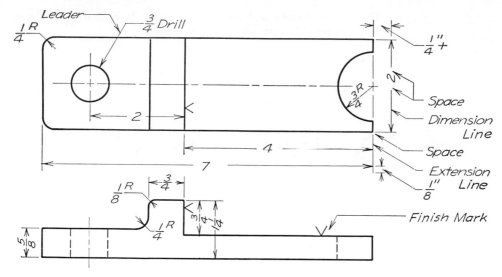

Fig. 10-2 Dimensioning.

scription, the two together give the complete working drawing of the object.

Size description is, then, an essential and important part of a working drawing. For some purposes, it is enough to specify nominal and ordinary sizes in common fractions of an inch. Sometimes a note should be added stating that dimensions are to be plus or minus a specified amount, as $\frac{1}{64}$ in. or $\frac{1}{32}$ in.; for large castings it might be that $\frac{1}{16}$ in. or more would be sufficiently close. Such a note may be placed on the drawing with the views, or it may be placed in the title block, usually in a space provided for this purpose. When accurate dimensions are required, they are given in decimals to hundredths or thousandths of an inch. In other cases extreme accuracy may be necessary, as illustrated in Fig. 10-1 and described by The Pratt & Whitney Company, a part of the Penn-Texas Corporation.

10·2 Dimensions. Although working drawings are made to scale, it would require too much time to take off distances by applying a scale to the drawing. Furthermore, the chances of making a mistake would be much too great, especially with small distances or on drawings made to a small scale. Distances on drawings vary as paper and cloth stretch and shrink with changes in the weather. It would be impossible to obtain measurements for the accuracy required for interchangeable manufacture where large numbers of the same piece must fit in place with neighboring parts. Notes such as "Do not scale this print. Work to dimensions shown" are sometimes placed on industrial prints as a warning.

For convenience in using, ensuring accuracy, and saving time, size description is given in the form of dimensions and notes arranged on the drawing in a definite manner.

122 MECHANICAL DRAWING

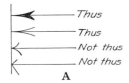 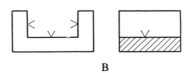 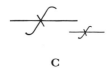

Fig. 10-3 Arrowheads and finish marks.

10·3 Lines, figures, arrowheads, etc. Certain lines and symbols are used on drawings. These lines and symbols are recognized easily by the many different kinds of people who use the drawings. Professional and trade associations, engineering societies, and certain industries have agreed upon the symbols they use in their drawings. The American Standards Association[1] in particular leads the work of standardization. To make a correct drawing, the draftsman must be familiar with these symbols, and he must know the principles of dimensioning. He must also be acquainted with the shop processes that will be used in building or making the object he is drawing. Symbols are sometimes used to show such processes.

The dimension line is a thin full line in contrast with the heavier shape outline (see Art. 11·3, Alphabet of lines). The line is ended by long pointed arrowheads (Fig. 10-2). Great care must be taken to have all arrowheads correctly shaped (Fig. 10-3 at A).

10·4 Finished or machined surfaces are indicated by the symbol ∨ touching the line that represents the finished surface as shown at B in Fig. 10-3. The old symbol ƒ shown at C is still in use but is being replaced by the ∨ symbol.

10·5 Use of extension lines. A space is left in the dimension line for a figure to

[1] American Standards Association, 70 East 45th Street, New York 17, N.Y.

tell the actual distance on the full-size piece. When the dimension is placed outside the outline of the view, *extension* or *witness* lines are drawn from the view to show the points or surfaces measured on the object. Extension lines are thin lines drawn from the outline and extending approximately ⅛″ past the arrowhead. Since extension lines are not part of the shape, they should not touch the outline (see Fig. 10-2).

10·6 Figures must be carefully made so that they are easy to read. Do not make them so large, however, that they overbalance the drawing. In general, make them about ⅛ in. high. To avoid crowding, dimension lines should be ⅜ in. or more from the lines of the drawing and from each other. Always make a fraction with a horizontal division line. Figures for fractions are made about two-thirds the height of whole numbers.

Light guidelines for figures and fractions may be drawn quickly and easily with the Braddock-Rowe triangle as illustrated in Fig. 10-4. The group of holes in the left-hand part of the triangle have been spaced for this purpose.

10·7 Placing dimensions. The important thing in placing dimensions is to keep in mind the man who has to read the drawing and make the piece from it. It is necessary to think of the actual piece in space. Start with the view which tells the most about the piece

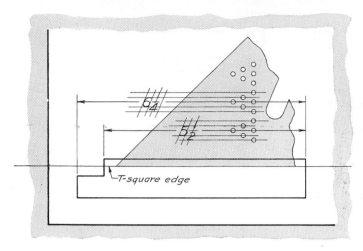

Fig. 10-4 Guidelines for fractions.

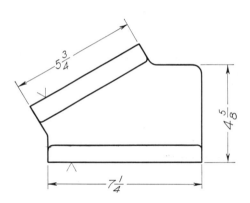

Fig. 10-5 Dimensioning—aligned system.

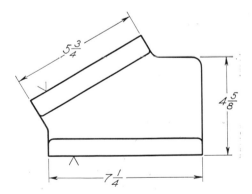

Fig. 10-6 Dimensioning—unidirectional system.

and give the dimensions which show on it. Then use other views to give the remaining dimensions. In general, it is better to place the dimensions between views so that they will be near both views.

Leaders are thin lines drawn from a note, at an angle, with an arrowhead at the place where the note applies (Fig. 10-2). When a leader is drawn to a circle or an arc, it should be drawn in a radial direction.

10·8 The aligned system of dimensioning (Fig. 10-5) has the dimensions placed in line with the dimension lines. Horizontal dimensions always read from the bottom of the sheet. Vertical dimensions read from the right-hand side of the sheet. Inclined dimensions may read in line with the inclined dimension line or be placed so as to read from the bottom of the sheet.

10·9 The unidirectional system of dimensioning (Fig. 10-6) has all the dimensions placed to read from the bottom of the sheet no matter where they occur. Aircraft companies have brought this system into use. It is accepted practice and is being adopted by many other industries.

10·10 Dimension symbols. Inches are shown by the symbol ″ and feet by the symbol ′. A dash is placed between feet and inches thus: 5′–7½″ or 0′–

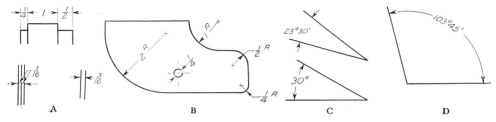

Fig. 10-7 Dimensioning—small spaces, radii, and angles.

9¼″. When the dimensions are all in inches, the inch marks may be omitted (Fig. 10-2). Most machine manufacturers follow this practice. The American Standards Association recommends that dimensions up to and including 72 in. be given in inches, and greater lengths in feet and inches. When the space is too small to admit arrowheads and figures, one of the methods in Fig. 10-7 at A and B is used.

Angles are dimensioned by drawing an arc, with the dimension horizontal (Fig. 10-7 at C), except for large arcs where the dimension may be placed as at D.

When there are few lines within the outline, dimensions may be placed inside, making it unnecessary to draw extension lines. The letters D or DIA should be placed after a dimension showing a diameter unless the diameter is evident from the drawing. The letter R should always be placed after the dimension for a radius (Fig. 10-7 at B). Dimension lines should not cross extension lines unless the conditions of the drawing make it necessary. Larger dimensions should be placed outside smaller dimensions.

10·11 Theory of dimensioning. The theory of dimensioning considers any object as made up of a number of geo-

metrical shapes, such as prisms, cylinders, pyramids, cones, and so forth, or parts of such shapes. A hole or hollow part can be considered as having the same outlines as one of these shapes. Such open spaces in an object may be considered as negative (not solid shapes).[2] It then becomes a matter of dimensioning a number of simple shapes. When the size of each simple piece is defined and the relative positions are given, the size description is complete. *Size dimensions* are used to define the simple pieces and *location dimensions* to give relative positions. When a number of pieces are assembled, each piece is first considered separately and then in relation to the other pieces. In this way the size description of a complete machine, a piece of furniture, or a building is no more difficult than the dimensioning of a single piece.

10·12 Size dimensions. The first shape is a flat piece, requiring the width (W), height (H), and depth (D) as indicated in the picture at A in Fig. 10-8 and shown by dimensions at B. Such an elementary shape may appear in a

[2] In the aircraft and some other industries the weights of parts are calculated by figuring volumes of parts as solid. From these solids, the volumes of holes and hollow or open spaces (negative or minus shapes) are subtracted. The result is then multiplied by the weight per cubic inch of the material.

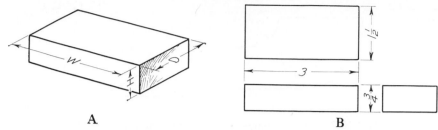

A
B

Fig. 10-8 The first shape.

great many ways, a few of which are shown in Figs. 10-9 and 10-10.

Flat pieces of irregular shape are dimensioned in a similar way (Figs. 10-11 and 10-12).

RULE: For any flat piece, give the thickness in the edge view or views and all other dimensions in the outline view or views.

The outline view is the one which shows the shape of the flat surface or surfaces. The front view in Fig. 10-11 is the outline view.

The second shape is the cylinder, which requires two dimensions: the diameter and the length (Fig. 10-13). Three cylinders are dimensioned in Fig. 10-14, one of which is the hole. A washer or other hollow cylinder may be thought of as two cylinders of the same length (Fig. 10-15).

RULE: For cylindrical pieces, give the diameter and length on the same view.

Notes are generally used to specify the sizes of holes. Such a note is generally placed on the outline view, especially when the method of forming the hole is specified (Fig. 10-16 at A). These notes show the operations necessary in forming or completing the hole, such as drilling, punching, reaming, lapping, tapping, countersinking, spot facing, and so forth. Either a dimension or a note may be used when a hole is to be formed by boring. When a hole in a casting is to be formed by a core, the word "core" is used in a note or with the dimension.

When parts of cylinders occur, such as fillets (Fig. 10-16 at B), rounds (Fig. 10-16 at C), and rounded corners, they are dimensioned in the views where the curves show (Fig. 10-16).

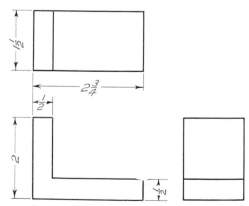

Fig. 10-9 The first rule applied.

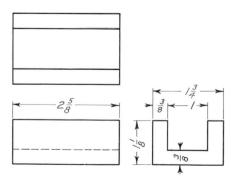

Fig. 10-10 The first rule applied.

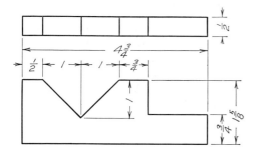

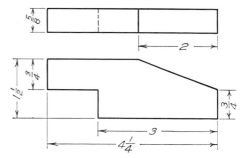

Fig. 10-11   An irregular flat shape.

Fig. 10-12   An irregular flat shape.

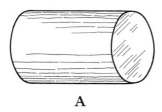

A

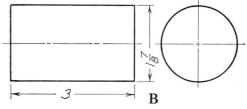

B

Fig. 10-13   The second shape, a cylinder.

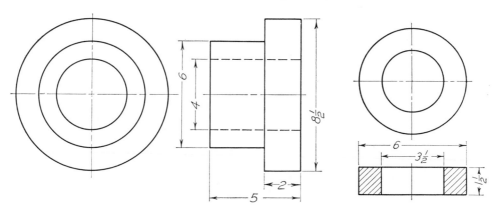

Figs. 10-14 and 10-15   Second rule applied.

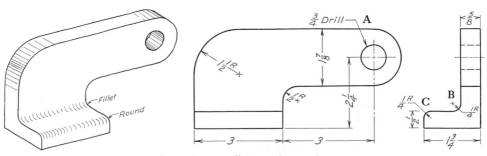

Fig. 10-16   Fillets and rounds.

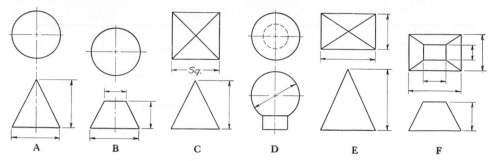

Fig. 10-17 Elementary shapes.

Other shapes include the cone, pyramid, and sphere. The cone, the frustum, the square pyramid, and the sphere may be dimensioned in one view (Fig. 10-17). The dimensions for rectangular or other pyramids and parts of pyramids require the use of two views.

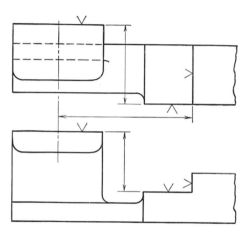

Fig. 10-18   Location dimensions for prisms.

10·13 Location dimensions are used to specify the relative positions of the parts which make up machines, buildings, bridges, and other engineering constructions. Such dimensions also locate holes, surfaces, and other features. The relative importance of the various surfaces and axes must be studied together so that the parts will go together as accurately as necessary. A knowledge of engineering practice in manufacture, assembling, and use is necessary if the draftsman is to do a good job of including the correct dimensions and notes on his drawing. Finished surfaces and center lines or axes are used to define positions with location dimensions. Two general rules will serve as a basis for showing location dimensions:

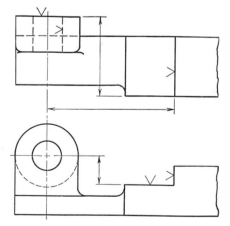

Fig. 10-19   Location dimensions for prisms and cylinders.

RULE: Prism forms are located by the axes and the surfaces (Fig. 10-18). Three dimensions are required.

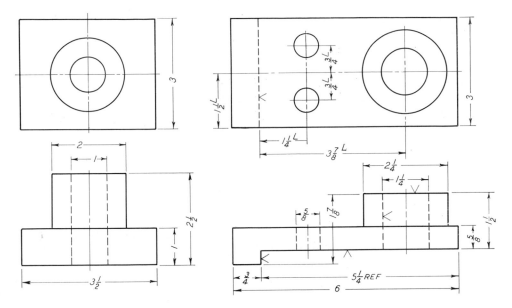

Fig. 10-20 First and second shapes.

Fig. 10-21 First and second shapes.

RULE: Cylinder forms are located by the axis and the base (Fig. 10-19). Three dimensions are required.

Combinations of prisms and cylinders are shown in Figs. 10-20 and 10-21. The dimensions at *L* (Fig. 10-21) are location dimensions.

10·14 General rules. In adding dimensions to drawings, draftsmen follow certain practices. These practices represent good form to the extent that they have the force of rules.

1) Dimension lines should be spaced about ⅜ in. apart and about ½ in. from the view outline.

2) If the *aligned system* is used, dimensions must read in line with the dimension line and from the lower or right-hand side of the sheet.

3) If the *unidirectional system* is used, all dimensions must read from the bottom of the sheet.

4) On machine drawings, detail dimensions up to 72 in. should be given in inches. Above this, feet and inches are generally used, except for gear drawings, bore of cylinders, length of wheel bases, and so forth. Aircraft and automotive drawings use inches.

5) When all the dimensions are in inches, the symbol ″ is preferably omitted.

6) On architectural and structural drawings, dimensions of 12 in. and over are given in feet and inches.

7) Sheet-metal drawings are usually dimensioned entirely in inches.

8) Furniture and cabinet drawings are usually dimensioned in inches.

9) Feet and inches are designated thus: 7′–3″ or 7 ft. 3 in. Where the dimension is in even feet, it is indicated thus: 7′–0″.

10) The same dimension is not repeated on different views unless

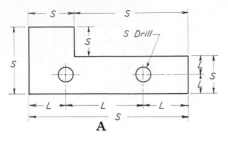
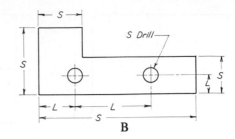

Fig. 10-22   Not required and required dimensions

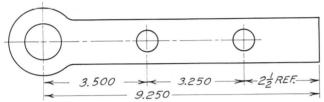

Fig. 10-23   "REF" dimension.

there is a special reason for it. In such cases the abbreviation "REF" is used after the dimension to indicate that it is given for *reference*.

11) Dimensions not required for making a piece should not be given. This is especially important for interchangeable manufacture, where limits are used (see Art. 10·16). Figure 10-22 at A has "not required" dimensions. These have been omitted in Fig. 10-22 at B.

12) Over-all dimensions should be placed outside of the smaller dimensions (Figs. 10-22 and 10-23). With the over-all dimension given, one of the smaller distances should not be dimensioned (Fig. 10-22 at B) unless it is needed for reference, and then it should be indicated by adding "REF" as in Fig. 10-23.

13) On circular end parts the center-to-center dimension is given instead of an over-all dimension (Fig. 10-24).

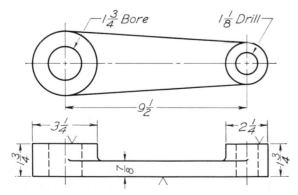

Fig. 10-24   Center-to-center dimension.

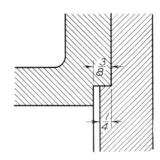

Fig. 10-25   Rule 14.

14) When it is necessary to place a dimension within a sectioned area, the sectioned lines are not run across the number (Fig. 10-25).

15) American Standard practice is to avoid placing dimensions in the area indicated by shading in Fig. 10-26.

16) Dimensions should be given from center lines or finished surfaces.

17) Never use a center line or a line of the drawing as a dimension line.

18) Never have a dimension line as a continuation of a line of a view.

19) Never place a dimension where it is crossed by a line.

20) Always give the diameter of a circle, not the radius. The abbreviation *D* or *DIA* is used after the dimension except when it is obviously a diameter.

21) The radius of an arc should always be given, with the abbreviation *R* placed after the dimension.

22) In general, place dimensions outside of views, preferably between them. See Fig. 10-28.

10·15 Use of decimals. Dimensions are given in feet, inches, and fractions of an inch for many purposes. In ordinary work, binary fractions such as ½″, ¼″, ⅛″, ¹⁄₃₂″, and ¹⁄₆₄″ are used. For parts which must fit accurately, the dimensions are given in decimals, and the workman is required to work within certain specified limits of accuracy. Such dimensions are used between finished surfaces, center distances, and places which must be held in a definite relation to each other. The basic decimal system uses a two-place decimal in place of fractions where such accuracy is required. Instead of the usual fractions, the two figures after

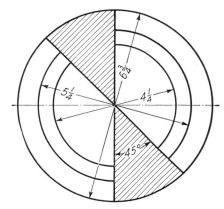

Fig. 10-26 Rule 15.

the decimal point are in fiftieths, such as .02, 04, .24, and so forth, which give two-place decimals. Such decimals can be divided by two and result in two-place decimals when used to obtain the radius from a diameter or for other purposes. In some cases other decimals may be required, but two-place decimals are used when possible. However, where extreme accuracy is necessary, three-, four-, or even five-place decimal dimensioning is used.

10·16 Limit dimensioning. When parts must have accurate measurements, the dimensions are given in decimals instead of the usual fractions. Micrometers (Fig. 10-37) and various kinds of gages or measuring devices, such as the gage blocks illustrated in Fig. 10-1, are used to check for accuracy.

Since absolute accuracy cannot be expected, a workman is required to keep within a fixed limit of accuracy. The number of *hundredths, thousandths,* or *ten-thousandths* of an inch that are allowed as a variation from absolute measurement is called the *tolerance.* The tolerance may be specified by a note on the drawing or in a

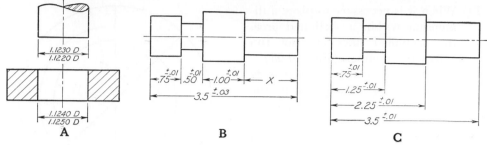

Fig. 10-27   Limit dimensions.

space provided in the title block as: "Dimension Tolerance 0.01± Unless Otherwise Specified." Limiting dimensions, or limits to specify the maximum and minimum dimensions permitted, are used to show the necessary degree of accuracy. This is illustrated at A in Fig. 10-27. Note that the maximum limiting dimension is placed above the dimension line for the shaft (external dimension) and that the minimum limiting dimension for the hole in the ring is placed above the dimension line.

At B and C in Fig. 10-27 the basic sizes are given and the tolerance specified, plus or minus, is shown. Consecutive dimensions are shown at B, where the dimension designated by X could have some variation. This dimension would not be given unless required for reference, in which case it would be followed by the abbreviation REF. Progressive dimensions are shown at C, where they are all given from a single surface (sometimes called *base-line dimensioning*).

Accurate or limiting dimensions should not be called for except where

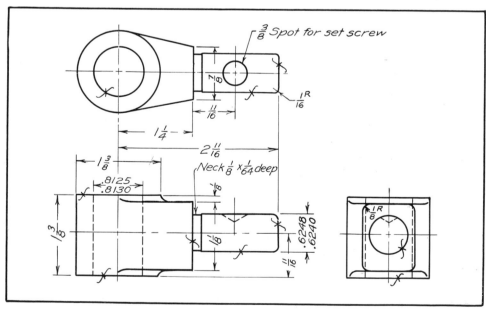

Fig. 10-28   A detail drawing with limits.

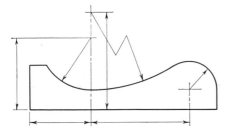

Fig. 10-29 Curve dimensions.

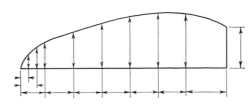

Fig. 10-30 Curve dimensions.

necessary, for they greatly increase the cost. The detail drawing in Fig. 10-28 has limits for only two dimensions; all others are nominal dimensions, with variations permissible according to the purpose for which the part is to be used.

10·17 Standard details. The shape of a part, the methods of manufacture, and the purpose for which the part is to be used generally indicate the kind and accuracy of the dimensions that must be given. A knowledge of manufacturing methods, patternmaking, foundry, machine-shop procedures, forging, welding, and so forth, is very useful when you are selecting and placing dimensions. In most cases such knowledge is essential. It is also important to consider whether only one part is to be made or whether quantity-production methods are to be used. In addition, there are purchased parts, identified by name or brand, that require few, if any, dimensions. Some companies have

their own standard parts for use in different machines or constructions, and these are dimensioned according to use and production methods.

There are, however, certain more or less standard details or conditions for which methods of dimensioning may be suggested.

10·18 Curves may be located by radii from centers as in Fig. 10-29, by offsets as in Fig. 10-30, or by naming the curve and giving the necessary specifications for describing it.

10·19 Ordinary angles are dimensioned as in Fig. 10-7. Angular tolerance is generally bilateral (two-sided) as $\pm\frac{1}{2}°$ for degrees, $\pm0°20'$ for minutes, and so forth. Angular tolerance is stated either on the drawing or placed in a space provided in the title block. Angular measurements on structural drawings are given by *run* and *rise* using $12''$ for the longer side of the triangle (Fig. 10-31 at A). A similar

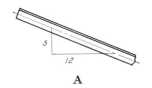

A

B

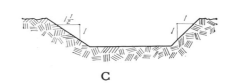

C

Fig. 10-31 Slopes.

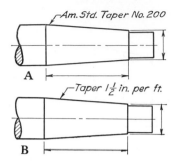

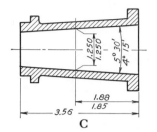

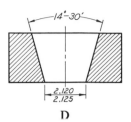

Fig. 10-32 Tapers.

method is used for slopes as at B and C where one side of the triangle is made equal to 1.

10·20 Tapers may be specified by giving one diameter or width, the length, and the American Standard taper number as in Fig. 10-32 at A. Another method is shown at B where the length, one diameter, and the taper are given. For a close fit the taper is dimensioned as at C where the diameter is given at a located gage line. At D one diameter and the angle are given.

10·21 Methods of dimensioning *chamfers* are shown in Fig. 10-33 at A for usual conditions and at B for accurate conditions.

10·22 Notes for dimensions. The use of notes for specifying dimensions and operations is indicated in Fig. 10-34 where A is for a *drilled* hole, B is for a hole to be *drilled* and *reamed*, C and D specify *counterbore*, E specifies *coun-*

tersink for a No. 24 *flat-head* screw, and F, G, and H are for countersunk and counterdrilled holes. Other dimensions with machining operations are suggested at I and J in Fig. 10-34.

When a hole is to be made in a piece after assembly with its mating piece, the note should read as previously stated but with the addition of the words "at assembly." Because such a hole is located when it is made during assembly with its mating part, no dimensions are required for its location.

10·23 Dimensioning assembled parts. The drawing of a separate part is called a *detail drawing.* When the parts of a machine are shown together in their relative positions, the drawing is called an *assembly drawing.* The rules and methods given for dimensioning apply to all cases where a complete description of size is required.

Drawings of complete machines, constructions, and so forth, are made for different uses and have to be di-

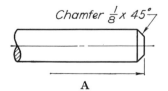

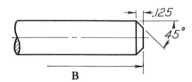

Fig. 10-33 Chamfers.

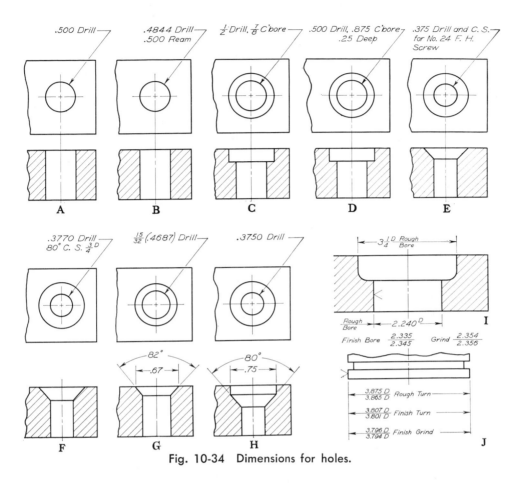

Fig. 10-34 Dimensions for holes.

mensioned to serve the purpose required of them. If the drawing is merely to show the appearance or arrangement of parts, the dimensions may be left off. When it is desired to tell the space required, give over-all dimensions. Where it is necessary to locate parts in relation to each other without giving all the detail dimensions, it is usual to give center-to-center distances and dimensions needed for putting the machine or construction together or erecting it in position. In some industries assembly drawings may be completely dimensioned either with or without extra part views (see Fig. 13-5). Such drawings serve the purpose of both detail and assembly drawings. These are often referred to as *composite drawings*.

For furniture and cabinetwork only the major dimensions sometimes are given, such as length, height, and sizes of stock. The details of joints are left to the cabinetmaker. This is common practice where machinery is used and where many details of construction are standardized.

10·24 Sketching and measuring. Sketching as a means of shape description and study was considered in Chap.

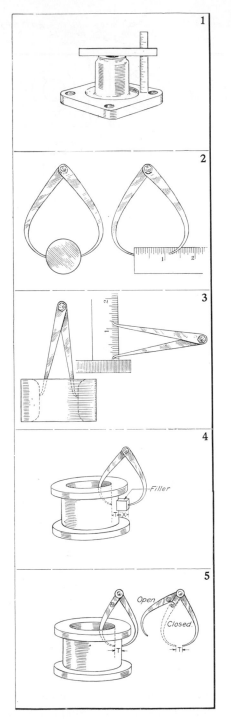

Fig. 10-35 Taking measurements.

6. When sketches that are to be used in making drawings are made from machine or furniture parts, it is necessary to define the size, the material, the kinds of surfaces (either finished or rough), the limits of accuracy, and all information that might have any future value.

10·25 After sketching the views of an object or part of an object, add all necessary dimension lines in exactly the same way as for views made with instruments. The piece should now be examined and the kind of material noted, together with the kinds of finish and location of all finished surfaces. When everything else is done, it is time to measure the piece and fill in the figures to tell the size. For this purpose various measuring tools will be needed. A 2-ft rule, a steel scale, and a pair of calipers will be sufficient for most purposes.

10·26 Other machinists' tools are often necessary or convenient for checking measurements an a workpiece with dimensions on a drawing. The student should know something about the tools that are available and how to use them.

The flat scale or the steel scale and straightedge can be used in many ways as suggested in Fig. 10-35, Space 1. The distances can be read directly on them.

Whenever possible, always take measurements from finished surfaces. Outside and inside calipers with their use illustrated are shown in Spaces 2 and 3. The distance between the contact points is read by applying the calipers to a scale.

When the calipers cannot be removed from a thickness, the plain calipers may be used by inserting an

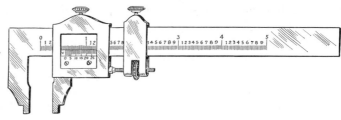

Fig. 10-36 Vernier calipers.

extra piece or filler (Space 4); or the transfer calipers (Space 5) may be used. The distance X must be subtracted from the total distance to obtain the desired thickness T when a filler is used. The transfer calipers are provided with a false leg, set so that the calipers may be opened and then brought back to the same position after being removed from the casting.

All measurements of wood construction can generally be obtained with sufficient accuracy by using the 2-ft rule. By way of contrast, photographic and electrical methods have been developed to make extremely accurate measurements necessary in connection with certain types of machining operations.

For accurate measurements vernier calipers and micrometer calipers (Figs. 10-36 and 10-37) are used. Other tools that are useful if at hand include the steel square, try square, combination square, surface gage, depth gage, radius and screw-thread gages, and protractor.

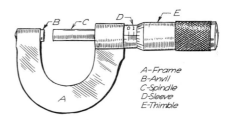

Fig. 10-37 Micrometer calipers.

A—Frame
B—Anvil
C—Spindle
D—Sleeve
E—Thimble

When a pictorial sketch is dimensioned, the only additional consideration is to use care to see that all extension lines are either in or perpendicular to the particular plane on which the dimension is being given (Fig. 10-38).

10·27 Notes and specifications. Information that cannot be represented graphically must be given in the form of lettered notes and symbols. Trade information that is understood generally by those on the job is often given in this way. Such notes include the following items: number required, material, kind of finish, kind of fit, method of machining, kinds of screw threads,

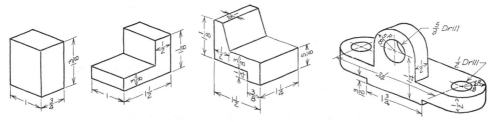

Fig. 10-38 Dimensioning on pictorial sketches.

kinds of bolts and nuts, sizes of wire, and thickness of sheet metal.

The materials in general use are wood, cast iron, wrought iron, steel, brass, aluminum, and various alloys. All parts to go together must be of the proper size so that they will fit. Some pieces may be left rough, partly finished or completely finished. The wood used for making furniture is first shaped with woodworking tools and machines. Many metals, such as cast iron, brass, aluminum, and so forth, are given the required form by molding, casting, and machining. First, a wood pattern of the shape and size required is made and placed in sand to make an impression or mold into which the melted metal is poured. Wrought iron and steel are made into shapes by rolling or forging in the rolling mill or blacksmith shop. Some kinds of steel may be cast as described.

There are many interesting ways of forming metals for special purposes and many special alloys that cannot be described in a drawing book, but the student will learn much by observing the shapes of parts of machinery and the materials of which they are made.

After a part is cast or forged, it must be *machined* on all surfaces that are to fit other surfaces. Round surfaces are generally formed on a lathe. Flat surfaces are finished or smoothed on a planer, milling machine, or shaper. Drill presses, boring mills, or lathes are used for making holes.

Extra metal is allowed for surfaces that are to be finished. To specify such surfaces the $\vee$ symbol or the f symbol is placed on the lines which represent the surfaces. If the entire piece is to be finished, a note such as

"Finish All Over" may be used and all other marks omitted.

Specifications as to methods of machining, finish, and other treatment are given in the form of notes, as spot-face, grind, polish, knurl, core, drill, ream, countersink, harden, caseharden, blue, and temper.

It is often necessary to add notes in regard to assembling, order of doing work, or other special directions.

10·28 Checking a drawing. After a drawing has been completed, it must be very carefully examined before it is used. This is called *checking the drawing.* It is very important work and should be done by someone who has not worked on the drawing.

Thorough checking requires a definite order of procedure and consideration of the following items. See that:

1) The views completely describe the shape of each piece.
2) There are no unnecessary views.
3) The scale is sufficiently large to show all detail clearly.
4) All views are to scale and correct dimensions are given.
5) Sufficient dimensions are given to define the size of all parts completely.
6) The kind of material and the number required of each part are specified.
7) The kind of finish is specified, all finished surfaces are marked, and finish is not called for where not needed.
8) All necessary explanatory notes are given and are properly placed.

Each draftsman is expected to inspect his own work for errors or omis-

sions before he gives his drawings to the checker.

10·29 Problem suggestions. Group H, page 422. Two lists are presented. List 1 includes basic and in general more elementary problems than List 2. Selections should be made according to the purpose of the course. List 2 may be used for additional assignments, or selections may be used for advanced students. Additional problems can be assigned from other groups. Review of Chap. 10 in connection with the problems in Groups J, K, and L should be assigned as part of the work.

LIST 1 Problems H·1, H·2, H·3, H·4, H·5, H·6, H·7, H·8, H·9, H·10, H·13, H·14, H·17, H·18, H·21, H·23, H·25, H·31

LIST 2 Problems H·11, H·12, H·15, H·16, H·19, H·20, H·22, H·24, H·26, H·27, H·28, H·29, H·30, H·32

FAITH OF THE ENGINEER

I AM AN ENGINEER. In my profession I take deep pride, but without vainglory; to it I owe solemn obligations that I am eager to fulfill.

As an Engineer, I will participate in none but honest enterprise. To him that has engaged my services, as employer or client, I will give the utmost of performance and fidelity.

When needed, my skill and knowledge shall be given without reservation for the public good. From special capacity springs the obligation to use it well in the service of humanity; and I accept the challenge that this implies.

Jealous of the high repute of my calling, I will strive to protect the interests and the good name of any engineer that I know to be deserving; but I will not shrink, should duty dictate, from disclosing the truth regarding anyone that, by unscrupulous act, has shown himself unworthy of the profession.

Since the Age of Stone, human progress has been conditioned by the genius of my professional forebears. By them have been rendered usable to mankind Nature's vast resources of material and energy. By them have been vitalized and turned to practical account the principles of science and the revelations of technology. Except for this heritage of accumulated experience, my efforts would be feeble. I dedicate myself to the dissemination of engineering knowledge, and especially to the instruction of younger members of my profession in all its art and traditions.

To my fellows I pledge, in the same full measure I ask of them, integrity and fair dealing, tolerance and respect, and devotion to the standards and the dignity of our profession; with the consciousness, always, that our special expertness carries with it the obligation to serve humanity with complete sincerity.

Published by Engineers' Council for Professional Development
29 West 39th Street, New York 18, N.Y.

11 Technique of the finished drawing

11·1 Making drawings for industrial use. It has been impressed upon us that in the language of drawing an object is described by telling its shape and its size. All drawings, whether for machines, buildings, airplanes, or automobiles, are made on the same principles.

Sometimes an unfavorable comparison is made between a student's drawing and a *real* drawing. The finished appearance of a real drawing as made by a draftsman or engineer is due to a thorough knowledge of commercial drafting. The correct order of going about the work and some of the procedures that draftsmen usually follow are described in this chapter. The student must become thoroughly familiar with this practice if his drawings are to have the style and good form that are so desirable and necessary.

11·2 An example of accuracy. Many uses are being found for photographic

Fig. 11-1   The Kodak Transfax Process. (*Eastman Kodak Company*)

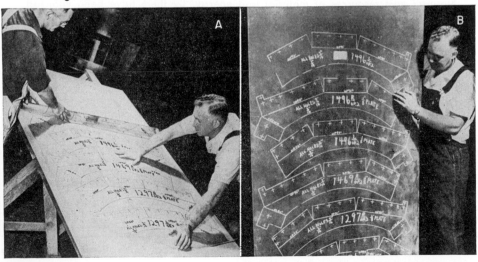

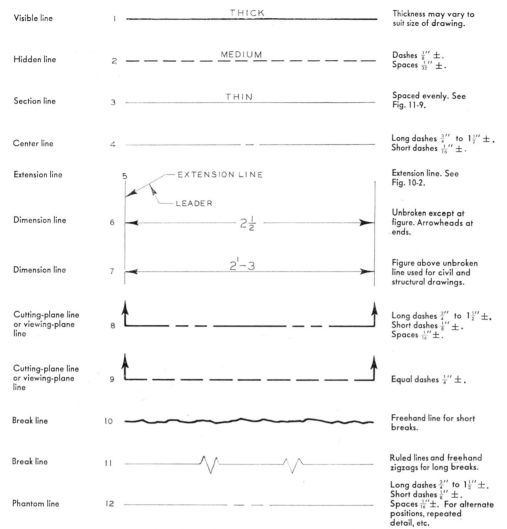

Visible line	1	THICK	Thickness may vary to suit size of drawing.
Hidden line	2	MEDIUM	Dashes $\frac{1}{8}''$ ±. Spaces $\frac{1}{32}''$ ±.
Section line	3	THIN	Spaced evenly. See Fig. 11-9.
Center line	4		Long dashes $\frac{3}{4}''$ to $1\frac{1}{2}''$ ±. Short dashes $\frac{1}{16}''$ ±.
Extension line	5	EXTENSION LINE / LEADER	Extension line. See Fig. 10-2.
Dimension line	6	$2\frac{1}{2}$	Unbroken except at figure. Arrowheads at ends.
Dimension line	7	$2'-3$	Figure above unbroken line used for civil and structural drawings.
Cutting-plane line or viewing-plane line	8		Long dashes $\frac{3}{4}''$ to $1\frac{1}{2}''$ ±. Short dashes $\frac{1}{8}''$ ±. Spaces $\frac{1}{16}''$ ±.
Cutting-plane line or viewing-plane line	9		Equal dashes $\frac{1}{4}''$ ±.
Break line	10		Freehand line for short breaks.
Break line	11		Ruled lines and freehand zigzags for long breaks.
Phantom line	12		Long dashes $\frac{3}{4}''$ to $1\frac{1}{2}''$ ±. Short dashes $\frac{1}{8}''$ ±. Spaces $\frac{1}{16}''$ ±. For alternate positions, repeated detail, etc.

Fig. 11-2   The alphabet of lines in ink.

methods in connection with the use of drawings. One such use is the process illustrated in Fig. 11-1 which shows why accurate drawings and a knowledge of technique of drafting are important.

The process illustrated uses Kodak Transfax, a light-sensitive solution that can be applied to surfaces with a spray gun. By using this solution, technicians can print drawings, layouts, wiring diagrams, and instrument dials directly on metals, plastics, or almost any smooth or semiporous material.

If necessary to obtain a good bond on the base material, it may be coated with a quick-drying lacquer. The surface is then sprayed with Transfax. When dry, a tracing or high-contrast photographic film negative is placed in contact as at A and exposed to light. Developing and clearing then follow

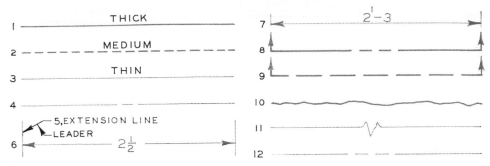

Fig. 11-3 The alphabet of lines in pencil.

to produce the copy at B. Where complete fabrication instructions are included on the tracing, they are reproduced, and the work can be done without further reference to the drawing.

11·3 Alphabet of lines. The kinds of lines given in the American Standards for use in making drawings are shown in Fig. 11-2. Each line is used for a definite purpose and must not be used for anything else. Detail drawings should have fairly wide (thick) outlines with thin center and dimension lines so that the drawing will have contrast and be easy to read. Hidden lines have a medium width. If all the lines are of the same width, the drawing will have a flat appearance and will be hard to read.

The lines shown are for inked drawings and tracings. On pencil drawings the lines may be in general proportion to ink lines (Fig. 11-3), where the lines are numbered to correspond with those of Fig. 11-2.

11·4 Engineering drawings are usually worked up on tracing cloth or tracing paper. The original layout may be on paper, then tracing cloth or tracing paper is placed over it, and the drawing traced with a firm pencil line. Good

sharp pencil work is essential. This requires neatness and the fewest unnecessary erasures. Blueprints or other reproductions are then made from the tracings. Most drawings used to be traced in ink on tracing cloth, but present practice is to use a pencil except for certain purposes or for especially permanent drawings.

11·5 Order of penciling. After shape and size description have been learned, the most important thing for the young draftsman to get is good form. A systematic method of working will help him achieve the desired results. The order of making the different parts of a drawing is the first item. A drawing is started by drawing the center and base lines as in Space 1 of Fig. 11-4. These form the skeleton for the views. Then block in the views as in Space 2. Next draw the arcs and complete the views as in Space 3. The views should be carried along together. Do not attempt to finish one view before making another. Finally, add the dimension lines and dimensions as in Space 4. Learn the following order of penciling and follow it as nearly as possible on every drawing:

1) Plan the arrangement of views.

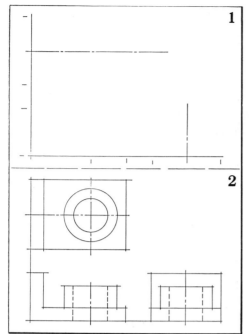
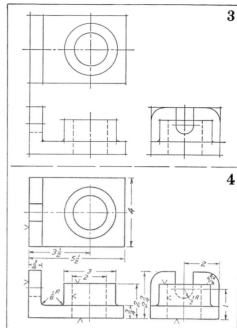

Fig. 11-4   Penciling.

2) Determine the scale to use.
3) Lay off the sheet to proper size and block in the title space or record strip.
4) Draw the primary center and base lines.
5) Lay off the principal measurements.
6) Block in the views by drawing the preliminary and final blocking-in lines.
7) Lay off the detail measurements.
8) Draw the center lines for details.
9) Draw all complete circles and the preliminary and final lines for details.
10) Draw part circles, fillets, and rounded corners.
11) Draw such lines that could not previously be drawn.
12) Draw all extension and dimension lines.

13) Put on dimensions and notes.
14) Section-line all sectioned surfaces.
15) Letter the title.
16) Check the drawing carefully.

11·6 Inking and tracing. The method of procedure in inking is the same, whether a tracing is made or whether the original drawing is finished by going over the penciled lines with drawing ink.

All straight lines are inked with the ruling pen. Hold the pen point downward and fill by touching the quill on the ink-bottle cork to the inside of the pen blades. The nibs of the pen are set to the desired width of line by turning the adjusting screw with the thumb and second finger of the pen hand. Then hold the pen against the T-square or triangle in the position shown in Fig. 11-5.

TECHNIQUE OF THE FINISHED DRAWING   143

Fig. 11-5 Correct position
for the pen.

Observe the following instructions:
1) Do not hold the pen over the drawing while filling.
2) Keep the blades of the pen parallel to the direction of the line.
3) Do not press the pen nibs hard against the T-square.
4) Do not screw the nibs of the pen too tight.
5) Have a pen wiper at hand (a soft lintless cloth or tissue paper).
6) Keep the pen clean by frequent wiping. Always wipe it carefully after using.
7) Never dip the pen into the ink bottle or allow ink to get on the outside of the blades.

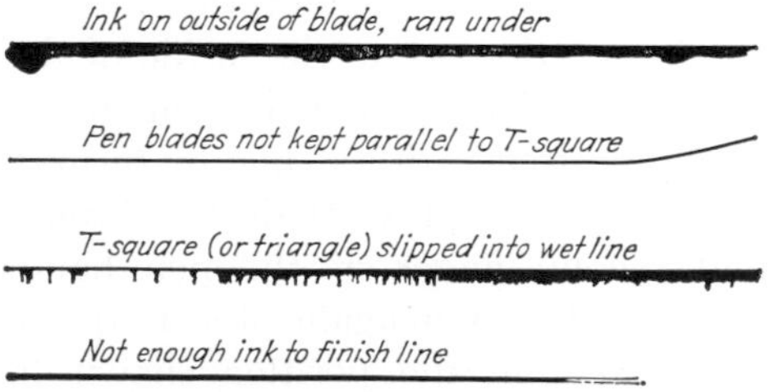

8) Do not put too much ink in the pen. About ¼ to ⁵⁄₁₆ in. is generally sufficient.

Faulty lines occur from different causes. The pen may need dressing or sharpening. The beginner should not attempt to do this himself but should ask the instructor to help him. Figure 11-6 shows some of the common faults and suggests the remedy.

The irregular curve (Fig. 2-28) is used for guiding the pen when curves other than circle arcs are to be inked. It is used by matching a portion of the curve and drawing a part of the line. Then the curve is moved to a new position. The new position of the irregular curve must always match a part of the line already inked.

For inking circles and arcs, the compasses and bow pen are used. Remove the pencil leg from the compasses and insert the pen leg, adjusting the needle point until it is very slightly longer than the pen. The joints of the compasses should be adjusted so that the legs are perpendicular to the paper. Always draw a circle in one stroke, inclining the compasses in the direction of the line and rolling the handle between the thumb and finger (Fig. 11-7).

Pen pressed against T-square too hard

Pen sloped away from T-square

Pen too close to edge, ink ran under

Ink on outside of blade, ran under

Pen blades not kept parallel to T-square

T-square (or triangle) slipped into wet line

Not enough ink to finish line

Fig. 11-6 Faulty lines.

11·7 To make a tracing. If you are using tracing cloth, first tear off the selvage and fasten the cloth down smoothly over the pencil drawing. Most draftsmen place the dull side up. Dust the surface with chalk dust (pounce) and rub a soft cloth over it to remove all traces of grease so that the ink will take. Be sure to remove all dust before starting to ink. In inking on paper, chalking is not necessary.

As tracing cloth is very sensitive to atmospheric changes and will stretch if left overnight, no view should be started that cannot be finished the same day. When work is again started, the cloth should be restretched. In restretching, adjust the cloth so that the work already done is in register (will match) with the new work.

11·8 Order of inking. Good inking is the result of two things: careful practice and a definite order of working. Smooth joints and tangents, sharp corners, and neat fillets not only improve the appearance of a drawing but make it easier to read.

The general order of inking or tracing is shown in stages in Fig. 11-8. The arcs are inked first as in Space 1 and should center over the pencil lines. Horizontal lines should be inked as in Space 2 and the drawing completed as in Space 3. Then the dimension lines, arrowheads, finish marks, and so forth, are added and the dimensions filled in.

1) Ink main center lines.
2) Ink small circles and arcs.
3) Ink large circles and arcs.
4) Ink hidden circles and arcs.
5) Ink irregular curves.
6) Ink horizontal full lines.
7) Ink vertical full lines.
8) Ink inclined full lines.

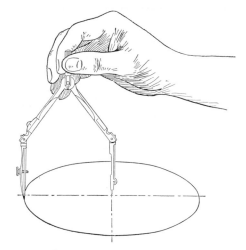

Fig. 11-7 Inking a circle.

9) Ink hidden lines.
10) Ink center lines.
11) Ink extension and dimension lines.
12) Ink arrowheads and figures.
13) Ink section lines.
14) Letter notes and titles.
15) Ink border lines.
16) Check drawing carefully.

11·9 Erasing. The ideal way, of course, is to complete a drawing or tracing without having to do any erasing. Sometimes, however, it is necessary to make an erasure because of a change or a mistake. Ink lines may be removed by rubbing with a pencil (ruby red) eraser, which does not rub off the surface of the paper or cloth as does an ink eraser. Ink may be erased more easily and with less damage to the drawing if a drafting triangle or other hard surface is placed under the part to be erased. *Do not use a knife or scratcher.* An erasing shield is very convenient. Thin metal shields have slots and openings of various sizes and shapes. Pencil lines are removed with artgum or a pencil eraser. Electric eras-

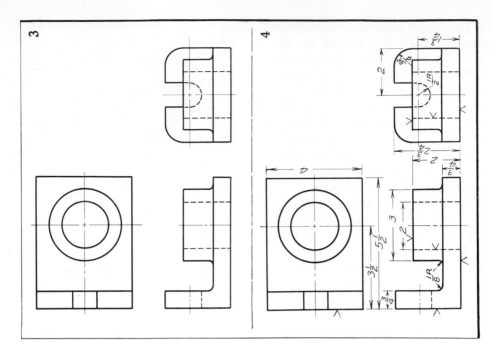

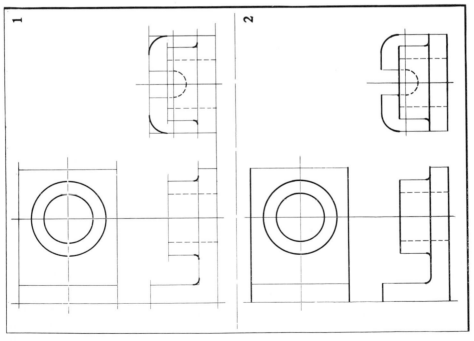

Fig. 11-8 Tracing or inking.

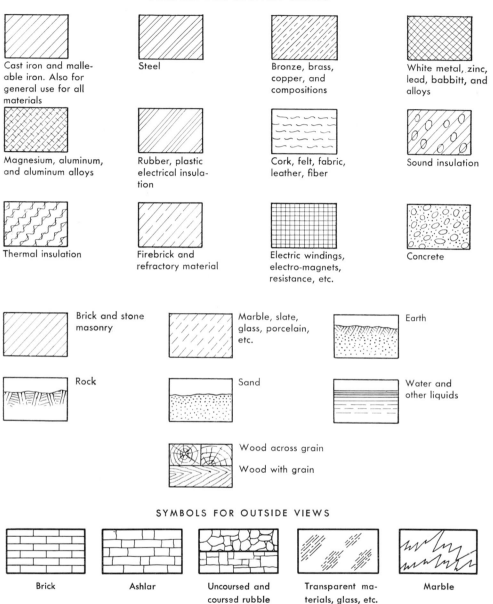

Cast iron and malleable iron. Also for general use for all materials

Steel

Bronze, brass, copper, and compositions

White metal, zinc, lead, babbitt, and alloys

Magnesium, aluminum, and aluminum alloys

Rubber, plastic electrical insulation

Cork, felt, fabric, leather, fiber

Sound insulation

Thermal insulation

Firebrick and refractory material

Electric windings, electro-magnets, resistance, etc.

Concrete

Brick and stone masonry

Marble, slate, glass, porcelain, etc.

Earth

Rock

Sand

Water and other liquids

Wood across grain

Wood with grain

SYMBOLS FOR OUTSIDE VIEWS

Brick

Ashlar

Uncoursed and coursed rubble

Transparent materials, glass, etc.

Marble

Fig. 11-9 Symbols for materials.

ing machines are now used in many drafting rooms. They consist of a small motor with provision for holding a cylindrical eraser on the end of a revolving shaft.

11·10 Conventional symbols. In drawing there are conventional methods of representing parts and materials that are designed for saving time and making reading easier. They might be

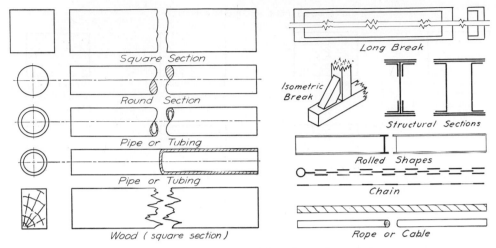

Fig. 11-10 Conventional breaks and symbols.

called "idioms" and "abbreviations" of the graphic language. The commonest are symbols for indicating screw threads, which are explained in Chap. 12. Other conventions are used for representing electrical apparatus, wiring, piping, and so forth.

For indicating the material of which a piece is to be made, the best rule is to letter the name of the material in a note. When pieces of different materials are shown side by side in a section, they can sometimes be shown to better advantage by using a symbolic section lining. The symbols for cut surfaces, as given by the American Standards Association, are shown in Fig. 11-9. Notes are generally used to tell the materials with outside views, but certain distinctive materials are sometimes indicated by the symbols shown in the lower row of Fig. 11-9. Architectural drawings involve the use of a large number of symbols or conventional representations, some of which are shown in Chap. 21. For showing the cross section of long, uniformly shaped pieces and for "breaking out" parts, the repre-

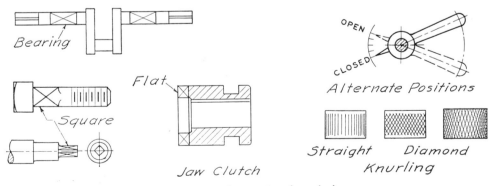

Fig. 11-11 Conventional symbols.

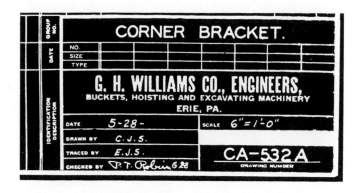

Fig. 11-12 Right, a boxed title. Below, a record strip.

CORNER BRACKET.							
GROUP NO.							
DATE	NO.						
	SIZE						
	TYPE						

G. H. WILLIAMS CO., ENGINEERS,
BUCKETS, HOISTING AND EXCAVATING MACHINERY
ERIE, PA.

IDENTIFICATION DESCRIPTION	DATE	*5-28-*	SCALE	*6"=1'-0"*
	DRAWN BY	*C. J. S.*		
	TRACED BY	*E. J. S.*		**CA–532A**
	CHECKED BY	*P. T. Robin 6.28*		DRAWING NUMBER

UNIT			NAME OF PIECE			
DR.	DATE	SYMBOL OF MACHINES USED ON		SUPERSEDES DRAW.	STOCK CASTING	
DR.					DROP FORGING	
TR.		THE LODGE & SHIPLEY MACHINE TOOL CO.		SUPERSEDED BY DR.	MATERIAL	PIECE NO
TR. CH.		FORM 795 CINCINNATI, OHIO. U. S. A.				

sentations of Fig. 11-10 are used. Some other symbols commonly used are shown in Fig. 11-11.

11·11 Titles. Every sketch and drawing must have some kind of title. The form, completeness, and location vary. On working drawings, the title is usually boxed in the lower right-hand corner (Fig. 11-12) or is included in the record strip extending across the bottom or end of the sheet (Fig. 11-12).

The title gives as much as is necessary of the following information:

1) The name of the construction, machine, or project.
2) The name of the part or parts shown, or simply details.
3) Manufacturer, company, or firm name and address.
4) Date—usually date of completion of the tracing.
5) Scale or scales.
6) Heat treatment, working tolerances, etc.
7) Numbers of the drawing, of the shop order, or customer's order, according to the system used.

8) Drafting-room record; names or initials with dates of draftsman, tracer, and checker; and approval of chief draftsman, engineer, etc.

In large drafting rooms, the title is generally printed in blank on the paper or cloth, leaving spaces to be filled in.

11·12 Bill of material. The names of the parts, material, number required, part number, and so forth, may be given in a note near the views of each part. Another method is to place the part number in a circle near the views, draw a leader from the circle to the part, and then collect all the information in a tabulated list called a *bill of material* or *material list* (Fig. 11-13).

BILL OF MATERIAL FOR TOOL POST				
Piece Number	Name	Quan	Mat.	Notes
1	BODY	1	S.A.E #1045	Forging
2	WEDGE	1	S.A.E #1045	Forging
3	RING	1	S.A.E #1045	Forging
4	BLOCK	1	S.A.E #1045	C.R.Steel 3×3×1¼
5	SCREW	1	S.A.E #1045	C.R Steel 1"Dia. x 3 15/16

Fig. 11-13 A bill of material.

Fig. 11-14 Blueprint machine. (*The C. F. Pease Company*)

This list is usually placed on the drawing above the title; sometimes it may be lettered or typewritten on a separate sheet. Bolts, nuts, washers, keys, and other similar or standard parts are often specified and marked with an identification number and listed in the bill of material. When this is done, the views of such parts do not need to be drawn. Some material lists are shown in Fig. L-3 on page 460, Fig. L-9 on page 465, and Fig. L-12 on page 467.

11·13 Blueprinting. Much of the work in shops or on structures is done from blueprints, or from other reproductions made by a large variety of available methods all called *prints*. A blueprint is a copy of a tracing. The paper used is chemically treated to give white lines on a blue background. As many copies as desired are made from a single tracing. Blueprints can be made from pencil or ink drawings on tracing cloth or tracing paper. The original drawing is kept in the files of the drawing room.

11·14 To make a blueprint. Blueprint paper is usually bought ready to expose

to the light. Some kinds work fast, some work slow, depending on the degree of rapidity for which they are made. When fresh, blueprint paper is of a yellowish-green color, and an unexposed piece should wash out perfectly white. With age or exposure to light or air, it turns to a darker gray-blue color and spoils in a short time. Blueprints used to be made by sunlight, but electric blueprint machines are now used because they give more uniform results, are faster, and can be used at any time. A continuous blueprinting machine made by The C. F. Pease Company is illustrated in Fig. 11-14 and includes washing and drying facilities.

Tracings are fed into the front of the printer onto blueprint paper. Together they are carried around a contact glass where they are exposed to the printing rays of electric lamps. After exposure, the blueprint paper passes through a water wash, potash applicator system, and then through drying drums. The finished prints are wound in a continuous roll to be delivered at the back of the machine.

Sometimes it is necessary or desira-

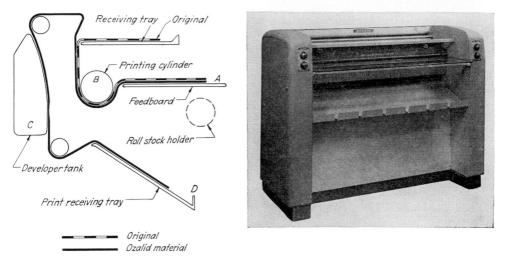

Fig. 11-15　Ozalid copying machine. (Ozalid Division of General Aniline and Film Corporation)

ble to make minor changes or corrections on blueprints. This can be done by using an alkaline solution in a writing or drawing pen.

11·15 Other methods of reproducing drawings include vandyke paper, which gives white lines on a dark brown background, and a number of special papers that give dark or black lines on a light background. Vandyke and similar negatives are used to make positive blue- or black-line prints.

Ozalid prints are made from tracings and provide dark reddish (or other color) lines on a light background. They are developed dry by exposing to ammonia vapor. An Ozalid copying machine is illustrated in Fig. 11-15. The tracing is placed on the Ozalid paper on the feedboard, *A,* and is carried on printer belts around a light source, *B.* Then it is conveyed across a perforated developer tank, *C,* from which ammonia vapor rises and develops the dry print. The print is then delivered on the front receiving tray, *D.* The machine is operated by an electric motor.

Prints with a light background, as described, are finding increasing favor. They are easier to read and they simplify changes and alterations. Photostats are made by a photographic method and may be the same size as the original drawing or a different size. For some purposes copies may be made by using the Mimeograph or the hectograph. Where a large number of copies are required, they may be reproduced in the same or a different size by the offset printing process.

11·16 Problem suggestions. Assign at least two problems to be drawn, traced, and blueprinted. Problems may be selected from Groups D, E, F, and H. Drawings previously made in pencil from Group H and which have been corrected may be saved and used for tracing. Review of Chap. 11 should be assigned in connection with problems in Groups J, K, and L.

12 Screws, bolts, and other fastenings

12·1 Standardized fastenings. The use of drafting in designing and building machines and other engineering projects requires a knowledge of certain parts that are often used in their construction. Such parts include screws, bolts, rivets, keys, pins, and shafting. These have been standardized and have well-defined characteristics and names. Threaded fastenings such as

Fig. 12-1 Threaded fastenings.

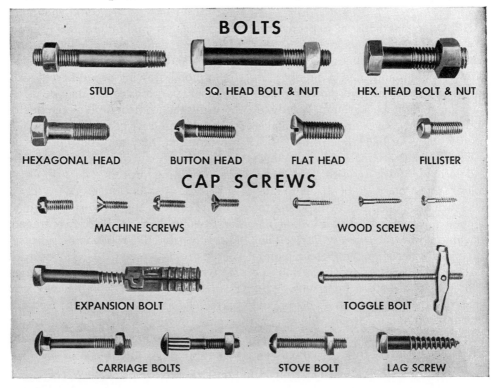

BOLTS

STUD   SQ. HEAD BOLT & NUT   HEX. HEAD BOLT & NUT

HEXAGONAL HEAD   BUTTON HEAD   FLAT HEAD   FILLISTER

CAP SCREWS

MACHINE SCREWS   WOOD SCREWS

EXPANSION BOLT   TOGGLE BOLT

CARRIAGE BOLTS   STOVE BOLT   LAG SCREW

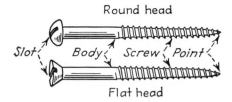

Round head

Slot — Body — Screw — Point

Flat head

Fig. 12-2 Wood screws.

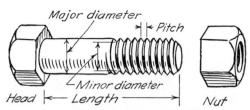

Major diameter — Pitch

Minor diameter

Head — Length — Nut

Fig. 12-3 Hexagonal-head bolt and nut.

screws, bolts, and nuts are made in a great variety of forms and sizes (Fig. 12-1).

12·2 Screw-thread standards in the United States were developed from a system presented by William Sellers in a report to the Franklin Institute in Philadelphia in 1864. Screw-thread standards in England came from a paper presented to the Institution of Civil Engineers in 1841.

Work on standards has continued with the growth of industry and the need for uniformity and interchangeable manufacture. In 1948 Unified Thread Standards were agreed upon by standardization committees of Canada, the United Kingdom, and the United States. The Unified Standards are now the basic American Standards

and are described in the American Standards *Unified and American Screw Threads for Screws, Bolts, Nuts, and Other Threaded Parts* (ASA B1·1–1949)[1] and in Handbook H-28, *Federal Screw Thread Specifications.*[2]

12·3 Screw threads. The use of screw threads is so frequent that the common forms and methods of representation must be understood. The most familiar occurrence of screw threads is on the ordinary wood screw (Fig. 12-2) and the common bolt (Fig. 12-3). Wood-screw threads have a space between them to allow for part of the difference in the strength of wood and metal.

[1] American Standards Association, 70 East 45th Street, New York 17, N.Y.
[2] U.S. Government Printing Office, Washington 25, D.C.

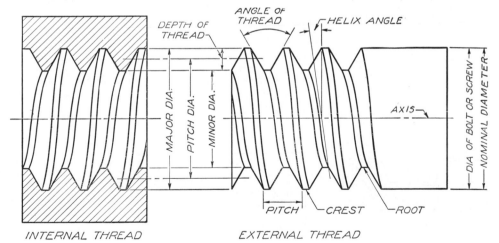

ANGLE OF THREAD

DEPTH OF THREAD

HELIX ANGLE

MAJOR DIA. PITCH DIA. MINOR DIA.

AXIS

DIA OF BOLT OR SCREW

NOMINAL DIAMETER

PITCH — CREST — ROOT

INTERNAL THREAD   EXTERNAL THREAD

Fig. 12-4 Screw-thread terms.

SCREWS, BOLTS, AND OTHER FASTENINGS **153**

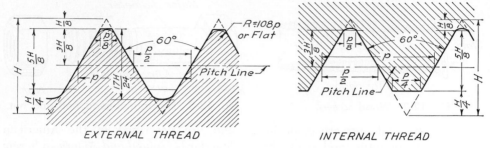

EXTERNAL THREAD   INTERNAL THREAD

Fig. 12-5   Unified and American (National) screw-thread profile.

12·4 Some screw-thread terms which should be known are illustrated in Fig. 12-4. The Unified and American (National) screw-thread profile shown in Fig. 12-5 is the form used for general fastening purposes. Other forms of threads are used to meet various requirements, and some of these are illustrated in Fig. 12-6. The sharp V is seldom used. The square thread and similar forms (worm thread and acme thread) are designed to transmit motion or power and to hold the forces in line with the axis. The knuckle thread is familiar on electric light sockets, and so forth, and as a "cast" thread. The Dardelet thread is a self-locking thread designed by a French military officer. The former British Standard (Whitworth), shown in a box, had rounded crests and roots and a 55° angle. The former United States Standard, not shown, had flat crests and roots and the 60° angle. The buttress thread takes pressure in one direction only—against the surface perpendicular to the axis.

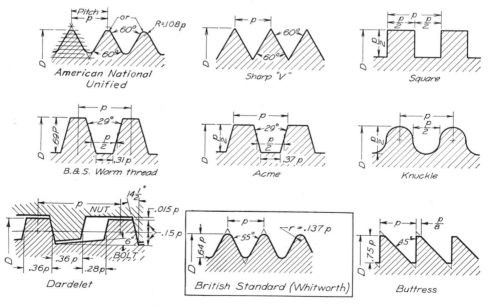

Fig. 12-6   Screw-thread profiles.

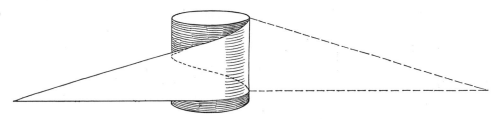

Fig. 12-7 Picture of a helix.

12·5 To draw a true representation of a screw thread, it is necessary to draw the projection of a helix (Figs. 12-7 and 12-8). A helix is a curved generated by a point moving uniformly around a cylinder and uniformly parallel to the axis of the cylinder. The hypotenuse of a right triangle will form one turn of a helix if the base of the triangle is equal to the circumference (Fig. 12-8). The altitude will be the pitch of the helix. A right triangle and the projections of the corresponding helix are shown in Fig. 12-8.

The method of drawing the projections of a helix is shown in Fig. 12-9 in Spaces 1 and 2. Draw two projections of a cylinder (Space 1). Divide the circumference into a number of equal parts and the pitch into the same number of equal parts. From each point in the circumference draw lines parallel to the axis to meet lines perpendicular to the axis drawn through the corresponding divisions of the pitch (Space 2). A smooth curve drawn through the points thus found will give the projection of the helix.

The application of the helix is shown in Space 3, which is the actual projection of a square thread. Such drawings are seldom made, since they require too much time and are no better practically than the conventional representations commonly used (see Art. 12·8).

12·6 Single and multiple threads. "A screw thread is a ridge of uniform section in the form of a helix on the external or internal surface of a cylinder, or in the form of a spiral on the external or internal surface of a cone or frustum of a cone."[3]

[3] *Unified and American Screw Threads for Screws, Bolts, Nuts, and other Threaded Parts* (ASA B1.1–1949). American Standards Association, 70 East 45th Street, New York 17, N.Y.

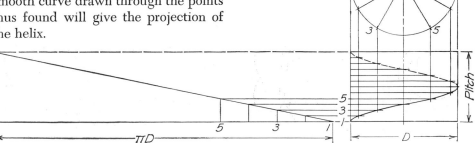

Fig. 12-8 Projection of a helix.

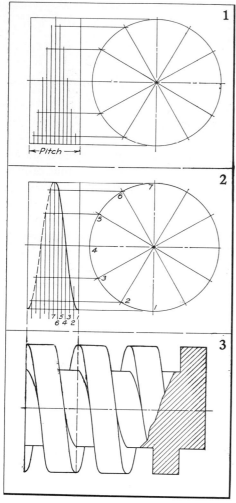

Fig. 12-9 Helix and square thread.

The *pitch* of a thread, *p*, is the distance from a point on the thread form to the corresponding point on the next form, measured parallel to the axis (Fig. 12-10). The *lead, l,* is the distance a threaded part would move parallel to the axis during one complete rotation, in relation to a fixed mating part (the distance a screw would enter a threaded hole).

Most screws have single threads and are so understood if not otherwise specified (Fig. 12-10 at A). A single thread has a single ridge in the form of a helix, and the pitch and lead are the same. A double thread (Fig. 12-10 at B) has two ridges in the form of helixes, and the lead is twice the pitch. A triple thread has three ridges, and the lead is three times the pitch. The number of threads per inch is one inch divided by the pitch. The number of turns per inch is one divided by the lead.

12·7 Right- and left-hand threads. A right-hand thread is one which turns in a clockwise direction to enter a threaded part when viewed from the outside end (Fig. 12-11 at A). A left-hand thread is one which turns in a counterclockwise direction when viewed from the outside end (Fig. 12-11 at B). Left-hand threads are always indicated as LH.

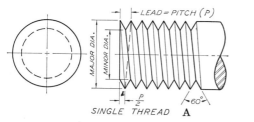
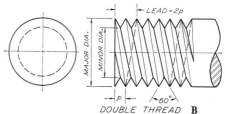

Fig. 12-10 Single and double threads.

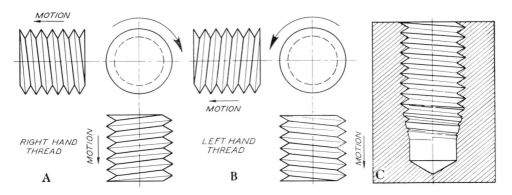

Fig. 12-11   Right- and left-hand threads.

A right-hand threaded hole is shown in section at C in Fig. 12-11. Thread lines slope opposite to external thread lines.

12·8 Screw-thread symbols are used for small diameters. American Standard *regular symbols* are shown at A and B in Fig. 12-12. The thick and thin lines at A represent the crests and roots of the thread. *Simplified symbols* are shown at C and D. The representations at E and F will be found on many shop drawings. The slope of the thread lines at F is equal to one-half the pitch. The actual pitch is not measured, but assumed to look well.

American Standard *regular symbols* for internal threads (threaded holes) in section are shown at A, B, and C in Fig. 12-13. The *simplified symbols* are shown at D, E, and F. End views are shown at G, H, and I. Symbols for threaded holes in elevation are shown at J, K, and L. The simplified symbols are used to save time on detail working drawings. If a *tapped* (threaded) hole does not go clear through a piece, the drill point or shape of the bottom of the hole is drawn as shown at B and C.

The same symbols are used for coarse or fine threads and for right-hand or left-hand threads, with notes to give the necessary information.

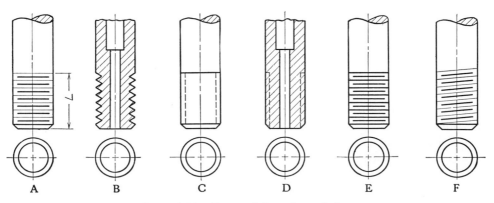

Fig. 12-12   External-thread symbols.

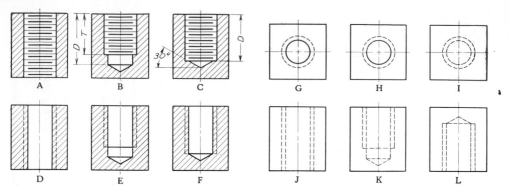

Fig. 12-13 Internal-thread symbols.

12·9 Screw threads larger than one inch in diameter. For diameters of more than this actual distance as drawn, the representations in Fig. 12-14 may be used. The V-form is shown in Space 1, the square thread in Space 2, and a more simplified representation of the square thread in Space 3. Screw threads in section are represented in Space 4. The order of drawing the lines for the V-form threads is shown in Fig. 12-15.

12·10 Thread series for Unified and American (National) screw threads. The number of threads per inch for a given diameter varies according to the purpose for which they are used. Several *series* of threads are provided in the American Standard. Letter symbols include: U, unified; N, National (American); C, coarse thread; F, fine thread; EF, extra fine thread; S, special thread.

Coarse thread series, UNC or NC. The pitch is relatively large for a specific diameter and is used for general engineering purposes.

Fine thread series, UNF or NF. The pitch is smaller (greater number of threads per inch) for a specific di-

ameter than for the coarse thread series. It is used where a finer thread is required, as in the automotive, aircraft, and similar industries.

Extra fine thread series, UNEF or NEF. The pitch is smaller than for the fine thread series. It is used where the depth of thread must be kept very small, as on aircraft equipment, thin-walled tubes, and so forth.

Three series provide for the same number of threads per inch regardless of the diameter. These are:

8-thread series, 8N. This series uses 8 threads per inch for all diameters.

12-thread series, 12N. This series uses 12 threads per inch for all diameters.

16-thread series, 16N. This series uses 16 threads per inch for all diameters.

Special threads, UN, UNS, or NS. These are nonstandard or special combinations of diameter, pitch, and length of engagement.

12·11 Classes of fits for Unified and American (National) screw threads. The amounts of tolerance and allowance specified to meet requirements for screw-thread fits are provided by *screw-thread classes.* Specific requirements can be met by the selection of

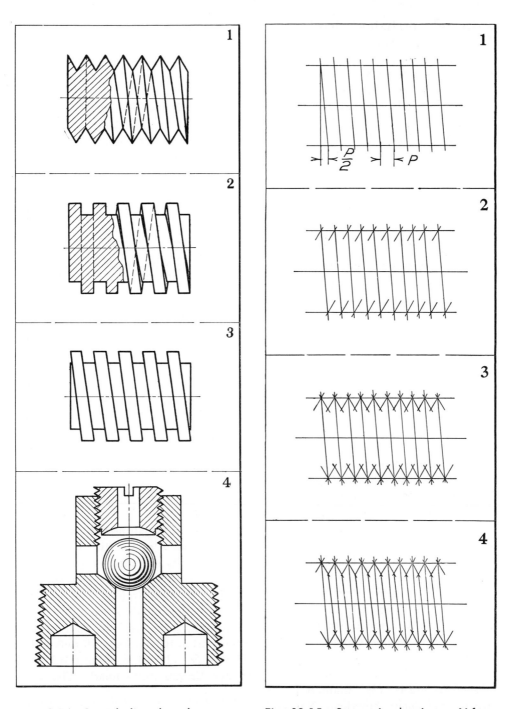

Fig. 12-14   Straight-line thread representations.

Fig. 12-15   Stages in drawing a V-form thread.

series and class. In brief, the classes for Unified and American (National) threads are: *classes 1A, 2A, and 3A* for external threads only; *classes 1B, 2B, and 3B* for internal threads only; *classes 3 and 2* for both external and internal threads.

Classes 1A and 1B. Replace former American Standard class 1, which was designated as "loose fit." Applied principally to ordinance.

Classes 2A and 2B. Include the great bulk of screw-thread work in the normal production of screws, bolts, nuts, and so forth.

Classes 3A and 3B. For the more accurate work. For class 3A maximum dimensions are basic and there is no allowance.

Classes 2 and 3. These are classes 2 and 3 of the former American Standard and are not Unified classes. No allowances are provided, and basic dimensions are used for maximum external and minimum internal thread dimensions.

12·12 Screw-thread specifications. Screw threads are specified by diameter (nominal or major diameter), number of threads per inch, initial letters of the series, and class of fit. If threads are to be left-hand, the letters LH should be added to the specifications; otherwise right-hand threads are understood.

1¼—7UNC—1A (1¼ diameter, 7 threads per inch, Unified American National threads, coarse thread, series 1, external)

½—13NC—2A (½ diameter, 13 threads per inch, American National threads, coarse threads, series 2, external)

⅞—14UNF—2B (⅞ diameter, 14 threads per inch, Unified American National threads, fine threads, series 2, internal)

1⅝—18NEF—3B—LH (1⅝ diameter, 18 threads per inch, American National threads, extra-fine threads, series 3, internal, left-hand)

Tapped (threaded) holes are specified by a note giving the diameter of the tap drill, depth of hole, thread information, and length of thread, as:

$$\tfrac{27}{64} \text{ drill} \times 1\tfrac{3}{8} \text{ deep}$$
$$\tfrac{1}{2}\text{—13NC—2B} \times 1 \text{ deep}$$

For complete information American Standard *Unified and American Screw Threads for Screws, Bolts, Nuts, and Other Threads* (ASA B1.1–1949) should be consulted.

12·13 Threaded fastenings are made in many forms for different uses. Enough information is included in the following articles to enable the student to identify and to draw the forms of bolts, nuts, and screws in most common use on machines and engineering constructions.

12·14 American Standard square and hexagon bolts and nuts.[4] Some terms used for bolts and nuts are given in Fig. 12-16 and should be learned as they are used in the descriptions which follow. Tables with some dimensions are in the Appendix, pages 531 to 534. Certain bolts and nuts have been designated as Unified Standard for use in the United States, Britain, and Canada. The series

[4] *Square and Hexagon Bolts and Nuts* (ASA B18.2–1955). The American Standards Association should be consulted for complete information.

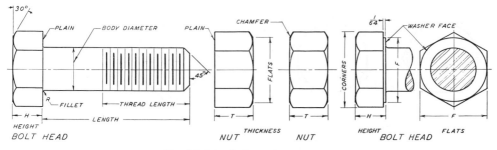

Fig. 12-16 Bolt and nut terms.

of standards for boltheads and nuts include:

Regular series for square bolts, hexagon bolts, semifinished hexagon bolts, square nuts, hexagon and hexagon-jam nuts, semifinished hexagon and hexagon-jam nuts, and semifinished slotted nuts. The regular series is used for general purposes.

Heavy series for hexagon bolts, semifinished hexagon bolts, square, hexagon, and hexagon-jam nuts, semifinished hexagon-jam nuts. The heavy series is used where a larger bearing surface is required or where a relatively larger hole is used.

Regular bolts and nuts are not finished on any surface. Semifinished bolts and nuts are processed to have a flat bearing surface. *Finished* bolts and

nuts refers to the quality of manufacture and the closeness of tolerance and does not mean that the surfaces are completely machined. Semifinished and semifinished bolts and nuts (Fig. 12-17) have a washer-faced bearing surface or have chamfered corners, with a diameter equal to the distance across flats. The thickness of the washer face is approximately ¹⁄₆₄ in.

12·15 Regular boltheads and nuts. For drawing purposes the dimensions may be obtained from the proportions given in Figs. 12-18 and 12-19. The chamfer angle may be drawn at 30° for either the hexagon or square forms. (The standard indicates 25° for the square form.) Radii for the arcs may be found by trial to suit the conditions. Note that

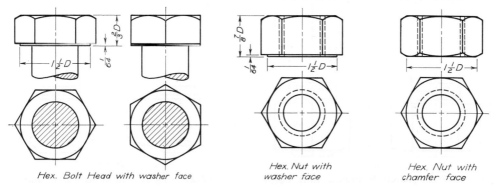

Hex. Bolt Head with washer face

Hex. Nut with washer face

Hex. Nut with chamfer face

Fig. 12-17   Boltheads and nuts with washer face or chamfer.

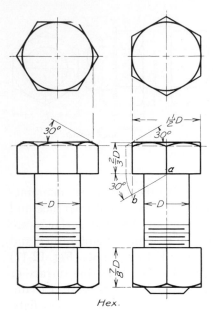

Fig. 12-18 Regular bolthead and nut—hexagon.

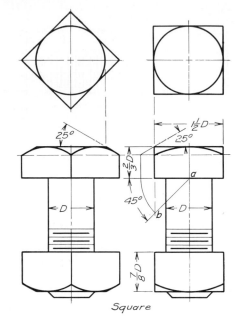

Fig. 12-19 Regular bolthead and nut—square.

one-half the distance across corners, *ab*, may be found by the construction shown.

12·16 Heavy boltheads and nuts. For drawing purposes the dimensions may be obtained from the proportions given in Figs. 12-20 and 12-21.

12·17 To draw a square bolthead across flats. (For regular series $W = 1\frac{1}{2}D$ and $H = \frac{2}{3}D$. For heavy series $W = 1\frac{1}{2}D + \frac{1}{8}$ and $H = \frac{2}{3}D$.) Start the top view as in Space 1 of Fig. 12-22 by drawing the chamfer circle with a diameter equal to the distance across flats. About this circle, draw a square.

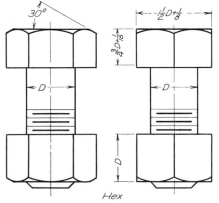

Fig. 12-20 Heavy bolthead and nut—hexagon.

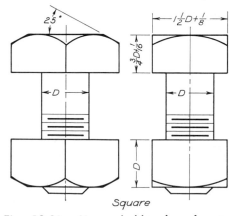

Fig. 12-21 Heavy bolthead and nut—square.

Draw a horizontal line in Space 2 representing the undersurface of the head and lay off the height of the head, H. Draw the top line of the head and project from Space 1 to obtain the vertical edges. Draw ox in the top view (Space 1), revolve to y, and project down to Space 2. From a in Space 2 draw the 30° chamfer line to b and project across to c and d. In Space 3 the edge view of the chamfer is drawn through c, e, and d by radius R. Radius R can be found by trial. Complete the view as in Space 4.

The same method may be used for drawing a nut with two exceptions: $T = \frac{7}{8}D$ for regular nuts and $T = D$ for heavy nuts.

12·18 To draw a square bolthead across corners. (For regular series $W = 1\frac{1}{2}D$ and $H = \frac{2}{3}D$. For heavy series $W = 1\frac{1}{2}D + \frac{1}{8}$ and $H = \frac{W}{2}$.)

Start the top view as in Space 1 of Fig. 12-23 by drawing the chamfer circle with a diameter equal to the distance across flats. About this circle, draw a square with the 45° triangle as shown. Draw a horizontal line in Space 2 representing the undersurface of the head and lay off the height of the head, H. Draw the top line of the head and project the vertical edges from Space 1. Project the diameter of the chamfer circle from the top view and draw 30° chamfer lines as shown (Space 2). Project point x down to obtain points f and g in Spaces 2 and 3 and draw line bcd. Then draw the edge view of the chamfer circle through bfc and cgd by radius R. Radius R can be found by trial. Now complete the view as shown in Space 4.

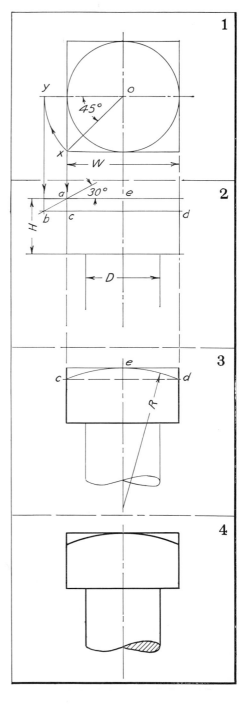

Fig. 12-22 Drawing a square bolthead across flats.

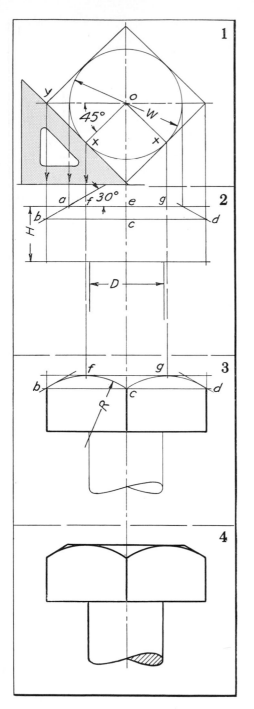

You can use the same method to draw a nut, except note that $T = \frac{7}{8}D$ for regular nuts and $T = D$ for heavy nuts.

Boltheads and nuts are usually drawn *across corners* on all views of design drawings, regardless of projection. This is done to show the largest space required in order to permit turning space or clearance. It also prevents hexagon heads and nuts being confused with square heads and nuts.

12·19 To draw a hexagon bolthead across corners (Fig. 12-24). Start the top view as in Space 1 by drawing the chamfer circle with a diameter equal to W, the distance across flats. For a head across corners draw a hexagon as indicated by the lines 1, 2, 3, 4, 5, 6.[5] For the front view, Space 2, draw a horizontal line representing the bearing or contact surface of the head. Lay off the height of the head and the top surface. Then project from the top view and draw the chamfer line as shown.

Draw line *abcd* (Space 3) to locate the chamfer intersections. Radius R_1 can be found by trial so that the arc will pass through points *b* and *c* and be tangent to the top line. Complete the front view as in Space 4 by drawing arcs with radii R_2 (tangent to top line and through point *a* and *b* at the left, and *c* and *d* at the right, by trial).

To draw a hexagon bolthead across flats, proceed as illustrated in Fig. 12-25.

You can draw hexagon nuts with the same construction, but note the difference between the height of the head and thickness of the nut.

Fig. 12-23 Drawing a square bolthead across corners.

[5] For methods of drawing a hexagon see Arts. 4·12 and 4·13.

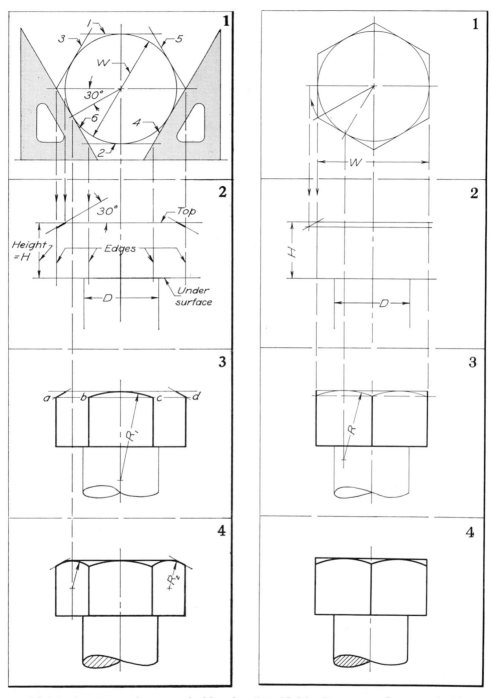

Fig. 12-24 Drawing a hexagon bolthead across corners.

Fig. 12-25 Drawing a hexagon bolthead across flats.

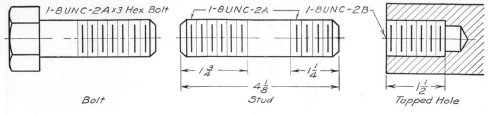

Fig. 12-26 Bolt.   Fig. 12-27 Stud.   Fig. 12-28 Tapped hole.

12·20 Boltheads and nuts have the dimensions so well standardized that they are not dimensioned on the drawings. For a standard bolt the necessary information is given in a note as in Fig. 12-26, which specifies 1″ diameter, 8 threads per inch, Unified coarse thread series, class 2A fit, 3″ long, hex bolt-head. If the standard minimum length of thread ($2D + \frac{1}{4}$″ for length up to 6″ inclusive and $2D + \frac{1}{2}$″ for lengths over 6″) is not used, the length of thread from the end of the bolt should be given.

A *stud* or stud bolt (Fig. 12-27), which has threads on both ends, is used

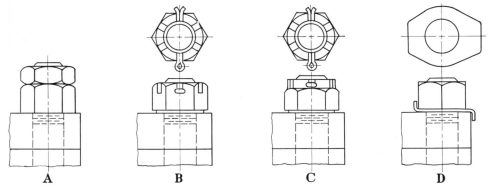

A   B   C   D

Fig. 12-29 Lock nuts.

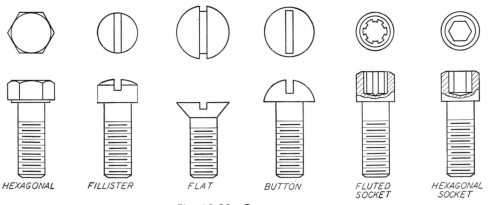

HEXAGONAL   FILLISTER   FLAT   BUTTON   FLUTED SOCKET   HEXAGONAL SOCKET

Fig. 12-30 Cap screws.

FLAT   OVAL   ROUND   FILLISTER   TRUSS   BINDING   PAN

Fig. 12-31   Machine screws.

where bolts are not suitable and for parts which must be removed often. One end is screwed permanently into place in a tapped hole, and a nut is screwed onto the projecting end. Sometimes a stud is used with a nut on both ends.

A *tapped* (threaded) hole is dimensioned as in Fig. 12-28.

12·21 Lock nuts and various devices (Fig. 12-29) are used to prevent nuts from working loose. Many patented devices are available. A jam nut is shown at A, a slotted nut at B, a castle nut at C, and a holding plate at D. A cotter pin is used with the slotted nut and the castle nut.

12·22 Cap screws are used for fastening two pieces together by passing through a hole in one and screwing into a tapped hole in the other. Some forms of American Standard cap screws are shown in Fig. 12-30; some general dimensions are given in the Appendix, page 535.

12·23 Machine screws are used where small diameters are required. Sizes below ¼ in. diameter are specified by number. Some American Standard machine screws are shown in Fig. 12-31 and some dimensions are given in the Appendix, page 536.

12·24 Setscrews (Fig. 12-32) are used for holding two parts in a desired position relative to each other by screwing through a threaded hole in one piece and bearing against the other. Some dimensions of American Standard setscrews are given in the Appendix, page 537.

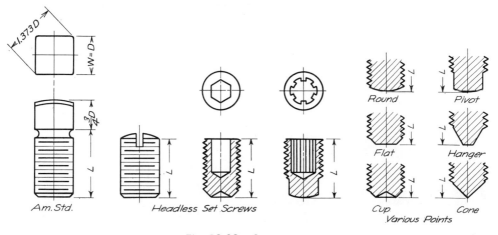

Am. Std.   Headless Set Screws   Cup   Cone

Round   Pivot

Flat   Hanger

Various Points

Fig. 12-32   Setscrews.

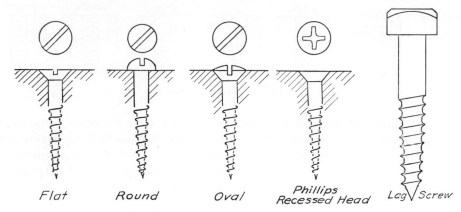

Flat Round Oval Phillips Recessed Head Lag Screw

Fig. 12-33 Wood screws and lag bolt.

12·25 Wood screws (Fig. 12-33) are made of steel, brass, or aluminum and are finished in various ways. Steel screws may be bright (natural finish), blued, galvanized, or copper-plated; both steel and brass screws are sometimes nickel-plated. Round-head screws have the head above the wood; flat-head screws are set flush or countersunk. Wood screws may be drawn as illustrated. They are specified by number, length, style of head, and finish.

Length of flat-head screws is measured overall; round-head screws from under head to point; oval-head screws from largest diameter of countersink to point. For sizes and dimensions, see the Appendix, page 538.

A lag screw, or lag bolt, is used for fastening machinery to wood supports and for heavy wood constructions when a regular bolt cannot be used. It is similar to a regular bolt but has wood-screw threads. Lag bolts are

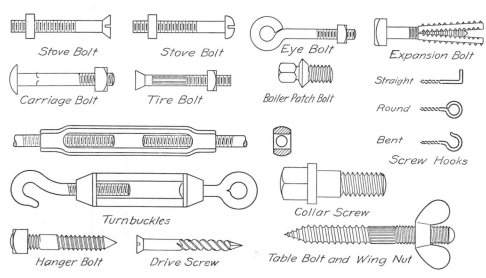

Stove Bolt Stove Bolt Eye Bolt Expansion Bolt

Carriage Bolt Tire Bolt Boiler Patch Bolt Straight

Round

Bent

Screw Hooks

Turnbuckles

Collar Screw

Hanger Bolt Drive Screw Table Bolt and Wing Nut

Fig. 12-34 Miscellaneous bolts and screws.

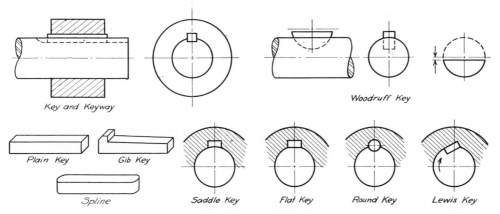

Key and Keyway   Woodruff Key

Plain Key   Gib Key

Spline   Saddle Key   Flat Key   Round Key   Lewis Key

Fig. 12-35   Keys.

specified by the diameter and length from under the head to the point. Proportions of the head are the same as for regular bolts.

12·26 Some miscellaneous threaded fastenings are shown in Fig. 12-34; the names indicate the purposes for which they are used. Screw hooks and screw eyes are specified by diameter and over-all length.

12·27 Keys (Fig. 12-35) are used to secure pulleys, gears, cranks, and similar parts to a shaft. The form of key is selected to suit the duty that it must perform. This ranges from the saddle key for light duty to special forms or two square keys for heavy duty. The common sunk key may have a breadth of about one-fourth the shaft diameter and a thickness of from five-eighths the

breadth to the full breadth. The Woodruff key is much used in machine-tool work. It is made in standard sizes and is specified by number (see Appendix, page 542). Special forms of pins have been developed to take the place of keys for some purposes They require only a drilled hole instead of the machining necessary for keys.

12·28 Rivets.[6] Sheet-metal plates, structural-steel shapes, and many other parts are put together with rivets, especially when permanent fastenings are required. See Chap. 22.

Structural rivets have the forms shown in Fig. 12-36. Boiler and tank rivets have the forms shown in Fig. 12-37. American Standard small rivets (Fig. 12-38) range from $\frac{3}{32}$ to $\frac{7}{16}$ in. in

[6] Welding is also used. See Chap. 17.

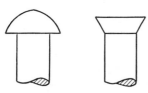

Fig. 12-36   Structural rivets.   Fig. 12-37   Boiler rivets.

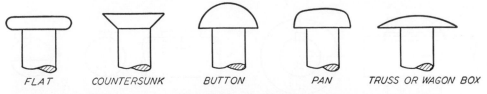

FLAT   COUNTERSUNK   BUTTON   PAN   TRUSS OR WAGON BOX

Fig. 12-38 Small rivets.

Fig. 12-39 Explosive rivet. (*Explosive Department, E. I. du Pont de Nemours & Company*)

diameter. See the Appendix, page 545, for rivet proportions.

The du Pont explosive rivet (Fig. 12-39) has a small explosive charge in the cavity when inserted. After the charge is exploded, a head is formed. This makes *blind* riveting possible since the head can be formed inside closed or inaccessible places.

12·29 Problem suggestions. Group I, page 431. Two lists are presented. List 1 includes basic problems. Selections from List 2 may be used for additional assignments, or selections may be made for more advanced students. Review of Chap. 12 should be assigned in connection with the problems in Groups J and L.

LIST 1 Problems I·3, I·4, I·7, I·9, I·13, I·14, I·18, I·21

LIST 2 Problems I·1, I·6, I·8, I·10, I·11, I·12, I·15, I·16, I·17, I·19, I·20, I·22, I·23, I·24, I·25

 The motion picture and follow-up filmstrip *Shop Procedures* are not directly correlated with any specific chapter but may be used to advantage with this chapter.

13 Mechanical drafting

13·1 Drafting practice. A working drawing is one that gives all the information necessary for making a single part or a complete machine or structure. The drawing completely describes the shape and size and gives specifications for the kinds of material to be used, the methods of finish, and the accuracy required. A picture and the working drawing of a simple machine part are shown in Fig. 13-1.

13·2 Working drawings are based upon orthographic projection (Chap. 5) with

Fig. 13-1   A working drawing.

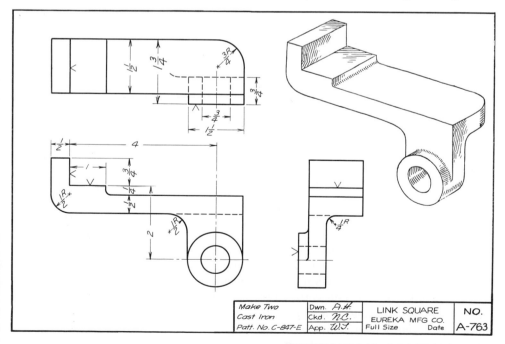

Make Two	Dwn. *A.H.*	LINK SQUARE	NO.
Cast Iron	Ckd. *N.C.*	EUREKA MFG CO.	
Patt. No. C-847-E	App. *W.J.*	Full Size Date	A-763

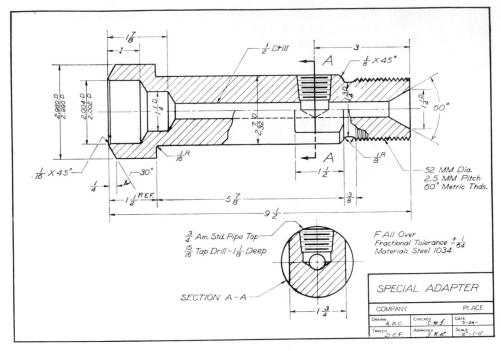

Fig. 13-2 A detail drawing.

dimensions and notes added as described in Chaps. 10 to 12.

Such drawings must conform in style with good practice as followed in the office where they are made. There must be contrast, which is obtained by giving proper values to the various lines that compose the views. Figures that are easy to read, uniform lettering, and the use of standard terms are essential. When completed, a working drawing must be thoroughly checked for errors and improvements before being submitted for approval.

13·3 Detail drawings. The drawing of a single piece that gives all the information necessary for making it is called a *detail drawing*. This is the simplest form of working drawing and must be a complete and an accurate

description of the piece, with carefully selected views and well-located dimensions. Sometimes separate detail drawings are made for the use of different workmen, such as the patternmaker, hammersmith, machinist, or welder. Such drawings have only the dimensions and information needed by the workmen for whom the drawing is made. An ordinary detail drawing is shown in Fig. 13-2.

When a large number of machines are to be manufactured, it is usual to make a detail drawing for each part on a separate sheet, especially when some of the parts are used on different machines. When several parts are used on a single machine, it is common practice in some industries to draw a number of detail drawings on large sheets.

Figure 13-3 shows a forging as

172 MECHANICAL DRAWING

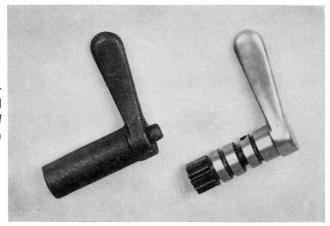

Fig. 13-3 Index-plunger operating handle—forging and finished part. (*The Hartford Special Machinery Company*)

formed and after it has been machined. The working drawing of the superspacer latch pinion, made by the Hartford Special Machinery Company, is shown in Fig 13-4. Notice how the parts to be removed after all work is done are shown. Also, notice the detailed list of machine operations.

13·4 Assembly drawings. A drawing of a completely assembled construction is called an *assembly drawing*. Such drawings vary greatly in regard to completeness of detail and dimensioning. Their particular value is in showing the way in which the parts go together and the appearance of the construction as a

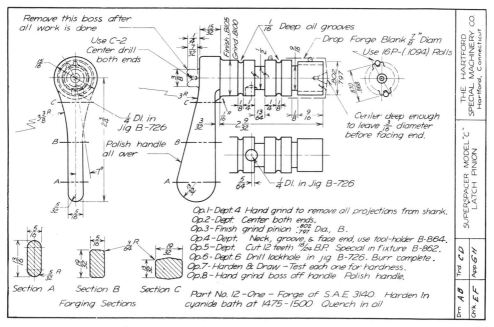

Fig. 13-4 Working drawing of the part shown in Fig. 13-3.

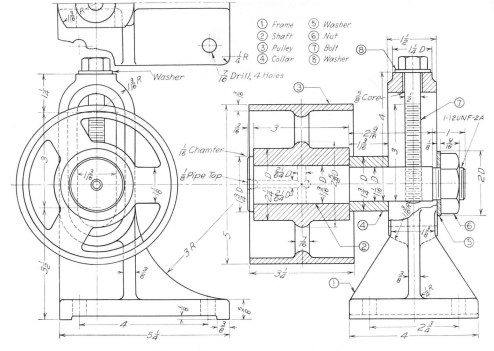

Fig. 13-5 An assembly working drawing.

① Frame	⑤ Washer
② Shaft	⑥ Nut
③ Pulley	⑦ Bolt
④ Collar	⑧ Washer

whole. When complete information is given, they may be used for working drawings. This is possible when there is little or no complex detail. Figure 13-5 shows such a drawing. Furniture and other wood construction can often be shown in assembly working drawings by adding necessary enlarged details or additional partial views.

Assembly drawings of machines are generally made to small scale. They have selected dimensions to tell over-all distances, important center-to-center distances, and location dimensions. All, or almost all, hidden lines may be left out and, if drawn to a very small scale, unnecessary detail may be omitted. Figure 13-6 is an example.

Either exterior or sectional views may be used. When the general appearance is the main purpose of the

drawing, only one or two views need to be used.

Because of the size of some assembled constructions, it may be necessary to draw different views of the assembly on separate sheets. The same scale should be used on all sheets.

13·5 Choice of views. A drawing can be used more easily if the draftsman properly selects the views. For the complete description of an object, at least two views are required. Although a drawing is not a picture, it is always advisable to select the views that require the least effort to read. Each view must have a part in the description; otherwise it is not needed and should not be drawn. In some cases one view is all that is necessary, provided a note is added or the shape and size are

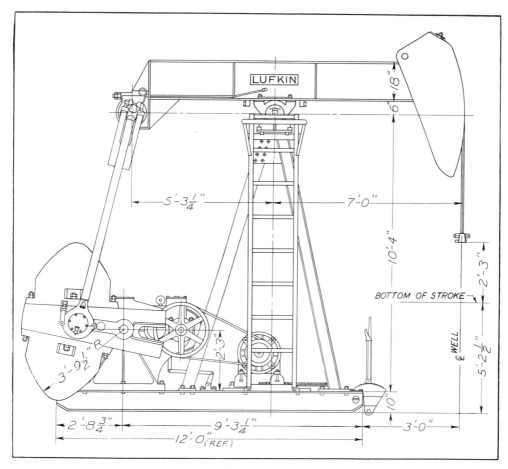

Fig. 13-6 An outline assembly drawing. (*Lufkin Foundry & Machine Company*)

standard or evident. Complex pieces may require more than three views, some of which may be partial views, auxiliary views, and sectional views. The reason for making the drawing must always be kept in mind when a question arises. The final test of the value of a drawing is its clearness and exactness in giving the complete information necessary for making the piece.

13·6 Choice of scale. The choice of scale for a detail drawing is governed by three things: (1) the size necessary for showing all details clearly, (2) the size necessary for carrying all dimensions without crowding, and (3) the size of paper used. It is always desirable to make detail drawings to full size. Other scales commonly used are half, quarter, and eighth (see Art. 2·23). Such scales as $2'' = 1'$, $4'' = 1'$, and $9'' = 1'$ are to be avoided. If a part is very small, it is sometimes drawn to an enlarged scale, perhaps twice full size.

When a number of details are drawn on one sheet, they should, if possible,

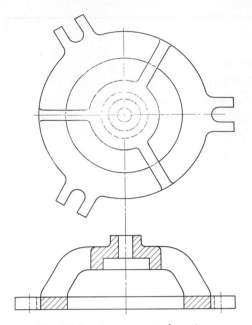

Fig. 13-7   A symmetrical section.

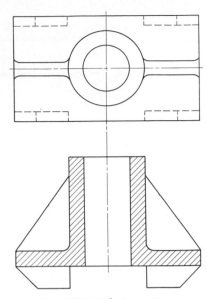

Fig. 13-8   Rib in section.

be made to the same scale. If different scales are used, they should be noted near each drawing. A detail or part detail drawn to a larger scale may often be used to advantage on assembly drawings. This will save the making of separate detail drawings. General assembly drawings can be made to the scale that will show the desired amount of detail and work up well on the size of paper used. Sheet-metal pattern drawings for practical use are always made full size, although practice models may be constructed from small-scale layouts.

13·7 Grouping and placing parts. When a number of details are used for one machine only, they are often grouped on a single sheet or set of

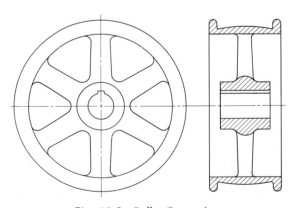

Fig. 13-9   Pulley in section.

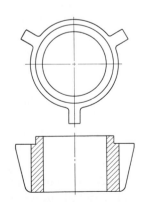

Fig. 13-10   Lugs in section.

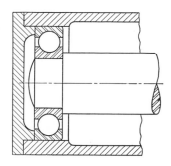

Fig. 13-11   Ball bearing in section.

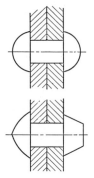

Fig. 13-12   Rivets.

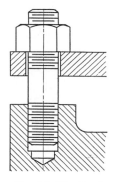

Fig. 13-13   Stud.

sheets. A convenient arrangement is to group the forging details together, the casting details together, the brass details together, and similarly other materials. In general, it is well to show parts in the position that they will have in the assembled machine, with related parts near each other. Long pieces, however, such as shafts and bolts, are drawn with their long dimensions parallel to the long dimension of the paper.

13·8 Adapting principles in the drafting room. The principles of shape description by means of views have been explained. They form the basis for working drawings. In the actual use of mechanical drawing, it is sometimes desirable to violate[1] these rules. The reason for each violation must be thoroughly understood, as well as the method of making the necessary changes in the drawing.

13·9 Sectional views. Regular sectional views were explained in Chap. 8. When regular sections result in complicated or misleading views, they are modified. Thus the sectional view of a symmetri-

[1] Such violations are called *conventional representations* and are used to make the drawings easier to read.

cal piece, drawn as in Fig. 13-7, gives a better representation than a true section.

13·10 Sections through ribs, arms, etc. When a section passes through a rib or pulley arm, the drawing is made as in Figs. 13-8 and 13-9, where the plane is thought of as being just in front of the rib or arm. In Fig. 13-10 the lugs are shown as symmetrical and are not sectioned. A true section in these figures would give the idea of a very heavy solid piece. Shafts, rivets, and bolts are represented in full as in Figs. 13-11 to 13-13. When a section or elevation of a drilled flange is drawn, the holes are shown at their true distance from the center regardless of where they would project (Fig. 13-14).

A revolved section is sometimes inserted in a view to show the shape as in Fig. 13-15.

13·11 Rule of contour. In general, preserve the characteristic contour of an object. Sections or elevations of symmetrical pieces are sometimes hard to read when drawn in true projection. It is usual in such cases to revolve a portion of the object until the characteristic contour shows. This has been done

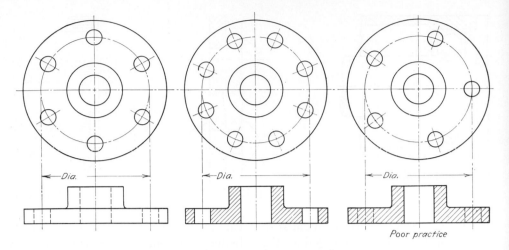

Fig. 13-14   Flanges in elevation and section.

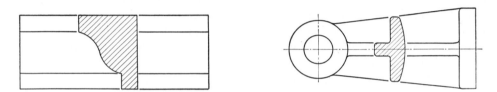

Fig. 13-15   Revolved section.

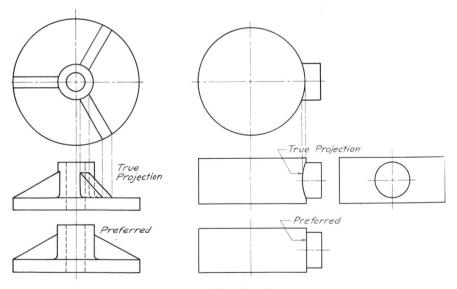

Fig. 13-16   The rule of contour.

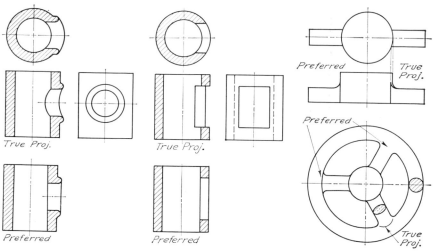

Fig. 13-17 The rule of contour.

in Figs. 13-16 and 13-17, which illustrate applications of the rule of contour.

It is always desirable to show true distances even though the views do not project. This may be illustrated by bent levers and similar pieces which are represented by revolved or stretched-out views as in Fig. 13-18.

13·12 Rough and finished castings. Castings are made by pouring melted metal, such as cast iron or aluminum, into molds formed in sand. Wooden patterns are used to form the molds. The cooled metal removed from each mold has surfaces roughened by contact with the sand. Sometimes the casting can be used in this form, but more often some of the surfaces must be finished or made smooth and brought to size by machining. Round surfaces are finished on a lathe or similar machine. Flat surfaces are finished on a shaper,

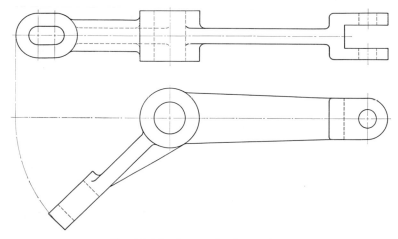

Fig. 13-18 A stretched-out view.

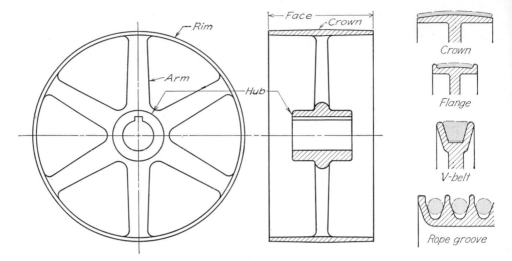

Fig. 13-19 Pulleys and flanges.

planer, milling machine, or similar machine.

Finished surfaces must always be indicated on a drawing and, when necessary, the degree of accuracy must be specified.

13·13 Fillets and rounds. Sharp corners and edges are generally undesirable on unfinished machine parts. Rounded corners and edges not only look better but are also stronger. For this reason, interior corners are filled in with fillets, and exterior corners are rounded.

13·14 Pulleys and flywheels. Included under this general head are pulleys that carry belts, flywheels for the storing of energy, and handwheels for adjustment. Each has a rim, arms, and a hub.

Belt pulleys (Fig. 13-19) are made of cast iron, steel, plastic, wood, paper, and so forth. The face of a belt pulley is generally crowned (made higher in the center). The crown tends to keep the belt centered. Sometimes flanges are used on small belt pulleys. For V-belts, specially shaped pulleys are used as illustrated. For rope or cable driving, such as in elevators or cable cars, grooved pulleys are used.

Flywheels have heavy rims which store up or give out energy when the speed changes. The rim of a flywheel is, therefore, thick in proportion to its width in order to concentrate weight. Flywheels are made in many forms for use on steam engines, gas engines, presses, and other machinery where their regulating action is needed.

13·15 Bearings. Bearings are supports for moving parts of machines. They may be either flat or round. The runner of a sled or an ice skate is essentially a flat bearing. A typewriter carriage slides on flat bearing surfaces known as a slide, or ways. The wheels of roller skates are built around ball bearings that roll around a round shaft. Sometimes rollers are used instead of steel balls. Plain, ball, or roller bearings are designed for use under varying conditions of load and speed.

Plain round bearings are usually lined with babbitt metal (a mixture of the three metals copper, antimony, and tin) or some other substance that slides easily against the shaft. Bearings are often oiled or greased by means of grooves to help the parts rub easily together. A hole through a piece of metal is the simplest type of bearing. It may or may not be bushed (lined) or oiled.

13·16 Shafting. Shafting drawings are of two general kinds. Transmission or line-shaft drawings are made to show the location of pulleys, gears, bearings, keyways, and so forth. The diameter and length of the shaft must be shown, together with the locating dimensions and notes specifying the sizes and kinds of the various features. Shafting is made of either hot-rolled or cold-rolled steel.

Drawings for machine shafts are made in the same way as other machine parts (Fig. 13-20). Complete information must be given by dimensions and notes. Shafts are made of steel of a grade suited to the purpose for which the shafts are used and are machined to size.

13·17 Shaft couplings. For joining lengths of line shafting end to end, couplings of various types are used. Two forms of sleeve couplings are illustrated in Figs. 13-21 and 13-22. A flange coupling is shown in Fig. J-17 in Chap. 24, and an Oldham coupling in Fig. L-11 in Chap. 24. The latter is used when the shafts are parallel, but they may be slightly out of line with each other.

13·18 Pipe. Pipe is used in conveying fluids and is made of various materials—lead, brass, wrought iron, steel, cast iron, wood, concrete, and so forth.

For steam, gas, and similar purposes,

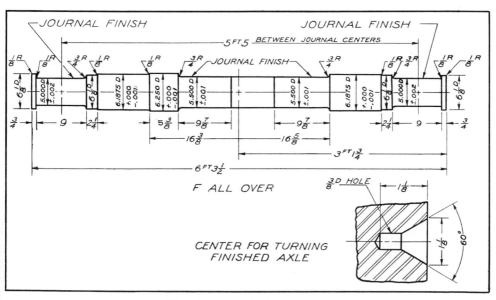

Fig. 13-20 A shaft drawing.

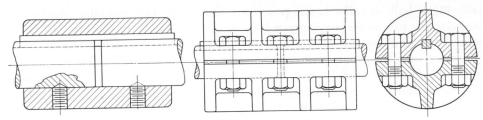

Fig. 13-21   Sleeve coupling.   Fig. 13-22   Split coupling.

standard pipe of steel or iron is commonly used. Such pipe is specified by the *nominal* inside diameter, which differs from the actual diameter. The dimensions for pipe in general use (formerly known as Standard) are given in the Appendix, page 544.

This former standard was used for ordinary pressures of around 125 lb per sq in. In addition extra-heavy (X) pipe was made with thicker walls for heavier pressures, but with the same outside diameter as the standard pipe. This reduced the inside diameter for the same nominal size. Double extra-heavy (XX) pipe kept the same outside diameter but reduced the inside diameter, and was used for still higher pressures. Large pipe, over 12 in. in diameter, was called *OD pipe* and was specified by the outside diameter and thickness of metal.

Present practice is covered in the published American Standard *Wrought-steel and Wrought-iron Pipe* (ASA B36·10-1950). This gives wall thicknesses and weights for different schedule numbers and replaces the former standard and the extra-heavy (X) and double extra-heavy (XX) standards.

13·19 Pipe threads and fittings. Ordinarily pipe is made up or put together with fittings. The ends of the pipe may be threaded or plain. Several forms of

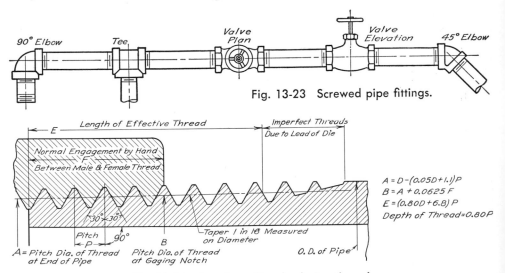

Fig. 13-23   Screwed pipe fittings.

Fig. 13-24   American Standard pipe thread.

$A = D-(0.05D+1.1)P$
$B = A+0.0625F$
$E = (0.80D+6.8)P$
Depth of Thread $= 0.80P$

screwed (threaded) fittings are shown in Fig. 11-23. The American Standard form of pipe thread (Fig. 13-24) is used on screwed pipe and fittings. Plain- (beveled) end pipe and fittings (Fig. 13-25) are welded together. Flanged fittings and pipe (Fig. 13-26) may be used for large sizes of pipe, or the pipe may be welded.

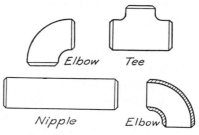

Fig. 13-25   Welded fittings.

13·20 Sizes of fittings are specified by the nominal size of pipe with which they are used. Reducing fittings are used to join different sizes of pipe. The size is specified by giving the largest run opening first and then the opposite end of the run. For tees and crosses the side outlets are given last (Fig. 13-27).

13·21 Piping drawings. Drawings for piping layouts are made as illustrated in Fig. 13-23, with dimensions and notes added to specify sizes, kinds, and location. For small-scale drawings and sketches, the single-line conventions of Fig. 13-28 are used. Welded piping may be shown as in Fig. 13-29. Pictorial

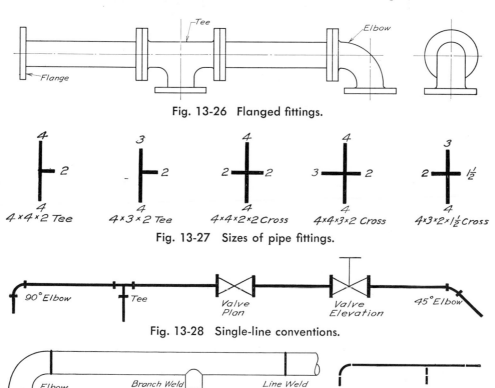

Fig. 13-26   Flanged fittings.

Fig. 13-27   Sizes of pipe fittings.

Fig. 13-28   Single-line conventions.

Fig. 13-29   Welded pipe representations.

methods of representation are often convenient.

13·22 Problem suggestions. Group J, page 436. Group K, page 450. Group L, page 459. Three lists are presented. List 1 includes more elementary problems. Selections of two or three problems should be made from List 1 for a brief course. Selections of a few drawings from List 2 may be used for alternate or additional problems. Selections from List 3 may be made for advanced students or for those taking a more extensive course. Review of Chaps. 10 to 12 should be assigned in connection with these problems. It will add interest and value to this chapter if a few parts of machines are available which can be sketched, measured, drawn, and traced.

Working Drawings, Group J
LIST 1   Problems J·1, J·2, J·4, J·6, J·12, J·14, J·15, J·17, J·19, J·25
LIST 2   Problems J·3, J·7, J·10, J·13, J·18, J·24, J·27

LIST 3   Problems J·5, J·8, J·9, J·11, J·16, J·20, J·21, J·22, J·23, J·26, J·28, J·29, J·30

Wood and Furniture Drawings, Group K
LIST 1   Problems K·1, K·3, K·4, K·6, K·8, K·11, K·12
LIST 2   Problems K·2, K·5, K·7, K·9, K·10, K·16, K·17
LIST 3   Problems K·13, K·14, K·15, K·18, K·19, K·20, K·21, K·22, K·23

Assembly and Detail Drawings, Group L
LIST 1   Problems L·2, L·4, L·7, L·8, L·12, L·15
LIST 2   Problems L·1, L·5, L·9, L·14, L·16, L·17
LIST 3   Problems L·3, L·6, L·10, L·11, L·13, L·18, L·19, L·20, L·21, L·22, L·23, L·24

Piping, Group M (page 473)
Problems M·1, M·2, M·3, M·4, M·5, M·6

The color filmstrip *Isometric Drawing* has been prepared to correlate with this chapter.

14 Pictorial drawing

14·1 Uses of pictorial drawing. On working drawings the shape description is always done by the exact method of separate views, or orthographic projection, as you have studied in previous chapters. In addition to a knowledge of this system of drawing, a draftsman should be able to make a pictorial view, either freehand or with instruments. The draftsman who

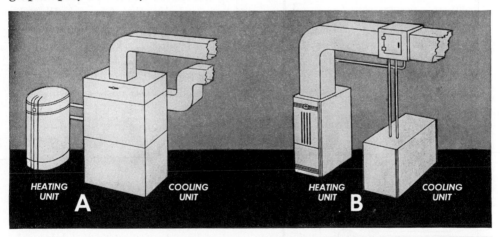

Fig. 14-1 All-year air-conditioning units represented by pictures. (*General Electric Company*)

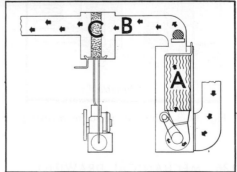

Fig. 14-2 All-year air conditioning.

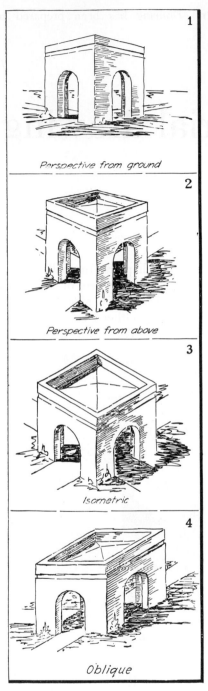

Perspective from ground

Perspective from above

Isometric

Oblique

Fig. 14-3 Kinds of pictorial drawing.

quickly and skillfully makes a pictorial sketch or drawing finds this ability very helpful in design work. Pictorial sketches help in reading and visualizing a drawing. They also show the appearance of an object to persons who cannot read orthographic projection. Notes, reports, and published articles are more helpful if they contain pictorial drawings. In the study of drawing, one of the best exercises is to translate orthographic drawings into pictorial drawings.

14·2 Pictorial exploded views. Pictorial drawings are used often to show *exploded views* on production drawings (Chap. 15); to illustrate parts lists; and to explain the operation of machines, apparatus, and equipment. For example, Figs. 14-1 and 14-2 are illustrations used by the General Electric Company to explain air-conditioning units for homes. The G-E boiler teamed with a G-E air conditioner is pictured at A in Fig. 14-1 and a G-E warm air conditioner teamed with a cooling unit is pictured at B. The working of a year-round air conditioner is shown in Fig. 14-2. In summer, air comes down the return duct to the conditioner (A) where it is first filtered and gently blown into the supply duct (B). The burner is off, but the cooling coil (C) in the supply duct is on. Air is cooled and relieved of moisture (dehumidified) before it goes upstairs to refresh your rooms. In winter, the cooling coil is off but the burner is in use. Returning air comes down the same duct, is cleaned by the same filter, circulated by the same blower, warmed, humidified, and sent up the same supply ducts. These two figures show how pictures and diagrams can be used together to explain operations and equipment.

14·3 Pictorial views. By those familiar with the subject, sketches are often made in *perspective*. This shows the object as it would actually appear to the eye (Fig. 14-3, Spaces 1 and 2). An easier way, although the result is not so pleasing in appearance as a well-made perspective, is to use one of the pictorial methods of projection, such as isometric drawing, Space 3, and oblique projection, Space 4. These all show three faces in one view. Their advantage is that the principal lines can be measured directly. Although similar in effect, these three methods should not be confused.

14·4 Isometric drawing. This simple method is based on revolution as illustrated in Fig. 14-4. Space 1 shows three views of a cube in the usual position. Space 2 shows three views when the cube has been revolved about a vertical axis. Two faces then show as equal rectangles in the front view (Space 2). When the cube has been revolved forward (tilted up on one corner) through the correct angle (35°16′), the front view shows three faces equal in shape and size (Space 3). This front view is called an *isometric* (equal measure) projection.

In this position, the edges would evidently not show in their true length. An isometric drawing of the same cube is of the same shape (Fig. 14-4 in Space 4) but a little larger in size, for the edges are drawn in their true length instead of in the shortened length. This variation in size does not affect the pictorial value of the view for shape description, but it does simplify the

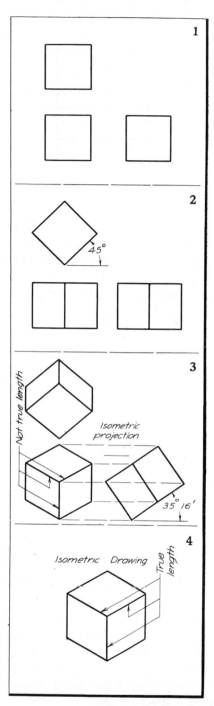

Fig. 14-4 The isometric cube.

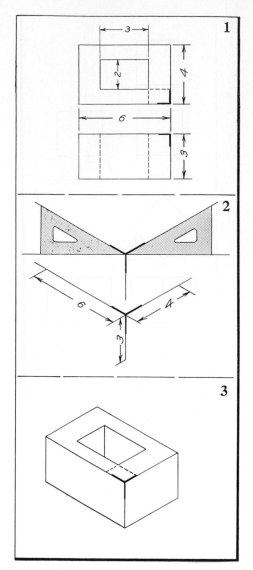

Fig. 14-5 Isometric axes. First position.

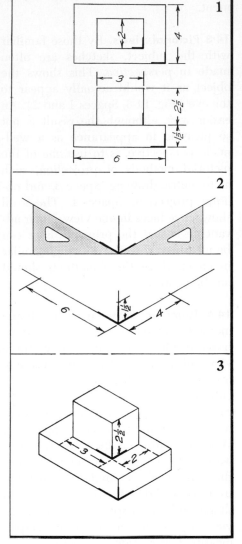

Fig. 14-6 Isometric axes. Second position.

drawing of the view because all measurements can be made with the regular scale. This makes it possible to draw the desired pictorial view at once without projecting from other views or using a special scale.

Isometric drawings are thus built on a skeleton of three lines representing

the three edges of the cube. These three lines form three equal angles of 120° and are called the *isometric axes*. One is drawn vertically, the others with the 30° triangle, as shown in Fig. 14-5. The intersection of these lines would be the front corner of a block with square corners. Measuring the length, breadth, and thickness of the block on the three axes and drawing lines through these points parallel to the axes will give the isometric drawing of the block. The arrangement of the axes in Fig. 14-5 is the first position and is based upon the three edges of the cube that meet at the front corner as in Fig. 14-4, Space 3. The axes may be arranged in different ways provided their relative positions are not changed. It is often more convenient to place the axes in the second position and use the lower corner (Fig. 14-6).

Any line on the object parallel to one of these edges is drawn parallel to it and is called an *isometric line*. The first rule of isometric drawing is: **Measurements can be made only on isometric lines.** The second rule is: **Remember the isometric cube.**

14·5 Nonisometric lines. Lines not parallel to any of the isometric axes are called *nonisometric* lines. Such lines will not show in their true length and cannot be measured; they must be drawn by locating their two ends.

Angles between lines on isometric drawings do not show in their true size and cannot be measured in degrees. All the angles of a cube are right angles, but in the isometric drawing some would measure 120° and some 60°. In the drawing of angles other than 90°, the lines forming them must be transferred from the orthographic views as shown in Fig. 14-7. To make an isometric drawing of the packing block shown (Space 1), first drop perpendiculars on the front view from the points D and E, giving the construction lines DF and EG. Then draw the two isometric axes, AB and AC, as in Space 2, and measure the distances AF and

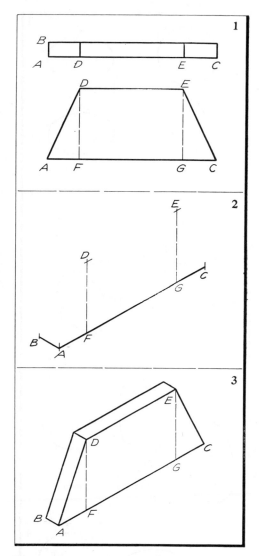

Fig. 14-7 Construction for nonisometric lines.

CG. Draw vertical construction lines at F and G equal in length to lines DF and EG taken from the front view in Space 1 to locate points D and E. The nonisometric lines AD and CE can then be drawn and the isometric view finished as in Space 3. The isometric representations of the angles will be

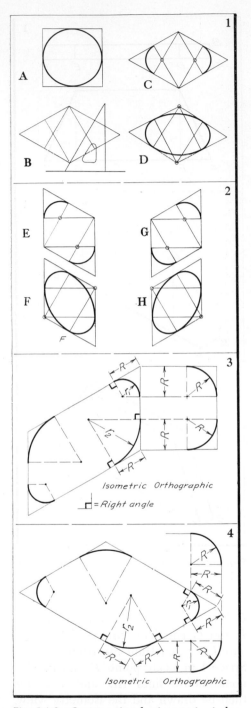

Fig. 14-8 Construction for isometric circles.

as shown at *DAF* and *ECG*. Any angle may be located on the isometric view by laying off the two legs of a right triangle.

14·6 Isometric circles. Circles will appear as ellipses in isometric drawing; but instead of a true ellipse being drawn, a four-centered approximation is usually made. To draw an isometric circle, first make the isometric drawing of the square that will contain it (Fig. 14-8, Space 1 at B). From the points of tangency, draw perpendiculars as indicated at B. Their intersections will give four centers from which arcs may be drawn tangent to the sides of the isometric square. Two of these centers will fall on the intersections of the perpendiculars as shown at C and two at the corners as shown at D. Thus the entire construction may be made with the 60° triangle. Circles on the left or right surfaces of the object may be drawn in the same way as shown at E, F, G, and H in Fig. 14-8, Space 2.

The construction for quarter rounds is the same as for one-quarter of a circle. This is illustrated in Spaces 3 and 4 of Fig. 14-8. Note that the radius is measured along the tangent lines from the corner in each case and that actual perpendiculars are then drawn to locate the centers for the isometric arcs. It will be observed that r_1 and r_2 are found in the same way as the short and long radii of a complete isometric circle.

When an arc is more or less than a quarter circle, it is sometimes possible to draw all or part of a complete isometric circle and use as much of it as is needed. In other cases it may be necessary to plot points as explained in Art. 14·8 for isometric curves.

14·7 Isometric templates. Templates of Celluloid or plastic are now made with elliptical openings of different sizes for drawing circles in isometric. The sides of the templates are cut at angles to permit the major axis of the ellipse to be placed in the required positions for drawing the ellipses. Such templates are convenient and timesaving when many isometric drawings are being made. They also give a better appearance because true ellipses are drawn.

14·8 Isometric curves. Curves other than circle arcs are drawn by plotting a series of points. This is illustrated in Fig. 14-9. First draw the orthographic view (Space 1) and locate a number of points by drawing lines as shown. Draw these same lines in isometric as illustrated for a vertical plane (Space 2) and a horizontal plane (Space 3). Then plot points by transferring distances from the orthographic to the isometric view. Draw a smooth curve through the points.

14·9 Isometric sections. Isometric drawings are generally made as outside views, but sometimes a sectional view is needed. The section is taken on an *isometric plane,* that is, on a plane parallel to one of the faces of the cube. Figure 14-10 shows isometric full sections taken on a different plane for each of the three objects (Spaces 1, 2, and 3). Note the fine lines indicating the part that has been cut away. Isometric half sections are illustrated in Fig. 14-11. The construction lines of Space 1 are for the object shown in Space 2. The construction lines of Space 3 are for the object shown in Space 4. Note the outlines of the cut surfaces in Spaces 1 and 3. The cut

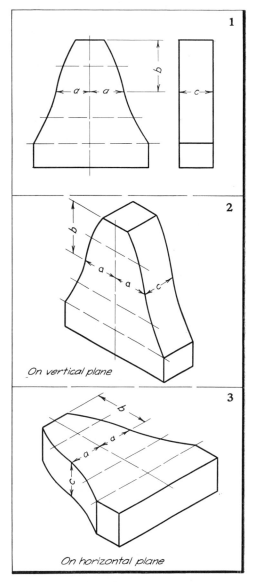

Fig. 14-9 Isometric curves.

surfaces are sectioned with lines drawn with the 60° triangle. The section lines are drawn in opposite directions on the two surfaces so that they would coincide if revolved together.

There are two general methods of constructing isometric sections. One

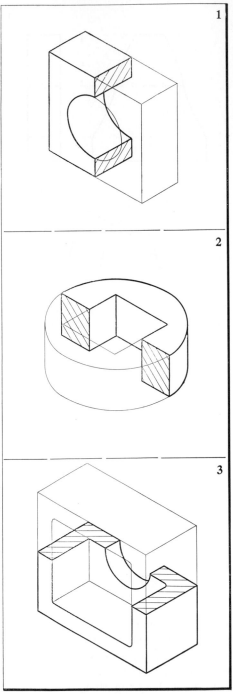

Fig. 14-10 Isometric sections.

method is to draw the complete outside view and the isometric cutting plane. The part of the view that has been cut away is then removed. A second method is to draw the section on the isometric cutting plane and then to work from it to complete the view.

14·10 Making an isometric drawing

PROBLEM: Make an isometric drawing of the guide shown in Fig. 14-12, Space 1.

1) Draw the axes *AB, AC,* and *AD* in second position (Fig. 14-12, Space 2).

Measure from *A* the length 3 in. on *AB.*

Measure from *A* the width 2 in. on *AC.*

Measure from *A* the thickness ⅝ in. on *AD.*

Through these points draw isometric lines, blocking in the base.

2) Block in the upright, making two measurements only, 2 in. and ¾ in.

3) Locate the center of the hole. Then draw its center lines as shown. Block in a ¾-in. isometric square and draw the hole as an approximate ellipse (Art. 14·6). At the upper corners measure the ½-in. radius on each line as in Space 3. Draw real perpendiculars to find the centers of the quarter circles.

4) Finish the drawing as in Space 4.

14·11 Reversed axes. Sometimes it is desirable to represent a part as viewed from below. This is done by reversing the axes as in Fig. 14-13. Draw the orthographic views as in Space 1; then draw the axes in *reversed position* as in Space 2. Lay off the measurements and complete the view as in Space 3.

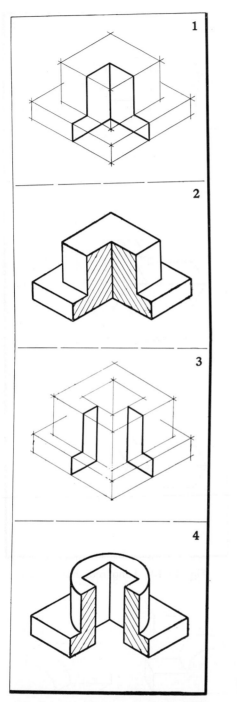

Fig. 14-11 Isometric half sections.

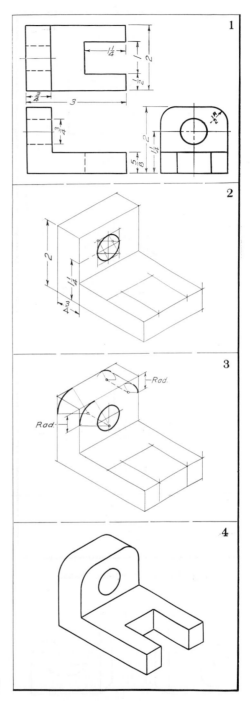

Fig. 14-12 Making an isometric drawing.

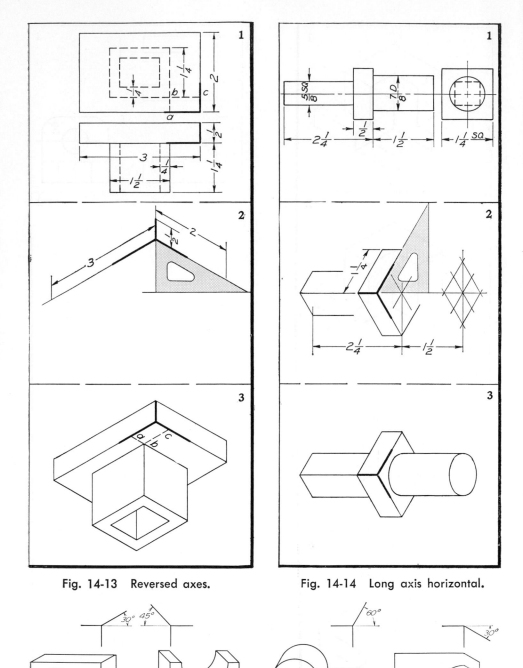

Fig. 14-13 Reversed axes.

Fig. 14-14 Long axis horizontal.

To right

To left

To right

Reversed axes to right

Fig. 14-15 Axes in oblique drawing.

14·12 Long axis horizontal. Long pieces may be drawn with one axis horizontal as in Fig. 14-14. For the object shown in Space 1, draw the axes as shown by the heavy lines in Space 2. Lay off the measurements given in Space 2 that are parallel to the axes and proceed in the usual way to complete the view as in Space 3. Except for the positions of the axes, the view is drawn in the same way as any other isometric view.

14·13 Oblique drawing. In this form of pictorial drawing the object is placed with one surface parallel to the picture plane (the frontal plane) instead of at an angle as in isometric drawing. The picture is then obtained by projection lines which make an angle with the picture plane instead of being perpendicular to it. These are called *oblique projecting lines*. Oblique drawings are constructed in the same manner as for isometric drawings, that is, on three axes. However, two of the axes always make right angles with each other; that is, one axis is drawn vertically, one horizontally, and the third at any convenient angle (Fig. 14-15).

The same methods and rules that were used in isometric drawing apply to oblique drawing, but compared with isometric, oblique drawing has the distinct advantage of showing one face without distortion. Thus objects with irregular outlines can be drawn by this method much more easily and effectively than in isometric. Many draftsmen prefer it for practically all pictorial work.

The first rule in oblique drawing is: Place the object so that the irregular outline or contour faces the front.

If there is no irregular outline, the second rule should be followed: Always place the object so that the longest dimension shows in the front.

14·14 Oblique circles. On the front face, circles and curves show in their true shape (Fig. 14-16, Space 1). On other faces, you can approximate circles and arcs as in isometric by drawing perpendiculars from the tangent points. In Space 1 a circle is shown as it would be drawn on a front plane, a side plane, and on a top plane. In Space 2 a circle is shown as it would appear on three faces of a cube, with the construction for locating the centers of the arcs. In Space 3, an oblique drawing is shown with arcs in a horizontal plane. In Space 4, an oblique drawing is shown with arcs in a side plane.

14·15 Making an oblique drawing
PROBLEM: Make an oblique drawing of the bearing of Fig. 14-17, Space 1. Observe that all but two small circles can be shown in their true shape.
1) Draw the axes *AB*, *AC*, and *AD* for the base in second position and measure on them the length, width, and thickness of the base as in Space 2. Draw the base; on it block in the upright, omitting the projecting boss, as shown in the figure.
2) Block in the boss as in Space 3 and find the centers of all circles and arcs.
3) Draw the circles and circle arcs.
4) Finish the drawing as in Space 4.

14·16 Cabinet drawings have the axes placed in the same positions as for oblique drawings, but all measurements parallel to the oblique axis are

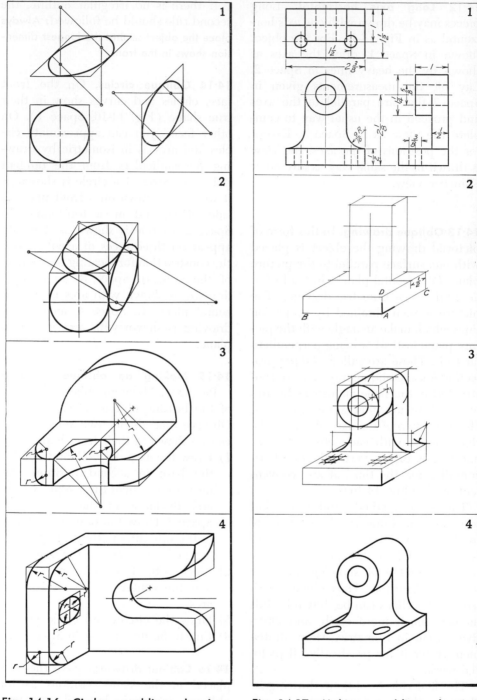

Fig. 14-16 Circles on oblique drawings.

Fig. 14-17 Making an oblique drawing.

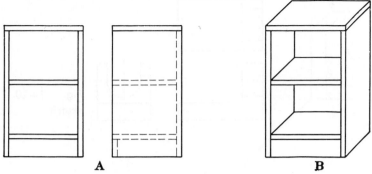

A   B

Fig. 14-18 Cabinet drawing.

reduced to one-half. The views of a case are shown at A in Fig. 14-18, and a cabinet drawing of the case is shown at B. Cabinet drawings are often used for furniture and wood constructions.

14·17 Isometric sketching. Freehand isometric sketches are of great help in reading orthographic views and in explaining objects or parts of constructions. Isometric sketching paper with lightly ruled, tinted lines for the directions of the axes furnishes a convenient aid in making isometric sketches. In Fig. 14-19 the orthographic views of a yoke bracket are shown at A and an isometric sketch is shown at B. The principles of isometric drawing form the basis of isometric sketching but, since sketches are not made to scale, their appearance may be improved by flattening. This can be done by giving the axes an angle less than 30° with the horizontal, and by slightly converging the lines, as well as shortening the lengths, to avoid distortion and give the effect of perspective. This is sometimes called *fake perspective.*

Always block in construction squares before sketching circles or arcs. Remember that the long axes of ellipses representing circles on the top face are horizontal.

Dimensioning a pictorial sketch is illustrated in Fig. 10-38.

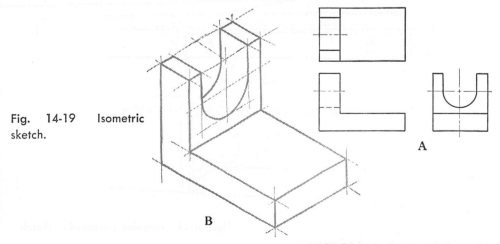

Fig. 14-19 Isometric sketch.

A

B

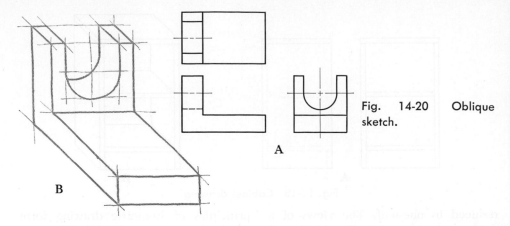

Fig. 14-20 Oblique sketch.

A

B

14·18 Oblique sketching. In Fig. 14-20 the orthographic views of a yoke bracket are shown at A and an oblique sketch is shown at B. The principles of oblique drawing form the basis of oblique sketching, but the appearance can often be improved by reducing the measurements on the oblique axis. Always block in construction lines before sketching circles, arcs, and curves (see Fig. 14-16).

14·19 Perspective drawing.[1] Perspective drawing is the representation of an object as it actually appears to the eye. A sketch made in perspective thus gives the best pictorial effect. The elementary principles of perspective are familiar to most students through the study of freehand drawing, and they will find this knowledge of value in studying shape description.

[1] In the scope of this book, the interesting subject of mechanical perspective construction cannot be taken up. With a knowledge of its methods, perspective drawings can be made from working drawings, as, for example, when an architect makes a picture of a proposed building. The result is as accurate as a photograph of the building (Fig. 21-1).

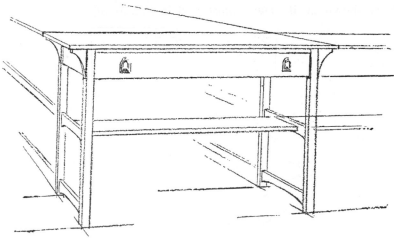

Fig. 14-21 Angular perspective sketch.

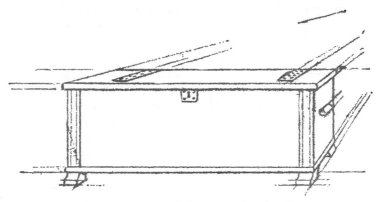

Fig. 14-22 Parallel perspective sketch.

In the perspective sketch shown in Fig. 14-21, it will be noted that the vertical lines remain vertical and that the two sets of horizontal lines each converge toward a point called the *vanishing point*. These two vanishing points lie on a horizontal line at the level of the eye called the *horizon*. The first rule is: All horizontal lines vanish on the horizon.

When the subject is turned at an angle as in Fig. 14-21, the drawing is said to be in *angular* or *two-point* perspective.

If the object is turned so that one face is parallel to the front plane, the horizontal lines on that face, or parallel to it, remain horizontal and have no vanishing point. Such a drawing is called *parallel*, or *one-point*, perspective (Fig. 14-22).

14·20 Making a perspective sketch from the object. In sketching from the object, place it below the level of the eye (unless it is very large) in order to show the outline of shape to the best advantage. Start by drawing a line for the nearest vertical corner. From this, sketch lightly the directions of the principal lines, running them past the limits of the figure. Test the directions and proportionate lengths with a pencil as follows: With the drawing board or sketch pad held *perpendicular* to the line of sight from the eye to the object, hold the pencil at arm's length *parallel* to the board and rotate the arm until the pencil appears to coincide with the line on the model. Then move the pencil parallel to this position back to the board. This gives the direction of the line. To estimate the apparent lengths, hold the pencil in the same way and mark with the thumb (Fig. 14-23) the

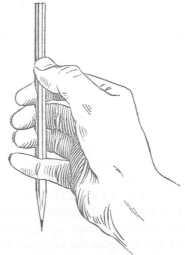

Fig. 14-23 Estimating proportions.

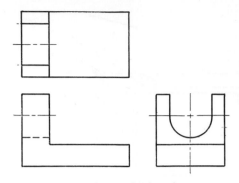

Fig. 14-24 Yoke bracket.

length of the pencil that covers the line. Rotate the arm with the thumb held in position until the pencil coincides with another line, and estimate the proportion of this measurement to the second line.

Block in the enclosing squares for all circles and circle arcs. Work with light, free sketch lines and do not erase any lines until the whole sketch is blocked in. Draw the main outlines first; then add details. Finally, brighten the sketch with heavier lines.

14·21 Making a perspective sketch from the views. Orthographic views of a yoke bracket are shown in Fig. 14-24 and are sketched in angular perspective in Fig. 14-25.

To make a sketch or drawing in angular perspective when the orthographic views are given instead of the object itself, the method generally used is what is known as the *cone of rays* method. In this method the plan is first drawn with its front corner against a line representing the picture plane as shown in Fig. 14-25. Think of this as the top view of the object, with the picture plane standing up against the front edge. Imagine the observer standing out in front of the plane at the point S, looking at the object through the plane. There will be a ray of light from each point of the object to the observer's eye. The picture as seen from this point will be the intersection of all these rays with the picture plane VV'. (To avoid distortion, the station point S is taken at a distance from the picture plane at least twice the width or height of the object.) Thus, if lines are drawn from the point S to the different points on the plan, their intersections with VV' will give the widths of the picture. Remember that so far we are looking down on the edge of the picture plane and that the picture is all in the line VV'. A horizontal line on the picture plane at a height above the ground equal to the height of the observer's eye will be the horizon. From S lines drawn parallel to the lines of the plan will pierce the picture plane on the horizon, giving the vanishing points V and V'. Now imagine the picture plane to be detached, moved forward, and then laid down into the plane of the paper. In the figure this has been done for convenience so that the horizon of the picture plane coincides with the line VV'. This means practically that the line GL, which is the bottom edge of the picture plane, was drawn as far below VV' as the height of the observer's eye. At the intersection of GL and a perpendicular from the front corner of the plan, draw a vertical line representing the front edge of the object, and lines to V and V' for the lower horizontal edges. Perpendiculars dropped from the intersection of the rays with the picture plane will give the length and width of the object. Vertical measurements must all

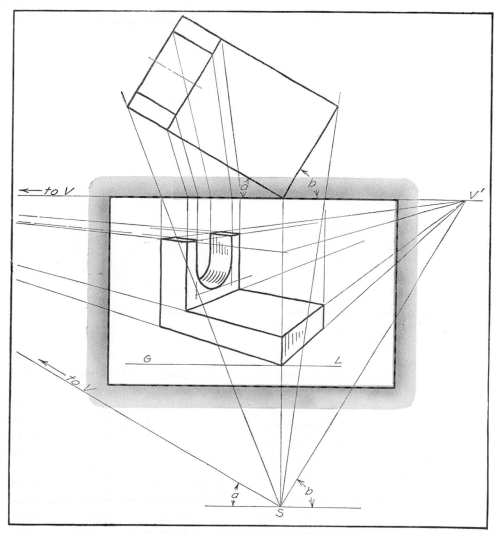

Fig. 14-25 Making a perspective sketch.

be made on the vertical line in the picture plane and vanished back to meet the location of the point to be measured. A study of Fig. 14-25 will show the method of finishing the sketch.

Compare the views in Figs. 14-19, 14-20, and 14-25, which are all pictures of the same object (the yoke bracket of Fig. 14-24).

A study of Figs. 14-26 and 14-27 will assist the student in making angular and parallel perspective sketches.

14·22 Problem suggestions. Group N, page 474. Three lists are presented. List 1 includes basic and more elementary problems from which selections may be made according to the purpose of the course. Selections may be made

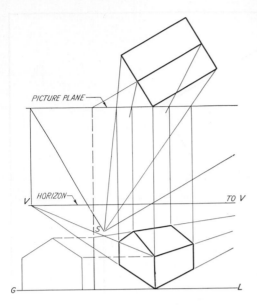

Fig. 14-26   Angular perspective.

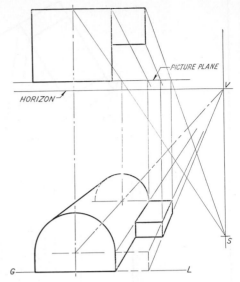

Fig. 14-27   Parallel perspective.

from List 2 for additional or alternate problems. These are a little more difficult than List 1. Selections may be made from Lists 2 and 3 for more advanced students or for those taking a more extensive course. A large number of problems are listed so that they may be varied from year to year. In some courses only a small number may be used to serve the purpose.

LIST 1   Problems N·1, N·2, N·5, N·8, N·11, N·13, N·15, N·17, N·18, N·21, N·24, N·25, N·28, N·31, N·33, N·35, N·37, N·38, N·41, N·42, N·43, N·46, N·47, N·49, N·53, N·56, N·59, N·60, N·64, N·66, and selections from Probs. N·67 to N·74

LIST 2   Problems N·3, N·4, N·7, N·9, N·14, N·16, N·22, N·23, N·26, N·27, N·30, N·44, N·50, N·54, N·61, and selections from Probs. N·75, to N·82

LIST 3   Problems N·29, N·32, N·34, N·36, N·39, N·40, N·45, N·48, N·51, N·52, N·55, N·57, N·58, N·63, N·65, and selections from Probs. N·83 to N·90

15 Production illustration

15·1 Production illustration has many uses in industry wherever pictorial drawings will do a better job of explaining the work. Pictorial drawings are easier for many people to understand and thus help them do their work faster and more accurately. In production illustration pictorial drawings are used to describe parts and the methods for making them. Pictorial drawings also show how the parts fit together and the steps that are followed to complete the product on the assembly line. Production illustrations were probably used to organize and set up the assembly line itself. They are useful for many industrial and engineering purposes. In Fig. 15-1, two production drawings are being explained at the Boeing Aircraft Company. These two drawings are shown separately in Figs. 15-2 and 15-3. Observe the broken-out and enlarged views to show details and the descriptive notes which are included.

Production drawings vary from simple sketches to elaborate shaded drawings. They may be based upon any of the pictorial methods: perspective, oblique, isometric, and so forth. The complete project may be shown or parts of groups of parts, and the views may be exterior, interior, sectional, *cut away, phantom* (see Fig. 8-11), and so forth. The purpose in all cases is to provide a clear and easily understood description. The previous chapters, in particular Chap. 6, "Sketching," and

Fig. 15-1 Explaining a production drawing. (*Boeing Aircraft Company*)

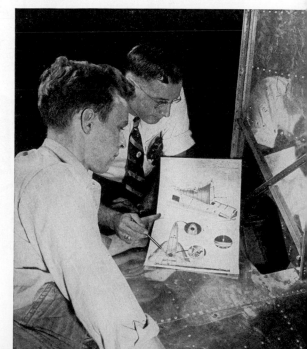

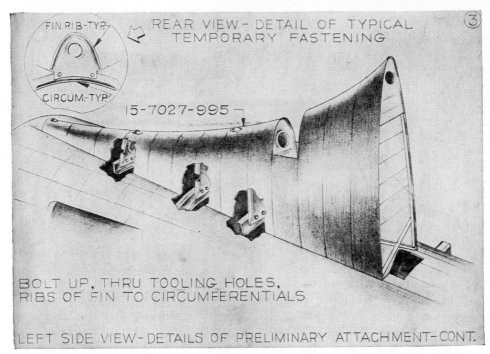

REAR VIEW – DETAIL OF TYPICAL TEMPORARY FASTENING

FIN RIB-TYP

CIRCUM.-TYP

15-7027-995

BOLT UP, THRU TOOLING HOLES, RIBS OF FIN TO CIRCUMFERENTIALS

LEFT SIDE VIEW – DETAILS OF PRELIMINARY ATTACHMENT – CONT.

Figs. 15-2 and 15-3 A production drawing. (*Boeing Aircraft Company*)

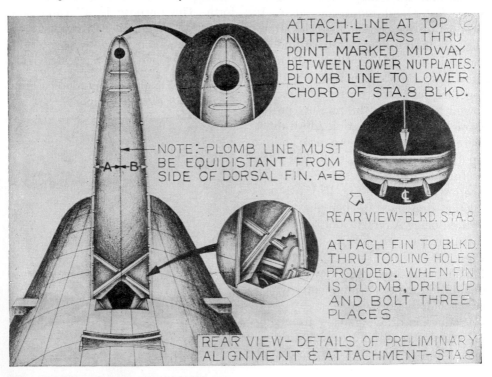

ATTACH LINE AT TOP NUTPLATE. PASS THRU POINT MARKED MIDWAY BETWEEN LOWER NUTPLATES. PLOMB LINE TO LOWER CHORD OF STA. 8 BLKD.

NOTE:- PLOMB LINE MUST BE EQUIDISTANT FROM SIDE OF DORSAL FIN. A=B

A → ← B

REAR VIEW – BLKD. STA. 8

ATTACH FIN TO BLKD. THRU TOOLING HOLES PROVIDED. WHEN FIN IS PLOMB, DRILL UP AND BOLT THREE PLACES

REAR VIEW – DETAILS OF PRELIMINARY ALIGNMENT & ATTACHMENT – STA. 8

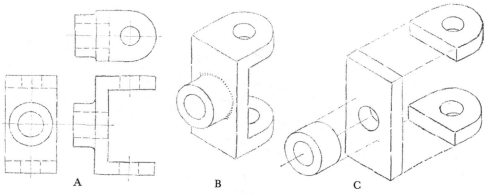

A   B   C

Fig. 15-4 An exploded view.

Chap. 14, "Pictorial Drawing," furnish the basis for making production illustrations. Drawings for use within the company's plant can be made by the regular draftsmen. Where artistic skill is necessary, the work is done by specially trained artist-draftsmen or commercial artists.

Production illustration (pictorial drawing) has been used for many years for illustrated parts lists, operation and service manuals, process manuals, and similar purposes. The aircraft industry in particular has found production illustration especially valuable. In building aircraft, pictorial drawings are used when the plane is first designed, at many stages of its manufacture, and as it is completed on the assembly line. When the plane is delivered to the customer, the industry supplies illustrated service, repair, and operation manuals.

15·2 Exploded views. A single piece may be shown separated into its individual parts, or a whole construction may be broken down into either single pieces or into part assemblies. Such pictures are called *exploded views.*

A single piece shown by orthographic views at A in Fig. 15-4 and pictorially at B may be exploded as at C, which illustrates the principle of

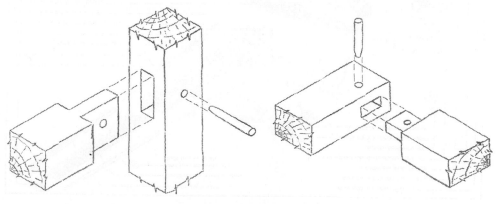

Fig. 15-5 Exploded views.

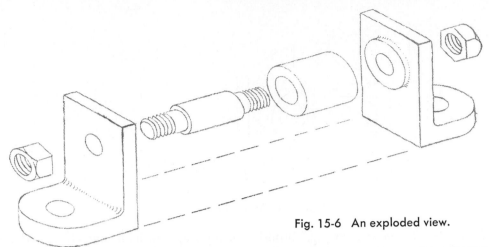

Fig. 15-6 An exploded view.

such views. The elementary parts are drawn as though projected from each other.

Exploded views of simple construc-tions are shown in Figs. 15-5 and 15-6 and for a large assembly in Fig. 15-7 (major-assembly breakdown for a bomber). All such views are based

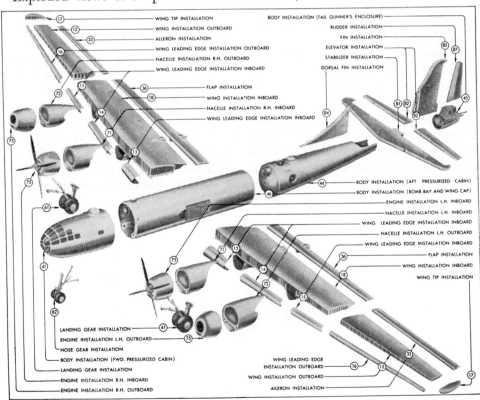

Fig. 15-7 Major-assembly breakdown. (*Boeing Aircraft Company*)

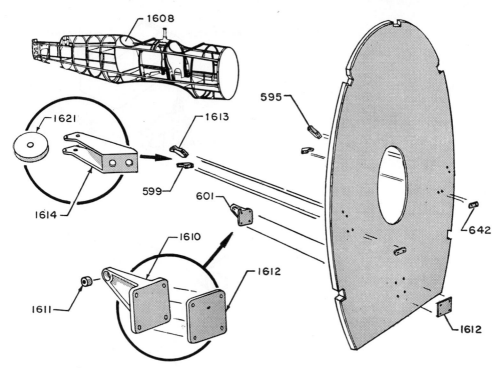

Fig. 15-8   Identification illustration. (*Timm Aircraft Corporation*)

Item	Part number	Nomenclature	Units per assembly
1608	3–31010	Ring Assembly Fuselage Sta. 100.375–106.25	1
595	3–71016	Assembly Control Cable Bracket Front	1
1621	AN210–1A	Pulley	2
599	3–70054	Bracket—Rudder Cable Pulley	2
642	3–70060	Backing Plate—Pulley Bracket	4
601	3–68015	Assembly Bearing Housing	1
1610	3–68015–2	Casting	1
1611	AN200–K4	Bearing	1
1612	3–68016	Plate Bearing Housing	1
1613	3–79020	Assembly—Glider Release Cable—Front	1
1614	3–79021	Bracket—Glider Release Cable—Front	1

upon the same principle—projecting the parts from the positions that they occupy when put together, or just *pulling them apart.*

15·3   Identification illustrations. Pictorial drawings are very useful for identifying parts, especially for those people who have difficulty in reading regular drawings or blueprints. Pictorial drawings help save time when the parts are manufactured or assembled in place. They are useful for illustrating operating instruction manuals and spare parts catalogues. One form of identification illustration is shown in Fig. 15-8, with the names of the parts given in tabular form below it.

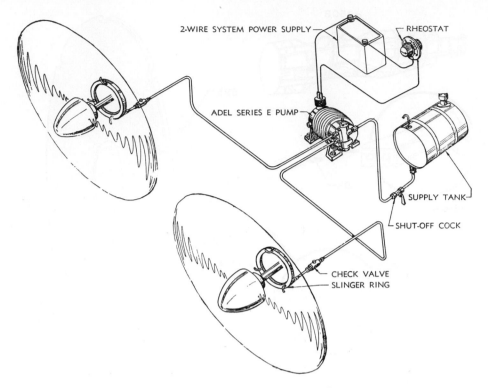

Fig. 15-9 Space drawing. (*Adel Precision Products Corporation*)

15·4 Space diagrams and installation illustrations. Pictorial drawings, by showing where parts go, save a lot of time. They are especially helpful in showing operating controls, piping installations for oil and hydraulic systems, wiring, and other complicated details. Such drawings vary according to the purpose for which they are used. The plane or machine may be shown in more or less outline form in order to fix the positions of the installations. A pictorial space drawing is shown in Fig. 15-9.

15·5 Rendering. For certain purposes or where shapes may be difficult to read, surface shading or rendering of some kind is desirable. A study of commercial art would be necessary to develop professional skill in the many ways of shading drawings, but the student should learn to recognize some of the methods that are used. A few illustrations are included for this purpose.

An explanation of the science of shades and shadows is too large a subject for this text. It is a subject for study as a separate course.

For most industrial production illustrations, accurate descriptions of shapes and positions are more important than fine artistic effects. Desired results can often be obtained without any shading. In general, when surface shading is used, it should be limited to the least amount necessary to define the shapes illustrated.

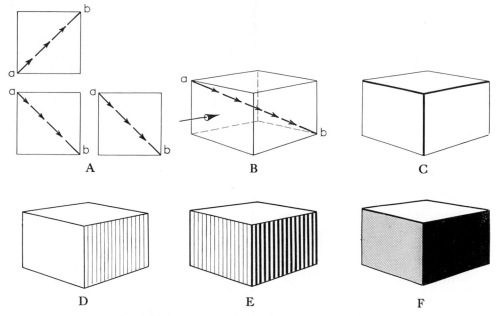

Fig. 15-10 Some methods of rendering a cube.

15·6 Line shading may be done mechanically, freehand, or sometimes by a combination of both. The light is generally considered to come from in back of and above the left shoulder of the observer in the direction of the body diagonal of a cube as at A and B in Fig. 15-10. The 45° lines at A show the direction of the light to be down, back, and to the right. This is a convention used by draftsmen and renderers.

In Fig. 15-10 the three lines meeting at the front corner accented as at C will bring out the shape where the surfaces are left plain. Since the top and front are lighted, they might be left clear with the right-hand surface shaded as at D. The front surface can have a light shading, with heavy shading on the right-hand surface as at E. Solid shading may be used as at F.

15·7 Some shaded surfaces are indi-

cated in Fig. 15-11. An unshaded view is shown in Space 1 for comparison. Ruled surface shading is shown in Space 2, freehand shading in Space 3, stippled shading in Space 4, Craftint shading in Space 5, and Ben Day shading in Space 6.

Stippling (Fig. 15-11, Space 4) consists of dots; short, crooked lines; or similar treatment to produce a shaded effect. It is a good method when well done but requires considerable time. Craftint paper (Fig. 15-11, Space 5) is made with a great variety of invisible allover dots, lines, and patterns which can be made visible by the application of a developing solution. The Ben Day process (Fig. 15-11, Space 6) uses films to cover the surface with dots or lines.

15·8 Airbrush rendering. (Fig. 19-9) produces pictures that resemble photo-

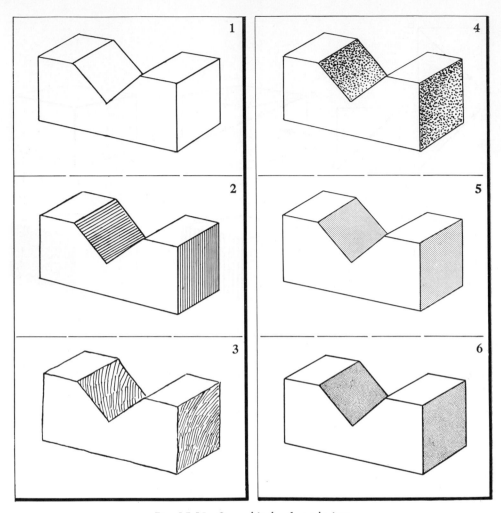

Fig. 15-11 Some kinds of rendering.

graphs. Compressed air is used to spray the solution to obtain the different shading effects in this process. Wash drawings of Sumi (Japanese ink with water added) produce similar results. In this method a brush like that in water color painting is used.

15·9 Cylinder shading is illustrated in Fig. 15-12, where shade lines follow the curvature at A, lines parallel to the elements are used at B, C, and E, stip-

pling is used at D, and surface shading at F.

15·10 Building construction illustration. Details of the construction for buildings can be made clearly and can be easily understood by pictorial sketches or drawings. Any of the methods may be used for this purpose, but simple isometric and oblique views are about all that are necessary in most cases as indicated in Fig. 15-13.

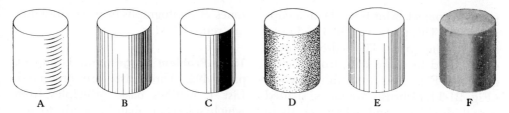

Fig. 15-12   Some methods of rendering a cylinder.

15·11 Furniture construction illustration. Pictorial methods have been much used for furniture and are especially adapted for this purpose. Isometric is useful, as well as other pictorial methods, for showing joints and how parts go together. Study the illustrations in Group K in Chap. 24, page 450.

15·12 Reproduction of illustrations. Illustrations made on tracing cloth or thin paper may be reproduced the same size by making direct contact prints as described in Arts. 11·13 and 11·14. Regular photographic paper may be used with such drawings or with photographic negatives at a reduced size. Photostats are frequently made by using a direct copying process that also reproduces drawings in their original size.

Where a large number of copies are required, line cuts, halftones, or offset prints are made.

Line cuts (Fig. 15-10) are photoengravings made on zinc or copper plates from black-line or pen-and-ink drawings. The drawing is generally made larger than the desired copy and reduced when photographed on the plate. All lines, dots, figures, lettering, and so forth, must be black in order to reproduce. The plate is etched and used in a printing press.

Halftones (Fig. 13-3) are photoengravings made by photographing through a screen formed by two glass plates. Lines are ruled at uniform distances apart and placed so that squares are formed. In this way, a negative is made showing the view as made up of minute dots, and from it a photo-

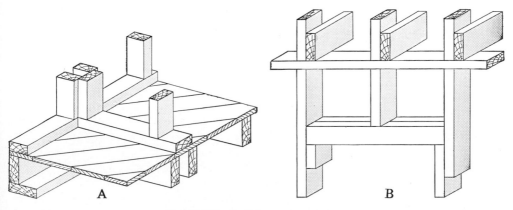

Fig. 15-13   Building construction.

graphic contact print is made on a copper plate. This plate is etched and used in a printing press. The halftone process is used to make cuts from photographs (Fig. 15-1), wash drawings (Fig. 21-1), airbrush drawings, shaded pencil drawings, and whenever there are different shades of gray as well as black and white to be reproduced.

The *offset* process can be used to reproduce any kind of drawing by photographing the drawing on a metal plate from which it is transferred to printing cylinders. It is a kind of mechanical lithograph. By this process solid lines as well as all the various tones of photographs or wash drawings are reproduced.

15·13 Problem suggestions. Group O, page 492. Three lists are presented. List 1 includes basic principles from which selections may be made to suit the purpose of the course. Selections from Lists 2 and 3 may be made for additional problems or for more advanced students.

LIST 1 Problems O·1, O·2, O·3, O·5, O·6, O·10, O·11

LIST 2 Problems O·4, O·7, O·8

LIST 3 Problems O·9, O·12, O·13, O·14, O·15, O·16

16 Aircraft drafting

16·1 The aircraft industry. An airplane includes many different kinds of parts of many different materials. There are also many different methods of making the parts and putting them together. There is the fuselage (Figs. 16-1 to 16-3) or central body of the airplane which contains the operating and passenger compartments (or fighting com-

partment on military craft). The fuselage may have welded truss construction (a rigid welded framework) or a metal skin braced on the inside. There are wings which are built of welded

Fig. 16-1 The Cutlass. A Navy two-engine jet-propelled airplane. (*Chance Vought Aircraft, Inc.*)

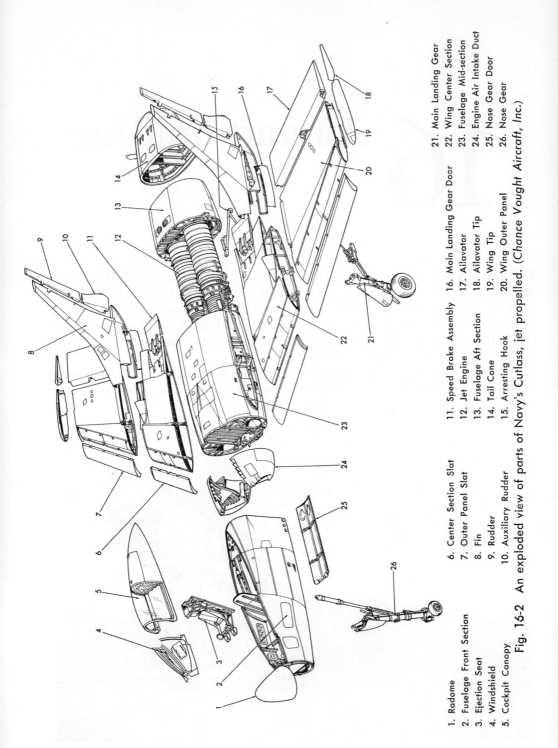

1. Radome
2. Fuselage Front Section
3. Ejection Seat
4. Windshield
5. Cockpit Canopy

6. Center Section Slat
7. Outer Panel Slat
8. Fin
9. Rudder
10. Auxiliary Rudder

11. Speed Brake Assembly
12. Jet Engine
13. Fuselage Aft Section
14. Tail Cone
15. Arresting Hook

16. Main Landing Gear Door
17. Ailavator
18. Ailavator Tip
19. Wing Tip
20. Wing Outer Panel

21. Main Landing Gear
22. Wing Center Section
23. Fuselage Mid-section
24. Engine Air Intake Duct
25. Nose Gear Door
26. Nose Gear

Fig. 16-2 An exploded view of parts of Navy's Cutlass, jet propelled. (Chance Vought Aircraft, Inc.)

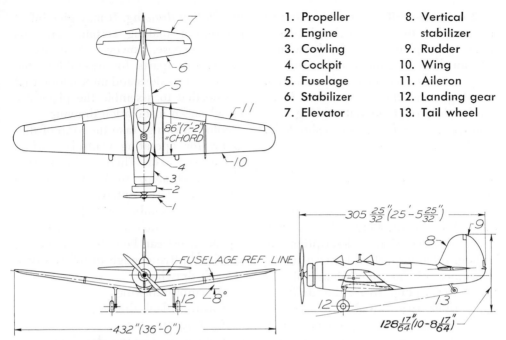

1. Propeller
2. Engine
3. Cowling
4. Cockpit
5. Fuselage
6. Stabilizer
7. Elevator
8. Vertical stabilizer
9. Rudder
10. Wing
11. Aileron
12. Landing gear
13. Tail wheel

Fig. 16-3   General arrangement. Three-view drawing. (*Timm Aircraft Corporation*)

light metal ribs covered with metal sheets (skin). Different methods are used for securing or fastening the wings to the fuselage. A wing is called an *airfoil*. Other support surfaces termed airfoils include ailerons, elevators, and rudders (Figs. 16-2 and 16-3). The leading edge is the front edge of an airfoil and the trailing edge is the rear edge. A chord is a straight line between the leading edge and the trailing edge. Elevators, ailerons, rudders, tabs and flaps are used to control the airplane in flight.

There is an undercarriage to absorb the shock of landing. There is the power plant, either piston-type engines or jet engines, and an arrangement for mounting and transmitting power. Of course, there are fuel tanks, electric circuits, lubricating systems, control-operating mechanisms, and so forth.

All of this means that different kinds of industry take part in making an airplane. Therefore, the drawings will be different in many ways from those used in other industries, as shown in the illustrations in this chapter. Some parts are made in different plants and have to be fitted as the plane is assembled. Some parts have to be laid out on sheets of metal or scribed from templates.[1] Casting, forging, welding, riveting, and other methods of forming and construction are used in the making of an airplane. Some drawings will, therefore, include more than one part or operation and may show undimensioned views (or few-dimensioned views) or part views to which other parts are to be attached or fitted.

[1] A template is a flat pattern of the required shape with holes, openings, location of bend lines, and other information. It is placed on the sheet and marked around to lay out the part.

16·2 Aircraft-drafting practice. Aircraft drafting has to do with the drawings made for airplanes: details, three-view exterior outlines, subassemblies such as wing construction, layouts, production drawings, and the many other kinds needed in aircraft manufacturing. The competent aircraft draftsman should be familiar with the variety of materials used as well as the different methods followed in manufacturing aircraft. However, the fundamental principles are the same for aircraft drawings as for all other drawings. A thorough knowledge of shape description by orthographic projection is necessary.

Because of the frequent use of pictorial views (Fig. 16-2), the ability to make them is a valuable accomplishment. Pictorial drawing has become a profession for many artist-draftsmen. A photograph is shown in Fig. 16-1 for comparison with Fig. 16-2.

The aircraft industry continually tries to improve its methods in order to manufacture aircraft more efficiently at lower cost. Different companies prepare engineering manuals so that their employees can follow the practices best adapted to their company's products. There are many such standards in general use and a draftsman should be familiar with his company's manual.

16·3 Classification of aircraft drawings. In general, aircraft drawings consist of assembly and detail drawings. However, these vary in some respects from the usual machine drawings. Thus assembly drawings may or may not contain some or all dimensions and information. They may show the whole plane, groups of parts, or just one or two parts.

One form of assembly drawing is the *installation drawing.* It may give information for making certain parts. Its major purpose, however, is to locate the various parts for assembling the plane. Dimensions and information that are needed to assemble the plane are found on an installation drawing.

Some drawings take the form of diagrams for operating controls, wiring, piping, and so on. There are lubrication *charts* and steps to be followed in proper aircraft maintenance.

Aircraft assembly and detail drawings include such a variety that only a general list can be given. The names are descriptive enough to tell the type of each drawing.

    Assembly drawings
    Casting blank drawings
    Casting drawings
    Casting machining drawings
    Chart drawings
    Design assembly or installation
      drawings
    Detailed subassembly drawings
    Diagram drawings
    Die-casting drawings
    Electrical drawings
    Equipment drawings
    Extrusion drawings
    Fairing drawings
    Forging drawings
    General arrangement drawings
    Installation drawings
    Layout drawings
    Milling design drawings
    Mock-up drawings
    Perspective drawings
    Production drawings
    Sheet-metal drawings
    Sketches
    Standard part drawings
    Tabulated drawings
    Tubing and cable drawings
    Welded drawings

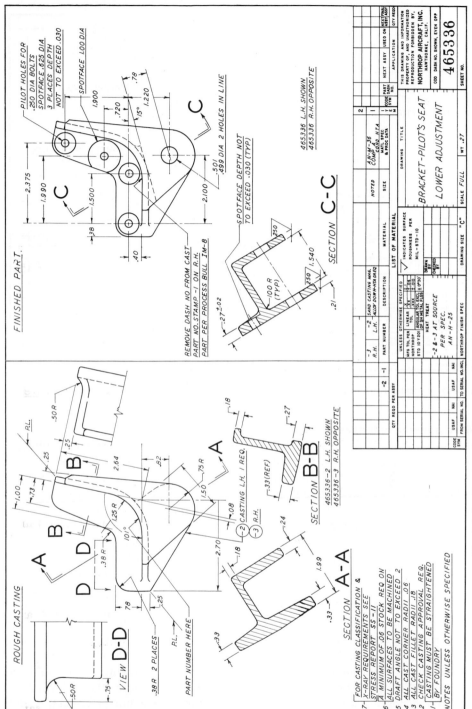

Fig. 16-4   Casting drawing—bracket. (Northrop Aircraft, Inc.) **Prob. P·9**

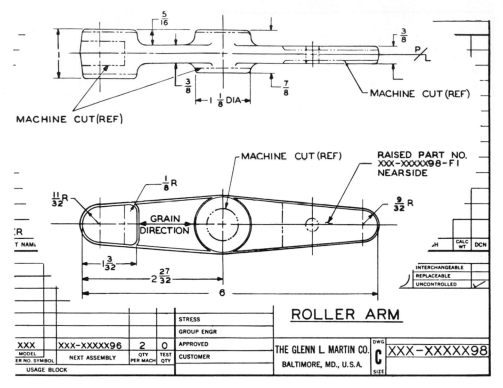

Fig. 16-5 Forging blank drawing—roller arm. (*The Glenn L. Martin Company*) **Prob. P·3.**

16·4 A general arrangement drawing is shown in Fig. 16-3. Note that the side view shows the front of the plane toward the left-hand end of the drawing. This is the standard arrangement for either assembly or detail drawings. Parts are left-hand or right-hand according to the position that they occupy relative to the pilot seated in the plane.

16·5 Casting drawings. Two drawings may be made for castings, one a casting blank drawing (*rough casting*) and the other a casting machining drawing (*finished part*). They may be on one sheet as in Fig. 16-4 or on separate sheets. In general, casting drawings should be made full size and should

have the views arranged with the center lines or datum planes parallel to the main part of the casting. Auxiliary and sectional views should be used where needed to show exact information for every detail of the casting.

Study the views of the casting blank drawing at the left in Fig. 16-4 and note the information given which refers only to the casting blank.

Dimensions on the casting blank are coordinated with the machining drawing, which is located from the same center or base lines used to locate the machined surfaces. Study the views of the machining drawing at the right on Fig. 16-4 and note the information given for the machinist, inspector, and others for all operations such as ma-

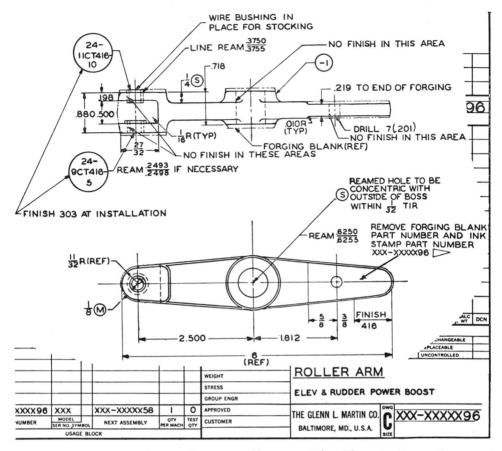

Fig. 16-6 Forging machining drawing—roller arm. (*The Glenn L. Martin Company*)
Prob. P·4.

chining, assembly of bushings, and so forth.

Fittings which may be used "as cast" or without any fabrication (machining, and so forth) may be completely detailed on a casting blank drawing.

16·6 Forging drawings. A forging blank drawing is shown in Fig. 16-5 and a forging machining drawing for the same part (*roller arm*) is shown in Fig. 16-6. These two drawings should be studied and compared. A single drawing may be made for fittings which may be used as forged (Fig. 16-7).

The forging blank drawing (Fig. 16-5) provides complete information for the diesinker, forger, inspector, and others with complete information for the forging blank only.

The forging machining drawing (Fig. 16-6) gives information for the machinist, inspector, and others for all operations such as machining, assembly of bushings, bearings, and so forth.

16·7 Sheet-metal drawings are based upon the principles of intersections and developments as discussed in Chap. 20. However, it is necessary to consider

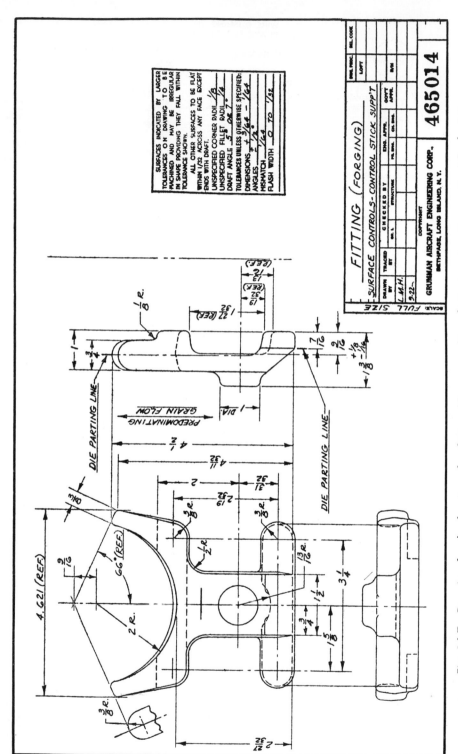

Fig. 16-7 Drawing for the forging of a fitting. (Grumman Aircraft Engineering Corporation) **Prob. P-5.**

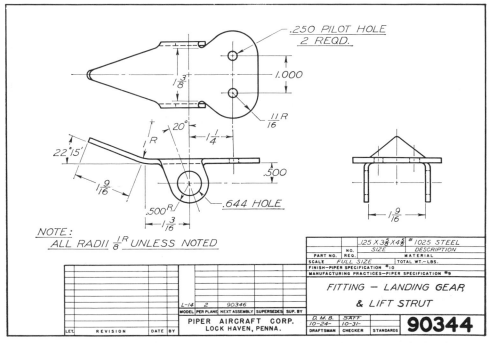

Fig. 16-8 Sheet-metal part. (*Piper Aircraft Corporation*) **Prob.P·2.**

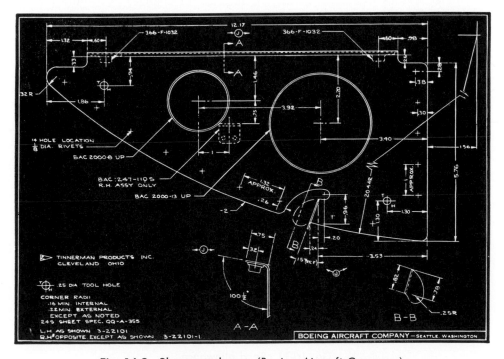

Fig. 16-9 Sheet-metal part. (*Boeing Aircraft Company*)

AIRCRAFT DRAFTING **221**

the thickness of metal, bend allowances, and other factors when laying out flat patterns (developments) or sheet-metal templates. The parts shown in Figs. 16-8 and 16-9 are made of sheet metal. In Fig. 16-9 note the use of decimal fractions exclusively. Design standards are used for lightening holes shown as in the note "BAC 2000-8 and -13 UP," which indicates direction of the flange.

Sheet metal is used extensively for forming parts of airplanes as well as for the curved skin covering. Many factors enter into the selection of the proper material, the design, and the forming of such parts. Only a few considerations can be indicated here because specialized knowledge and experience are necessary for a complete understanding of this part of airplane design.

Bend relief is an allowance made at

the corners when plates are bent. A method of bend relief is shown in Fig. 16-10. Allowance must be made for bends (Fig. 16-11). The minimum bend radius depends upon the material and the thickness. Values can be found in the engineering manuals of aircraft companies or in the Appendix of *A Manual of Aircraft Drafting.*[2]

Joggling (Fig. 16-12) is used when plates or structural shapes overlap in order to present an unbroken surface for the skin.

16·8 Sketching (Chap. 6) is used in many ways in connection with the design of aircraft and in making information more readable. Sketches may contain complete information for the fabrication of small parts, to forward (present) small parts, to forward small portions of information on large drawings, or for changes in manufacture of the aircraft. Sketch pads with printed forms are used for such purposes. The views may be freehand sketches or "drawings." Figure 16-13 illustrates a sketch-pad sheet for an addition to a rib assembly.

[2] *A Manual of Aircraft Drafting* by Carl L. Svensen, D. Van Nostrand Company, Inc., Princeton, N.J.

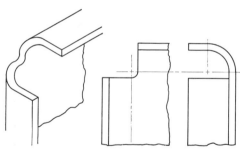

Fig. 16-10 Bend relief.

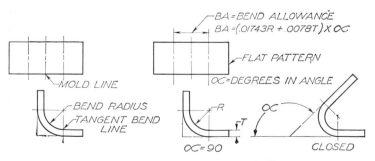

Fig. 16-11 Bend allowance.

Fig. 16-12 Joggling.

16·9 Tabulated drawings may be used for either assembly or detail drawings where only a few of the dimensions are different as in Fig. 16-14 for the dimensions A, B, C, and D.

16·10 Assembly drawings show two or more parts joined together to form a unit (Figs. 16-15 and 16-16). They call out (specify) all the parts which are required, including such details as bolts, screws, and fasteners of any kind needed to join the parts. Clips, brackets, and so forth, may be detailed on sheet-metal assembly drawings by assigning dash numbers (Art. 16·14) to

identify them. Such dash numbers for details shown on assembly drawings save the time and expense of making separate drawings for each part. A subassembly drawing for a stabilizer is shown in Fig. 16-17. Note the call-outs. Note also that only assembling dimensions are given.

16·11 Layouts of various kinds form an important part of aircraft design and drafting from the general over-all design to pencil layouts for subassemblies and groups of parts. Such drawings provide for the relations of the parts, manufacturing procedure, operating

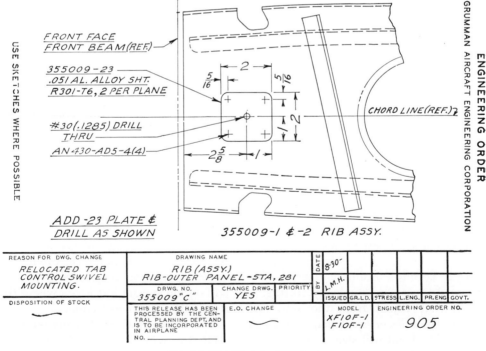

Fig. 16-13 Sketch drawing.

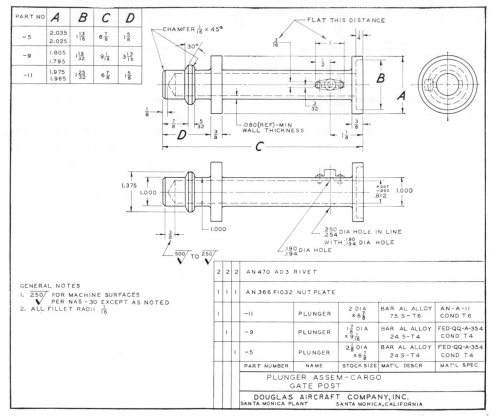

Fig. 16-14 Tabulated drawing. (*Grumman Aircraft Engineering Corporation*) **Prob. P·6.**

and other equipment, and so forth. Layout drawings are extremely accurate drawings and show all necessary information for making details and assembly drawings, for determining clearances, for stress analysis, for calculation of weights, for detailing shapes, for dimensioning, and for specifying materials and treatments.

16·12 Lofting. Full-size layouts for large projects are made by lofting, a term that comes from the ship loft where the lines or exact shapes of ships are worked out full size. Lofting is an important kind of layout for airplane

design. Accurate full-size contours and sections are developed by lofting. Curves are faired (adjusted or smoothed out) to obtain smooth surfaces, and templates are made for use where necessary.

Specialized knowledge of materials and their properties as well as experience and good judgment are necessary for this work. Such work cannot be done on drawing boards but must be laid out on special loft floors where the required areas are available.

Part of a drawing of a master template for wing contours is shown in Fig. 16-18.

(*Text continued on page 228.*)

224 MECHANICAL DRAWING

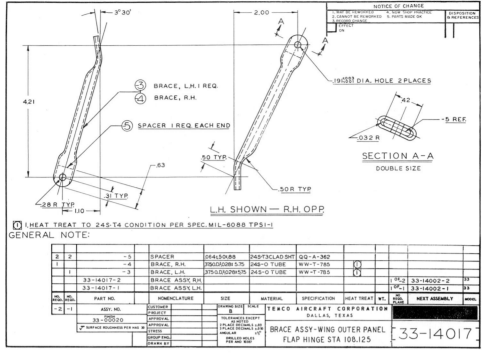

Fig. 16-15   Brace assembly (*Temco Aircraft Corporation*) **Prob. P·8.**

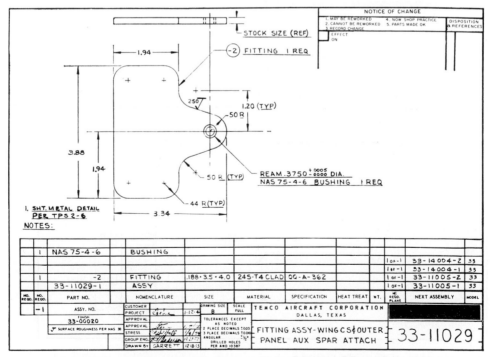

Fig. 16-16   Fitting assembly (*Temco Aircraft Corporation*) **Prob. P·1.**

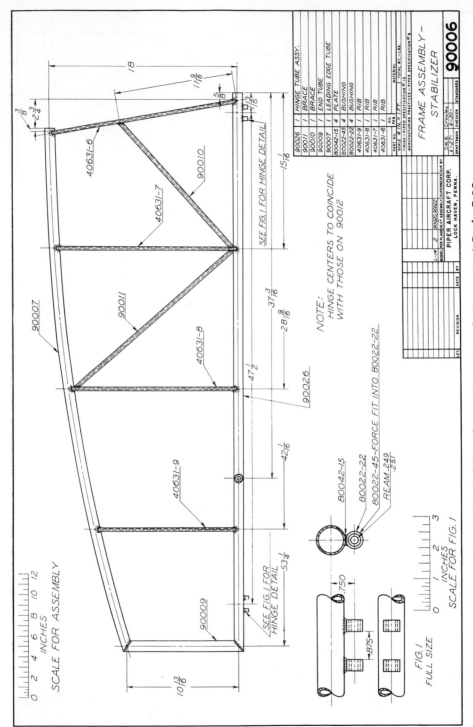

Fig. 16-17 Stabilizer frame. (Piper Aircraft Corporation) **Prob. P·10.**

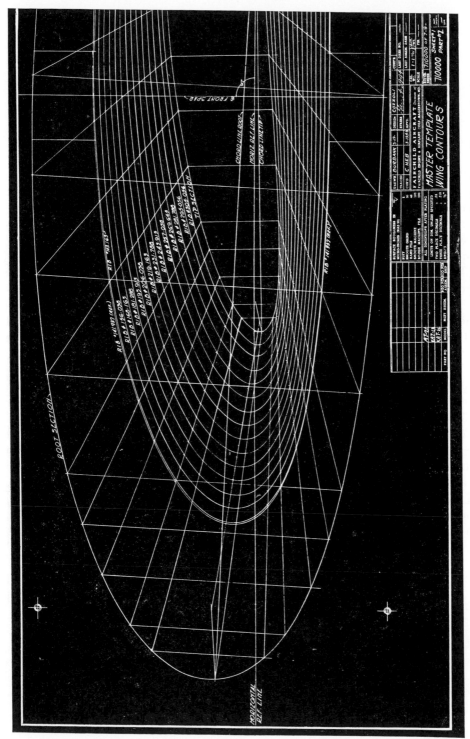

Fig. 16-18 Master template. (Fairchild Aircraft Division of Fairchild Engine and Airplane Corporation)

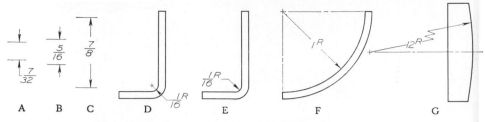

Fig. 16-19 Dimensions for vertical distances and radii.

16·13 Dimensions and notes. The usual practice is to give all dimensions in inches and to omit the inch mark except as on the three-view assembly drawing (see Fig. 16-3) where feet and inches are used.

All notes and dimensions are placed to read from the bottom of the drawing, regardless of the direction of the dimension lines, whether they are horizontal, vertical, or at an angle, as shown on the illustrations in this chapter. Dimensions less than ⁵⁄₁₆ are shown as at A in Fig. 16-19 and ⁵⁄₁₆ and larger as at B and C. Capital letters are generally used for all lettering, either vertical or inclined, according to the practice of the particular company.

Radii are given for the inside radius on all bends (Fig. 16-19 at D, E, F, and G). Progressive dimensioning is sometimes used with regular dimensioning (Fig. 16-20). Linear dimensions are preferred to degrees for angles (Fig. 16-21), but degrees may be given for reference.

Notes are used to give necessary information and instructions. They should not be used in place of dimensions. However, when used to specify an operation, the dimension may be included for such purposes as the diameter and depth of drilled or reamed holes. Other notes are indicated on the illustrations.

The basic principles of dimensioning as described in Chap. 10 apply with the exceptions here noted together with exceptions made by any special company practice.

Large drawings which have much information, such as views of several parts, extra part views, sectional views, references to other views, and so forth, are marked off in zones (vertical strips 11 in. wide) as in Fig. 16-22. The zones

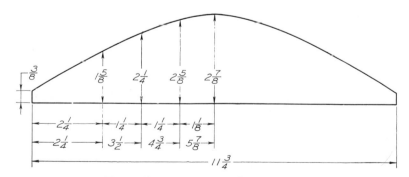

Fig. 16-20 Progressive dimensioning.

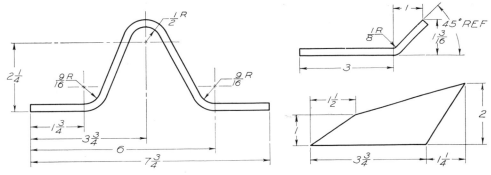

Fig. 16-21   Dimensioning for angles.

are numbered in small squares along the bottom border lines as shown. The numbers in the zone column of the title tell the zone in which the views or other items will be found and save the time which would be spent in searching for them.

16·14 Dash numbers. When two or more parts are drawn on a detail drawing or an assembly drawing, they are identified by dash numbers of the drawing. The basic number is the drawing number. This number followed by a dash number identifies a piece shown on that drawing. Thus 3279-3 would indicate part -3 on drawing 3279. On the drawing the -3 may be enclosed in a circle or left in the clear, but it must be placed close to the part that it identifies. Even dash numbers

may be used for right-hand parts and odd dash numbers for left-hand parts, or the numbers may be followed by the letters R or L.

Particular practice in the use of dash numbers varies with different companies.

16·15 Titles and nomenclature. Titles used on aircraft drawings vary according to the practice of different companies. In general, the title may include such information as model, title of assembly or detail, drawing number, calculated weight, actual weight, dimensional limits, scale, date, identification of draftsman, tracer, checker, engineer, and so forth, and provision for a material list.

The name on an aircraft part should locate the part as to the group or sub-

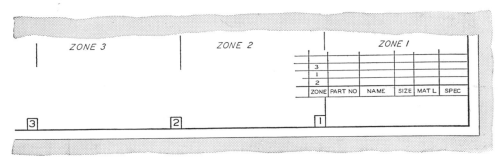

Fig. 16-22   Zone marking.

group to which it belongs so far as possible. Breakdown parts lists are available in company drafting rooms. In general, the name of the part or noun is placed first, followed by the main group and subgroup. This is well explained in the following, which gives the practice of the Aeronca Aircraft Corporation.

Drawing titles. In naming drawings, U.S. Air Force standard practice is followed. The drawing title must consist first of the basic identifying word (noun) entered on the top line of the title block, followed on the second line by a suitable description and modifying words. For example:

BRACKET—
WING AILERON HINGE

This is read: "WING AILERON HINGE BRACKET" and the title will be entered in the number book thus: Bracket—"Wing Aileron Hinge."

No basic names of more than one word can be used.

Names such as "tie rods," "push rods," and "push tubes" can be written similar to the following example:

ROD—AILERON CONTROL PUSH

The details of an assembly must be named in agreement with the name of the assembly and consistently with each other as follows:

a) ASSEMBLY—FLOATING INSTRU-
MENT PANEL BOTTOM BRACKET

b) BRACKET—FLOATING INSTRU-
MENT PANEL BOTTOM

The parts may be further identified, when there is danger of confusion of parts with similar names, by the addition of such words as "right," "left," "upper," "lower," "end," and "center" or by such words as "long," "short," "main," or "auxiliary."

The words "and" and "for" can be omitted from the title as the title should be as concise as possible.

16·16 Standard parts. Some parts are manufactured for general use and are available in standard sizes and dimensions. Such parts are "called out" or identified by numbers or symbols. Some companies make their own standard parts for their own use which are called out in a similar manner.

There are standard sections for various extruded shapes and tubes, standard fabrics, bolts, eyebolts, nuts, castle nuts, stop nuts, cotter pins, taper pins, turnbuckles, bushings, rivets, keys, sheet-metal screws, and so forth. Other standards include those of the American Standards Association (ASA), Society of Automotive Engineers (SAE), and other societies, and the government standards as used by the Air Corps, the Army, and the Navy. Until the Armed Forces merged, government standards were designated for the Air Corps (AC) and jointly for the Army and Navy (AN). Recently a new set of standards has been organized for all the services. The new standards, known as *Military Standards* or *Mil Standards,* are replacing the AC and AN numbers. Some AC and AN Standards will continue until the new Mil Standards are complete. Books of standards, kept up to date, are used for reference when drawings are made in aircraft drafting rooms.

16·17 Aircraft rivets. Some aircraft rivets are illustrated in Fig. 16-23. For

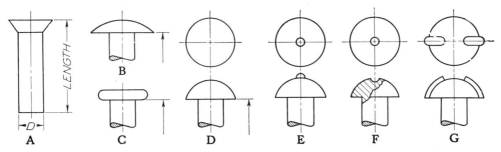

Fig. 16-23 Aircraft rivets.

complete dimensions and information, access should be had to AN Standard sheets. A countersunk head (AN425) is shown at A, a brazier head (AN455) at B, a flat head (AN442) at C, and a round head (AN430) at D. Identification markings indicate the material: Type A (aluminum, 3S) without marking is shown at D; Type D (aluminum alloy, 17S) with raised dot is shown at E, Type AD (aluminum alloy, A17S) with depression is shown at F, and Type DD (aluminum alloy, 24S) is shown at G.

Codes are used for calling out rivets, as, for example, AN425AD4-8. AN425 means Army-Navy Standard countersunk head, AD means A17S material, 4 means the diameter in thirty-seconds of an inch, and 8 means the length in sixteenths of an inch.

16·18 Aircraft bolts. An AN aircraft bolt is shown in Fig. 16-24, with some dimensions in the table. Sheets of AN standards are used in aircraft plants to give all dimensions and other information for each diameter of bolt. Identification marks, three of which are shown, are used on the head: for aluminum alloy specification QQ-A-351, the head is left unmarked as at B; for aluminum alloy QQ-A-354, the head is marked as at C; for steel, the head is marked as at D.

Code symbols are used to call out bolts, as, for example, AN4-7. AN means steel, Army-Navy Standard; 4 means the diameter in sixteenths of an inch of $\frac{4}{16} = \frac{1}{4}$ diameter; 7 means the length in eighths of an inch, or $\frac{7}{8}$ in. long. For aluminum alloy, the dash is replaced by a letter (or letters) to indicate the alloy as in AN4D7. If the hole for a pin at the end of a bolt is to be omitted, the letter A is added as in AN4D7A.

The length of bolts is given by the

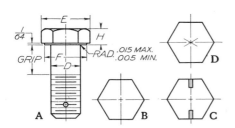

Fig. 16-24 Aircraft bolt.

D	Threads per in.	E	F	D	Threads per in.	E	F
No. 10				$\frac{1}{2}$	20	$\frac{7}{8}$	0.750
0.189	32	$\frac{7}{16}$	0.375	$\frac{9}{16}$	18	$1\frac{1}{64}$	0.875
$\frac{1}{4}$	28	$\frac{1}{2}$	0.4375	$\frac{5}{8}$	18	$1\frac{3}{32}$	0.9375
$\frac{5}{16}$	24	$\frac{37}{64}$	0.500	$\frac{3}{4}$	16	$1\frac{5}{64}$	1.0625
$\frac{3}{8}$	24	$\frac{21}{32}$	0.5625	$\frac{7}{8}$	14	$1\frac{7}{16}$	1.250
$\frac{7}{16}$	20	$\frac{23}{32}$	0.625	1	14	$1\frac{21}{32}$	1.4375

For bolthead, $H = \frac{1}{2}D + \frac{1}{32}''$. For nut, $H = \frac{3}{4}D$.

number of eighths up to ⅞ in. in diameter; for 1 in. or more, it is given in inches and eighths. Thus 1 in. is given as 10 or 1 in. and no eighths; 1⅛ in. is given as 11 or 1 in. and one-eighth.

For other aircraft threaded fastenings, clevis bolts, eyebolts, special lock nuts, and so forth, reference should be made to the latest AN Standard sheets on hand in the company drafting room.

16·19 A check list of procedures used as a guide for group drawing checkers by the Grumman Aircraft Engineering Corporation includes the following items for consideration. It may also be utilized by the man on the drawing board in the final analysis of a completed drawing.

Drawing arrangement
Selection of sheet size
Placement of notes, stamps, etc.
Drawing appearance
  General simplicity and neatness—useless waste of time in unnecessary detail
  Lettering—$\frac{5}{32}$ high
Part numbering and unnecessary notes regarding same
Title block and bill of materials
Model block
General make-up of drawing—call-outs, drill notes, sections, views, etc.

Applicable stamps
Applicable notes
  General
  Commercial articles
  Interchangeability and replaceability
  Tool engineering information
Zoning (where applicable)
Drawing number on roll sizes (reverse side, opposite corners along margin)
Installations, for proper next assembly call-out(s)
Assemblies (major)—for applicable installations
Special drawings
  Participating and/or licensee contractor's drawings
  Altered government standards
  Specification control drawings
  Altered commercial and/or patented articles
  Matched parts

16·20 Problem suggestions. Group P, page 493. Three lists are represented. List 1 is elementary. Selections from Lists 2 and 3 may be made for more advanced students according to the purpose of the course.

LIST 1 Problems P·1, P·3, P·5, P·8, P·9, P·10, P·12
LIST 2 Problems P·2, P·4, P·7
LIST 3 Problems P·6, P·11, P·13, P·14, P·15

17 Welding drawings

17·1 Welding is being used for an ever-increasing variety of mechanical and structural purposes, such as building up and fastening parts together. Welding has become common practice for steel buildings (Fig. 17-1). Standard steel shapes, plates, and bars may be welded together to make machine frames, bases, jigs and fixtures, and so forth. The greater strength of steel in tension is often an advantage that permits a design of less weight and complication for parts that were formerly made of cast iron. Sheet-metal work, such as tanks and other containers, can be simplified by welding instead of riveting the joints.

Fig. 17-1 Welding steel on a building. (*Courtesy Engineering News-Record*)

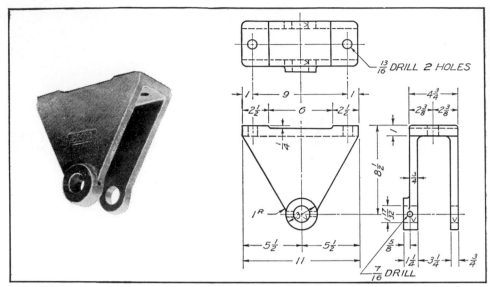

Fig. 17-2 Cast-sheave housing. (*Wellman Engineering Company and Lincoln Electric Company*) **Prob. Q·3.**

The aircraft, automotive, and shipbuilding industries have developed welding as a major fabricating method for aluminum and magnesium, as well as for steel.

17·2 Welding processes. The two basic processes are fusion welding and resistance welding. Fusion welding makes use of welding material in the form of a wire or rod which is added to the

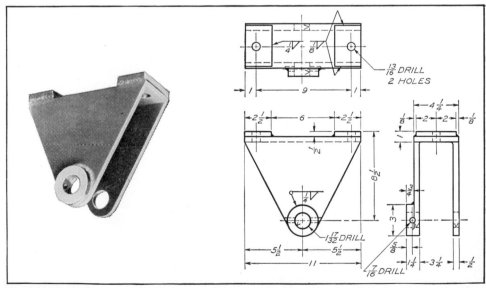

Fig. 17-3 Welded-sheave housing. (*Wellman Engineering Company and Lincoln Electric Company*) **Prob. Q·4.**

234 MECHANICAL DRAWING

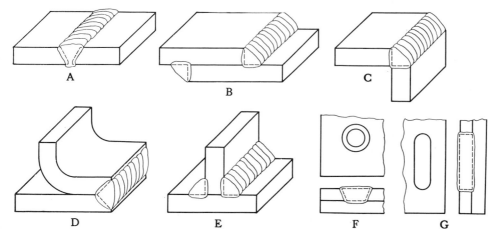

Fig. 17-4 Basic types of joints. (A) Butt joint (V-groove weld). (B) Lap joint (fillet weld). (C) Corner joint (fillet weld). (D) Edge joint (V-groove weld). (E) T-joint (fillet welds). (F) Plug weld. (G) Slot weld. **Prob. Q·1.**

weld. These filler rods combine with the metal being welded. Gas or a carbon arc is used to create the heat so that the metals flow together. Resistance welding uses an electric current to generate welding heat by the resistance of the parts to an electric current. The parts are welded by pressure. Welding processes include forge welding, resistance welding, arc welding, gas welding, thermit welding, induction welding, flow welding, cold welding, and soldering and brazing. There are many books[1] on welding which can be used for reference or study of this important subject.

17·3 Welding drawings make use of ideographic (picture-writing) symbols to give the necessary welding information (Art. 17·5). These symbols have been developed by the American Weld-

ing Society and provide a flexible means of giving specifications, type, location, size of weld, and various combinations to suit any condition. Every drafting room should be provided with one or more copies of the latest edition of *Welding Symbols and Instructions for Their Use.*[2] These symbols have been adopted as American Standard.[3]

Compare the photograph and drawing of a casting for a sheave housing in Fig. 17-2 with the same part made by welding in Fig. 17-3.

17·4 Types of joints are shown and named in Fig. 17-4. There are many variations in the kinds of welds used in making these joints. These are further influenced by the preparation of the parts as illustrated for a few joints which are named in Fig. 17-5. The preparation of the groove is shown by

[1] *Welding Engineering* by B. E. Rossi, McGraw-Hill Book Company, Inc., New York. *Procedure Handbook of Arc Welding Design and Practice,* The Lincoln Electric Company, Cleveland, Ohio.

[2] The American Welding Society, New York 18, N.Y.
[3] *Graphical Symbols for Welding* (ASA Z32.2.1–1949).

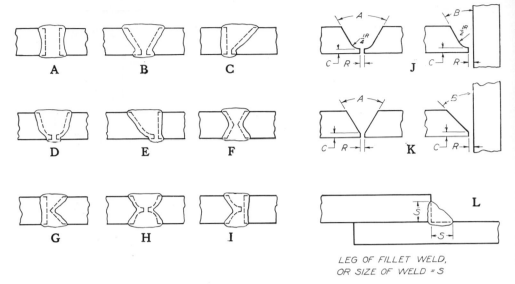

LEG OF FILLET WELD,
OR SIZE OF WELD = S

Fig. 17-5 Groove joints. (A) Square groove. (B) Single V-groove. (C) Single bevel groove. (D) Single U-groove. (E) Single J-groove. (F) Double V-groove. (G) Double bevel groove. (H) Double U-groove. (I) Double J-groove. (J) $A = 45°$ min $C = \frac{1}{16}''$ to $\frac{3}{16}''$ $R = 0$ to $\frac{9}{16}''$ $B = 35°, 25°$. (K) $A = 60°$ min $C = 0$ to $\frac{1}{8}''$ $R = \frac{1}{8}''$ to $\frac{1}{4}''$ $B = 45°$ min. **Prob. Q·2.**

the hidden lines at A to I inclusive. The size of the *root opening* is shown by R and the amount of the *angle* by A at J and K. The *size of weld,* or leg of a fillet weld, is indicated by S at L.

Many combinations and varieties of joints are used to meet the great number of different conditions that occur in welding practice. Knowledge of conditions together with experience are necessary to make a proper selection of the types and sizes of welds.

17·5 Basic arc- and gas- (fusion) welding symbols of the American Welding Society are given in Fig. 17-6, which shows both basic and supplementary symbols. Separate symbols may be selected to describe any desired weld since they may be assembled to describe simple or complicated joints.

The standard location of information on welding symbols is shown on Fig. 17-7. The notes indicate how symbols and data are placed in relation to the

BASIC ARC AND GAS WELD SYMBOLS								SUPPLEMENTARY SYMBOLS			
TYPE OF WELD											
Bead	Fillet	Plug or slot	Groove					Weld all around	Field weld	Contour	
			Square	V	Bevel	U	J			Flush	Convex
⌒	△	▽	||	∨	✓	∪	⨆	○	●	—	⌒

Fig. 17-6 Arc- and gas-welding symbols.

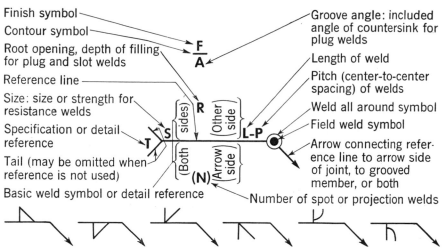

Finish symbol

Contour symbol

Root opening, depth of filling for plug and slot welds

Reference line

Size: size or strength for resistance welds

Specification or detail reference

Tail (may be omitted when reference is not used)

Basic weld symbol or detail reference

Groove angle: included angle of countersink for plug welds

Length of weld

Pitch (center-to-center spacing) of welds

Weld all around symbol

Field weld symbol

Arrow connecting reference line to arrow side of joint, to grooved member, or both

Number of spot or projection welds

Fig. 17-7 Location of welding information on welding symbols.

reference line. The perpendicular leg of the fillet, bevel-, and J-groove weld symbol is always placed to the *left*.

The words "near side" and "far side," formerly used, have been replaced by the words "arrow side" and "other side" (Fig. 17-8). The symbol is shown at the left and the desired weld at the right at A to E. Note that the weld symbol for the arrow side is placed on the side of the reference line toward the reader; for the other side it is placed on the side of the reference line away from the reader; for both sides it is placed on both sides of the reference line. The arrow is drawn to point with a *definite break toward the member to be grooved* when the bevel- or J-groove weld symbol is used (Fig. 17-9). At A, the meaning is not clear.

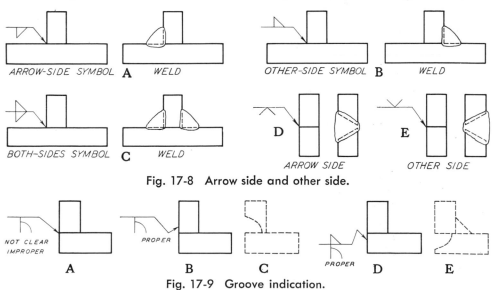

ARROW-SIDE SYMBOL **A** WELD

OTHER-SIDE SYMBOL **B** WELD

BOTH-SIDES SYMBOL **C** WELD

D ARROW SIDE

E OTHER SIDE

Fig. 17-8 Arrow side and other side.

NOT CLEAR IMPROPER **A**

PROPER **B**

C

PROPER **D**

E

Fig. 17-9 Groove indication.

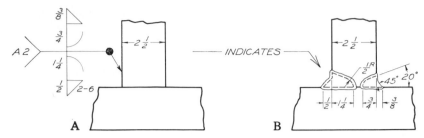

Fig. 17-10 Symbols applied.

At B, the arrow clearly indicates that the vertical member is to be grooved on the arrow side as at C. At D, the symbol clearly indicates the desired welds as at E.

The tail of the arrow is used for specification reference. See Fig. 17-10, where A2 placed in the tail signifies the specification described in connection with that figure. Also, see Fig. 17-7, where the letter *T* is placed in the tail of the arrow to refer to a specification. The tail of the arrow may be omitted when a specification reference is not needed, as in drawings where standard company specifications are used.

17·6 An example of the way in which the symbols are used to give welding information is illustrated in Fig. 17-10 at A and B. This joint is described as follows: Double-filleted-welded, partially grooved, double-J tee joint with incomplete penetration (type of joint shown by the drawing). Grooves of standard proportion (which are ½ in. *R*, 20° included angle, edges in contact before welding) ¾ in. deep for other (or far) side weld and 1¼ in. deep for arrow (or near) side fillet weld with increments 2 in. long, spaced 6 in. center-to-center. All fillets standard 45° fillets. All welding done in field in accordance with welding specification

number A2 (which requires that weld be made by manual DC shielded metal-arc process using high-grade, covered, mild steel electrode; that root be unchipped and welds be unpeened but that joint be preheated before welding).

17·7 Meaning of symbols. Some symbols used to indicate various welded joints and their meaning are shown in Figs. 17-11 to 17-13. In each case the symbol is shown on the top row, and the preparation of the joint before welding is shown by hidden lines on the bottom row.

Welding symbols are shown on a machine drawing in Fig. 17-3 and on a structural drawing in Fig. 17-14.

17·8 "Resistance welding[4] differs from other forms of welding in that no extraneous materials, such as fluxes[5] or filler rods, are used. . . ." The welding heat is generated by the resistance of the parts to the electric current. For contact welding, the parts are placed

[4] *Resistance Welding Manual*, Resistance Welder Manufacturers' Association, Philadelphia, Pa.
[5] Fluxes are fusible materials or gases that are used to cleanse metals for welding by dissolving oxides. They also are used to prevent the possible formation of oxides and release gases during the welding process.

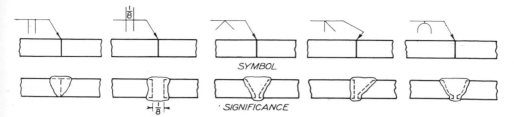

SYMBOL

SIGNIFICANCE

Fig. 17-11 Butt joint.

together, electric current is passed through, and pressure is applied to force the parts together to produce a forge weld. For flash welding, the parts are placed either in very light contact or with a very small air gap; the electric current "flashes" or arcs and melts the ends of the parts.

17·9 Resistance welds. There are two major classes of resistance welds: spot welding (including spot, projection, seam, cross-wire, and contact) and butt welding (including butt-flash, push-butt, percussive, and contact).

A few definitions formulated by the Nomenclature Committee of the Resistance Welder Manufacturers' Association are as follows:

SPOT WELDING. A resistance process wherein the fusion is confined to a relatively small portion of the area of the lapped parts to be joined by the shape or contour of one or both welding electrodes (Fig. 17-15 at A).

PROJECTION WELDING. A resistance-welding process wherein localization of heat between two or more surfaces or between the end of one member and surface of another is effected by projections (Fig. 17-15 at B and C).

BUTT SEAM WELDING. A welding process with the pieces positioned edge to edge (Fig. 17-15 at D).

LAP SEAM WELDING. A seam-welding process wherein overlapping or tangent spot welds are made progressively (Fig. 17-15 at E).

FLASH BUTT WELDING. A resistance butt-welding process wherein the necessary heat is derived from an arc or series of arcs established between the parts being welded prior to the application of the weld consummating pres-

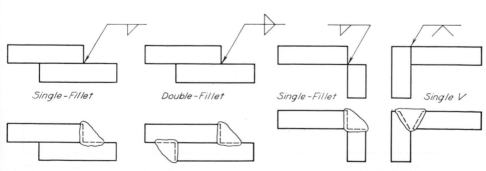

Single-Fillet   Double-Fillet   Single-Fillet   Single V

Fig. 17-12 Lap joints.   **Fig. 17-13 Corner joints.**

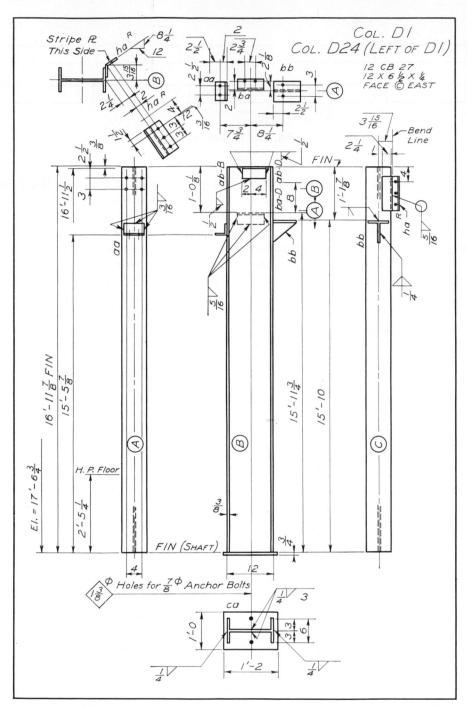

Fig. 17-14 Welding symbols on a structural drawing. (*American Bridge Company*) **Prob. Q·12.**

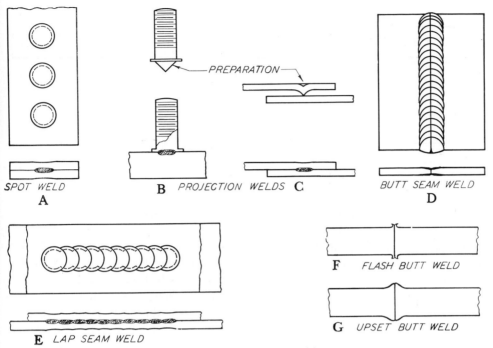

Fig. 17-15 Resistance welds.

BASIC RESISTANCE WELD SYMBOLS				SUPPLEMENTARY SYMBOLS			
TYPE OF WELD				Weld all around	Field weld	Contour	
Spot	Projection	Seam	Flash or upset			Flush	Convex
✕	✕	✕✕✕	|	◯	●	—	⌢

Fig. 17-16 Resistance-welding symbols.

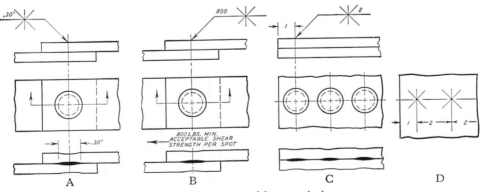

Fig. 17-17 Spot-welding symbols.

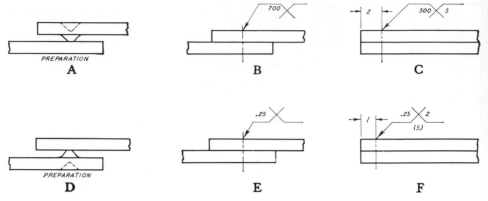

Fig. 17-18 Projection-welding symbols.

sure. The pressure is applied when the heat thus obtained has produced proper welding conditions (Fig. 17-15 at F).

UPSET BUTT WELDING. A resistance-welding process wherein the current is applied after the parts to be welded are brought in contact and wherein the heat is derived from the flow of current (Fig. 17-15 at G).

Basic resistance-welding symbols are given in Fig. 17-16. The basic reference line and arrow are used as with arc- and gas-welding symbols, but in general there is no "arrow side" or "other side." Figure 17-7 covers both resistance welds and gas welds.

The spot-welding symbol is shown in Fig. 17-17 in the top row. The second row shows a plan view. The third row shows a section through the weld. At A the minimum diameter of each weld is specified as 0.30 in. At B the minimum shearing strength of each weld is specified as 800 lb. At C and D are two methods of specifying that the welds start 1 in. from the left end and are spaced 2 in. center to center.

The projection-welding symbol is shown in Fig. 17-18, with the preparation at A and D. At A the embossment (projection) is on the "arrow side" member, in which case the symbol is placed as at B and C. At B the "700" means that the acceptable shear strength per weld is to be not less than 700 lb. At C the minimum shear strength per weld is 500 lb, and the welds are to be spaced 5 in. center to

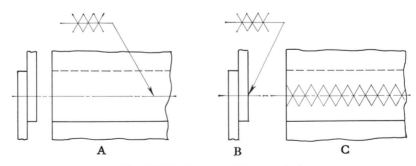

Fig. 17-19 Seam-welding symbol.

center. At D the embossment (projection) is on the "other side" member. At E the minimum diameter of the weld is 0.25 in.; at F the minimum diameter of the weld is 0.25 in., spaced 2 in. center to center. There are five welds. The symbol for seam welding is shown in Fig. 17-19. Here the arrow is used at A and B, and the alternative method of placing the symbol on the view is shown at C.

17·10 Problem suggestions. Group Q, page 496. Three lists are presented. The more elementary problems are included in List 1. Other problems may be assigned from Lists 2 and 3 for advanced students. Reference books on welding, if available, are very desirable.

LIST 1 Problems Q·1, Q·2, Q·3, Q·4, Q·5, Q·8
LIST 2 Problems Q·6, Q·7, Q·9
LIST 3 Problems Q·10, Q·11, Q·12

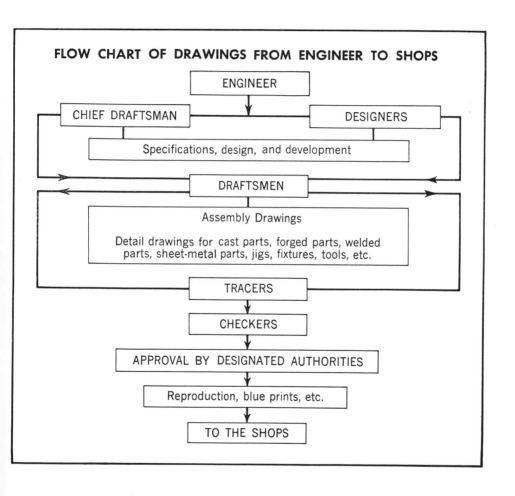

FLOW CHART OF DRAWINGS FROM ENGINEER TO SHOPS

ENGINEER

CHIEF DRAFTSMAN   DESIGNERS

Specifications, design, and development

DRAFTSMEN

Assembly Drawings

Detail drawings for cast parts, forged parts, welded parts, sheet-metal parts, jigs, fixtures, tools, etc.

TRACERS

CHECKERS

APPROVAL BY DESIGNATED AUTHORITIES

Reproduction, blue prints, etc.

TO THE SHOPS

18 Electrical drafting

18·1 Electrical drafting for machinery and details is based upon the same principles as for all other drafting. In addition to the usual views a great many symbols and schematic or line diagrams (Fig. 18-1) are used for showing wiring, circuits, and arrangements of electrical equipment.

A simple one-tube coil-condenser tuned radio receiver is illustrated in Fig. 18-1 with the parts named. If you are interested, you will find that you can actually build this set by some further study and investigation. The completed radio will appear as shown in the picture. As a help in becoming familiar with the symbols, this figure shows the various parts of the receiver in their approximate positions. Wiring diagrams, however, do not always indicate the positions of the parts. Such diagrams are made only to show the parts which make up the set and the connections.

Electrical drafting requires a knowledge and understanding of electricity in addition to the ability to make drawings. However, this chapter will enable

the student to learn to draw some of the symbols and to learn how they are used. Students who have had a course in physics will find their knowledge of electricity of much help in understanding and drawing schematic diagrams.

18·2 Graphical symbols are used on electrical diagrams to represent electric circuits with connections, equipment, instruments, and so forth. There are a large number of graphical symbols and variations of symbols used to show different conditions. For a complete set of symbols the American Standards' *Graphical Symbols for Electrical Diagrams*[1] should be available for reference. A selection from American Standards is shown in Fig. 18-2 and some applications are shown in the illustrations which follow. Symbols which differ from American Standard will be found on the diagrams of some companies, and in such cases care must be used to identify the devices and conditions.

[1] ASA Y32.2–1954. American Standards Association, 70 East 45th Street, New York 17, N.Y.

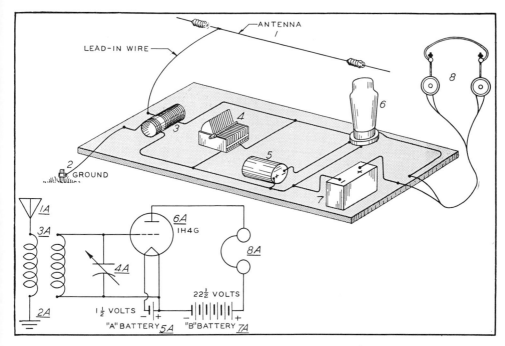

Fig. 18-1   A schematic diagram (lower left) and a picture (above) for a simple radio receiver. **Prob. R·23.**

Picture	Symbol	Part
1	1A	Antenna (aerial)
2	2A	Ground connection
3	3A	Antenna coil
4	4A	Variable condenser
5	5A	A battery
6	6A	Triode vacuum tube 1H4G
7	7A	B battery
8	8A	Earphones

Graphical symbols for use on electrical diagrams for radio, and so forth, are shown in Fig. 18-24. A variety of transparent plastic templates can be purchased for use in drawing uniform symbols quickly and easily. One of a number of such templates is shown in Fig. 18-3. Symbols for use in connection with architectural plans are shown in Fig. 21-52.

18·3 Position and scale. Electrical diagrams using graphical symbols are made to show relations of various parts and wiring connections. Such diagrams are not drawn to scale and there are no specified sizes for the symbols. However, some symbols may be made larger or smaller in order to give a better representation of the conditions being described. Also, the symbols have the

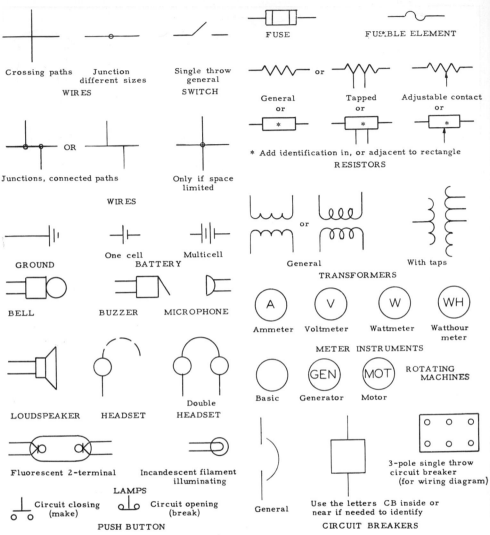

Fig. 18-2 Electrical symbols. (*Extracted from American Standards' "Graphical Symbols for Electrical Diagrams," ASA Y32.2–1954, with the permission of the publisher, Institute of Radio Engineers, Inc.*)

same meaning when drawn in different positions. As many thin or heavy lines may be used for parts, or all, of a diagram as may be desirable to clarify conditions.

Electrical equipment, such as switchboards, transformers, and so forth, if not represented by symbols are drawn

to scale when necessary. Plant layouts and other drawings for electrical installations are drawn to scale in the same way as other engineering projects.

18·4 Pictorial drawings (Chap. 14) are often useful for explaining electrical devices, electrical installations, and

246 MECHANICAL DRAWING

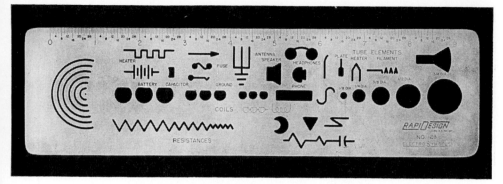

Fig. 18-3 Template for drawing symbols.

other features. The isometric drawing of the transformer yard (Fig. 18-4) shows the relation of the electrical equipment to the supporting structure. Such a drawing is useful during assembly and erection as well as for record and reference. Details and specifications for insulators, bus clamps, cutouts, mounting brackets, lightning arresters, and so forth, are carried on other drawings to avoid complicating this assembly or erection drawing.

One of the primary purposes of such erection drawings is to show the location at which the conduits (such as at C and so forth) are to be brought up (stubbed out) out of the concrete slab or ground. The dimensions are important in order to have the connections for the equipment at the proper places since conduit is installed in almost all cases before equipment is received and installed.

Another use of pictorial drawing in electrical work is illustrated in the isometric drawing of Fig. 18-5, which shows the arrangement of part of a bus duct system. This drawing is one of many bus ducts that carry electric current to various parts of the Republic National Bank Building in Dallas, Texas. The purpose of this drawing is to take actual field measurements and convert them into an itemized schedule of component parts to be manufactured. At the same time the drawing serves as an assembly drawing for their actual identification for installation in the building. It is necessary to show the various elbows and offsets (items 1, 5, 6, 8, and 10) in the drawing so that a suitable path for the ducts can be found around job conditions of beams, columns, shafts, or other obstacles. In the insert in Fig. 18-5 is a photograph of a duct.

18·5 Basic electric circuits include series circuits, parallel circuits, and combinations of series and parallel circuits.

Series circuits are those where the current flows from the source (battery, generator, and so forth) through one resistance (lamp, motor, and so forth) after another as shown in Figs. 18-6 to 18-8. In Fig. 18-6 a bell, A, is operated from a battery, C, when the circuit is closed by the normally open (NO) type push button, B. In Fig. 18-7 a buzzer, A, is operated by the current from the transformer, C. What is item B and what function does it have in this circuit? In Fig. 18-8 four lamps, C, D, E, and F, are operated from a generator,

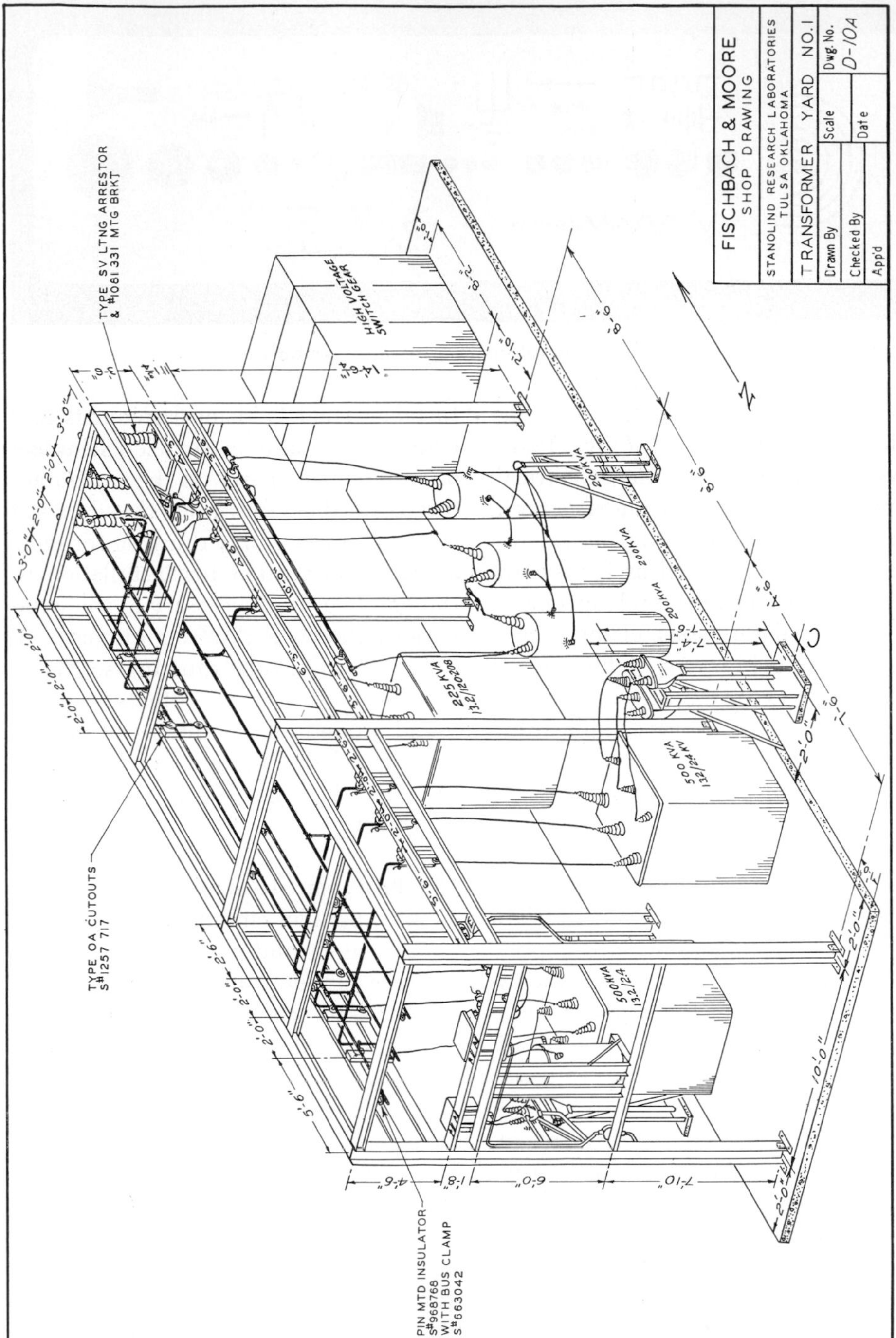

Fig. 18-4 Pictorial drawing of a transformer yard.

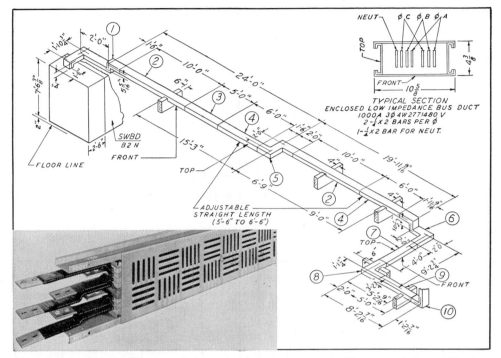

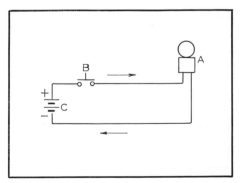

Fig. 18-5　Isometric drawing of part of a bus duct system. (*Photograph from Westinghouse Electric and Manufacturing Company*)

A, when the fused switch, *B*, is closed. All the lights must be on, for if any one is not, the circuit will be open. Remember the Christmas tree string of lights that went out completely when just one lamp burned out? This was a series string of lights.

Parallel circuits provide for the current to flow through more than one path. Three separate branches (paths), *C*, *D*, and *E*, with lamps are shown in Fig. 18-9. Each lamp is independent of the others. If one lamp is burned out, the others will continue to operate.

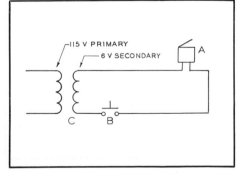

Fig. 18-6　A series-circuit diagram. **Prob. R·2.**

Fig. 18-7　A series-circuit diagram. **Prob. R·3.**

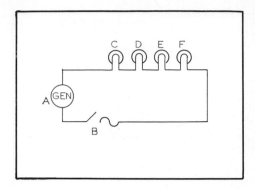

Fig. 18-8   A series-circuit diagram. **Prob. R·4.**

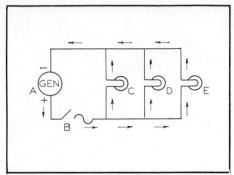

Fig. 18-9   A parallel-circuit diagram. **Prob. R·5.**

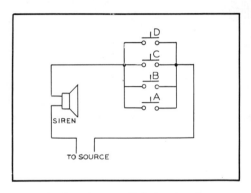

Fig. 18-10   A parallel-circuit diagram. **Prob. R·6.**

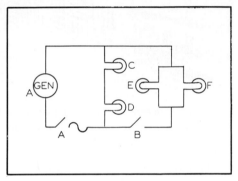

Fig. 18-11   A combination series and parallel circuit. **Prob. R·7.**

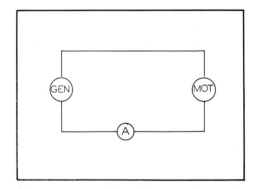

Fig. 18-12   Ammeter connection. **Prob. R·8.**

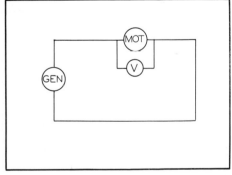

Fig. 18-13   Voltmeter connection. **Prob. R·9.**

250   MECHANICAL DRAWING

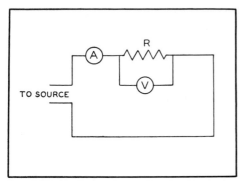

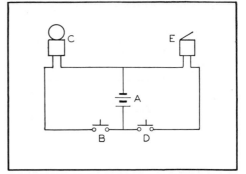

Fig. 18-14 Ammeter and voltmeter connections. **Prob. R·10.**

Fig. 18-15 Bell and buzzer circuit. **Prob. R·11.**

With a parallel string of lights on your Christmas tree, the remaining lights will continue to burn if some are missing, loose, or burned out.

A siren is shown in Fig. 18-10. It may be activated by any one of the push buttons, A, B, C, or D, which are all in parallel. An application of this would be in an alarm system to give warning of an attempted holdup in a store. The push buttons, connected in parallel, would be located under counters and in the cashier's cage.

Observe that the symbol for the siren is the same as for a loudspeaker (Fig. 18-2) but that here it is accompanied by a note "Siren" to identify it.

Combination series and parallel circuits provide many different arrangements combining both series and parallel connections. In Fig. 18-11 lamps C and D are in series and lamps E and F are in parallel. Both lamps C and D must be on if switch A is closed since they are in series. When switches A and B are closed, *all* the lamps (C, D, E, and F) are lighted. Lamps E and F will operate independently. If one fails, the other will remain lighted since they are in parallel. However, because lamps C and D are in series, as we have learned from the example of the Christ-

mas tree lights, when one fails, the other will not light.

18·6 Electrical instruments of many kinds have been developed for measuring purposes. Two principal ones are the *ammeter* and the *voltmeter*. The ammeter is an instrument which measures electric current in amperes. To measure the amount of current flowing through a resistance, the ammeter is connected directly in series with the resistance (motor, appliance, and so forth) as indicated in Fig. 18-12.

The voltmeter is an instrument which measures the electromotive force (pressure) in volts. A voltmeter is connected in parallel with that part of a circuit across which the voltage is to be measured as indicated in Fig. 18-13.

Figure 18-14 shows both an ammeter and a voltmeter connected in a circuit to measure the current flowing through and the voltage flowing across the resistance R.

18·7 Some electric circuits. In Fig. 18-15 the bell, C, and the buzzer, E, are operated independently from the same battery, A, by the push buttons, B and D.

In Fig. 18-16 the current is from an

ELECTRICAL DRAFTING **251**

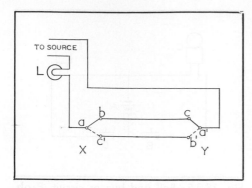

Fig. 18-16   Three-way switch diagram. **Prob. R·12.**

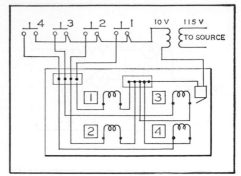

Fig. 18-17   Annunciator diagram. **Prob. R·13.**

outside source. The three-way switches, X and Y, are used so that the light at L may be turned off or on by either of the switches. Switch X might be at the garage and switch Y at the house. Each switch has three terminals. If either switch is opened, the light will be turned off; but the light may be turned on by the switch at the opposite end.

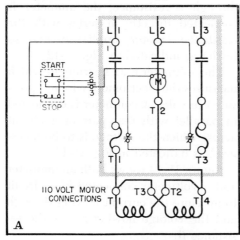

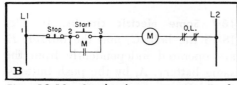

Fig. 18-18   Single-phase starter. **Prob. R·20.**

A circuit diagram is shown in Fig. 18-17 for an *annunciator* (an arrangement for signaling from different places to a station or post). It provides for ringing a buzzer in the annunciator when any of the buttons are pressed. Each button releases or allows a tab to drop down to identify the place where the button is pressed. Trace the circuits which are operated by each of the buttons. The source of the current is from the secondary of a step-down transformer.

A motor-starter wiring diagram is shown at A in Fig. 18-18 and a schematic or one-line diagram is shown at B for the same circuit. A motor starter is required for the following purposes:

1) To give the proper protection against burnouts caused by sustained overloads. This is known as *thermal overload protection,* a protection not afforded by ordinary fuses.

2) To provide for remote control by manual start-stop buttons or automatic devices, such as thermostats, pressurestats, limit switches, and so forth.

3) To furnish provisions for sequence control. This is illustrated in Fig. 18-19.

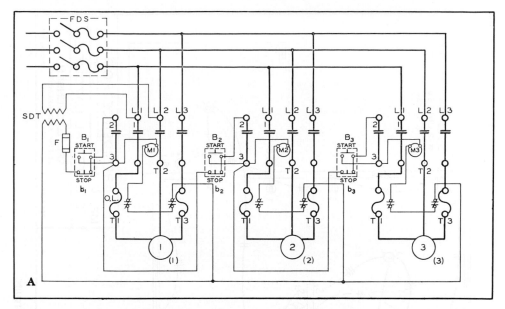

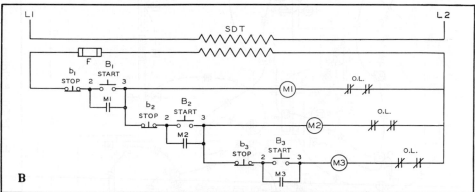

Fig. 18-19 Three-way conveyor system. **Prob. R·21.**

Figure 18-19 illustrates a wiring diagram at A and a schematic or one-line diagram at B for the same circuit. This figure shows the sequence control for a conveyor system consisting of three separate motors. Notice that a thin line (light value line) is used to indicate the pilot circuit (low voltage) in contrast to a thick line (heavy value line) to indicate the line voltage part of the circuit. The low voltage is obtained from the step-down transformer SDT.

A *transformer* is an electrical device which changes the voltage of alternating current, the type used in most electrical systems. In this case, the step-down transformer changes the current from a higher to lower voltage.

In Fig. 18-19 at A (upper rectangle) start button B_1 will start the No. 1 conveyor motor at (1), but start button B_2 will not start the No. 2 conveyor motor at (2) unless conveyor motor No. 1 has started. Likewise start button B_3 starts

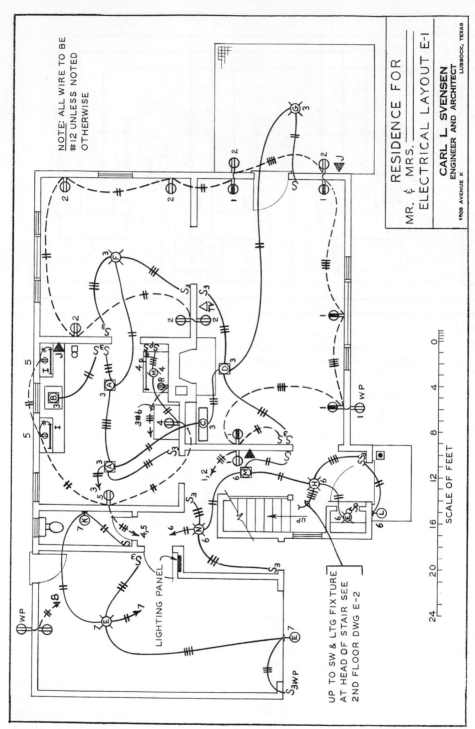

Fig. 18-20 Building wiring circuits.

254

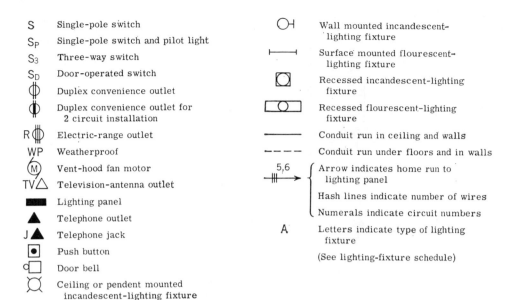

S	Single-pole switch		Wall mounted incandescent-lighting fixture
S_P	Single-pole switch and pilot light		Surface mounted flourescent-lighting fixture
S_3	Three-way switch		
S_D	Door-operated switch		Recessed incandescent-lighting fixture
	Duplex convenience outlet		Recessed flourescent-lighting fixture
	Duplex convenience outlet for 2 circuit installation		Conduit run in ceiling and walls
R	Electric-range outlet		Conduit run under floors and in walls
WP	Weatherproof		
M	Vent-hood fan motor	5,6	Arrow indicates home run to lighting panel
TV	Television-antenna outlet		Hash lines indicate number of wires
	Lighting panel		Numerals indicate circuit numbers
	Telephone outlet		
J	Telephone jack	A	Letters indicate type of lighting fixture
	Push button		(See lighting-fixture schedule)
	Door bell		
	Ceiling or pendent mounted incandescent-lighting fixture		

Fig. 18-21   Symbols used in Fig. 18-20.

conveyor motor No. 3 at (3) only after conveyor motor No. 2 has started. The conveyor system may be completely stopped by the fused disconnect switch FDS, by stop button b_1, or by its overload O.L. The stop button b_2 or the No. 2 motor overload will stop both conveyors Nos. 2 and 3. The stop button b_3, or overload, will only stop the No. 3 conveyor. The fuse, F, is for protection of the low-voltage control circuit.

In Fig. 18-19 at B (lower rectangle) the same circuit is shown by a one-line diagram. The fuse, F, is for the protection of the low-voltage control circuit.

18·8 Electrical layouts for buildings. The usual architect's indication of electrical outlets and switch locations is shown in Fig. 21-56. This plan only indicates the location of lights, base plugs, and desired switching arrangements. To provide a satisfactory and adequately wired electrical system upon completion of the structure, it is

necessary to have a complete and detailed set of electrical drawings and specifications prepared by someone who knows the engineering requirements. Such an electrical layout drawing is shown in Fig. 18-20, which indicates the circuit arrangements, and so forth, for the first floor of a two-story residence. A schedule of the symbols used is shown in Fig. 18-21. The two floors are indicated in Fig. 18-22, which is a riser diagram. Riser diagrams are used to show the interconnection between the various outlets of a system. The precise locations of the outlets are given on the electrical layouts, but not the interconnections. This is to avoid crowding.

The specifications will indicate the quality and type of materials, and the workmanship that will be acceptable.

The schedule of fixtures given in Fig. 18-23 illustrates the required information for the residence shown in Fig. 18-20.

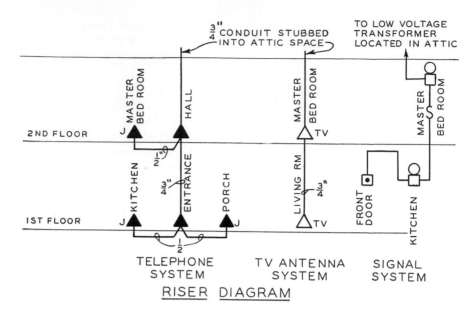

Fig. 18-22 Riser diagram.

FIXTURE SCHEDULE

TYPE	FIXTURE DESCRIPTION	LAMP	REMARKS
A	Marco #J1-95P	150W	Recessed
B	Marco #J8-106P	100W	Recessed
C	Industrial Fluorescent	30W Fluorescent	Recessed (See Arch. Detail #10)
D	Marco #J121P	150W R40	Recessed
E	Porcelain Keyless Socket	60W	
F	Lightolier #7936	150W	
G	Lightolier #6464	150W	
H	Lightolier #4085	12-6W(656)	
I	Fluorescent Strip	30W Fluorescent	Built in under kitchen cabinet with switch
K	Lightolier #4305	2-60W	With convenience outlet
L	Marco #924SC	75W	
M	Marco #J1-96P	100W	Recessed
N	Lightolier #4321	2-60W	
P	Fluorescent Strip	30W	Built in ventahood

Fig. 18-23 Schedule of fixtures.

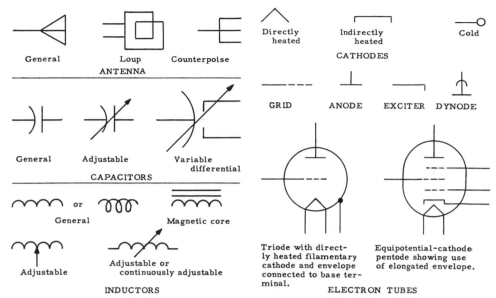

General   **Loup**   **Counterpoise**

ANTENNA

Directly heated   **Indirectly heated**   **Cold**

CATHODES

General   **Adjustable**   **Variable differential**

CAPACITORS

GRID   **ANODE**   **EXCITER**   **DYNODE**

General   or   **Magnetic core**

Adjustable   **Adjustable or continuously adjustable**

INDUCTORS

Triode with direct-
ly heated filamentary
cathode and envelope
connected to base ter-
minal.

Equipotential-cathode
pentode showing use
of elongated envelope.

ELECTRON TUBES

Fig. 18-24 Electrical symbols. (*Extracted from American Standards' "Graphical Symbols for Electrical Diagrams," ASA Y32.2–1954, with the permission of the publisher, Institute of Radio Engineers, Inc.*)

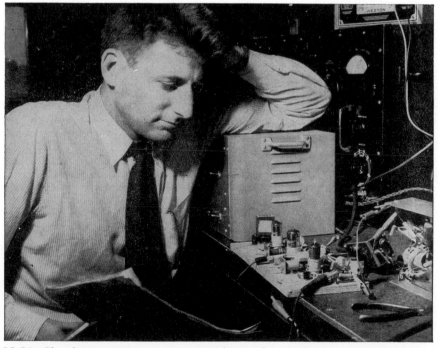

Fig. 18-25 The design engineer. (*From "Understanding Radio," by H. M. Watson, H. E. Welch, G. S. Eby, McGraw-Hill Book Company, Inc.*)

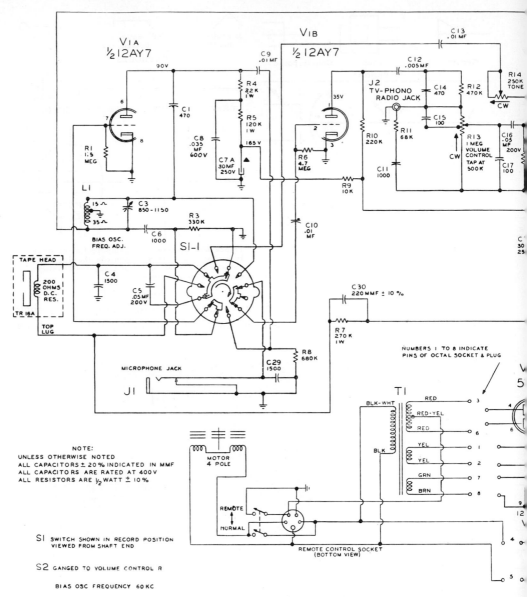

Fig. 18-26   Knight model 96R X 635 tape recorder.

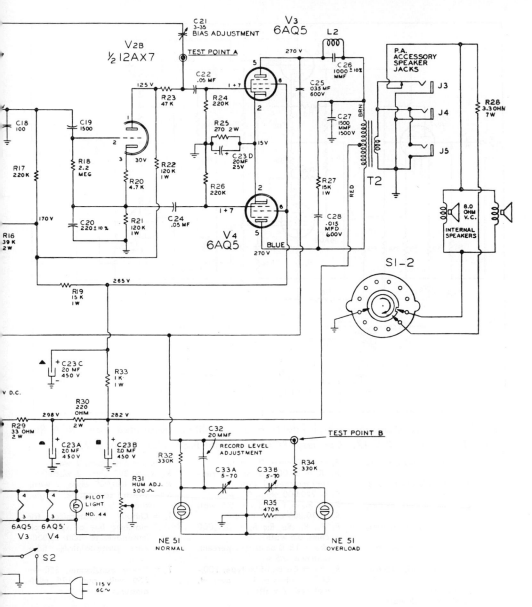

(Allied Radio Corporation) **Prob. R·30.**

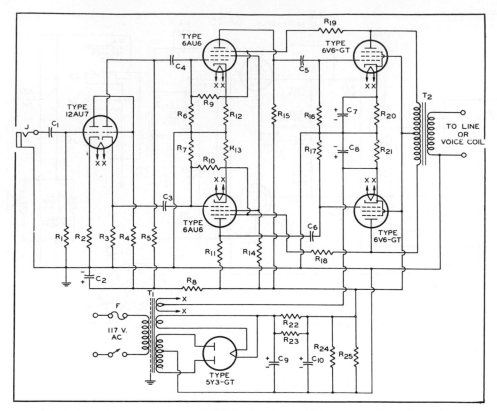

Fig. 18-27 Circuit diagram of high-fidelity audio amplifier. (*Reprinted from "RCA Receiving Tube Manual R-C 17." Courtesy, RCA, Copyright Proprietor*) **Prob. R·27.**

$C_1 = 0.1$ microfarad, paper, 600 volts

$C_2 = 40$ microfarad, electrolytic, 450 volts

C_3 $C_4 = 0.02$ microfarad, paper, 600 volts

C_5 $C_6 = 0.05$ microfarad, paper, 600 volts

C_7 $C_8 = 50$ microfarad, electrolytic, 50 volts

C_9 $C_{10} = 80$ microfarad, electrolytic, 450 volts

$F = $ Fuse, 1 ampere

$R_1 = 470,000$ ohms, 0.5 watt

$R_2 = 6800$ ohms, 0.5 watt

R_3 $R_5 = 39,000$ ohms ± 1 percent matched, 1 watt

$R_4 = 220,000$ ohms, 0.5 watt

R_6 R_7 $R_{14} = 1$ megohm, 0.5 watt

$R_8 = 10,000$ ohms, 1 watt

R_9 R_{10} R_{11} R_{15} R_{16} $R_{17} = 330,000$ ohms, 0.5 watt

R_{12} $R_{13} = 1800$ ohms ± 1 percent, matched, 0.5 watt

R_{18} $R_{19} = $ Carbon-film type, 100,000 ohms ± 1 percent, matched, 2 watts

R_{20} $R_{21} = 510$ ohms, 2 watts

R_{22} $R_{23} = 390$ ohms, 2 watts

R_{24} $R_{25} = 150,000$ ohms, 2 watts

$S = $ Switch, single-pole, single-throw

$T_1 = $ Output transformer for matching line or voice coil impedance to 9000–10,000-ohm plate-to-plate tube load

$T_2 = $ Power transformer, 350–0–350 volts rms, 125 milliamperes

18·9 Electronic circuit diagrams. Radio diagrams vary greatly from the circuit diagrams for a simple one-tube coil-condenser tuned circuit receiver shown in Fig. 18-1 to extremely complicated circuits described in books dealing solely with the subject.[2]

A few electronic symbols from American Standards are shown in Fig. 18-24.

In Fig. 18-25 the design engineer is trying out a radio circuit with the units

[2] *Essentials of Radio* by Morris Slurzberg and William Osterheld and *Understanding Radio* by Herbert M. Watson, Herbert E. Welch, and George S. Eby are both published by McGraw-Hill Book Company, Inc., New York.

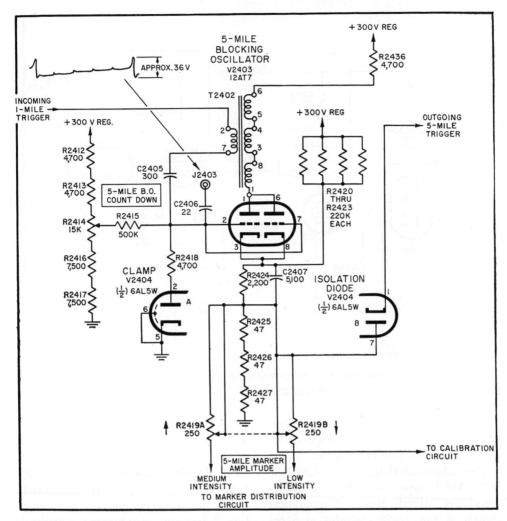

Fig. 18-28 Circuit diagram, count down block oscillator with clamp and isolation diode. *(Raytheon Manufacturing Company)* **Prob. R·28.**

arranged on a "breadboard." Parts can be removed or changed until the required quality of reception can be obtained and mass-produced at an economical cost as determined by the planning section. Sketches of circuits are an important part of design studies from which draftsmen work.

Diagram drawings made in the electrical and electronics industries may become complicated as illustrated in Figs. 18-26 to 18-29. Such drawings are generally made by draftsmen from designers' sketches. The templates mentioned in Art. 18·2 are much used for this purpose.

Actually these electronic drawings are made up of various components (or smaller units), as arranged by designers, to produce the desired results just

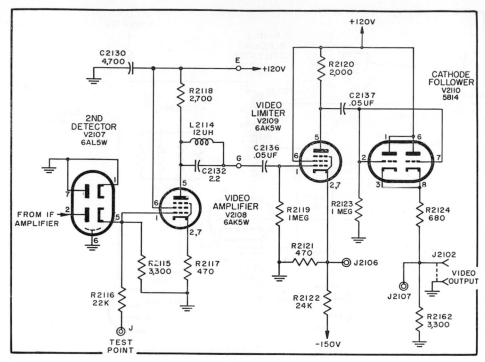

Fig. 18-29 Circuit diagram, second detector, and video amplifier and limiter. (*Raytheon Manufacturing Company*) **Prob. R·29.**

as a building is made up of simple parts or as a machine is composed of shafts, bearings, and other units.

The schematic diagram for a Knight 96R X635 tape recorder manufactured by Allied Radio Corporation shown in Fig. 18-26 operates as a recorder and public address system separately or simultaneously.

The circuit diagram for a high-fidelity audio amplifier shown in Fig. 18-27 contains conventional tubes and electronic components. It illustrates one of the important applications of RCA receiving tubes.

The schematic diagrams in Figs. 18-28 and 18-29 represent parts of a storm detector radar (AN/CPS-9) manufactured by Raytheon Manufacturing Company for the Signal Corps of the

U.S. Army. The circuit names are given in the legends under the figures.

18·10 Problem suggestions. Group R, page 497. Three lists are presented. List 1 includes elementary problems. List 2 has somewhat more advanced problems for students who are interested and have studied electricity. The problems in List 3 are for those students who have made a hobby of radio and radar.

LIST 1   Problems R·1, R·2, R·4, R·5, R·8, R·9, R·11, R·14, R·17, R·22, R·23, R·25

LIST 2   Problems R·3, R·6, R·7, R·10, R·15, R·18, R·24, R·26

LIST 3   Problems R·12, R·13, R·16, R·19, R·20, R·21, R·27, R·28, R·29, R·30

19 Cams and gears

19·1 Cams and gears (Fig. 19-1) are machine parts that frequently occur on working drawings. The theory and specification of cams and gears are important divisions of the study of mechanism, to which the student is referred. The student should, however, know how to represent them on drawings as indicated in this chapter.

19·2 Cams. A cam is a machine element used to obtain an irregular or special motion not easily obtained by other means. Its shape is derived from the motion required of it. *Plate cams* are illustrated in Figs. 19-1 and 19-2. As the cam in Fig. 19-2 revolves, it moves the *follower* up and down for one-half revolution and allows it to remain at rest for the remaining one-half revolution. The *cylindrical cam* in Fig. 19-3 revolves and moves the follower back and forth parallel to the axis of the shaft. Some cam terms are given in Fig. 19-4, which also illustrates how the cam acts.

Fig. 19-1 Cam installation using the Mc-Gill cam follower. The small gear at the lower left-hand corner meshes with a large gear (covered with a guard) secured to a shaft. The cam shown at the center is secured to the same shaft. As the cam revolves, it moves the cam follower (a hollow cylinder) attached to the link and gives it a variable motion. The link is pivoted near the upper right-hand corner in the illustration. (*McGill Manufacturing Company, Inc.*)

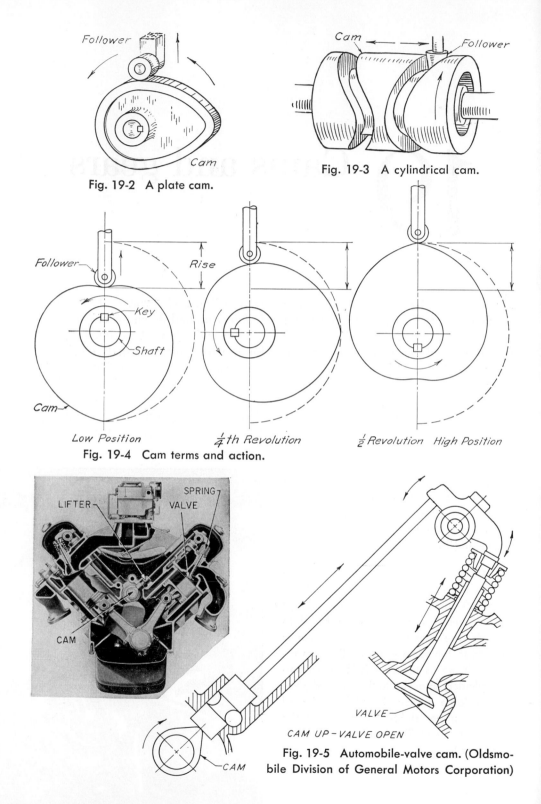

Fig. 19-2 A plate cam.

Fig. 19-3 A cylindrical cam.

Fig. 19-4 Cam terms and action.

Low Position

$\frac{1}{4}$th Revolution

$\frac{1}{2}$ Revolution   High Position

Fig. 19-5 Automobile-valve cam. (Oldsmobile Division of General Motors Corporation)

CAM UP - VALVE OPEN

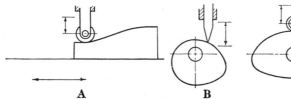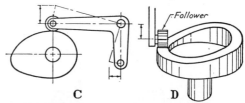

Fig. 19-6 Some kinds of cams.

19·3 Kinds of cams. A cam for operating the valve on an automobile engine is illustrated in Fig. 19-5. This cam has a *flat follower* which rests against the face of the cam. The *slider cam* in Fig. 19-6 at A moves the follower up and down as the cam moves back and forth. A cam with a *point follower*, off center, is shown at B. A lever cam is shown at C and a cylindrical cam, edge-type, is shown at D. Plate and grooved cams are illustrated in Fig. 19-7. The roll of the follower is guided by the groove, which has a width equal to the diameter of the roller. A grooved cam being machined is shown in Fig. 19-8 at A, and forms of cylindrical cams are shown at B and C.

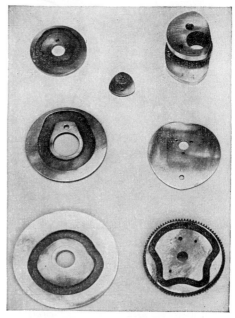

Fig. 19-7 Plate and grooved cams. (*The Rowbottom Machine Company*)

Fig. 19-8 Machining cams. (*The Rowbottom Machine Company*)

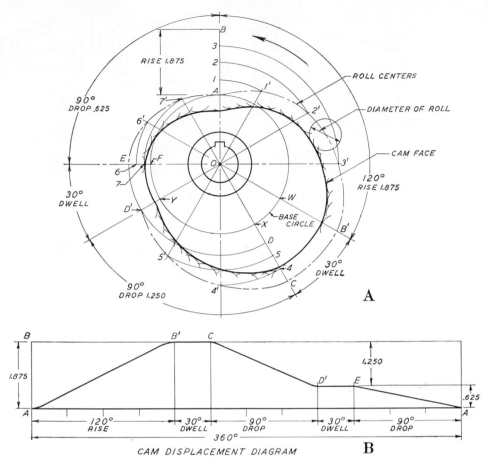

Fig. 19-9 Drawing a plate cam.

19·4 To draw a cam outline. Given point O, the center of the shaft, and point A, the lowest position of the center of the roller, Fig. 19-9 at A. It is required to raise the center of the roller 1.875″ with uniform motion during 120° of a revolution of the shaft, remain at rest (*dwell*) for 30°, drop 1.250″ during 90°, remain at rest for 30°, and drop 0.625″ during the remaining 90°. The shaft revolves uniformly.

The *cam displacement diagram* at B in Fig. 19-9 indicates the desired mo-

tion. The horizontal line represents one revolution of the base circle, 360°, and is divided in parts proportional to the number of degrees for each action. Vertical distances show the actual rise and fall.

To draw the cam shown at A in Fig. 19-9: Divide the rise, *AB*, into a number of equal parts (four parts are used for clearness; but to obtain a more accurate solution, more parts would be used). Divide the arc *AW* (120°) into the same number of equal parts as in the rise and draw radial lines from O.

With center O draw arcs with radii $O1$, $O2$, $O3$, and OB to locate points $1'$, $2'$, $3'$, and B' on the line of roller centers. Using an irregular curve, draw a smooth curve through these points.

Draw arc $B'C$ (30°) with radius OB'. This will allow the follower to be at rest, for it will be at a constant distance from O.

Lay off $CD = 1.250''$ and divide it into a number of equal parts (three are shown). Divide arc XY (90°) into the same number of equal parts (three) and draw radial lines from O. Draw arcs with center O and radii $O4$, $O5$, and OD to locate points $4'$, $5'$, and D'. Draw a smooth curve through points $4'$, $5'$, and D'.

Draw arc $D'E$ (30°) with radius OD to provide for the 30° dwell.

The distance EF will be $0.625''$ (the remaining part of the drop to the base circle). Divide EF into a number of equal parts (three shown). Divide arc FA into the same number of equal parts (three) and draw radial lines. Draw arcs with radii $O6$ and $O7$ to locate points $6'$ and $7'$. Using an irregular curve, draw a smooth curve through points E, $6'$, $7'$, and A.

With centers on the line of roll centers, draw successive arcs with the radius of the roll as indicated. Then, using an irregular curve, draw a smooth curve tangent to the arcs as shown by the cam face line.

19·5 Motion. The motion of the follower of a cam may be *uniform, harmonic,* or *uniformly accelerated.* At A in Fig. 19-10 the thin line AC represents uniform motion. Equal distances on the rise are made for equal distances on the travel (equal intervals of time). To avoid a sudden jar at the beginning and end of motion, arcs are used to modify the motion as shown by the heavy line. Harmonic motion, shown at B, is smoother. Draw a semicircle with the rise as a diameter. Divide it into a number of equal parts and the travel into the same number of equal parts. Project across and up to locate the points as shown and draw a smooth curve through them. Uniformly accelerated motion, represented at C, is still smoother. The rise is divided into parts proportional to 1, 3, 5, . . . 5, 3, 1. The travel is divided into the same number of parts (equal parts). Project across and up to locate points through which to draw a smooth curve as shown.

19·6 Cam drawings. A drawing for a face (plate) cam is shown in Fig. 19-11. Note that the amount of movement is given by the radii for the dwells, $4\frac{1}{2}''$ radius and $7''$ radius. Harmonic motion is used and there are two rollers. A drawing for a barrel (cylindrical) cam is shown in Fig. 19-12. Note the displacement diagram. There are two

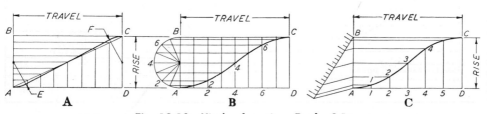

Fig. 19-10   Kinds of motion. **Prob. S·1.**

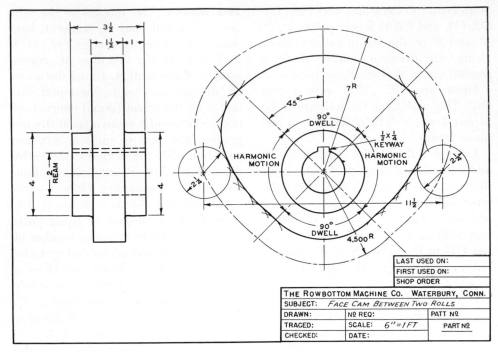

Fig. 19-11   Drawing of a face (plate) cam. **Prob. S·9.**

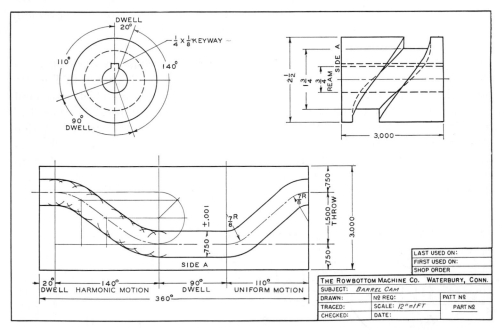

Fig. 19-12   Drawing of a barrel (cylindrical) cam. **Prob. S·10.**

268   MECHANICAL DRAWING

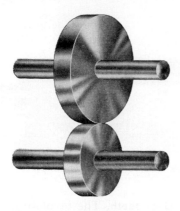

Fig. 19-13   Friction wheels.

Fig. 19-14   Gear and pinion.

dwells and two kinds of motion. For laying out harmonic motion, refer to Art. 19·5, Fig. 19-10.

19·7 Gears. If two wheels or circular disks are in contact as in Fig. 19-13, both will revolve if one is turned. If the smaller wheel is two-thirds the diameter of the larger wheel, it will make one and one-half revolutions for one revolution of the larger wheel, provided that no slipping occurs. If the driven wheel is hard to turn, there will be slipping. To prevent this, *teeth* are added to the wheels (Fig. 19-14) to form *spur gears*. The shape of the

Fig. 19-15   Cut spur gear (*The Fellows Gear Shaper Company*)

teeth is such that the same kind of motion is obtained as with rolling wheels that do not slip. A *spur gear* and *pinion* are illustrated in Fig. 19-14. The small gear is the pinion. A cut spur gear is shown in Fig. 19-15.

A *rack and pinion* are illustrated in Figs. 19-16 and 19-17. A rack is simply a gear with a straight pitch line in place of a circular pitch line.

19·8 Gear terms. Names of some parts of gears are illustrated in Fig. 19-18. Note the three diameters: *outside diameter, root diameter,* and *pitch diameter.* The pitch diameter corresponds to the diameter of the rolling wheel that is replaced by the gear. There are two kinds of pitch: *circular pitch* (illus-

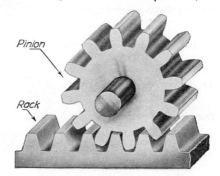

Fig. 19-16   Rack and pinion.

Fig. 19-17 Rack and pinion (*The Fellows Gear Shaper Company*)

trated) and *diametral pitch*. The circular pitch is the distance from a point on one tooth to the same point on the next tooth measured along the pitch circle and equals the circumference of the pitch circle divided by the number of teeth. The diametral pitch is a ratio, or number, obtained by dividing the number of teeth by the pitch diameter. The *addendum* is the distance that the gear tooth extends above (outside) the pitch circle. The *dedendum* is the distance that the gear tooth extends below (inside) the pitch circle.

19·9 Gear teeth. The involute and cycloidal curves are used for gear-teeth forms. The information given in this chapter is for the 14½° involute system (14½° or 20° is generally used). The 14½° or 20° refers to the pressure angle (Fig. 19-19). The pressure angle and the distance between centers determines the diameters of the base circles. Note that the base circle (from which the involute is derived) is smaller than the pitch circle (Figs. 19-19 and 19-20).

In Fig. 19-20, R_A is the radius of the

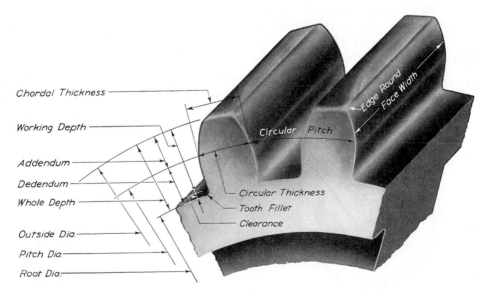

Chordal Thickness

Working Depth

Addendum
Dedendum
Whole Depth

Outside Dia.
Pitch Dia.
Root Dia.

Edge Round
Face Width

Circular Pitch

Circular Thickness
Tooth Fillet
Clearance

Fig. 19-18 Gear terms.

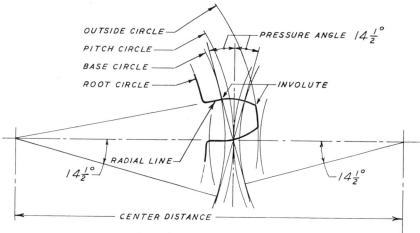

Fig. 19-19   Pressure angle.

pitch circle of the gear with center at A, and R_B is the radius of the pitch circle of the pinion with center at B. $R_A + R_B$ equals the distance between centers. The line of pressure, T_A T_B, through O (the point of tangency of the pitch circles) makes the pressure angle ϕ (Greek letter phi) with the perpendicular to the line of centers. Angle ϕ is shown extra large for clearness. Then AT_A and BT_B, drawn to the tangent points T_A and T_B, are the radii of the base circles. A point, x, on a cord (line of pressure T_A T_B) will describe involutes from the base circles as the cord winds and unwinds, and represents the outlines of gear teeth outside of the base circles. The part of the gear tooth inside the base circle is a radial line.

19·10 Gear terms, abbreviations, and formulas. The following information and formulas are for use in finding required dimensions, and so forth, for standard $14\frac{1}{2}°$ involute gears:

$$N = \text{number of teeth} = DP = \frac{\pi D}{p} = D_o P - 2$$

$$a = \text{addendum} = \frac{1}{P} = \frac{P}{\pi}$$

$$b = \text{dedendum} = \frac{1.157}{P} = \frac{1.157p}{\pi}$$

$$c = \text{clearance} = \frac{0.157}{P} = \frac{0.157p}{\pi}$$

$$h_t = \text{whole depth} = a + b = \frac{2.157}{P} = \frac{2.157p}{\pi}$$

$$D = \text{pitch diameter} = \frac{N}{P} = D_o - 2a$$

$$D_o = \text{outside diameter} = \frac{N+2}{P} = D + 2a = \frac{(N+2)p}{\pi}$$

$$D_R = \text{root diameter} = D - 2b = D_o - 2(a+b)$$

$$P = \text{diametral pitch} = \frac{N}{D} = \frac{\pi}{p}$$

$$p = \text{circular pitch} = \frac{\pi D}{N} = \frac{\pi}{P}$$

19·11 Gear drawings. It is not necessary to show the teeth on drawings of

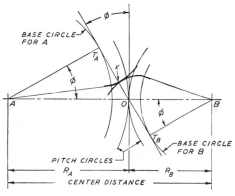

Fig. 19-20   Gear action, base circle, etc.

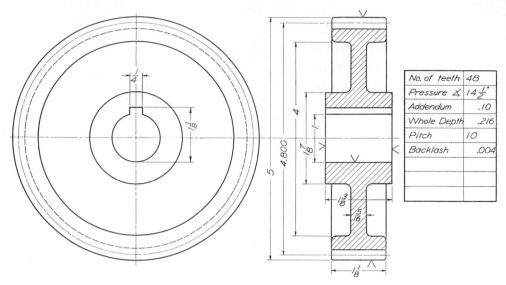

No. of teeth	48
Pressure ∡	$14\frac{1}{2}°$
Addendum	.10
Whole Depth	.216
Pitch	10
Backlash	.004

Fig. 19-21 Working drawing of a cut spur gear.

gears. A drawing for a cut spur gear is shown in Fig. 19-21. The gear *blank* should be drawn with dimensions for making the pattern and for the machining operations. Notes should also be included giving the necessary information for cutting the teeth, the accuracy required, the material, and so forth. On assembly drawings the representation shown in Fig. 19-22 may be used with such notes as may be necessary.

19·12 Bevel gears. When two gear shafts intersect, bevel gears are used. These gears may be thought of as replacing rolling cones (Fig. 19-23, at A, B, C, and D). If the gears are the same size and the shafts are at right angles, they are called *miter gears*. A single bevel gear is shown in Fig. 19-24 and a pair of bevel gears in Fig. 19-25. The smaller of two bevel gears is called the *pinion*.

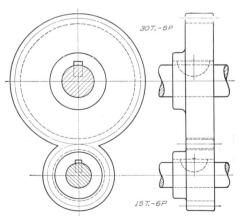

Fig. 19-22 Gears in elevation.

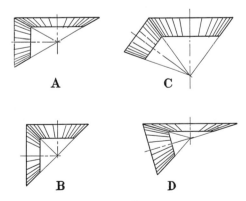

Fig. 19-23 Rolling cones.

272 MECHANICAL DRAWING

Fig. 19-24 A bevel gear. (*The Fellows Gear Shaper Company*)

Fig. 19-25 A pair of bevel gears.

19·13 Bevel-gear terms. Some information about bevel gears is given in Fig. 19-26. The Greek letters in the illustration are identified in the following list:

GREEK LETTERS

α = alpha, δ = delta, Γ = gamma

α	= addendum angle
δ	= dedendum angle
Γ	= pitch angle
Γ_R	= root angle
Γ_0	= face angle
a	= addendum
b	= dedendum
a_N	= angular addendum
A	= cone distance
F	= face
D	= pitch diameter
D_o	= outside diameter
N	= number of teeth
P	= diametral pitch
R	= pitch radius

Fig. 19-26 Some bevel-gear terms.

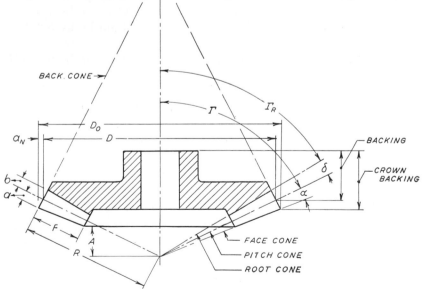

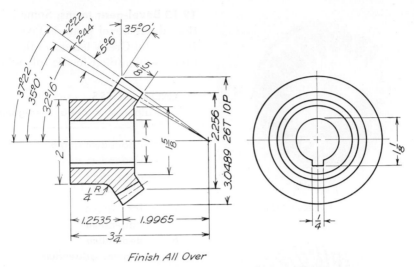

Fig. 19-27 Working drawing of a cut bevel gear.

19·14 Bevel-gear drawing. Working drawings of bevel gears require the dimensions for machining the blank, together with the necessary gear information. An example of a working drawing for a cut bevel gear is shown in Fig. 19-27.

19·15 Gear information may be obtained from the publications of the American Standards Association and by a study of books on mechanism, machine design, and the subject of gears.

19·16 Problem suggestions. Group S, page 500. Three lists are presented. List 1 includes basic elementary problems. Selections from Lists 2 and 3 may be made for more advanced students when time permits.

LIST 1   Cam Probs. S·1, S·3, S·4, S·5, S·7
          Gear Probs. S·12, S·13
LIST 2   Cam Probs. S·2, S·6, S·9
          Gear Probs. S·11, S·14
LIST 3   Cam Probs. S·8, S·10

The color filmstrips *Developments* and *Intersections* have been prepared to correlate with this chapter.

20 Sheet-metal drafting

20·1 Sheet-metal drafting. A large class of metalwork is made from sheets of metal which are formed into the required shape by bending or folding up and fastening by rivets, seams, soldering, or welding. Figure 20-1 shows a schematic arrangement of the Kennedy stratified air-swept-tube mill system for raw ore and clinker grinding. For sheet-metal work, the drawings consist of the representation of the finished object and the drawing of the shape of the flat sheet, which, when rolled or folded and fastened, will form the object.[1] This second drawing is called the *development* or *pattern* of the piece; making it comes under the term *sheet-metal pattern drafting*.

20·2 Development. There are two gen-

---

[1] A great many thin metal objects without seams are formed by die-stamping or by pressing a flat sheet into shape under very heavy presses. Examples range from brass cartridge cases to steel wheelbarrows. Other kinds of thin metal objects are made by spinning, for example, some brass and aluminum ware. In stamped and spun work, the metal is stretched out of its original shape.

eral classes of surfaces: plane and curved. The six faces of a cube are plane surfaces. The bases of a cylinder are plane surfaces, whereas the lateral surface is curved.

It is possible to cut a piece of paper so that it can be folded into a cube as in Fig. 20-2. The shape cut out is the *pattern* of the cube. There are five regular solids and their patterns are made as shown in Fig. 20-3. A good understanding of the nature of developments may be had by laying out the foregoing shapes on rather stiff drawing paper. These shapes can then be cut out and their patterns folded to form the figures. The joints can be easily secured with cellulose tape.

Thus the pattern for any piece that has plane surfaces may be made by first deciding where the seam is to be. Usually, for economy of solder or rivets and time, the seam is taken on the shortest line. Then each face is opened in order so that the pattern shows each face in its true size. One example, the development of a prism, is illustrated in Fig. 20-4. The lines inside the pattern are called *folding*, or *crease*, lines. The

Fig. 20-1 Schematic arrangement of Kennedy stratified air-swept tube mill system. (Kennedy-Van Saun Manufacturing & Engineering Corporation)

1 Belt Conveyor—Feed to Crusher
2 Vibrating Screen
3 Oversize Return Chute
4 Gearless Gyratory Crusher
5 Belt Conveyor—Closing Crusher Circuit
6 Traveling Crane
7 Clamshell Bucket
8 Mill Feed Hopper

9 Weighing Feeder
10 Stratified Air-swept Tube Mill
11 Cross Conveyor for Oversize
12 Return Conveyor for Oversize
13 Radial Flow Classifier
14 Cyclone Collector
15 Mill Exhauster
16 Dust Filter

17 Dust Filter Exhauster
18 Rotary Air Locks
19 Finished Material Conveyor
20 Automatic Pneumatic Transport Pump
21 Hot Air Furnace
22 Instrument and Control Cubicle
23 Automatically Controlled Tempering
   Air Damper

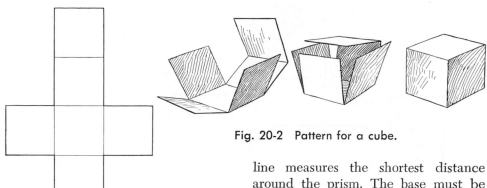

Fig. 20-2 Pattern for a cube.

dotted lines on the second figure indicate extra material to allow for lap in making joints.

The length of the pattern for a prism is measured on a straight line called the *stretchout line* (Fig. 20-4). This

line measures the shortest distance around the prism. The base must be perpendicular to the edges so that it will form the stretchout line when the faces of the prism are unfolded in contact with a plane surface.

20·3 Development of prisms. To develop the prism in Fig. 20-5, draw the stretchout line *SL* and on it lay off 1–2,

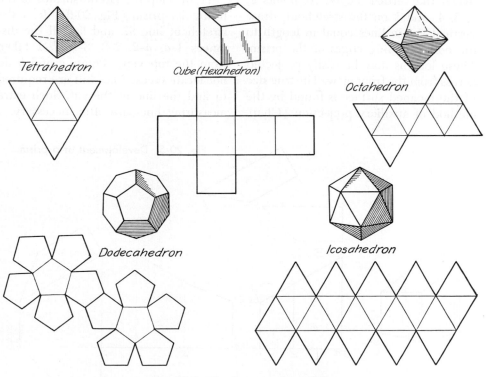

Tetrahedron

Cube(Hexahedron)

Octahedron

Dodecahedron

Icosahedron

Fig. 20-3 The five regular solids.

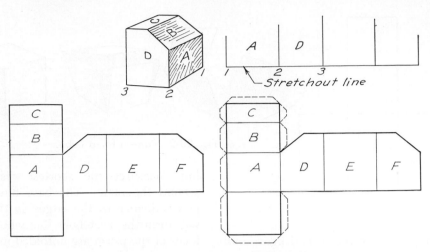

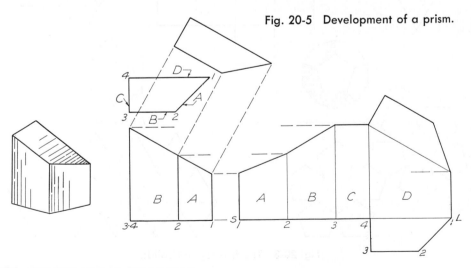

Fig. 20-4 A pattern showing lap.

2–3, 3–4, and 4–1 obtained from the top view. This gives the length of the stretchout and the true distances between the vertical edges. At points 1, 2, 3, 4, and 1 on the stretchout, draw vertical crease lines equal in length to the corresponding edges of the prism. These lengths may be easily projected across from the front view. The true size of the inclined surface is found by the method of auxiliary projection (Chap.

9) and is attached to one of the sides in its proper relation. The development of the bottom may be added if desired.

To develop the lateral surface of the triangular prism (Fig. 20-6), draw the stretchout line SL and lay off the distances 1–a, a–2, 2–3, 3–b, b–1 taken from the top view. Points a and b do not locate crease lines but are required to find the line of the cut. Such extra measuring lines are often necessary.

Fig. 20-5 Development of a prism.

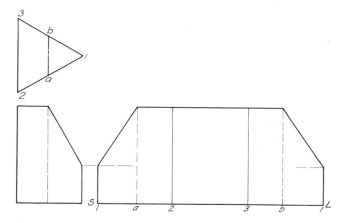

Fig. 20-6 Development of a prism.

20·4 Cylinders. In geometry we learn that a cylinder may be thought of as a prism with an infinite number of sides. The development of the curved surface of a cylinder, then, might be obtained by opening up each face, in order, and placing it in contact with a plane surface. The result would be a rectangle having a width equal to the height of the cylinder (an element) and a length equal to the distance around the cylinder. The developed surface of a cylinder is illustrated in Fig. 20-7. For a cylinder the stretchout line is a straight line equal in length to the circumference of the cylinder. If the base of the

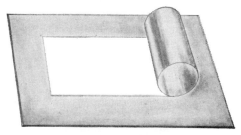

Fig. 20-7 Developed surface of a cylinder.

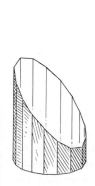
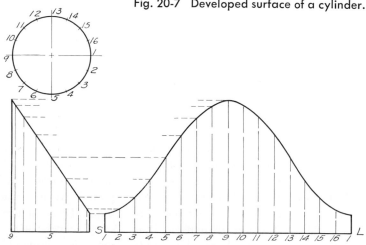

Fig. 20-8 Development of a cylinder.

SHEET-METAL DRAFTING **279**

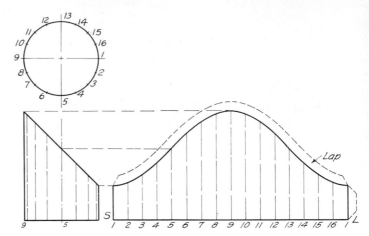

Fig. 20-9 Pattern for a square elbow.

cylinder is perpendicular to the axis, it will roll out into a straight line and form the stretchout line. If a prism or cylinder does not have a base perpendicular to the axis, a right section must be taken to obtain the stretchout line.

20·5 Development of cylinders. Consider a cylinder as being a many-sided prism. To develop the cylinder (Fig. 20-8), assume the position of any convenient number of imaginary edges. For ease of working, these are equally spaced. This makes it possible to obtain the length of the stretchout by stepping off as many spaces along SL as there are on the top view. At each point on the stretchout, draw a vertical measuring line. Project the length of each imaginary edge across from the front view to the corresponding line of the development and draw a smooth curve through these points of intersection.

Since the surface is curved, the stretchout as obtained is only approximate. The more edges assumed, the closer will be the approximation. It is seldom necessary to have the points less than ¼ in. apart. The accuracy in

length of the stretchout may be tested by measuring on it the figured length of the circumference, which equals 3.1416 times the diameter, or πd.

20·6 To draw the pattern for a two-piece or square elbow (Fig. 20-9). Since this elbow consists of two cylinders cut off at 45°, only one needs to be developed for a pattern. The explanation of Fig. 20-8 applies to this figure. Lap is allowed as indicated.

20·7 The development of a four-piece elbow is illustrated in Fig. 20-10. To draw the elbow, first draw arcs having the desired inner and outer radii as shown at A. Divide the outer quarter circle into six equal parts. Draw radial lines from points 1, 3, and 5 to locate the joints. Draw tangents to the arcs at points 2 and 4 and complete the figure as shown at B by tangents to the inner quarter circle. With this view completed, we are ready to start development. Draw a circle representing the cross section of the pipe (one-half this view is sufficient). Divide it into a number of equal parts and lay out the

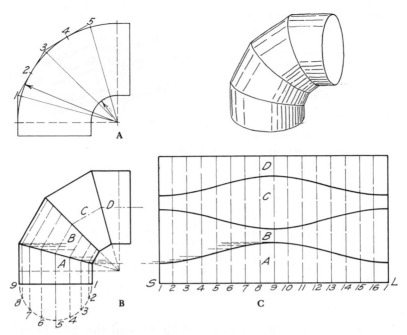

Fig. 20-10   Pattern for a four-piece elbow.

stretchout line with the same equal parts. From the circle, project to the elevation to locate the imaginary edges. The pattern for the first section is obtained by projecting across from the elevation as shown at C, in the same way as in Figs. 20-8 and 20-9.

The patterns for the four pieces may be cut without waste from a rectangular piece if the seams are made alternately on the inside, or throat line, and the outside line. To draw the pattern for the second section, extend the measuring lines of the first section and with the dividers take off the lengths of the imaginary edges on the front view, starting with the longest one. The third and fourth sections are made in a similar way. Since the curve is the same for all sections, only one need be plotted and that one can be used as a template (pattern) for the others.

20·8 Galvanized-iron and copper moldings and cornices are made up of a combination of cylinder and prism parts. A practical problem in developments is to make the pattern for a mitered piece "return" around a corner as shown in Fig. 20-11. An inspection of the figure shows the method of working to be the same as in Fig. 20-8. Here, however, the section of the molding takes the place of the top view, and its length is laid out on the stretchout line.

20·9 Development of pyramids and cones. In the case of prisms and cylinders, the stretchout was a straight line with the measuring lines perpendicular to it and parallel to each other. As their edges were all parallel to the front plane, their true lengths were always shown in the front view. Pyramids and cones, or any objects larger at one end

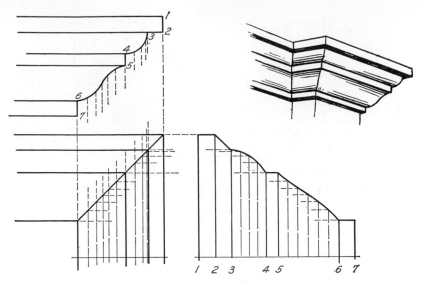

Fig. 20-11　Pattern for a return miter.

than at the other, will not roll straight; hence their stretchouts are not straight lines. Since they have sloping sides, their edges will not always show in their true lengths.

20·10 To find the true length of the edge of a pyramid or cone, revolve the line it projects until the line is parallel to one of the planes of projection. The line's projection on that plane will then

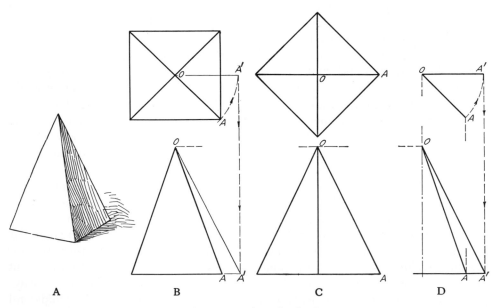

Fig. 20-12　True length of a line.

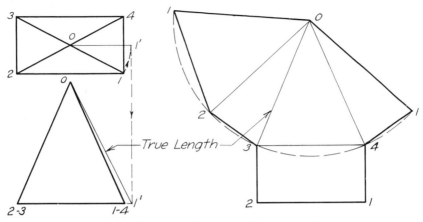

Fig. 20-13   Development of a pyramid.

be the true length of the edge in question. The pyramid at A in Fig. 20-12 is shown by top and front views at B. The edge *OA* does not show in its true length in either view. However, if we draw the pyramid in the position shown at C, the true length of *OA* is shown in the front view. At C the pyramid has been revolved from the position of B about a vertical axis until the line *OA* is parallel to the vertical plane. At D the line *OA* is shown before and after revolving. Thus the construction for finding the true length of a line is as follows: In the top view, with radius *OA* and center *O*, revolve the top view of *OA* until it is horizontal. Project the end of the line down to meet a horizontal line through the front view of *A*. Join this point of intersection with the front view of *O*. The true length is shown at *OA'*.

20·11 To draw the pattern for a rectangular pyramid (Fig. 20-13). Find the true length of one of the edges by swinging it around as shown. With this true length as a radius, draw an arc of indefinite length for a stretchout line.

On this, mark off as chords the four edges of the base 1–2, 2–3, 3–4, 4–1. Connect these points with each other in turn and draw the crease lines by joining each point with the center.

20·12 Cones. The curved surface of a cone may be thought of as being made up of an infinite number of triangles. The development of the curved surface might be obtained by placing each triangle, in order, in contact with a plane surface. The result would be a sector of a circle having a radius equal to an element of the cone and an arc equal in length to the circumference of the base of the cone. The developed surface of a cone is illustrated in Fig. 20-14.

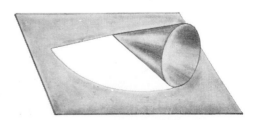

Fig. 20-14   Developed surface of a cone.

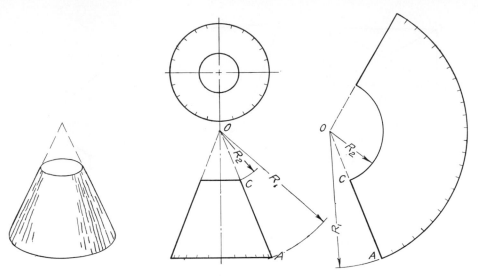

Fig. 20-15   Developed surface of a frustum of a cone.

20·13 To draw the pattern for a cone.
From Fig. 20-14 it will be seen that the
stretchout line for a cone is a circle arc
with a radius equal to the slant height
of the cone. Considering the cone as a
many-sided pyramid, draw on the top
view a convenient number of imaginary edges (elements) with a large
number of equal spaces. With the slant
height taken from the front view as a

radius (*OA* in Fig. 20-15), draw an arc
of indefinite length as a stretchout. On
this, step off as many spaces as were
assumed in the top view and at the
same distances apart. Connect the end
points with the center. The resulting
sector is the developed surface. If the
cone is cut off straight across as in Fig.
20-15, draw another arc with *OC* as a
radius after developing the full cone.

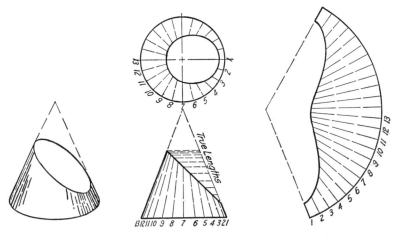

Fig. 20-16   Developed surface of a truncated cone.

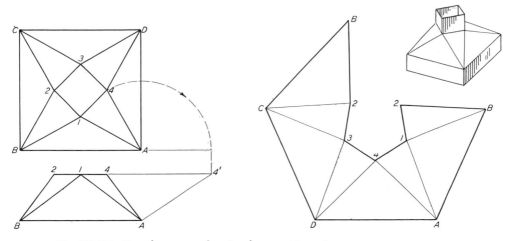

Fig. 20-17   Development of a simple transition piece—square to square.

20·14 The pattern for a truncated cone. If the cone is cut off at an angle as in Fig. 20-16, first develop the full cone, drawing the developed position of each element and numbering it to avoid mistakes. Then find the true length of each element from the base to the cut surface by revolving it around the axis until it is parallel to the front plane or, in other words, by projecting it across to the outside line in the front view. Lay off these true lengths on the corresponding lines on the pattern and connect the points. The elements and lines have been stopped at the cut surface to preserve clearness.

20·15 Development of a transition piece. A transition piece is used to connect a pipe of one shape with another of a different shape. Transition pieces are made up of parts of different kinds of surfaces and are developed by triangulation. This consists of dividing a surface into triangles (exact or approximate) and laying them out on the developed pattern in regular order.

The example shown in Fig. 20-17 connects two square ducts, one of which is at 45° with the other. It will be seen that this piece is made up of eight triangles, four of one size and four of another size. To draw the developed surface find the true size of each triangle and place them in the proper order. Lines 1–2, 2–3, 3–4, and 4–1 show in their true size as do lines AB, BC, CD, and DA. Find the true length of one of the other lines as for A4. Revolve it parallel to the frontal plane and the true length shows at $A4'$ in the front view. Start the development by drawing line DA. Then with centers at A and D and radius $A4'$ taken from the front view (true length of $A4 = D4 = D3$, etc.) draw intersecting arcs to locate point 4 on the development. With D as a center draw an arc with radius $A4'$ and intersect it with an arc of radius 4–3 and center 4 to locate point 3. Proceed to lay off the remaining triangles until the development is completed.

The example shown in Fig. 20-18 connects a round pipe with a rectangular one. From the picture, it is seen that this piece is formed by four triangles. Be-

SHEET-METAL DRAFTING   **285**

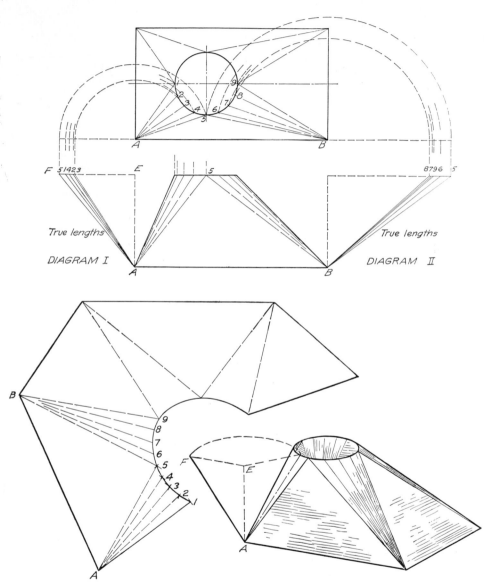

Fig. 20-18 Development of a simple transition piece—round to rectangular.

tween these triangles are four conical parts, with apexes at the corners of the rectangular opening and bases each one-quarter of the round opening.

Starting with the cone whose apex is at A, divide its base 1–5 into a number of equal parts as 2, 3, 4 and draw the lines A2, A3, A4 to give triangles approximating the cone. Find the true length of each of these lines. This is done in practical work by constructing a separate diagram, as at I. The construction is based on the fact that the true length of each line is the hypotenuse of a triangle whose altitude is the altitude of the cone and whose base is the length of the top view of the line.

On the front view, draw the vertical line AE as the altitude of the cone. On the base EF lay off the distances A1, A2, and so forth. This is done in the figure by swinging each distance about the point A in the top view and dropping perpendiculars to EF. Connect the points thus found with the point A in diagram I to obtain the desired true lengths. Diagram II, constructed in the same way, gives the true lengths of lines B5, B6, and so forth, of the cone whose apex is at B. After the true-length diagrams are constructed, start the development with the seam at A1. Draw a line A1 equal to the true length of A1. With 1 as a center and radius 1–2 taken from the top view, draw an arc. Intersect this arc with an arc from center A and radius equal to the true length of A2, thus locating the point 2 on the development. With 2 as center and radius 2–3, draw an arc and intersect it by an arc with center A and radius of the true length of A3. Proceed similarly with points 4 and 5 and draw a smooth curve through the points 1, 2, 3, 4, and 5 thus found. Then attach the

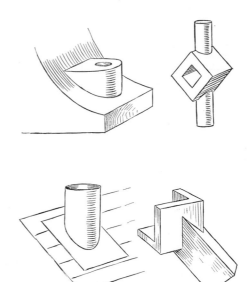

Fig. 20-19   Intersections.

true size of the triangle A5B, locating point B on the development by intersecting arcs from A with radius AB taken from the top view, and from 5 with the radius the true length of B5. Continue until the piece is completed.

20·16 Intersections. Whenever surfaces come together, there is a line common to both called the *line of intersection*. In Fig. 20-19 a number of lines of intersection are shown. It is necessary for both the machine designer and the sheet-metal worker to be able to locate a line of intersection when one occurs.

20·17 Intersecting prisms. Several examples of intersecting prisms are illustrated in Fig. 20-20.

To draw the intersection of two prisms, first start the orthographic views. In Fig. 20-21 a square prism passes through a hexagonal prism.

SHEET-METAL DRAFTING   **287**

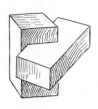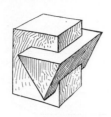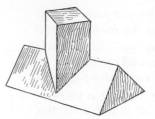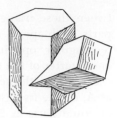

Fig. 20-20 Intersecting prisms.

Through the front edge of the square prism, pass a plane parallel to the vertical plane. The top view of this plane appears as a line *AA*. The intersection of the plane *AA* with one of the faces of the vertical prism shows in the front view as line *aa* and is crossed by the front edge of the square prism at point 1. Point 1 is a point on both prisms and, therefore, a point in the desired line of intersection. Plane *BB* is parallel to plane *AA* and contains an edge of the vertical prism and an edge of the inclined prism, which meet at point 2 in the front view. Plane *BB* also determines point 3.

These planes are called *cutting planes*, and they may be used for the solution of most problems in intersections. For intersecting prisms, pass planes through all the edges of both prisms within the limits of the line of intersection. Where the lines that are cut from both prisms by the same plane cross, there is a point on the required line of intersection. In Fig. 20-22 four cutting planes are required. The limiting planes are *AA* and *DD*, as a plane in front of *AA* or in back of *DD* would cut only one of the prisms.

20·18 Intersecting cylinders. To draw the line of intersection of two cylinders (Fig. 20-23). Since there are no edges on the cylinders, it will be necessary to assume positions for the cutting planes.

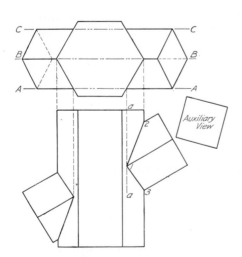

Fig. 20-21 Intersecting prisms.

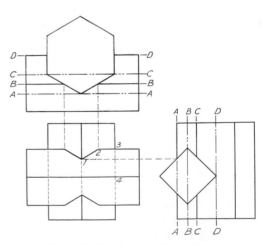

Fig. 20-22 Intersecting prisms.

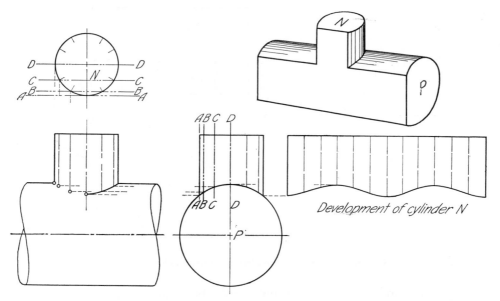

Fig. 20-23 Intersecting cylinders.

Plane *AA* contains the front line of the vertical cylinder and cuts a line from the horizontal cylinder. Where these two lines intersect in the front view, there is a point on the required curve. Each plane cuts lines from both cylinders, which intersect at points common to both cylinders. The development of

Fig. 20-24 Intersecting cylinders.

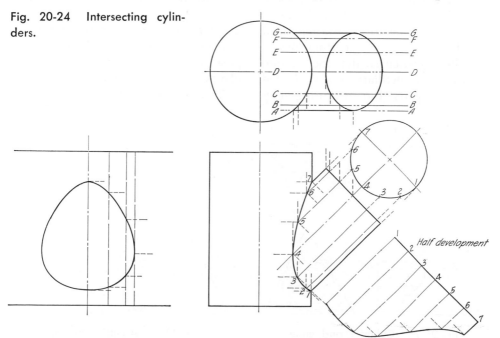

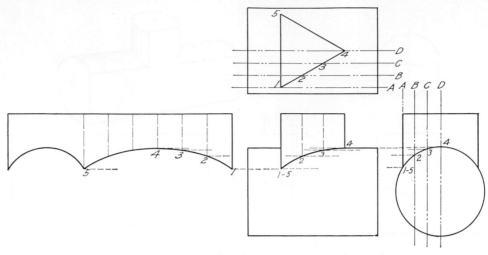

Fig. 20-25 Intersection and development of a cylinder and a prism.

the vertical cylinder, obtained by the method of Art. 20·5, is shown in the figure.

The solution for an inclined cylinder is given in Fig. 20-24, where the positions of the cutting planes are located by an auxiliary view. In the development of the inclined cylinder, the auxiliary view is used to get the length of the stretchout. If the cutting planes have been chosen so that the circumference of the auxiliary view is divided into equal parts, the measuring lines will be equally spaced along the stretchout.

To develop the portion of the vertical cylinder having the hole for the inclined cylinder, lay out a portion of the stretchout and project from the front view to the measuring lines as shown.

20·19 Intersecting cylinders and prisms. The intersection of a cylinder and a prism is found by the use of cutting planes as already described. In Fig. 20-25 a triangular prism intersects a

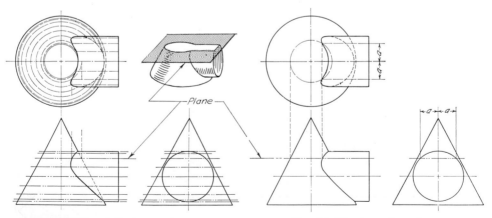

Fig. 20-26 Cylinder and cone.   Fig. 20-27 A cutting plane.

cylinder. The planes *A, B, C,* and *D* cut lines from the prism and lines from the cylinder which cross in the front view and determine the curve of intersection as shown. The development of the triangular prism is found by taking the length of the stretchout line from the top view and the lengths of the measuring lines from the front view. Note that one plane of the triangular prism (line 1–5 in the top view) is perpendicular to the axis of the cylinder. The curve of intersection on that face is the radius of the cylinder.

20·20 Intersection of cylinders and cones. The intersection of a cylinder and a cone may be found by passing planes parallel to the horizontal plane as shown in Fig. 20-26. Each plane will cut a circle from the cone and two straight lines from the cylinder. The straight lines of the cylinder cross the circle of the cone in the top view at points on the curve of intersection. These lines are then projected to the front view, as in Fig. 20-27, where the construction is shown for a single plane. Use as many planes as are necessary to obtain a smooth curve.

20·21 Intersection of planes and curved surfaces. The line of intersection of a cone cut by a plane *MM*, as in Fig. 20-28, may be found by horizontal cutting planes *A, B, C,* and *D*. Each plane cuts a circle from the cone and a straight line from the plane *MM*. Thus points common to both the plane *MM* and the cone are located, as shown in the top view. These points, when projected to the front view, give the curve of intersection.

The intersection at the end of a connecting rod is found by passing planes

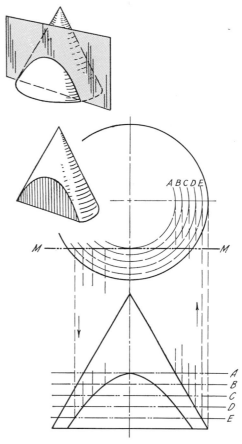

Fig. 20-28 Cone and plane.

perpendicular to the axis, which cut circles as shown in the end view of Fig. 20-29. The points at which these circles cut the "flat" are projected back as points on the curve.

20·22 Development of a measure. To draw the development of a measure (Fig. 20-30 at A), draw the view shown in Fig. 20-30 at B with the half circles at top and bottom. Observe that the body is a frustum of a cone. Extend the outline to complete the cone. With *MN* as a radius, draw an arc. Step off one-half the circumference of the base on

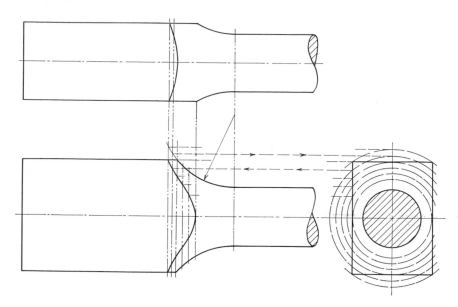

Fig. 20-29 Intersection of plane and turned surface.

this arc and draw the radial lines MK and ML. With M as a center and MD as a radius, draw arc PQ, completing the development of the body. Add the necessary allowance for lap.

To develop the handle, divide it into a number of spaces and step these spaces off on the stretchout RS. At R lay off one-half the width of the upper end of the handle on each side of the stretchout; and at S lay off one-half the width of the lower end of the handle on each side. Add allowance for laps and hems. The true development of the lip would require the drawing of lines through each point and finding the length of each line as described for the truncated cone (Fig. 20-16). The usual practical (approximate) method is as follows: On a center line oa draw an arc with OA as a radius, and space one-half the circumference of the top of the body on each side as shown by dad. Draw the radii od. Increase OA by ac

$= AC$, and increase od by $de = DE$, as obtained from the elevation. Draw ce and the perpendicular bisector of ce intersecting the center line at g. With g as a center and gc as a radius, draw arc ece to complete the pattern. Add the necessary material for seams and hems.

20·23 Seams and laps. The basis of sheet-metal pattern drafting is development. For practical work, it is necessary to know the processes of wiring, seaming, and hemming and the allowances of material to be made. Open ends of articles are usually reinforced by enclosing a wire in the edge as shown at A in Fig. 20-31. The amount added to the pattern may be taken as 2½ times the diameter of the wire. Edges are also stiffened by hemming. Single- and double-hemmed edges are shown at B and C. Edges are fastened by soldering on lap seams D, folded seams E, or, the commonest way,

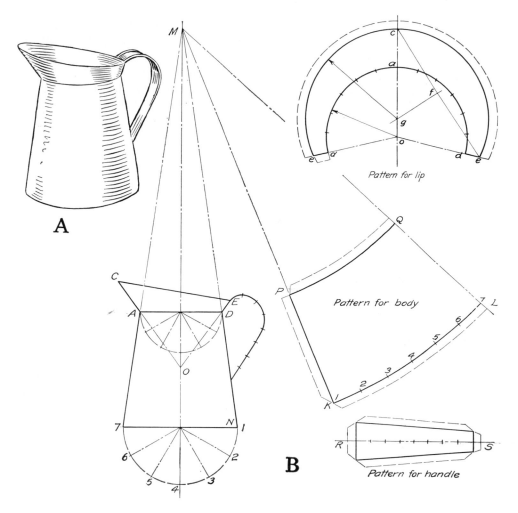

Fig. 20-30 Pattern for a measure.

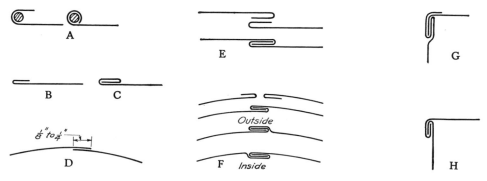

Fig. 20-31 Wiring, seaming, and hemming.

grooved seams. The grooved seams are shown in three stages, both inside and outside, at F. The Pittsburgh corner lock joint is shown at G and the cup joint at H. An important consideration in allowing lap on patterns is the shape of the space left at the corners to prevent thick places in the seam. This is called *notching* and is illustrated on Fig. 20-30B at corners P and K.

20·24 Problem suggestions. Group T, page 503. Three lists are presented. List 1 includes elementary problems from which a selection can be made for the time available. Selections from List 2 can be made for somewhat more difficult problems to give a more complete course. List 3 may be used according to the ability of the students and the time available, or it may be used in an advanced course. All three lists include a large number of problems to permit a selection to suit the purpose of the course.

LIST 1   Development Probs. T·1, T·2, T·4, T·5, T·9, T·10, T·14, T·17, T·20, T·22, T·25, T·30, T·33, T·35
Intersection Probs. T·38, T·39, T·42, T·43, T·54

LIST 2   Development Probs. T·3, T·6, T·11, T·13, T·15, T·19, T·23, T·26, T·28, T·34, T·36
Intersection Probs. T·40, T·41, T·44, T·45, T·48, T·51, T·53, T·56, T·58

LIST 3   Development Probs. T·7, T·8, T·12, T·16, T·18, T·24, T·27, T·29, T·31, T·32, T·37
Intersection Probs. T·46, T·47, T·49, T·50, T·52, T·55, T·57, T·59, T·60

21 Architectural drafting

21·1 Architectural drawings are concerned with the representation and specification of buildings and structures of various kinds. Although the general principles are the same as for other technical drawings, there are certain methods of representation, conventional symbols, and practices that are necessary because of the relatively small scale used for architectural plans.

In addition to working drawings, pictorial drawings are used to show how the completed structure will look (see wash drawing, Fig. 21-1). Such pic-

tures together with preliminary or sketch plans (Fig. 21-2) present both exterior and interior features and arrangements and provide a basis for starting the working drawings.

However, before starting the working drawings, several preliminary drawings may need to be made for consideration of the general design, exterior appearance, and plan layout. These are gone over until they are satisfactory and meet with the client's ap-

Fig. 21-1 Perspective. Contemporary house. (*Herbert Brasher, Architect, Lubbock, Texas*)

DR. & MRS. HAYMES RESIDENCE
HERBERT BRASHER & ASSOCIATES
ARCHITECTS - LUBBOCK, TEXAS

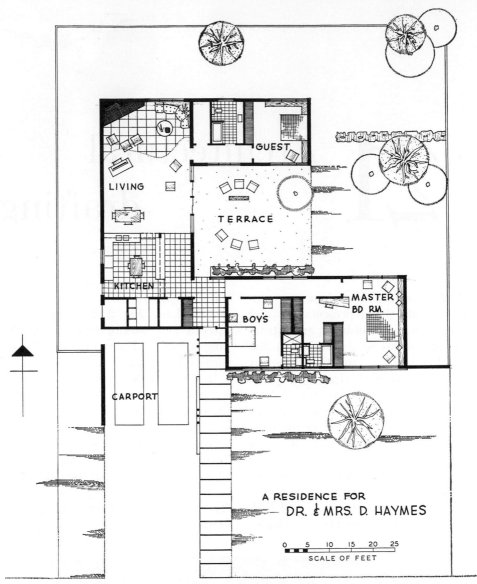

LIVING

GUEST

TERRACE

KITCHEN

MASTER BD RM.

BOY'S

CARPORT

A RESIDENCE FOR
DR. & MRS. D. HAYMES

0 5 10 15 20 25
SCALE OF FEET

Fig. 21-2 Plan. House of Fig. 21-1. (*Herbert Brasher, Architect*) **Prob. U·81.**

proval. Drawings such as Figs. 21-1 and 21-2 may then be made to clarify the whole design.

21·2 Lettering. Making architectural drawings in common with all drawings requires the ability to letter. The tradi-tional lettering used on architectural drawings is based on the Old Roman alphabet (Fig. 21-3). The letters may be *solid* or in *outline*. Such letters are used for inscriptions, in titles on im-portant drawings, and on display draw-ings.

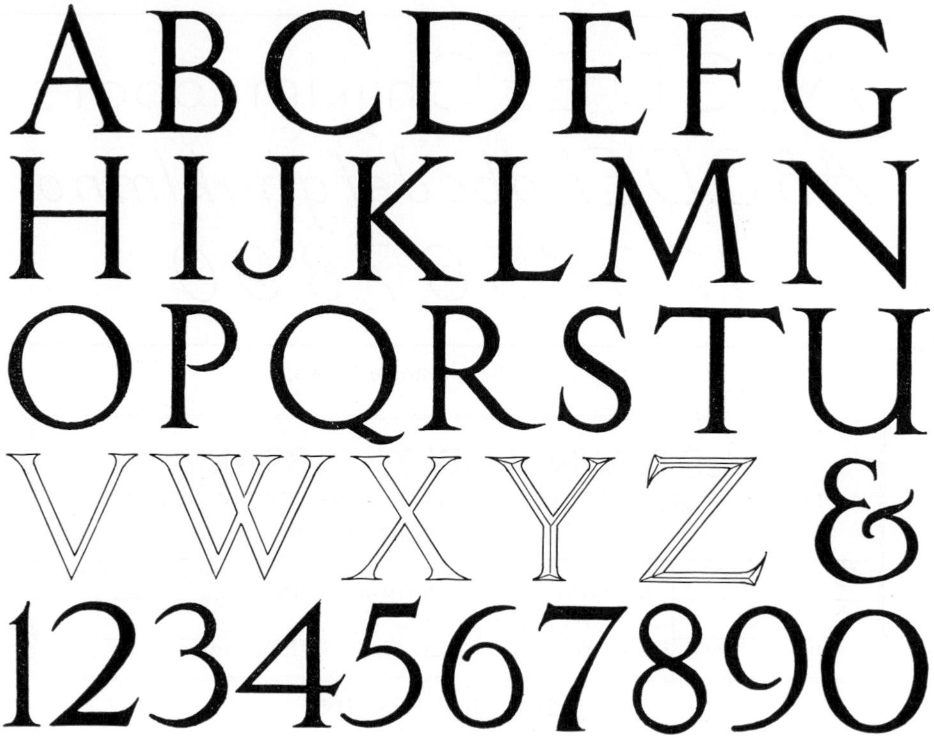
ABCDEFG
HIJKLMN
OPQRSTU
VWXYZ&
1234567890

Fig. 21-3 An Old Roman alphabet. **Prob. U·8.**

For architectural working drawings, the lettering is usually done in single-stroke letters as shown in Figs. 21-4 and 21-5. In Fig. 21-4 the Old Roman form is retained. In the interest of speed the terminals may be left off as in Fig. 21-5. The letters may be inclined to provide italic letters. Some architectural draftsmen use the single-stroke letters of Figs. 3-6 and 3-10 or

ABCDEFGHIJKLMN
OPQRSTUVWXYZ&
1234567890
abcdefghijklmnopqrstuvwxyz

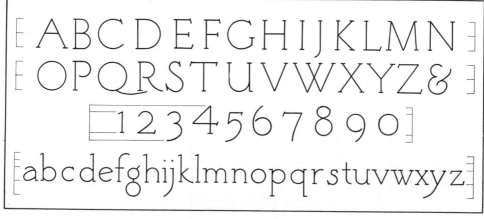

Fig. 21-4 Single-stroke Roman letters. **Probs. U·1 to U·7.**

ABCDEFGhijklmnopqrs
ABCDEFabcdefghijklmno
1234567890

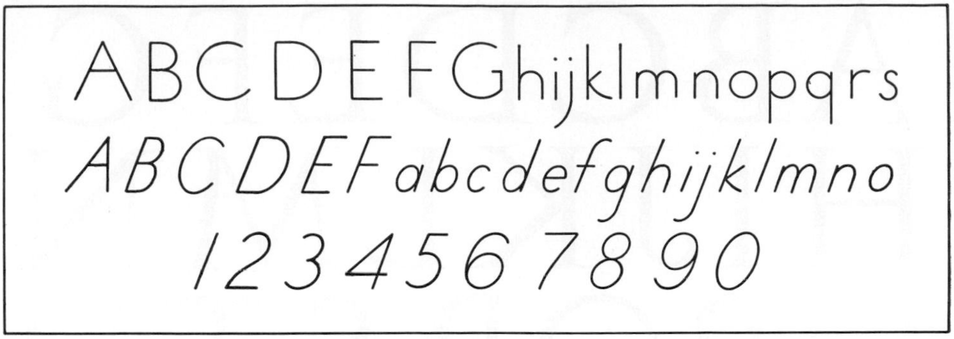

Fig. 21-5 Single-stroke letters.

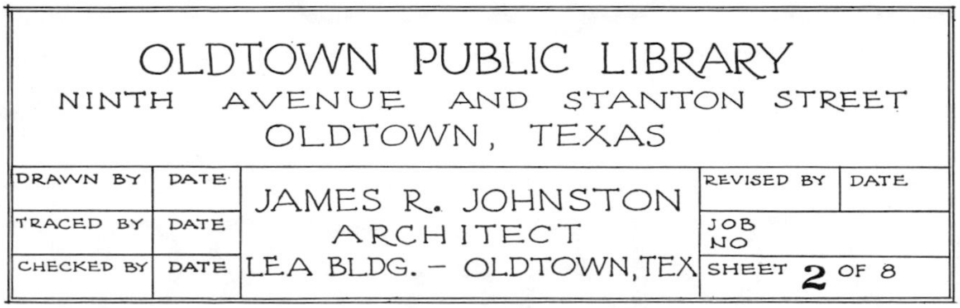

OLDTOWN PUBLIC LIBRARY
NINTH AVENUE AND STANTON STREET
OLDTOWN, TEXAS
DRAWN BY
DATE
TRACED BY
DATE
CHECKED BY
DATE
JAMES R. JOHNSTON
ARCHITECT
LEA BLDG. – OLDTOWN, TEX
REVISED BY
DATE
JOB NO
SHEET 2 OF 8

Fig. 21-6 Title. **Prob. U·8.**

Figs. 3-12 and 3-16 for office lettering on working drawings.

Many variations of the standard alphabet are used on drawings and for titles. Basically they are derived from the Roman alphabet, and the student should learn it first. In practice every draftsman develops his own individual style.

Many offices now use the lettering guides illustrated in Figs. 3-26 to 3-29 in Chap. 3.

21·3 Titles. Elaborate and important titles may be designed with the Old Roman letters of Fig. 21-3. The single-stroke letters of Figs. 21-4 and 21-5 serve for titles on working drawings. The titles shown in Figs. 21-6 and 21-7 indicate the usual content and treatment of titles for architectural drawings. Some offices use sheets with parts of the title printed or put on with a rubber stamp (Fig. 21-8).

Lettering for titles should conform with the design. For example, plain single-stroke letters should be used with the simple design of a contemporary structure. All lettering should be clear and easy to read.

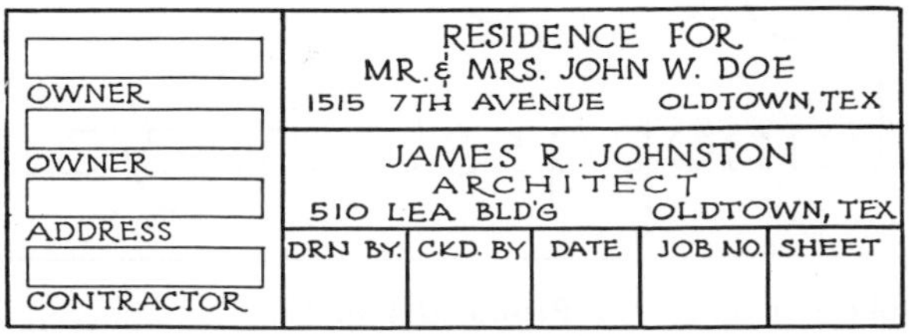

OWNER
OWNER
ADDRESS
CONTRACTOR
RESIDENCE FOR
MR. & MRS. JOHN W. DOE
1515 7TH AVENUE
OLDTOWN, TEX
JAMES R. JOHNSTON
ARCHITECT
510 LEA BLD'G
OLDTOWN, TEX
DRN BY.
CKD. BY
DATE
JOB NO.
SHEET

Fig. 21-7 Title.

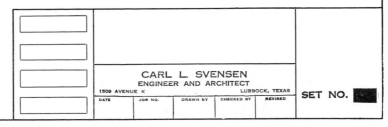

Fig. 21-8
Printed-title form.

CARL L. SVENSEN
ENGINEER AND ARCHITECT
1509 AVENUE K   LUBBOCK, TEXAS

DATE	JOB NO.	DRAWN BY	CHECKED BY	REVISED

SET NO.

21·4 House styles. The construction, appearance, and plans of houses have developed from the materials available, the climate conditions, and the needs of the occupants. From simple shelters, houses have progressed in convenience with the growth of civilization. Present-day equipment and utilities have removed the restrictions of climate and made it possible to have a comfortable home of any arrangement or design in any part of the country. Electricity provides for conveniences from lighting and cooking to refrigeration and heating or cooling the house. Gas provides for both heating and refrigeration. The latest information on both electrical and gas conveniences can always be obtained from catalogues and descriptive literature of the manufacturers. There are many kinds of equipment and materials which should be investigated and understood regardless of the style of house that is being considered.

Some traditional types of houses are illustrated in Figs. 21-9 to 21-14 with

Fig. 21-9 Cape Cod house. **Prob. U·66.**

Fig. 21-10 Dutch colonial house. **Prob. U·67.**

Fig. 21-11 Monterey house. **Prob. U·68.**

(Figs. 21-9 to 21-14 drawn by William Allen.)

Fig. 21-12 Traditional Tudor house. **Prob. U·69.**

Fig. 21-13 Georgian house. **Prob. U·70.**

Fig. 21-14 Georgian house with addition.

Fig. 21-15 An urban (city) or suburban (metropolitan) dwelling. (*George Hay, Architect, Media, Pa. Photo, courtesy "Better Homes & Gardens" magazine*)

brief notes to enable the student to identify them.

The Cape Cod house of Fig. 21-9 is a fundamentally American design which has come down from colonial times. It is a conservative type which has retained continuous popularity.

The Dutch colonial house of Fig.

Fig. 21-16 Plan. House of Fig. 21-15. (*George Hay, Architect. Photo, courtesy "Better Homes & Gardens" magazine*)

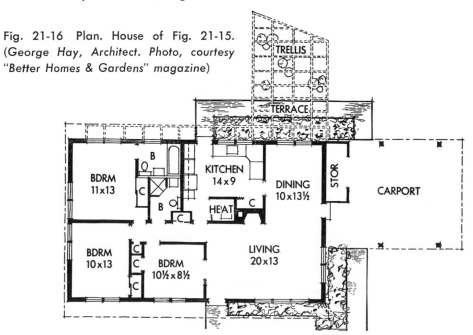

Fig. 21-17 Western house. (*Wurster, Bernardi, and Emmons, Architects, AIA, San Francisco, Calif.*)

21-10 is a modification of early designs. It is identified by the slightly overhanging upper story and contrasting brick or stone lower story.

The Monterey house of Fig. 21-11 is of Spanish origin and was developed on the west coast. It is identified by its graceful lines and by the upper porch, which should face in a southerly direction.

The traditional Tudor house of Fig. 21-12 is basically English. It is identified by its half-timbered exterior, separate chimney stacks, arched recessed doorway, and small-paned windows. It presents a certain seventeenth century feudal air.

The Georgian house of Fig. 21-13 is another design from England. It is identified by the simple, bold cornice line and the arched doorway with fanlight above. A larger house would be symmetrical as suggested in Fig. 21-14.

21·5 Contemporary houses. Contemporary architecture of today has many forms. For example, there are houses with hip roofs, with gable roofs, or with flat roofs (see Art. 21·13). A multitude of materials are used for walls, from stone to Fiberglas. However, most of this chapter will have to do with the use of wood.

Three examples of contemporary architecture are (1) the *urban,* or city, dwelling shown in Figs. 21-15 and 21-16; (2) the *suburban* house shown in Figs. 21-17 and 21-18; and (3) the *split-level* or hillside house shown in Figs. 21-21 and 21-22.

The house in Figs. 21-15 and 21-16 is described as a ranch type of slab construction. It is 28 ft 6 in. wide and 69 ft long (or deep). The small width makes this plan suitable for a narrow city lot. There is no basement. A concrete slab foundation is used. The rectangular shape and simple roof line make the construction less expensive than irregular shapes and "cut-up" roofs with valleys and other joining surfaces.

The house in Figs. 21-17 to 21-20 is described as a Western house for young homemakers. This type of house

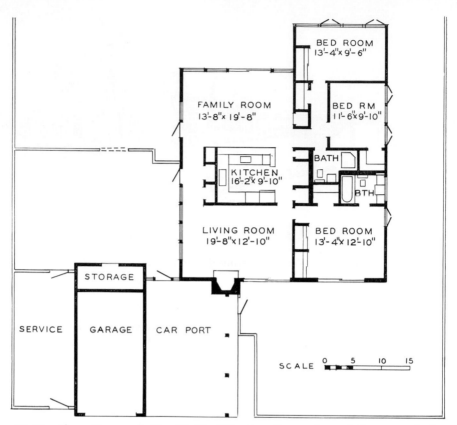

Fig. 21-18 Plan. House of Fig. 21-17. (*Wurster, Bernardi, and Emmons, Architects, AIA*)

provides for outdoor living in a suburban location and has picture windows. It is of frame construction with exterior walls of vertical sheathing. There is no basement, but a concrete slab may be used for the foundation.

A study of the plan (Fig. 21-18) will show that the kitchen is located without outside walls. To make up for this, it has a monitor (Fig. 21-19) to provide window space. The general construction can be understood from the sections (Fig. 21-20).

The house in Figs. 21-21 and 21-22 is described as a split-level (there are three levels) home with simple lines. Over-all dimensions are 44 ft by 32 ft.

There is a family room and a garage on the exposed basement level. All three levels meet as they lead from a central entrance. The bedroom wing is slightly higher than the living area. Exterior plywood and battens every 16 in. give the house strong vertical lines. These vertical lines are relieved by horizontal grouping of dark panels, windows, and siding at the gable ends of the house.

Comparison of the traditional houses of Figs. 21-9 to 21-14 with the contemporary designs of Figs. 21-1 and 21-2 and Figs. 21-15 to 21-22 will reveal some of the developments in design which have taken place. Architects

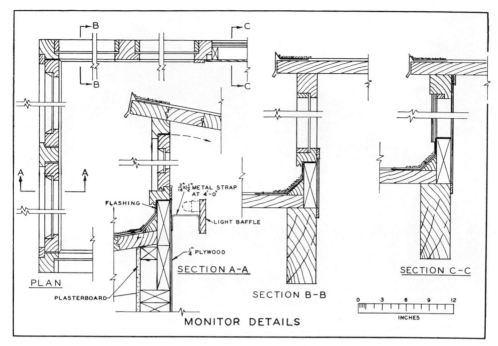

Fig. 21-19 Monitor details. House of Fig. 21-17. (*Adapted from drawings of Wurster, Bernardi, and Emmons, Architects, AIA*)

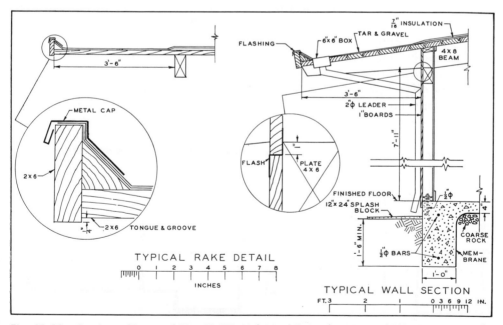

Fig. 21-20 Sections. House of Fig. 21-17. (*Adapted from drawings of Wurster, Bernardi, and Emmons, Architects, AIA*)

ARCHITECTURAL DRAFTING **303**

Fig. 21-21   A split-level house. (George Hay, Architect, Media, Pa. Photo, courtesy "Better Homes & Gardens" magazine)

have made use of new types of materials, more efficient methods of construction, and modern conveniences now available. As a result new architectural designs have been developed that have helped to provide the improved living conditions of the present day. Other contemporary houses are illustrated later in this chapter (Art. 21·31).

21·6 Parts of a house. The essential parts of a house are illustrated in Fig. 21-23. All these parts do not appear in every house, and different materials may be used for some of the parts.

Wood frame walls are first built up with studs or other structural members and with sheathing and sheathing paper. After the sheathing paper has

Fig. 21-22   Plan. House of Fig. 21-21. (George Hay, Architect. Photo, courtesy "Better Homes & Gardens" magazine)

Fig. 21-23 Essential parts of a house. (*From National Bureau of Standards Circular 489*)

1. Gable end.
2. Louver.
3. Interior trim.
4. Shingles.
5. Chimney cap.
6. Flue linings.
7. Flashing.
8. Roofing felt.
9. Roof sheathing.
10. Ridge board.
11. Rafters.
12. Roof valley.
13. Dormer window.
14. Interior wall finish.
15. Studs.
16. Insulation.
17. Diagonal sheathing.
18. Sheathing paper.
19. Window frame and sash.
20. Corner board.
21. Siding.
22. Shutters.
23. Exterior trim.
24. Waterproofing.
25. Foundation wall.
26. Column.
27. Joists.
28. Basement floor.
29. Gravel fill.
30. Heating plant.
31. Footing.
32. Drain tile.
33. Girder.
34. Stairway.
35. Subfloor.
36. Hearth.
37. Building paper.
38. Finish floor.
39. Fireplace.
40. Downspout.
41. Gutter.
42. Bridging.

been put on, wood or asbestos siding, shingles, stucco, or veneers of brick or stone are added. A typical wall with wood siding is shown at A in Fig. 21-24 and with brick veneer at B.

Interior walls may be finished with lath and plaster, gypsum wallboard, interior plywood, fiberboard, asbestos-cement board, wood paneling, wall tile, and so forth.

21·7 Classes of drawings. There are three general classes of architectural drawings: (1) preliminary sketches, (2) display and competitive drawings, and (3) working drawings.

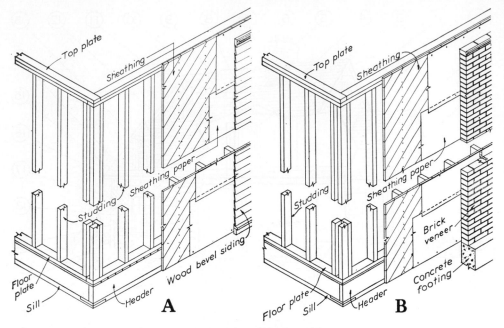

Fig. 21-24 (A) Wall with wood siding. (B) Wall with brick veneer. (*From National Bureau of Standards Circular 489*)

21·8 Preliminary sketches. These include freehand studies of the arrangement of rooms, general appearance of elevations, and other matters for study and consideration. A number of small freehand plans (called *thumbnail sketches* because of their small size) are made at first. Although these are made somewhat in proportion, they are not drawn to scale. Schemes that show promise of a satisfactory solution are then worked up in larger sketches using an approximate scale for the larger dimensions. Tracing paper is often used to work out and preserve different arrangements by making one sketch over another. The best layout can then be selected, drawn to scale, and worked up in greater detail.

21·9 Display and competitive drawings. These are more or less elaborate

preliminary drawings of a proposed building. Plans and elevations, often including a perspective, are used but without working information. They are rendered in water color, airbrush, pen and ink, pencil, pastels, or crayon to make them legible and attractive. An airbrush-rendered perspective of a contemporary house is shown in Fig. 21-1 and a pen-and-ink perspective of a traditional house is shown in Fig. 21-54.

21·10 Working drawings. These form the most important class of drawings and include plans, elevations, sections, and detail drawings which, when read with the specifications for details of materials, finish, and so forth, give the working information for the erection of the building. Working drawings for a house are in Figs. 21-56 to 21-60.

21·11 Scales. The architect's scale is described in Art. 2·19. Ordinary house plans and plans for small buildings are drawn to the scale of ¼″ = 1′. The usual scale for larger buildings is ⅛″ = 1′. Plot plans (Art. 21·28) may be drawn at ¹⁄₁₆″ = 1′ or ¹⁄₃₂″ = 1′. Larger scales are used for drawings of parts that cannot be shown with sufficient detail on the small-scale drawings. Wall sections may be drawn at 1″ = 1′ or 1½″ = 1′. Other scales used for details include ½″ = 1′, ¾″ = 1′, 3″ = 1′, 6″ = 1′, and full size.

21·12 House framing. The framework of a building must be strong and rigid to ensure low maintenance costs over

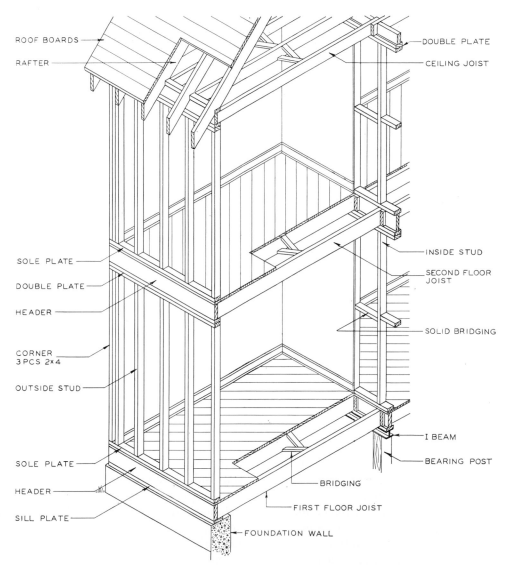

Fig. 21-25 Western or platform framing. **Prob. U·11.**

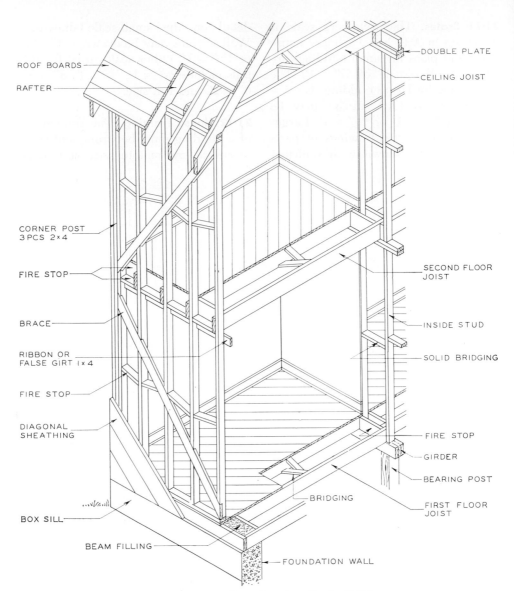

ROOF BOARDS

RAFTER

CORNER POST
3 PCS 2 × 4

FIRE STOP

BRACE

RIBBON OR
FALSE GIRT 1 × 4

FIRE STOP

DIAGONAL
SHEATHING

BOX SILL

BEAM FILLING

DOUBLE PLATE

CEILING JOIST

SECOND FLOOR
JOIST

INSIDE STUD

SOLID BRIDGING

FIRE STOP

GIRDER

BEARING POST

FIRST FLOOR
JOIST

BRIDGING

FOUNDATION WALL

Fig. 21-26   Balloon framing. **Prob. U·10.**

a long period of years. For residences, light frame construction is used. This varies somewhat with different builders and in different parts of the country.

Western or platform framing has each floor framed separately as in Fig. 21-25. The first floor is built on top of the foundation walls as a platform.

Studs one story in height are used for wall and partition framing to support another platform for the second floor.

Balloon framing has the studs extending the full height of the house from sill to plate as in Fig. 21-26. The second-floor joists are spiked to the studs and rest upon a false girt notched

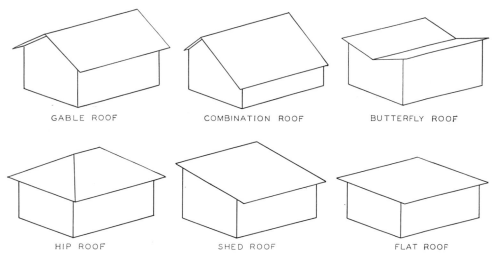

GABLE ROOF   COMBINATION ROOF   BUTTERFLY ROOF

HIP ROOF   SHED ROOF   FLAT ROOF

Fig. 21-27 Types of roofs.

into the studs. A box sill is used, and fire stops are fitted in the walls and floors.

21·13 Roofs. Some basic roof types are illustrated and named in Fig. 21-27. Each one has a use which may be in-fluenced by the shape and interior arrangement as well as by the method of supporting the roof (rafters, trusses, or posts).

21·14 Sizes of lumber are specified by *nominal* dimensions which differ from

Lumber

Nominal size	2×4	2×6	2×8	2×10	2×12
Dressed size	$1\frac{5}{8} \times 3\frac{5}{8}$	$1\frac{5}{8} \times 5\frac{1}{2}$	$1\frac{5}{8} \times 7\frac{1}{2}$	$1\frac{5}{8} \times 9\frac{1}{2}$	$1\frac{5}{8} \times 11\frac{1}{2}$
Nominal size	4×6	4×8	4×10	6×6	6×8
Dressed size	$3\frac{5}{8} \times 5\frac{1}{2}$	$3\frac{5}{8} \times 7\frac{1}{2}$	$3\frac{5}{8} \times 9\frac{1}{2}$	$5\frac{1}{2} \times 5\frac{1}{2}$	$5\frac{1}{2} \times 7\frac{1}{2}$
Nominal size	6×10	8×8	8×10		
Dressed size	$5\frac{1}{2} \times 9\frac{1}{2}$	$7\frac{1}{2} \times 7\frac{1}{2}$	$7\frac{1}{2} \times 9\frac{1}{2}$		

Boards

Nominal size	1×4	1×6	1×8	1×10	1×12
Actual size, common boards	$\frac{25}{32} \times 3\frac{5}{8}$	$\frac{25}{32} \times 5\frac{5}{8}$	$\frac{25}{32} \times 7\frac{1}{2}$	$\frac{25}{32} \times 9\frac{1}{2}$	$\frac{25}{32} \times 11\frac{1}{2}$
Actual size,* shiplap	$\frac{25}{32} \times 3\frac{1}{8}$	$\frac{25}{32} \times 5\frac{1}{8}$	$\frac{25}{32} \times 7\frac{1}{8}$	$\frac{25}{32} \times 9\frac{1}{8}$	$\frac{25}{32} \times 11\frac{1}{8}$
Actual size,* tongue and groove	$\frac{25}{32} \times 3\frac{1}{4}$	$\frac{25}{32} \times 5\frac{1}{4}$	$\frac{25}{32} \times 7\frac{1}{4}$	$\frac{25}{32} \times 9\frac{1}{4}$	$\frac{25}{32} \times 11\frac{1}{4}$

* Face width.

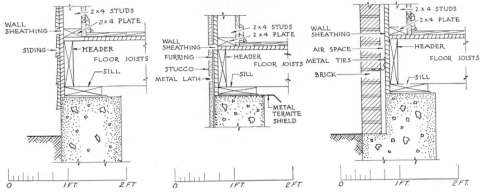

Fig. 21-28　Box sill, wood siding. **Prob. U·12.**

Fig. 21-29　Box sill, stucco wall. **Prob. U·13.**

Fig. 21-30　Box sill, brick-veneer wall. **Prob. U·12.**

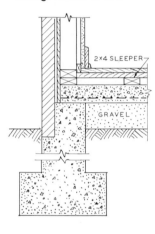

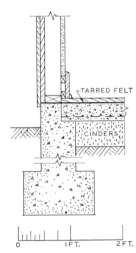

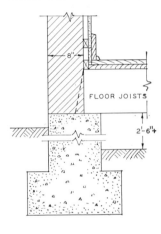

Fig. 21-31　Sill for slab foundation, brick-veneer wall. **Prob. U·13.**

Fig. 21-32　Sill for slab foundation, frame. **Prob. U·14.**

Fig. 21-33　Sill for basementless house. **Prob. U·14.**

the actual dimensions of the *surfaced* or smoothed pieces as, for example, S4S, which means surfaced on four sides. Dimensions of some common sizes of lumber and boards are given in the table.

21·15 Sill details. Sill construction (box sill) with wood-siding wall is shown in Fig. 21-28, with stucco in Fig. 21-29, and with brick veneer in Fig. 21-30. Note the increased thickness of the

foundation wall in Fig. 21-30 and the metal shield for protection against termites in Fig. 21-29. Sill details when slab foundations are used are shown in Figs. 21-31 and 21-32. Another arrangement when a basement is not used is shown in Fig. 21-33.

21·16 Corner studs and sheathing. The arrangement of corner studs shown in Fig. 21-34 is simple and satisfactory. Another arrangement, shown in Fig.

310　MECHANICAL DRAWING

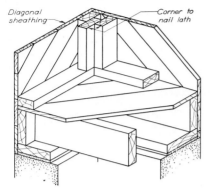

Fig. 21-34 Diagonal sheathing. **Prob. U·15.**

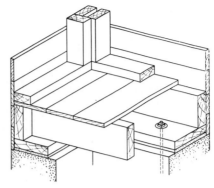

Fig. 21-35 Horizontal sheathing. **Prob. U·16.**

21-35, requires greater care in making it up. Diagonal sheathing and subflooring are shown in Fig. 21-34 and horizontal sheathing and subflooring in Fig. 21-35. Anchor bolts (Fig. 21-35) are used to anchor the building to the foundation. The diameter of these bolts should be from ⅝ to ¾ in. They should be spaced about 8 ft apart and should extend through the sill and about 18 in. into the foundation.

Three constructions for girders supporting the inside ends of floor joists are shown at A, B, and C in Fig. 21-36.

21·17 Roof framing and cornice details. The usual roof-framing members are shown and named in Fig. 21-37. The joints between the walls and roofs of houses are finished by cornices. Box cornices, which conceal the rafters, are shown at A and B in Fig. 21-38. An open cornice, which exposes the rafters, is shown at C in Fig. 21-38. A closed cornice with a hanging gutter is shown at A in Fig. 21-39. An overhanging ranch-style cornice with exposed lookouts is shown at B in Fig. 21-39. Note the use of dots instead of arrowheads

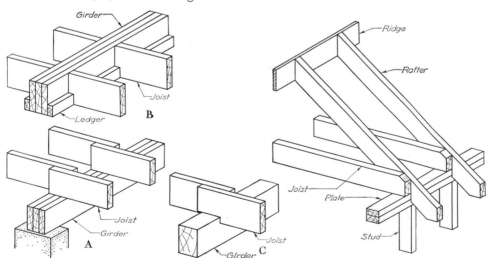

Fig. 21-36 Girders to support floor joists.

Fig. 21-37 Roof framing.

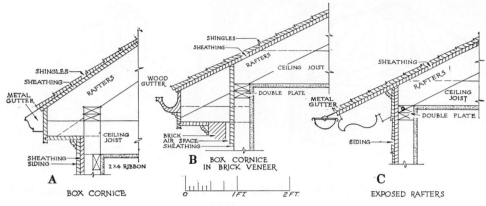

A BOX CORNICE

B BOX CORNICE IN BRICK VENEER

C EXPOSED RAFTERS

Fig. 21-38 (above) and Fig. 21-39 (below). Cornice details. **Prob. U·17.**

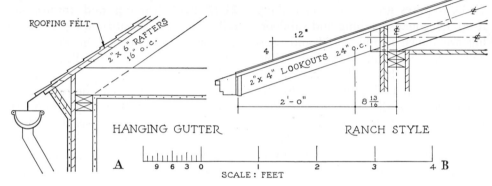

HANGING GUTTER

RANCH STYLE

A SCALE : FEET **B**

Fig. 21-40 (below) Stairs. **Prob. U·18.**

PLAN

UP 17 RISERS   DOWN 17 RISERS

WEDGES

2ND FLOOR

7'-0" HEAD ROOM

FLOOR TO FLOOR HEIGHT

1ST FLOOR

NOSING

TREAD

RISER

STRINGER

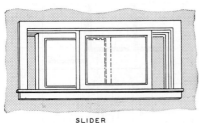
SLIDER

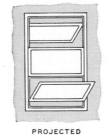
PROJECTED

CASEMENT

Fig. 21-41   Types of windows.

to indicate the dimensions—a practice used by some architectural draftsmen.

21·18 Stairways. In drawing an inside stairway (Fig. 21-40), first make a diagram to find the number of steps and the space required. The riser, or height from one step to the next, is generally about 6½ to 7½ in. The width of the tread is such that the sum of riser and tread is about 17½ in. (a 7-in. riser and 11-in. tread is a general standard). On

the plan the lines represent the edges of the risers and are drawn as far apart as the width of the tread as shown in the illustration. Note the use of the scale to divide the floor-to-floor height into the number of risers. On working drawings, the entire flight is not drawn but is broken to show what is on the floor under it. The other end is shown on the floor above.

For outside stairs or steps, as in a garden, and so forth, the risers are

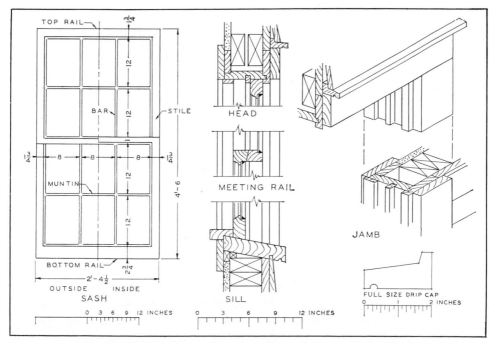

Fig. 21-42   Window sash and sections of frame. **Prob. U·19.**

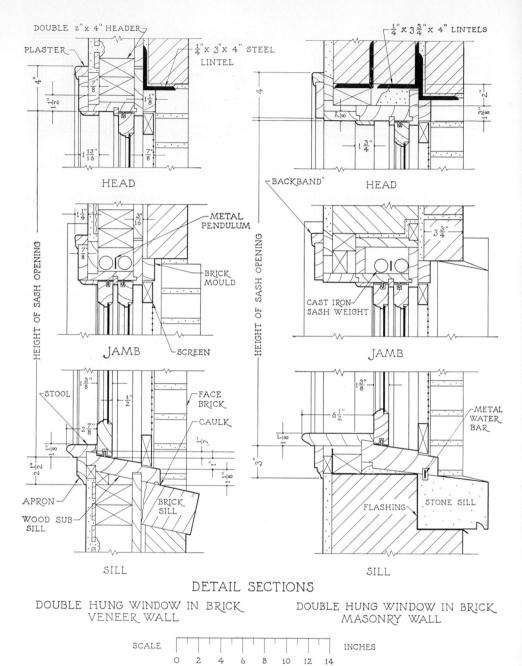

HEAD (left) — DOUBLE 2"x 4" HEADER, PLASTER, $\frac{1}{4}$"x 3"x 4" STEEL LINTEL

HEAD (right) — $\frac{1}{4}$"x 3$\frac{3}{4}$"x 4" LINTELS, BACKBAND

JAMB (left) — METAL PENDULUM, BRICK MOULD, SCREEN, HEIGHT OF SASH OPENING

JAMB (right) — CAST IRON SASH WEIGHT, HEIGHT OF SASH OPENING

SILL (left) — STOOL, FACE BRICK, CAULK, APRON, WOOD SUB SILL, BRICK SILL

SILL (right) — METAL WATER BAR, FLASHING, STONE SILL

DETAIL SECTIONS

DOUBLE HUNG WINDOW IN BRICK VENEER WALL

DOUBLE HUNG WINDOW IN BRICK MASONRY WALL

SCALE 0 2 4 6 8 10 12 14 INCHES

Fig. 21-43 Detail sections of double-hung windows. **Probs. U·20, U·21.**

made lower and the treads are made wider. A person's gait and stride increase and lengthen unconsciously when he is outdoors.

21·19 Windows. Different types of windows are being used in contemporary house designs, some of which are indicated in Fig. 21-41. Casement windows

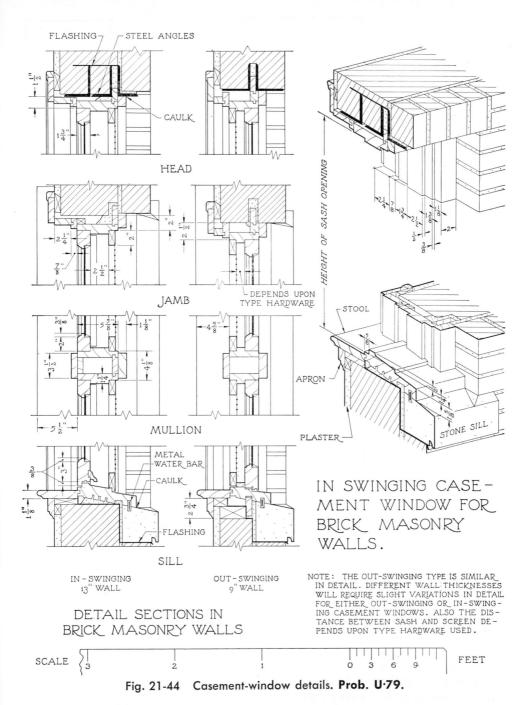

FLASHING — STEEL ANGLES

$1\frac{1}{2}"$

CAULK

$1\frac{3}{4}"$

HEAD

$2\frac{1}{4}"$ $2"$

$\frac{7}{8}"$ $2\frac{1}{2}"$ $2"$

$2\frac{1}{2}"$

DEPENDS UPON
TYPE HARDWARE

JAMB

$\frac{3}{8}"$ $5\frac{5}{8}"$ $1\frac{1}{8}"$

$3\frac{1}{2}"$ $4\frac{2}{8}"$

$4\frac{2}{8}"$

$5\frac{1}{2}"$

MULLION

METAL
WATER BAR

CAULK

$\frac{3}{8}"$ $3"$

$1\frac{1}{8}"$ $2\frac{3}{4}"$

FLASHING

SILL

HEIGHT OF SASH OPENING

$2\frac{1}{4}"$ $\frac{7}{8}"$ $\frac{3}{4}"$ $2\frac{1}{2}"$ $\frac{3}{8}"$ $2"$

$\frac{1}{2}"$

$\frac{3}{8}"$

STOOL

APRON

PLASTER

STONE SILL

IN SWINGING CASE-
MENT WINDOW FOR
BRICK MASONRY
WALLS.

IN - SWINGING
13" WALL

OUT - SWINGING
9" WALL

NOTE: THE OUT-SWINGING TYPE IS SIMILAR
IN DETAIL. DIFFERENT WALL THICKNESSES
WILL REQUIRE SLIGHT VARIATIONS IN DETAIL
FOR EITHER OUT-SWINGING OR IN-SWING-
ING CASEMENT WINDOWS. ALSO THE DIS-
TANCE BETWEEN SASH AND SCREEN DE-
PENDS UPON TYPE HARDWARE USED.

DETAIL SECTIONS IN
BRICK MASONRY WALLS

SCALE   3   2   1   0 3 6 9   FEET

Fig. 21-44 Casement-window details. **Prob. U·79.**

are hinged at the sides to swing open.
Projected windows are hinged at the
top or bottom. Slider windows move
sidewise instead of up and down as
ordinary double-hung windows do.
Steel and aluminum are being used as

ARCHITECTURAL DRAFTING 315

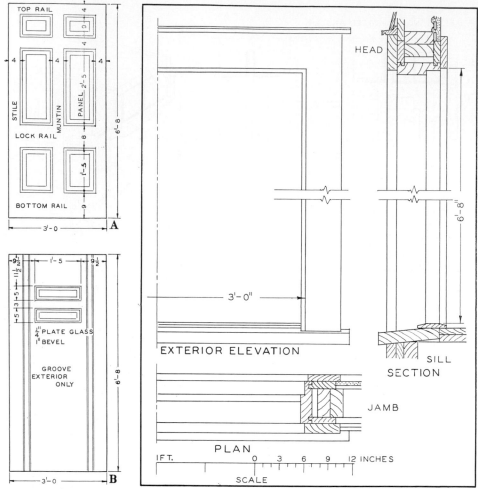

Fig. 21-45 Doors.
Prob. **U·22.**

Fig. 21-46 Door-framing details. **Prob. U·23.**

well as wood for sash and frames. Fixed and picture windows are coming into greater use with the increased use of air conditioning.

Sizes of windows depend upon the sizes of the glass panes and the number of panes. Lists giving the sizes of sash can be obtained from window companies or suppliers of building materials. A wood sash drawing with the names of the parts is shown in Fig. 21-42. The thickness of the sash is 1⅜ in. Small sash may be 1⅛ in. thick, and

large ones may be up to 2¼ in. thick. Sections of an ordinary double-hung window in a wood-frame wall are shown in Fig. 21-42. Detail sections for double-hung windows in brick-veneer and brick-masonry walls are shown in Fig. 21-43. Some casement-window details are shown in Fig. 21-44.

21·20 Doors. Usual heights of doors are 6'–8" and 7'–0", but they may vary by 2" intervals from 6'–6" to 8'–0". Width may vary for some purposes from 2'–0"

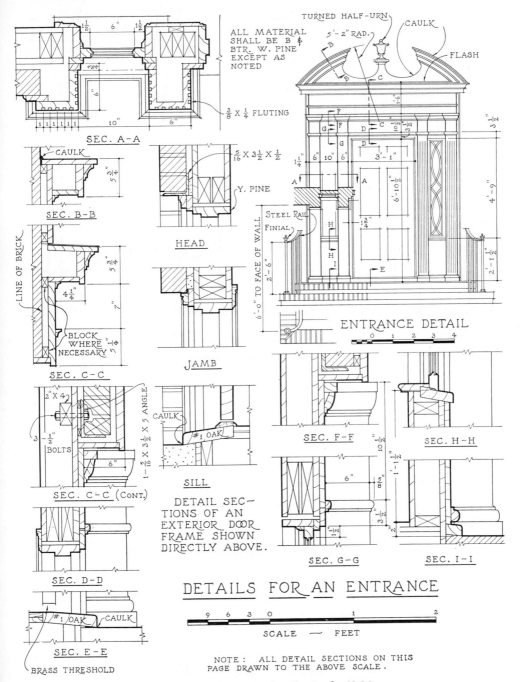

SEC. A-A

ALL MATERIAL
SHALL BE B &
BTR. W. PINE
EXCEPT AS
NOTED

$\frac{3}{8} \times \frac{1}{4}$ FLUTING

CAULK

SEC. B-B

$\frac{5}{16} \times 3\frac{1}{2} \times \frac{1}{2}$

Y. PINE

HEAD

LINE OF BRICK

BLOCK
WHERE
NECESSARY

SEC. C-C

JAMB

TURNED HALF-URN

CAULK

5'-2" RAD.

FLASH

ENTRANCE DETAIL
0 1 2 3 4

STEEL RAIL
FINIAL

6'-0" TO FACE OF WALL

2'-6"

SEC. F-F

SEC. H-H

2" X 4

3-½"
BOLTS

$1-\frac{5}{16} \times 3\frac{1}{2} \times 5$ ANGLE

CAULK

#1 OAK

SILL

DETAIL SEC-
TIONS OF AN
EXTERIOR DOOR
FRAME SHOWN
DIRECTLY ABOVE.

SEC. C-C (CONT.)

SEC. G-G

SEC. I-I

SEC. D-D

DETAILS FOR AN ENTRANCE

9 6 3 0   1   2

SCALE — FEET

#1 OAK   CAULK

SEC. E-E

BRASS THRESHOLD

NOTE: ALL DETAIL SECTIONS ON THIS
PAGE DRAWN TO THE ABOVE SCALE.

Fig. 21-47 Entrance details. **Prob. U·80.**

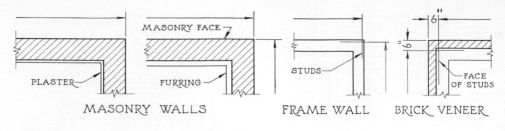

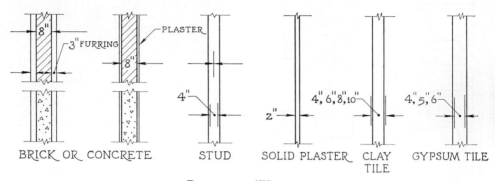

EXTERIOR WALLS

PARTITION WALLS

Fig. 21-48   Wall symbols.

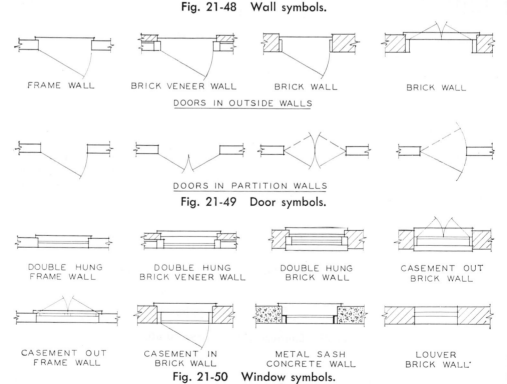

FRAME WALL   BRICK VENEER WALL   BRICK WALL   BRICK WALL

DOORS IN OUTSIDE WALLS

DOORS IN PARTITION WALLS

Fig. 21-49   Door symbols.

DOUBLE HUNG
FRAME WALL

DOUBLE HUNG
BRICK VENEER WALL

DOUBLE HUNG
BRICK WALL

CASEMENT OUT
BRICK WALL

CASEMENT OUT
FRAME WALL

CASEMENT IN
BRICK WALL

METAL SASH
CONCRETE WALL

LOUVER
BRICK WALL'

Fig. 21-50   Window symbols.

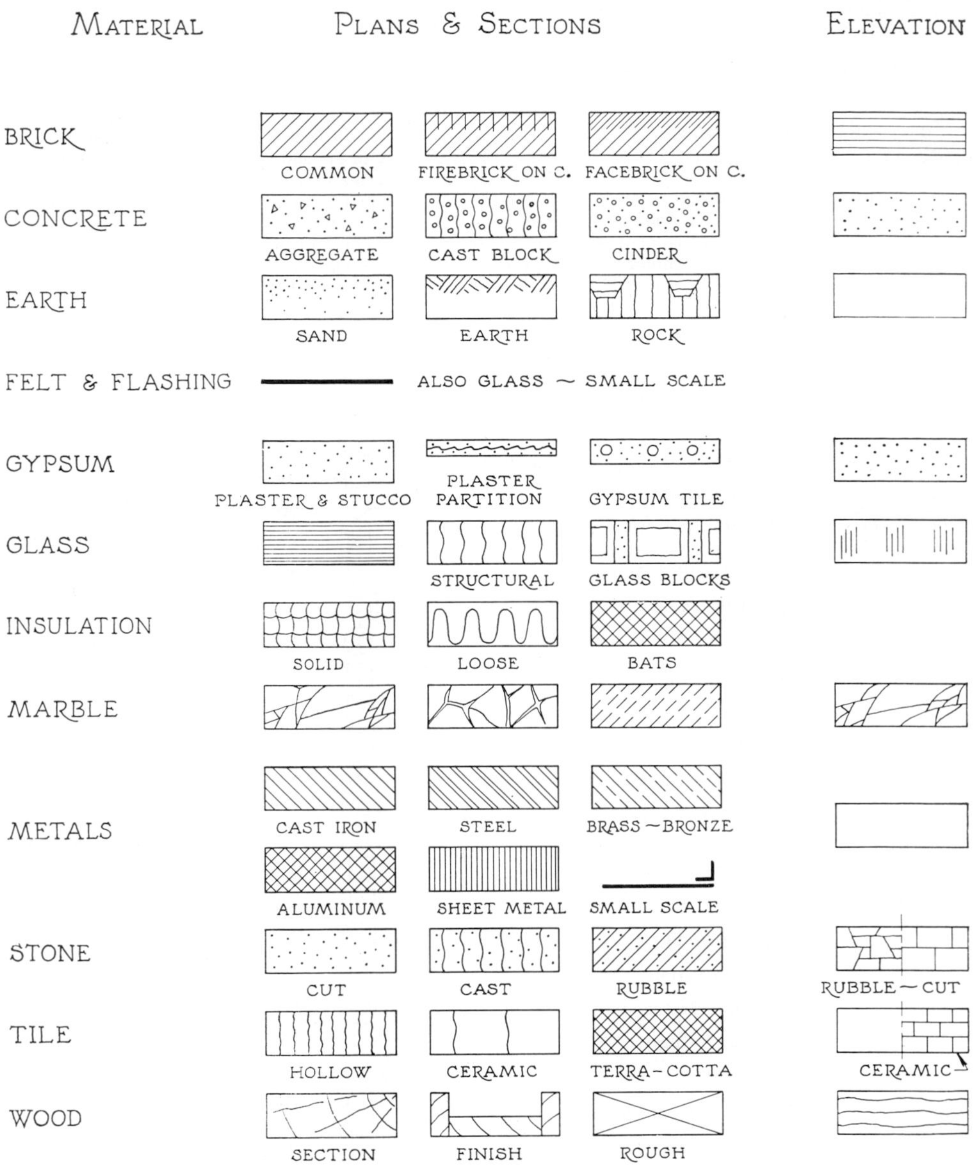
MATERIAL
PLANS & SECTIONS
ELEVATION
BRICK
COMMON
FIREBRICK ON C.
FACEBRICK ON C.
CONCRETE
AGGREGATE
CAST BLOCK
CINDER
EARTH
SAND
EARTH
ROCK
FELT & FLASHING
ALSO GLASS ~ SMALL SCALE
GYPSUM
PLASTER & STUCCO
PLASTER PARTITION
GYPSUM TILE
GLASS
STRUCTURAL
GLASS BLOCKS
INSULATION
SOLID
LOOSE
BATS
MARBLE
METALS
CAST IRON
STEEL
BRASS ~ BRONZE
ALUMINUM
SHEET METAL
SMALL SCALE
STONE
CUT
CAST
RUBBLE
RUBBLE ~ CUT
TILE
HOLLOW
CERAMIC
TERRA-COTTA
CERAMIC
WOOD
SECTION
FINISH
ROUGH

Fig. 21-51 Symbols for building materials.

to 3′–0″, but the usual widths are 2′–8″ and 3′–0″. Thicknesses may be 1⅜″ or 1¾″ for interior doors and from 1¾″ to 2½″ for exterior doors. An interior door with the names of parts is shown at A in Fig. 21-45, and one exterior door is shown at B. Door-framing details for a wood wall are shown in Fig. 21-46. Details for an entrance are shown in Fig. 21-47.

21·21 Symbols. The small scale ⅛″ = 1′–0″ or ¼″ = 1′–0″ used on general plans makes it necessary to use symbols

Ceiling	Wall	GENERAL OUTLETS

GENERAL OUTLETS

- Outlet
- Blanked Outlet
- Drop Cord
- Electric Outlet
  For use only when circle used alone might be confused with columns, plumbing symbols, etc.
- Fan Outlet
- Junction Box
- Lamp Holder
- Lamp Holder with Pull Switch
- Pull Switch
- Outlet for Vapor Discharge Lamp
- Exit-light Outlet
- Clock Outlet (Specify Voltage)

CONVENIENCE OUTLETS

- Duplex Convenience Outlet
- Convenience Outlet other than Duplex
  1=Single, 3=Triplex, etc.
- Weatherproof Convenience Outlet
- Range Outlet
- Switch and Convenience Outlet
- Radio and Convenience Outlet
- Special Purpose Outlet (Des. in Spec.)
- Floor Outlet

SWITCH OUTLETS

S — Single-pole Switch
S_2 — Double-pole Switch
S_3 — Three-way Switch
S_4 — Four-way Switch
S_D — Automatic Door Switch
S_E — Electrolier Switch
S_K — Key-operated Switch
S_P — Switch and Pilot Lamp
S_{CB} — Circuit Breaker
S_{WCB} — Weatherproof Circuit Breaker
S_{MC} — Momentary Contact Switch
S_{RC} — Remote-control Switch
S_{WP} — Weatherproof Switch
S_F — Fused Switch
S_{WF} — Weatherproof Fused Switch

SPECIAL OUTLETS

$\ominus$a,b,c,etc. $S_{a,b,c,etc.}$

Any standard symbol as given above with the addition of a lower-case subscript letter may be used to designate some special variation of standard equipment of particular interest in a specific set of architectural plans.

When used they must be listed in the Key of Symbols on each drawing and if necessary further described in the specifications.

AUXILIARY SYSTEMS

- Pushbutton
- Buzzer
- Bell
- Annunciator
- Outside Telephone
- Interconnecting Telephone
- Telephone Switchboard
- Bell-ringing Transformer
- Electric Door Opener
- Fire-alarm Bell
- Fire-alarm Station
- City Fire-alarm Station
- Fire-Alarm Central Station
- Automatic Fire-alarm Device
- Watchman's Station
- Watchman's Central Station
- Horn
- Nurse's Signal Plug
- Maid's Signal Plug
- Radio Outlet
- Signal Central Station
- Interconnection Box
- Battery
- Auxiliary System Circuits

Note: Any line without further designation indicates a 2-wire system. For a greater number of wires designate with numerals in manner similar to —·— 12-No. 18W-3/4"C., or designate by number corresponding to listing in Schedule.

$\square$a,b,c Special Auxiliary Outlets

Subscript letters refer to notes on plans or detailed description in specifications.

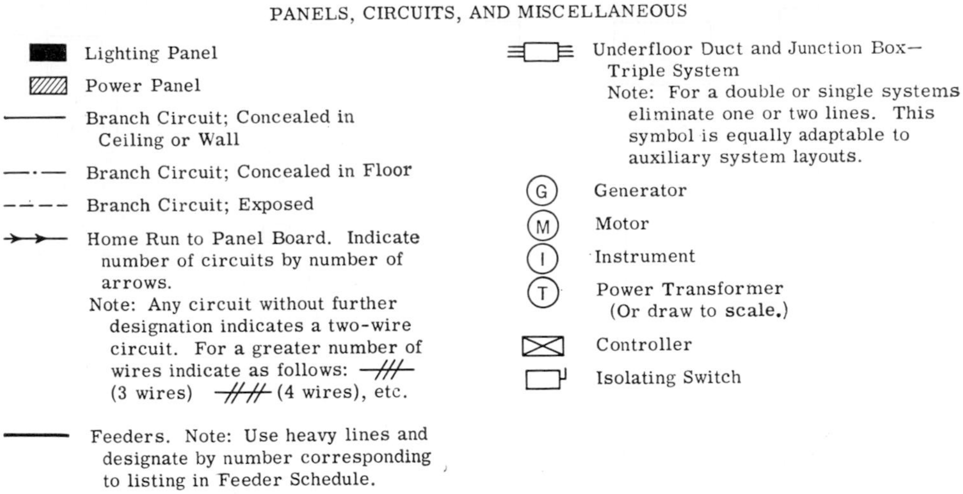

■ Lighting Panel

▨ Power Panel

——— Branch Circuit; Concealed in Ceiling or Wall

—·— Branch Circuit; Concealed in Floor

— – – – Branch Circuit; Exposed

→→ Home Run to Panel Board. Indicate number of circuits by number of arrows.
Note: Any circuit without further designation indicates a two-wire circuit. For a greater number of wires indicate as follows: —///—
(3 wires) —////— (4 wires), etc.

——— Feeders. Note: Use heavy lines and designate by number corresponding to listing in Feeder Schedule.

≡▭≡ Underfloor Duct and Junction Box— Triple System
Note: For a double or single systems eliminate one or two lines. This symbol is equally adaptable to auxiliary system layouts.

Ⓖ Generator

Ⓜ Motor

Ⓘ Instrument

Ⓣ Power Transformer (Or draw to scale.)

⊠ Controller

▭ Isolating Switch

Fig. 21-52 Electrical symbols. (*Extracted from American Standards' "Graphical Electrical Symbols for Architectural Plans," ASA Y32.9–1943, with the permission of the publisher, American Institute of Electrical Engineers*)

since it would not be possible to show actual details. Such details where required are drawn to a larger scale. Details in some cases, such as those showing sections of trim and moldings, may be full size.

21·22 Wall symbols consist of parallel lines drawn to represent the thickness (Fig. 21-48). Some symbols for doors are shown in Fig. 21-49; single lines show the direction of opening or swing. Various windows are represented by the symbols in Fig. 21-50. Symbols for building materials are shown in Fig. 21-51.

21·23 Electrical symbols to represent wiring, outlets, switches, and so forth, are shown by the American Standards symbols of Fig. 21-52. Their use on a house plan is shown on Fig. 21-56.

21·24 Plumbing symbols from American Standards are shown on Fig. 21-53,

and some of them are represented on the plan in Fig. 21-56.

21·25 Plans. A plan is a drawing of a horizontal section taken above the floor represented and at such places as will show the walls, doors, windows, and other structural features. It is drawn to include all details relating to the story, such as built-in construction, cabinets, stairways, heating, plumbing, and lighting outlets in walls and ceiling. Ordinary house plans are drawn to the scale of $\frac{1}{4}'' = 1'$.

A set of working drawings for a house is generally called a *set of plans* and includes a basement plan, plot plan, wall section, floor plan, elevations, details, and so forth. Such a set of plans for the house illustrated in Fig. 21-54 is shown in Figs. 21-56 to 21-60.

21·26 Floor plan. The sketch plan of a house is shown in Fig. 21-55. The floor plan developed from this sketch is

ARCHITECTURAL DRAFTING **321**

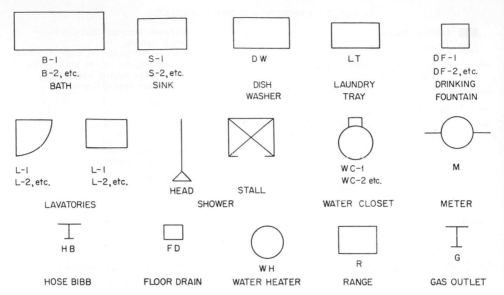

Fig. 21-53 Graphical symbols for plumbing. One symbol is used for each item. For example, the one symbol for sink is used for sinks of all types with letters S-1, S-2, etc., for reference in describing the sink in the specifications. (*Extracted from American Standards' "Graphical Symbols for Plumbing," ASA Y32.4–1955, with the permission of the publisher, The American Society of Mechanical Engineers*)

shown in Fig. 21-56. The following procedure is used: Draw a horizontal line representing the outside face of the front of the house; then draw the interior walls and the interior partitions. Frame walls are drawn 6 in. thick. Locate the doors and windows and draw them with conventional symbols. For sizes of doors and windows refer to the schedules of Fig. 21-58.

The stairway shown can be laid out as described for Fig. 21-40. Note that a landing is used in place of one of the treads in Fig. 21-56.

Only one floor plan is required for the house shown. When a second floor is to be drawn for a two-story house, it is best planned by laying a piece of tracing paper over the first-floor plan. The exterior walls are then traced and the stairways and chimney flues lo-

cated. The interior partitions need not be continuous with the first floor. Closets should be provided in the bedrooms and elsewhere as required.

21·27 Basement plan. The basement plan or foundation layout (Fig. 21-57) must be completely dimensioned because the construction of the house is begun with this plan. It should be checked with the first-floor plan and may be traced from it. Note the foundations for the chimney, porches, and so forth, and the other details. Windows should be under the first-floor windows.

21·28 Plot plan. This is a plan of the site showing the locations of the house and accessory buildings on the lot. It should give complete and accurate dimensions; indicate all driveways and

Fig. 21-54 Pen-and-ink perspective of a house.

walks; show the location of electric, gas, water, sewer, and telephone lines; and give all other pertinent information. A plot plan is shown as a part of Fig. 21-57.

21·29 Elevations. A front elevation is shown in Fig. 21-58 and a side elevation in Fig. 21-59. Four elevations (front, back, and both sides) are included in a complete set of plans and are required for Federal Housing Administration (FHA) loans. The elevations show the exterior appearance of the house, floor and ceiling heights, openings for windows and doors, roof pitch, and so forth. To draw an elevation, start with the grade line. Then lo-

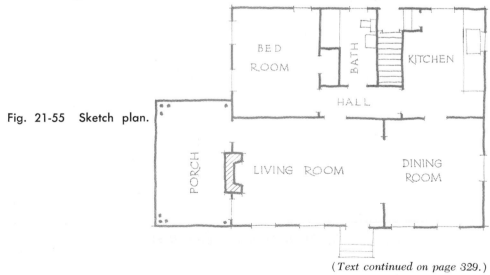

Fig. 21-55 Sketch plan.

(*Text continued on page 329.*)

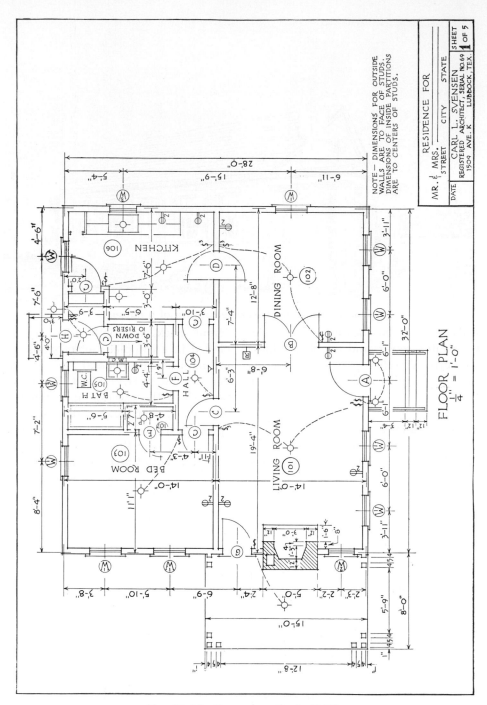

Fig. 21-56 Floor plan. **Prob. U·51.**

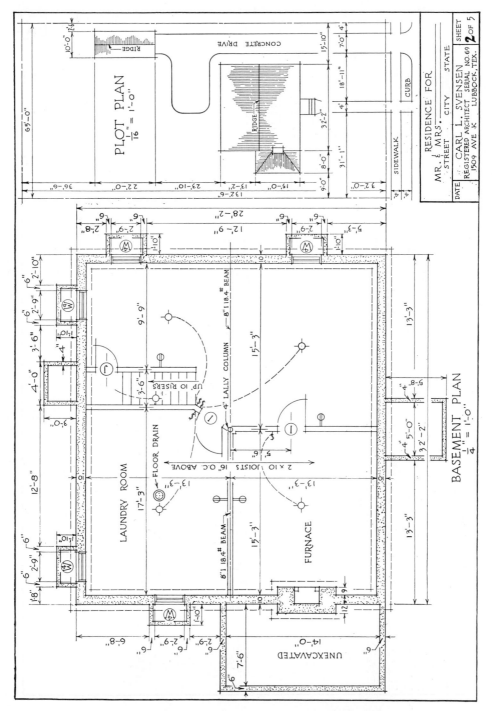

Fig. 21-57 Basement plan and plot plan. **Prob. U·51.**

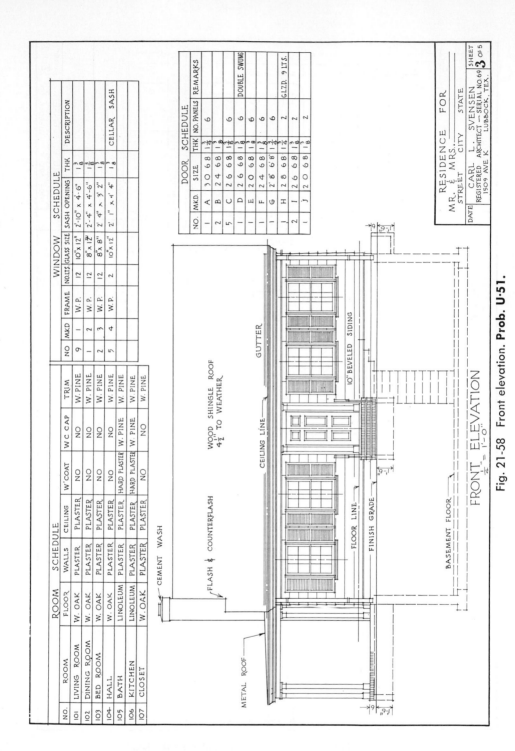

Fig. 21-58 Front elevation. **Prob. U-51.**

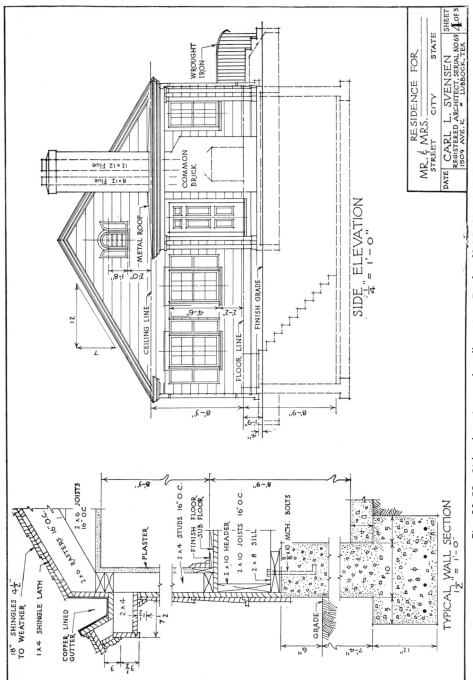

RESIDENCE FOR

MR. & MRS.

CARL L. SVENSEN

STREET   CITY   STATE

DATE

REGISTERED ARCHITECT, SERIAL NO 69

1509 AVE. K   LUBBOCK, TEX

WROUGHT IRON

12 × 12 Flue

8 × 12 Flue

COMMON BRICK

METAL ROOF

CEILING LINE

1'-8"

2'-0"

12

7

FLOOR LINE

FINISH GRADE

2'-2"

4'-6"

8'-3"

1'-6"

8'-0"

SIDE ELEVATION

1/4" = 1'-0"

18" SHINGLES 4½" TO WEATHER

1 × 4 SHINGLE LATH

2 × 6 RAFTERS 16" O.C.

2 × 6 JOISTS 16" O.C.

8'-3"

PLASTER

2 × 4 STUDS 16" O.C.

FINISH FLOOR

SUB FLOOR

2 × 10 HEADER

2 × 10 JOISTS 16" O.C.

2 × 8 SILL

⅝ × 10 MCH. BOLTS

8'-0"

COPPER LINED GUTTER

2 × 4

7½"

3½"

3

GRADE

10

5

6"

7'-4"

12"

TYPICAL WALL SECTION

1½" = 1'-0"

Fig. 21-59 Side elevation and wall section. **Probs. U-25, U-26, U-51.**

ARCHITECTURAL DRAFTING   **327**

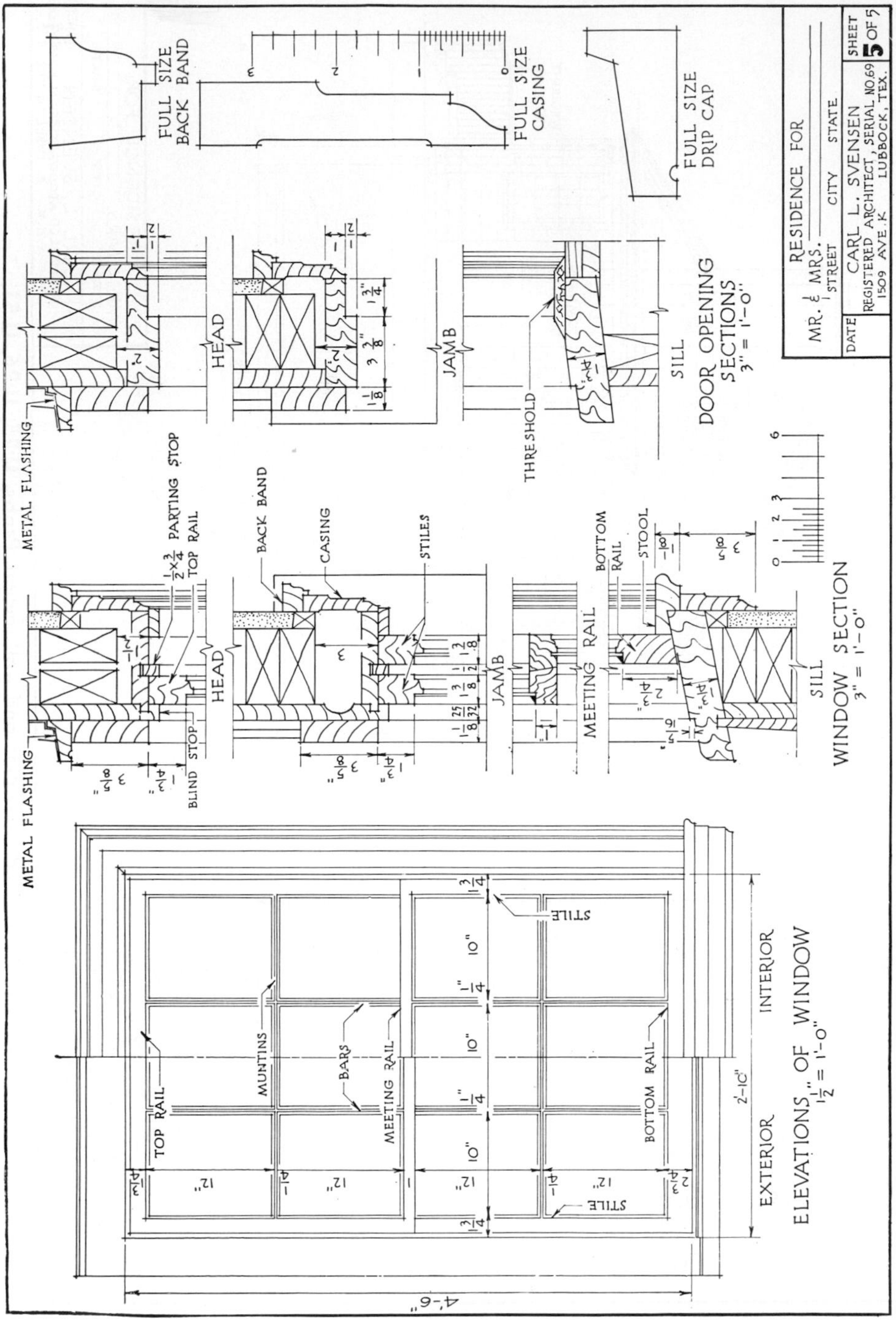

Fig. 21-60 Details. Prob. U-51.

FULL SIZE BACK BAND

FULL SIZE CASING

FULL SIZE DRIP CAP

HEAD

JAMB

SILL

DOOR OPENING SECTIONS
3" = 1'-0"

METAL FLASHING

THRESHOLD

HEAD

JAMB

MEETING RAIL

SILL

WINDOW SECTION
3" = 1'-0"

METAL FLASHING

PARTING STOP

TOP RAIL

BACK BAND

CASING

STILES

BOTTOM RAIL

STOOL

BLIND STOP

EXTERIOR

INTERIOR

TOP RAIL

MUNTINS

BARS

MEETING RAIL

BOTTOM RAIL

STILE

STILE

ELEVATIONS, 1½" = 1'-0" OF WINDOW

RESIDENCE FOR
MR. & MRS.
STREET   CITY   STATE
DATE   CARL L. SVENSEN
REGISTERED ARCHITECT, SERIAL NO.69
1509 AVE. K   LUBBOCK, TEX.
SHEET
5 OF 5

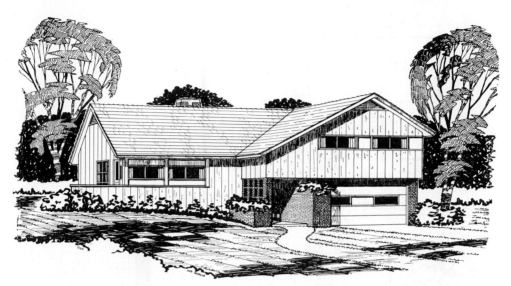

Fig. 21-61 A split-level house. (*Herman H. York, Architect, AIA, Jamaica, N.Y.*)

cate the floor levels and the vertical dimensions of other features. Horizontal dimensions can be obtained by placing a plan above the elevation, or underneath if tracing paper is used.

21·30 Details. A wall section to a larger scale is shown at the left in Fig. 21-59. Other larger scale drawings are made of the parts that cannot be shown with sufficient detail on the ¼-in. scale drawings. A typical sheet of such details is shown in Fig. 21-60. As the building progresses, the architect furnishes full-size drawings, made with a soft pencil, for millwork, moldings, and any special details.

21·31 Contemporary houses for study and comparison. Designs by representative architects are shown in Figs. 21-1, 21-2, 21-15 to 21-22, and 21-61 to 21-80. The house in Figs. 21-61 to 21-64 is described as a split-level house. It is of frame construction with exterior walls of vertical boards for the upper level

and brick veneer for the lower level. Foundation walls are of poured concrete. The roof has asphalt shingles and copper flashing. The girders are 6″ I 12# (I beams, 6″ high, weight 12 lb per ft). Inside walls are ⅜″ gypsum wallboard that are painted or papered except where wainscots or other finishes are desired. Wood-sliding windows are used except in the basement where top-hinged windows are put in. All floors are oak except those in the bathrooms, recreation room, and kitchen. Both the bathroom floor and walls are of ceramic tile, the recreation room floor is of asphalt tile, and the kitchen floor is of linoleum. There are three levels for the house and a lower level for the garage.

The front elevation in Fig. 21-63 shows the general appearance and gives some dimensions. Complete plans would require elevations from all four directions. The sections in Fig. 21-64 indicate the different floor levels, the walls, and the slope of the roof (7″ vertically for 12″ horizontally).

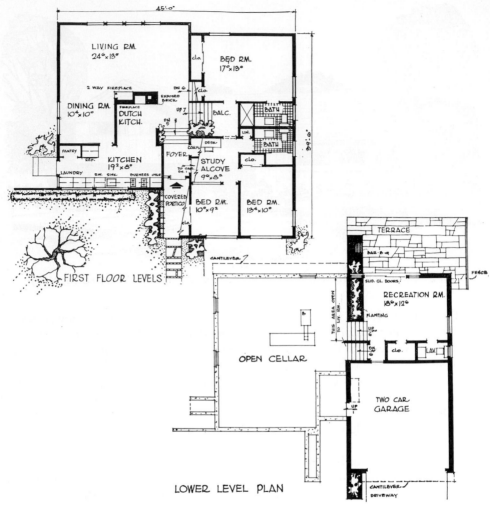

FIRST FLOOR LEVELS

LOWER LEVEL PLAN

Fig. 21-62 Plan. House of Fig. 21-61. (*Herman H. York, Architect, AIA*)

The house in Figs. 21-65 and 21-66 is described as a distinctly contemporary design, the features of which are evident in the illustrations.

The house of Figs. 21-67 and 21-68 is described as a compact house with simple lines and of frame construction. Note the use of sliding windows (Fig. 21-67). On the plan (Fig. 21-68) see the indication of folding doors (by the use of wavy lines) between the dining room and the family room. The patio and terrace, with sliding doors from the family room and rear bedroom, provide for outdoor living.

The house in Figs. 21-69 to 21-71 illustrates the use of steel framing for residential construction. The walls are of concrete brick, concrete blocks, and plate glass. Note the overhanging upper level (Fig. 21-69) and identify it with the partial west elevation shown at A in Fig. 21-71. The view at A is from the right on the plan in Fig. 21-70.

(*Text continued on page 334.*)

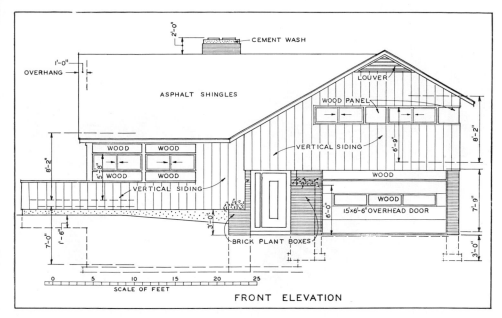

Fig. 21-63 Front elevation. House of Fig. 21-61. (*Adapted from drawings of Herman H. York, Architect, AIA*)

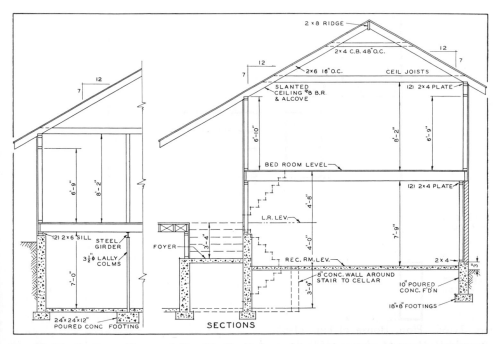

Fig. 21-64 Sections. House of Fig. 21-61. (*Adapted from drawings of Herman H. York, Architect, AIA*)

ARCHITECTURAL DRAFTING 331

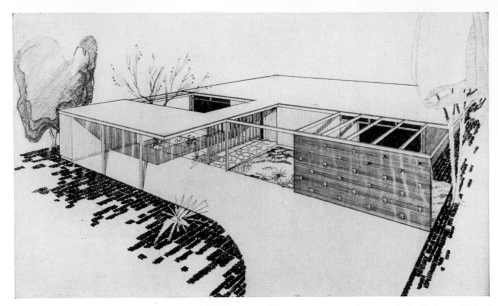

Fig. 21-65 A house for outdoor living. (*Donald H. Honn, Architect, AIA. Tulsa, Okla.*)

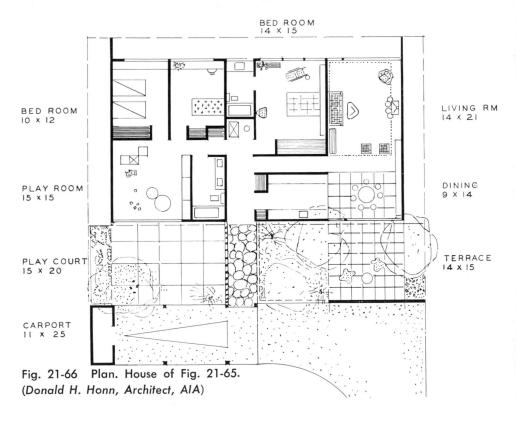

BED ROOM
14 x 15

BED ROOM
10 x 12

PLAY ROOM
15 x 15

PLAY COURT
15 x 20

CARPORT
11 x 25

LIVING RM
14 x 21

DINING
9 x 14

TERRACE
14 x 15

Fig. 21-66 Plan. House of Fig. 21-65.
(*Donald H. Honn, Architect, AIA*)

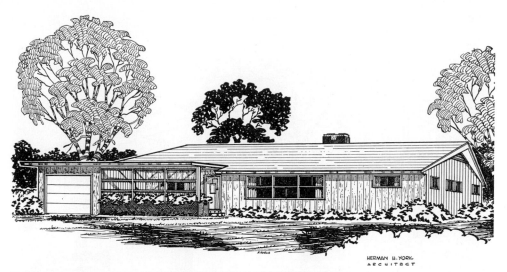

Fig. 21-67 A one-level house. (*Herman H. York, Architect, AIA, Jamaica, N.Y.*)

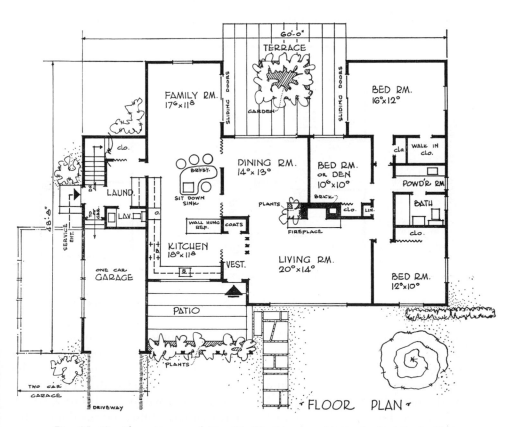

Fig. 21-68 Plan. House of Fig. 21-67. (*Herman H. York, Architect, AIA*)

ARCHITECTURAL DRAFTING **333**

Fig. 21-69 A house with steel framing. (*Donald H. Honn, Architect, AIA. Tulsa, Okla.*)

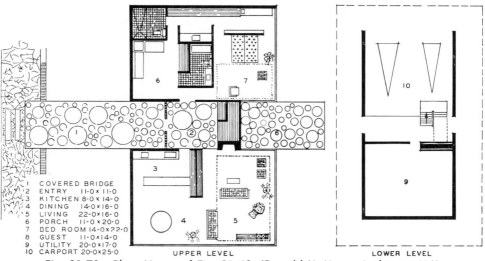

1 COVERED BRIDGE
2 ENTRY   11-0 x 11-0
3 KITCHEN 8-0 x 14-0
4 DINING   14-0 x 16-0
5 LIVING   22-0 x 16-0
6 PORCH   11-0 x 20-0
7 BED ROOM 14-0 x 22-0
8 GUEST   11-0 x 14-0
9 UTILITY   20-0 x 17-0
10 CARPORT 20-0 x 25-0

UPPER LEVEL   LOWER LEVEL

Fig. 21-70 Plan. House of Fig. 21-69. (*Donald H. Honn, Architect, AIA*)

A typical wall section is shown at B in Fig. 21-71. Some detail sections are shown at C in Fig. 21-71 and have been numbered to correspond with the numbers on the partial west elevation at A.

The house in Figs. 21-72 to 21-74 is described as in the Northwest mood, that is, simple. This house is constructed entirely of wood. Laminated beams are used over long spans. The exterior is sheathed with vertical grain redwood left without finish to weather. The roof has white asbestos shingles for fire protection.

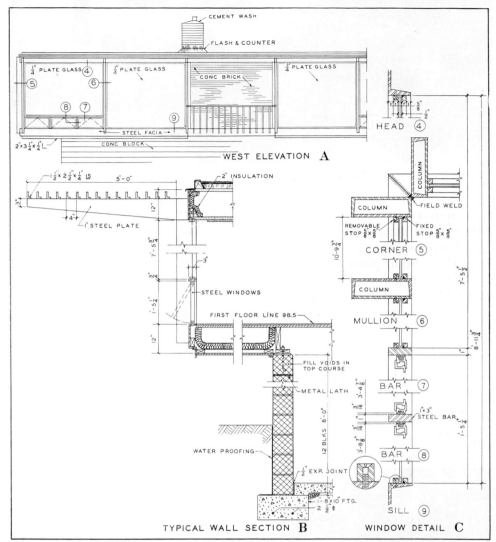

Fig. 21-71 A partial elevation and some sections. House of Fig. 21-69. *(Adapted from drawings of Donald H. Honn, Architect, AIA)*

The house in Figs. 21-75 and 21-76 is described as a symmetrical plan and structure. The architect states: "The fundamental decisions of orientation and lot use permitted a building form based on symmetry about two axes." The structure is of wood, with gray cyprus siding, white trim, and orange or brown cement asbestos panels.

The small house in Figs. 21-77 to 21-80 is designed to give the most comfortable living conditions at the lowest cost for those who do not require a lot of room.

The straight-forward post and beam construction is quick, and the heavy Douglas fir plank ceiling and floor give strength and character to the design of

Fig. 21-72 Northwest house, front. (*Paul Thiry, Architect, FAIA, Seattle, Wash.*)[1]

the house. The construction of this house differs from the usual method of framing with studs (Figs. 21-23 to 21-26). It is framed with posts and beams. After these are in place, the floor and roof planks are put on. Then the milled trim, which is used for jamb trim, head, and sill, is put directly on the frame of the windows, doors, and so forth. Milled trim is finished to desired form in the mill or factory.

The large glass areas are protected by overhang from summer sun and sky glare. Such areas give a large feeling

of space. The screen panel of Celloglass framing the balcony rail achieves privacy without obstructing the view.

Note the curved folding partition between the living and sleeping rooms on the plan (Fig. 21-78). This figure shows the floor and foundation plans. Compare the floor plan (Fig. 21-78) with the elevations (Fig. 21-79) and then with the sections (Fig. 21-80). In order to show the construction more clearly, most of the dimensions have been left off the views. However, the graphic scales will give a comparative idea of the sizes of the various parts.

(*Text continued on page 342.*)

Fig. 21-73 Northwest house, rear. (*Paul Thiry, Architect, FAIA, Seattle, Wash.*)[1]

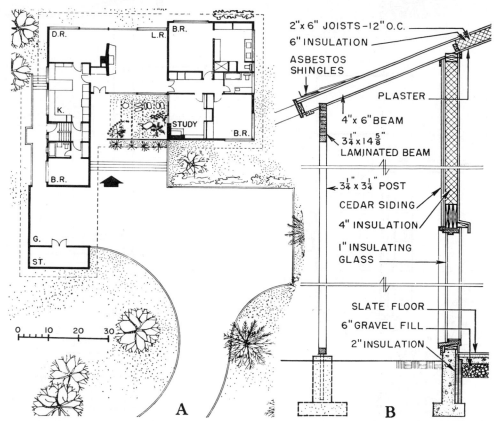

2"x 6" JOISTS-12" O.C.
6" INSULATION
ASBESTOS
SHINGLES

PLASTER

4"x 6" BEAM
$3\frac{1}{4}$" x $14\frac{5}{8}$"
LAMINATED BEAM

$3\frac{1}{4}$" x $3\frac{1}{4}$" POST
CEDAR SIDING
4" INSULATION
1" INSULATING
GLASS

SLATE FLOOR
6" GRAVEL FILL
2" INSULATION

0   10   20   30

D.R.   L.R.   B.R.
K.
STUDY
B.R.
B.R.
G.
ST.

A   B

Fig. 21-74 Plan and section. House of Figs. 21-72 and 71-73. (Paul Thiry, Architect, FAIA, Seattle, Wash.)[1]

Fig. 21-75 House of symmetrical design. (Cecil D. Elliott, Architect, AIA. Mervin R. A. Johnson, Associate Architect. Raleigh, N.C.)[1]

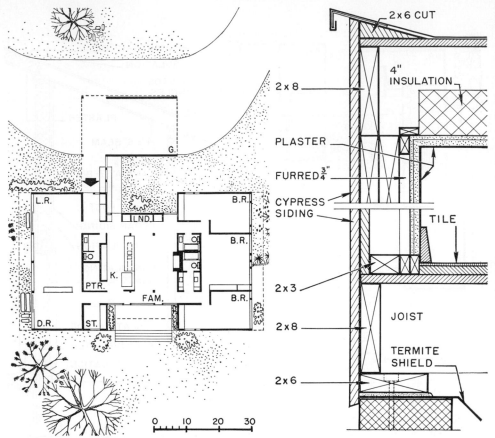

Fig. 21-76 Plan and section. House of Fig. 21-75. (Cecil D. Elliott, Architect, AIA. Mervin R. A. Johnson, Associate Architect. Raleigh, N.C.)[1]

Fig. 21-77 A small house. (Henry Hill, Architect, AIA, and John W. Kruse, AIA, Associate. San Francisco, Calif.)

338 MECHANICAL DRAWING

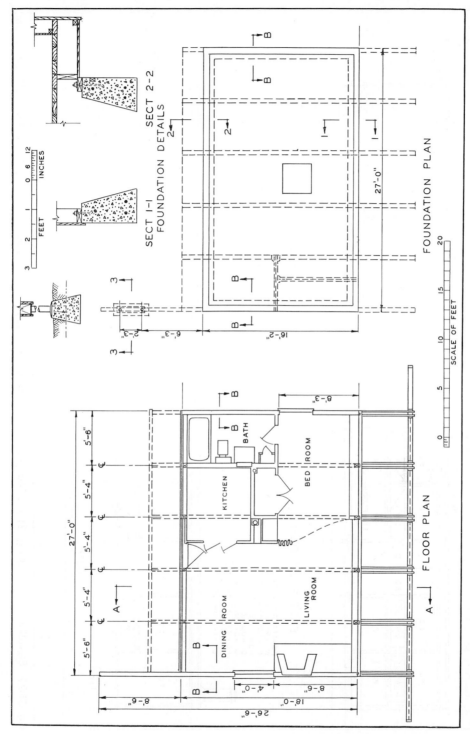

Fig. 21-78   Plans. House of Fig. 21-77. (Adapted from drawings of Henry Hill, Architect, AIA, and John W. Kruse, AIA, Associate)

ARCHITECTURAL DRAFTING   **339**

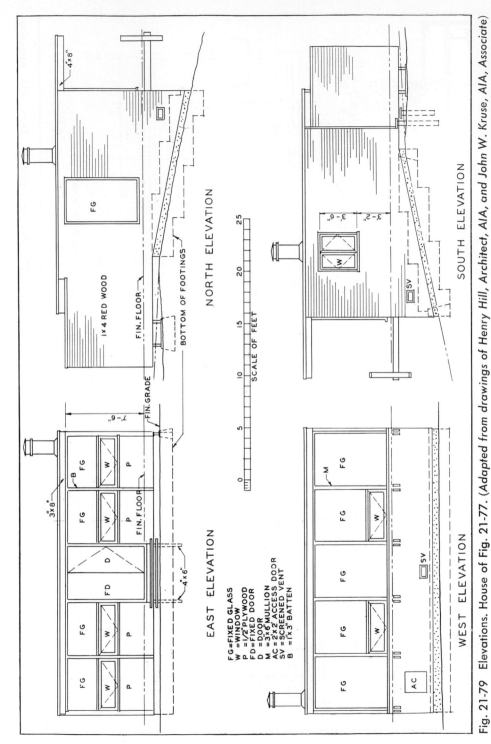

NORTH ELEVATION

SOUTH ELEVATION

EAST ELEVATION

WEST ELEVATION

SCALE OF FEET

FG = FIXED GLASS
W = WINDOW
P = 1/2"PLYWOOD
FD = FIXED DOOR
D = DOOR
M = 3"x6"MULLION
AC = 2'x2'ACCESS DOOR
SV = SCREENED VENT
B = 1"x3" BATTEN

Fig. 21-79 Elevations. House of Fig. 21-77. (Adapted from drawings of Henry Hill, Architect, AIA, and John W. Kruse, AIA, Associate)

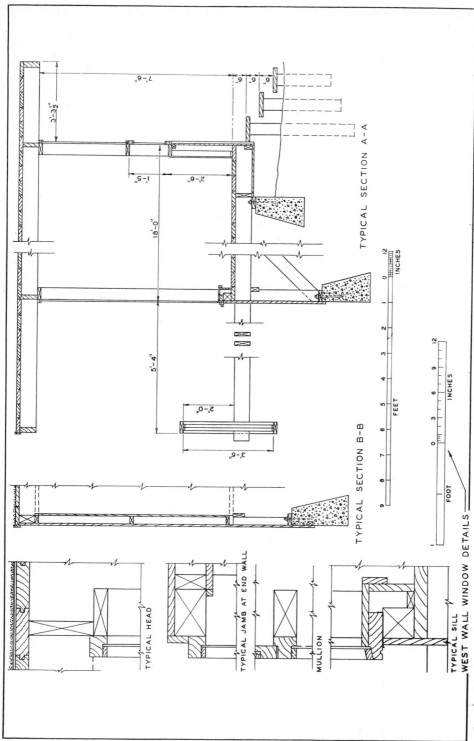

TYPICAL SECTION A-A

TYPICAL SECTION B-B

INCHES

FEET

INCHES

FOOT

TYPICAL HEAD

TYPICAL JAMB AT END WALL

MULLION

TYPICAL SILL
WEST WALL WINDOW DETAILS

Fig. 21-80 Sections. House of Fig. 21-77. (Adapted from drawings of Henry Hill, Architect, AIA, and John W. Kruse, AIA, Associate)

21·32 Problem suggestions. Group U, page 515. Three lists are presented. Selections may be made for as extensive a course as desired. For an elementary survey course, problems may be selected from List 1. Problems in Lists 2 and 3 in addition to List 1 provide for a separate course in architectural drafting. Visits to houses under construction should be a part of the course, with notes and sketches required. It is also desirable to have available for reference a few sets of prints of houses that have been designed by local architects.

[1] Reprinted by permission from *Record Houses of 1956*. Copyright 1956 by F. W. Dodge Corporation. Photographs for Figs. 21-72 to 21-74 by Art Hupy; for Figs. 21-75 and 21-76 by Joseph W. Molitor.

LIST 1 Lettering Probs. U·1, U·2, U·3, U·4, U·5, U·6, U·7, U·8
Architectural Probs. U·12, U·15, U·17, U·18, U·19, U·22, U·23, U·27, U·29, U·31, U·50, U·51, and selections from Probs. U·34 to U·41

LIST 2 Lettering Probs. U·9
Architectural Probs. U·20, U·24, U·25, U·32, U·33, and selections from Probs. U·42 to U·49

LIST 3 Architectural Probs. U·10, U·11, U·21, U·26, U·30, selections from Probs. U·52 to U·57, U.58 to U·65, U·66 to U·70, U·71 to U·78, and Probs. U·79, U·80, U·81

22 Structural drafting

22·1 Structural drafting has to do with the drawings made for the framework and supporting members of structures, such as columns, floor members, roof trusses, and bridge trusses. Rigid frames of steel for the Allen County War Memorial, Fort Wayne, Indiana, are shown in Fig. 22-1. The *span*, or distance, across the building is 224 ft. A steel truss bridge over the Watauga River on Tennessee State Highway No. 67 is shown in Fig. 22-2.

The picture of a part of a flat steel truss for a building is presented in Fig. 22-3. Some structural terms are given in Fig. 22-4. This truss has been *fabri-*

Fig. 22-1 Allen County War Memorial, Fort Wayne, Ind. 224-foot rigid steel frames. (*Courtesy, Engineering News-Record*)

Fig. 22-2 Watauga River Bridge on Tennessee State Highway No. 67. (*Courtesy, Engineering News-Record*)

cated, or made up, in the shop, and, as shown, is ready for shipment to the site of the building. The top horizontal member, or *top chord,* is made of two *angles* (Fig. 22-5). The *bottom chord* is made of two smaller angles, and the *diagonals* are made of single angles.

Fig. 22-3 Riveted joints in steel construction.

Notice how the various members are connected by riveting to steel *gusset plates.* The design of structures requires a knowledge of the many subjects included in structural engineering, such as mathematics, stresses, mechanics, properties of materials, methods of fabricating, and methods of erection. However, the student should know some of the characteristics of drawings made for such purposes and how they differ from other drawings.

22·2 Structural shapes. Structural members are built up of standard rolled shapes, some of which are shown in section in Fig. 22-5. Such shapes are made in a great variety of sizes and weights, lists of which may be found in the handbook *Steel Construction*[1] or in

[1] *Steel Construction,* or as it is sometimes called, the "AISC Handbook," is published by the American Institute of Steel Construction, New York.

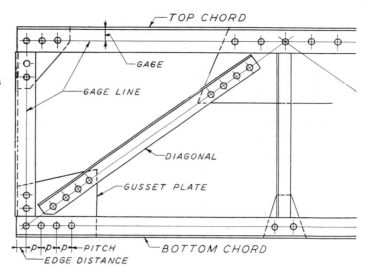

Fig. 22-4 Some terms in steel construction.

TOP CHORD

GAGE

GAGE LINE

DIAGONAL

GUSSET PLATE

P+P+P+PITCH

EDGE DISTANCE

BOTTOM CHORD

the handbooks published by the various steel companies. The AISC Handbook contains tables of the properties of the various shapes and of many combinations of shapes; beam and column data; details of standard beam connec-

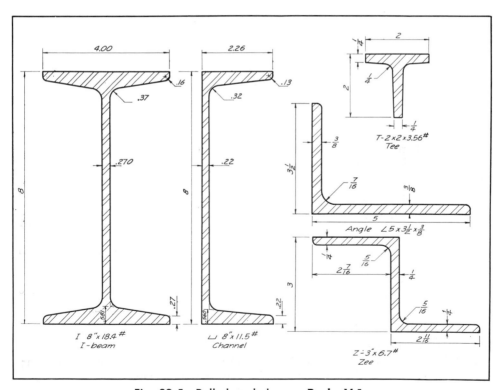

Fig. 22-5 Rolled-steel shapes. **Prob. V·1.**

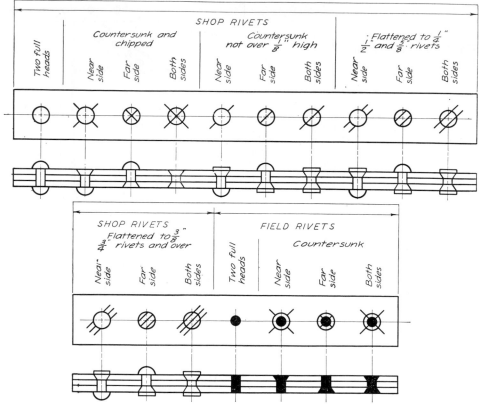

Fig. 22-6   Rivet symbols. **Prob. V·2.**

tions; specifications for the design, fabrication, and erection of structural steel for buildings; and a large amount of related information. Dimensions of steel plates are specified by giving the width, thickness, and length thus: Pl. $12 \times \frac{3}{8} \times 24$. Angles are specified by dimensions giving the length of the legs and thickness of material thus:

$$\llcorner 5 \times 3\frac{1}{2} \times \frac{3}{8}$$

Other shapes are specified by the main dimension and weight per foot:

18 W̅ 64 means 18″ wide flange I-beam, 64 lb per ft.

Bar 2 ⏹ means 2″ square bar.

Bar 1 ⏀ means 1″ diameter round bar.

22·3   Riveting. Structural rivets are shown in Fig. 12-36. The Standard symbols for riveting are given in Fig. 22-6. Riveting done in the shop is called *shop riveting,* whereas that done in the field where the work is being erected is called *field riveting* (shown in black on drawings). Lines on which rivets are spaced are called *gage lines.* The distance between centers along these lines is called the *pitch.* Welding (Chap. 17) is increasing in use for fabricating structural steel shapes.

Many buildings of steel construction are welded throughout. Others are partly welded and partly riveted.

Sometimes steel construction is put

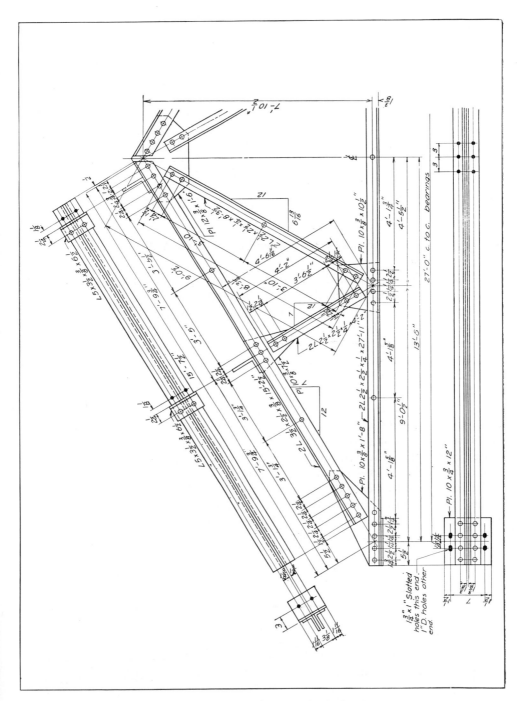

Fig. 22-7   A structural drawing. **Prob. V·4.**

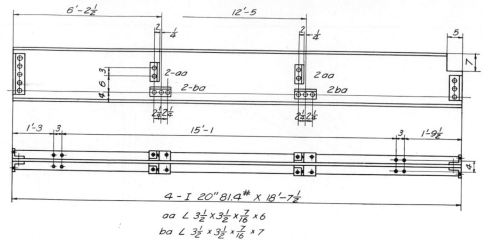

Fig. 22-8 A structural detail. **Prob. V·3.**

together by bolting, especially in locations that are remote from facilities for welding or riveting, or where it may be desirable to provide for dismantling or to avoid the noise of riveting. In some cases the use of special bolts has provided for economical and quick construction.

22·4 Structural drawings. Assembly or part-assembly working drawings form a large class of structural drawings. These include the "skeleton" or basic and center lines to locate the working points, the structural members, gage lines, location dimensions, notes, and other necessary information. Such a

general working drawing is shown in Fig. 22-7 for a small steel roof truss. Since the truss is symmetrical about a vertical center line, it is necessary to show only one-half of it in the drawing. Notice the lines upon which the design is built and the notes used to designate the various features. The sizes of the gusset plates are given in notes as are the number and sizes of angles ($\llcorner$ s). The slope or inclination is indicated by a right triangle, one leg of which is 12 in. A study of the drawing will show that each member is completely dimensioned or described and that dimensions are given to fix the location of each member.

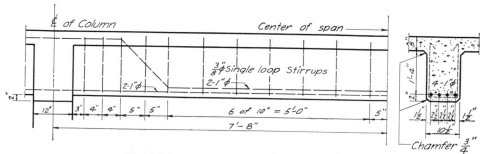

Fig. 22-9 Reinforced concrete. **Prob. V·5.**

Fig. 22-10   Precast concrete wall panel for NBC television studios, Fairbanks, California.

Separate shop drawings are made for complicated or special details and for repeated details.

22·5 Detail drawings. Shop detail drawings give all the dimensions and information necessary to fabricate (or make) the parts. The location and kind of rivets are shown with everything drawn to scale. The simple beam detail of Fig. 22-8 shows the general characteristics of such drawings. Notice that the dimensions are placed above the dimension lines. The lower view is a section and, on structural drawings, is shown as seen from above.

The connections or angles at the ends of the beam are Standard Beam Connections; it is not necessary to dimension them. At the left end a B5 connection is used and at the right end, a B3 connection. For the sizes of these angles and dimensions, see a steel handbook (the rivets are ¾ in. in diameter).

22·6 Reinforced concrete. Drawings made for reinforced-concrete structures show the dimensions of the concrete members and sections, and they give the sizes and locations of the steel reinforcing material. A part of such a drawing is shown in Fig. 22-9. Notice the symbol for the diameter of the steel rods and the representation of the rods by long dashes and blacked-in circles. The rods are drawn as though on different levels on the elevation in order to show how two of them are bent. The section shows them on the same level along the bottom of the beam. The symbol for concrete is shown in Fig. 11-9. Reinforced-concrete design requires a good knowledge of mathematics, mechanics, and materials and is a specialized field of structural engineering.

The proportions of the materials to be used to give the required strength must be understood—the amounts of cement, sand, gravel or crushed rock, and water—as well as the computation of the size and amount of steel and the placing of the steel.

Many interesting applications of reinforced-concrete construction, such as for dams, retaining walls, bridges, roads, walls, beams, and floors of buildings, can be found in the pages of *Engineering News-Record* and similar magazines.

A method of shortening erection time is the use of precast concrete wall panels which are cast flat and then tilted up into place. This is illustrated in Fig. 22-10, which shows a panel being tilted into position with a four-point pickup by a large mobile crane operating from the floor of the building.

22·7 Problem suggestions. Group V, page 526. These problems are designed to give an elementary idea of structural drafting and should be accompanied by inspection of buildings under construction, inspection of bridges, and so forth. The purpose of the chapter is to give general information since structural drafting requires some knowledge of the principles of structural design. Problems V·1, V·2, V·3, V·4, V·5

23 Map drafting

23·1 Maps are essentially one-view drawings of part of the earth's surface. There are so many features to be represented and so many uses for maps that they are made in a great variety. Some maps, such as city plats, must be extremely accurate and made to a relatively large scale (50 to 200 ft to the inch), whereas geographic maps of states or countries, which show boundary lines, streams, lakes, coast lines, and relative locations, may use a scale of several miles to the inch. The civil engi-

Fig. 23-1 Plat of a survey. **Prob. W·1.**

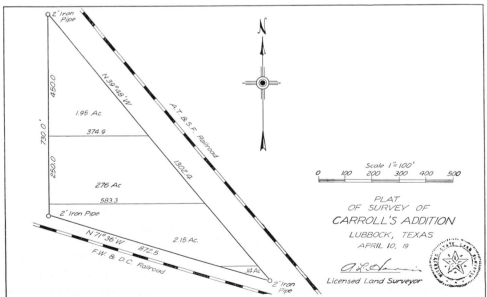

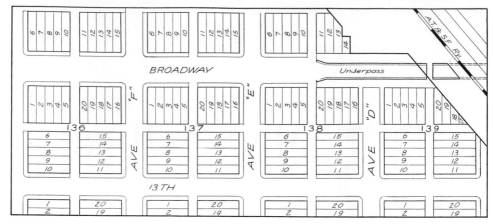

Fig. 23-2　A city map. **Prob. W·2.**

neer's scale (Art. 2·20, Fig. 2-16) is used for map drawings. Distances are given in decimals of a foot, such as in tenths, hundredths, and so forth. (See the maps in your geography and history books.)

23·2 Plats of a survey. A map to record the boundaries of a tract of land and to identify it is called a *plat*. The amount and kind of information will depend upon the purpose for which the map is required. The plat of a plane survey, which was made to record the legal description of the property, is shown in Fig. 23-1.

23·3 City plat. Maps of cities are made for many purposes, such as to maintain a record of street improvements and to show the location of utilities and sizes and location of property for tax assessments. A part of such a city plat is shown in Fig. 23-2. Notice the numbering of the lots and the location of streets, alleys, sidewalks, and so forth.

23·4 Contours. Since maps are one-view drawings, vertical distances or

variations in ground levels do not show. They can, however, be indicated by lines of constant level called *contours*. This is illustrated in Fig. 23-3 where the contours show the location of lines on the ground that are at stated heights above the ocean (sea level). Contour lines close together indicate a steeper slope than lines farther apart. This can be seen by projecting up the intersections of the horizontal level lines with the *profile* section of Fig. 23-3 as shown.

It will be observed that the contour map and the profile correspond to the plan and section of an ordinary drawing. Note the horizontal line or cutting plane on the contour map, which shows the position or line on which the profile is taken. Notice how the profile would change if the cutting plane were moved toward the ocean or to some other new position.

Contour lines are usually taken at 10-ft *intervals* (vertical distances) or levels on the profile (or section). For a larger scale, 5-ft intervals may be used. For very small scales, 20, 50, 100, or 200-ft intervals may be used. When extremely detailed information is re-

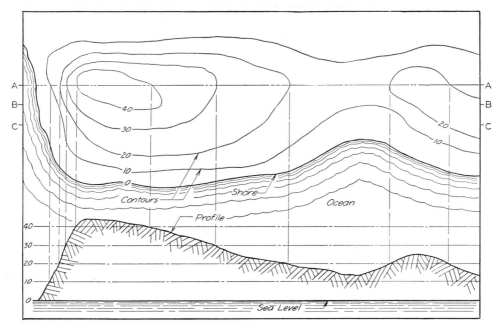

Fig. 23-3 Contours. **Probs. W·3 and W·4.**

quired, a large-scale drawing may have intervals of 0.5, 1, or 2 ft.

23·5 A contour map is shown in Fig. 23-4 with contour intervals of 50 ft (distance between contour levels). When there are many contour lines, every fifth one is drawn heavier to make them easier to follow. The elevation in feet is marked in a break in the line. Notice the *water lining* used on the representation of the river.

Before a contour map can be drawn, levels must be run in the field to obtain and record the necessary information. This requires experience in surveying, an important part of civil engineering.

23·6 Topographic maps are made to give rather complete descriptions of the areas shown. This includes such infor-

mation as boundaries, natural features, the works of man, vegetation, and relief (elevations and depressions). Symbols are used for many of the features shown on topographic maps, some of which are given in Fig. 23-5. Maps using topographic symbols can be obtained at nominal cost from the Director, U.S. Geological Survey, Department of the Interior, or U.S. Coast and Geodetic Survey, Department of Commerce, Washington, D.C. Naval charts (maps) come from the Hydrographic Office in the Bureau of Navigation of the Navy Department. Government maps represent the finest kind of map drafting.

Aeronautical maps make use of special symbols, which need to be understood in order to read them. Some symbols from the U.S. Coast and Geodetic Survey are shown in Fig. 23-6.

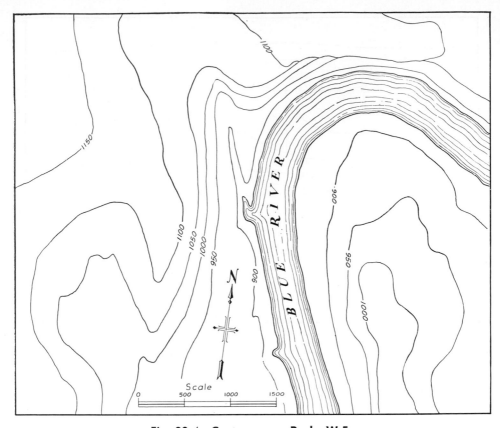

Fig. 23-4 Contour map. **Prob. W·5.**

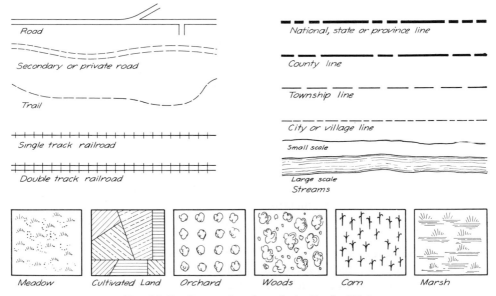

Road

Secondary or private road

Trail

Single track railroad

Double track railroad

National, state or province line

County line

Township line

City or village line

Small scale

Large scale
Streams

Meadow Cultivated Land Orchard Woods Corn Marsh

Fig. 23-5 Conventional symbols. **Prob. W·6.**

Fig. 23-6 Some aeronautical chart symbols. (*From U.S. Coast and Geodetic Survey*)

The making of maps is an important part of civil engineering and requires thorough training. Books on surveying and mapping and United States government bulletins should be studied before undertaking work on any important maps.

23·7 Problem suggestions. Group W, page 526. These problems are designed to give an elementary idea of map drawing. It would add to the value of this study if maps of various kinds could be on hand for inspection.

Problems W·1, W·2, W·3, W·4, W·5, W·6

24 Problems

24·1 The important part of any course in mechanical drawing consists of the working of a large number of properly selected and graded problems. The problems that follow are arranged somewhat in the order of difficulty in each of the divisions of the subject, and the methods of presentation are varied to suit the objectives and requirements of the problems. Graphic layouts are given when practicable, as they are definite and save time for both instruc-

tor and student. It is not necessary or intended that all the problems be worked; a selection to fit the course should be made by the instructor. A large number of references to text material are given with the problems. These references should be studied by the student before asking for assistance from the instructor.

Any or all of the drawings may be inked, but the best results are generally obtained by delaying this operation un-

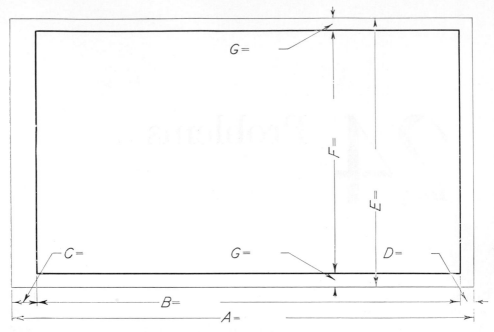

Fig. A-1 Adjustable layout for any size sheet.

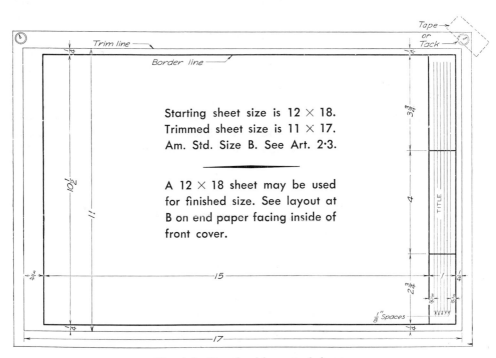

Starting sheet size is 12 × 18.
Trimmed sheet size is 11 × 17.
Am. Std. Size B. See Art. 2·3.

A 12 × 18 sheet may be used
for finished size. See layout at
B on end paper facing inside of
front cover.

Fig. A-2 Standard layout of sheet.

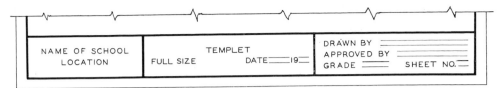

Fig. A-3   Record strip, or long block title.

til the ability to make a good pencil drawing has been acquired.

24·2 General instructions. The trim sizes of sheets recommended by the American Standards Association, as given in Art. 2·3, are in almost universal use in industry and are, therefore, recommended for use in drawing courses. Most of the problems are planned for working on 11″ × 17″ sheets. It is, of course, possible to use other sizes and arrangements where necessary and desired by the instructor. To assist in such cases, Fig. A-1 is given with letters to indicate the dimensions. The desired numerical values can be filled in after the equality signs (=) on the figure.

Most of the problems in this book are designed for use on the American Standard Size "B" sheet with the lay-

out shown on Figs. A-2 and A-3. Other layouts are suggested on Fig. A-4.

On the following figures the numbers enclosed in circles are for locating the starting lines and are always measured full size regardless of the scale of the views of the drawing. When such dimensions are given, the lines that they locate should be drawn first. (These dimensions are not to be put on the completed drawing as they are simply to locate the lines upon which the drawing is built.) Use light, sharp pencil lines and work as accurately as possible. Errors made in starting are not often evident until the drawing is nearly completed. The title for each sheet is given in italics.

If a different size of sheet is used, the figures in the circles should be adjusted to allow more or less space. This is best

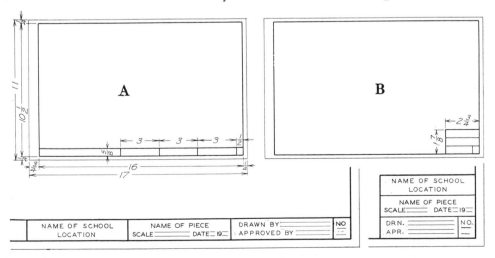

Fig. A-4   Alternate layouts.

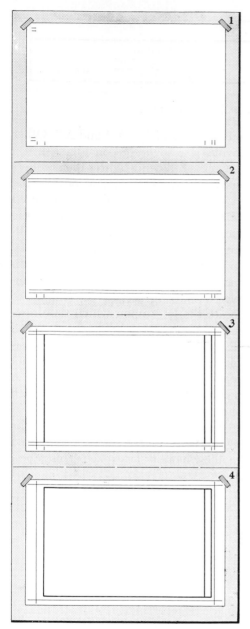

Fig. A-5 Two-minute method.

Since most drawings are now finished in pencil, careful attention should be given to developing the ability to make bright contrasty drawings on either drawing paper or tracing paper. This requires firm, black pencil lines for the view lines and thin, sharp pencil lines for dimension lines, extension lines, and so forth.

A minimum amount of erasing is essential if clean, professional-appearing drawings are to be obtained. A great deal depends upon the care that is given to keeping the pencil point in proper condition at all times. Never sharpen it over the drawing board!

24·3 Layout of the sheet. Read Arts. 2·1 to 2·6. Fasten the paper to the board as described in Art. 2·2. The outside dimensions to which the finished sheet will be trimmed are 11″ × 17″, with border line and record strip as shown in Fig. A-2. The guide lines for lettering in the record strip, Fig. A-3, are not to be put in until the drawing is finished and ready for the title. By following the method illustrated in progressive steps, the layout of a sheet should not take more than two minutes.

Two-minute method (Fig. A-5). With the scale measure 17″ near the bottom of the sheet (or on the bottom of the sheet), making short vertical marks, not dots. Measure and mark ¾″ in from the left-hand mark and ¼″ in from the right-hand mark (Fig. A-5, Space 1). From this last mark measure 1″ toward the left and mark. Lay the scale vertically near the left of the paper (or on the left edge) and make short horizontal marks 11″ apart. Make short marks ¼″ down from the top mark and ¼″ up from the bottom mark. With the T-square draw horizontal lines through

done by the instructor at first. The students can learn how to locate the views after a little practice. With further experience his judgment will improve.

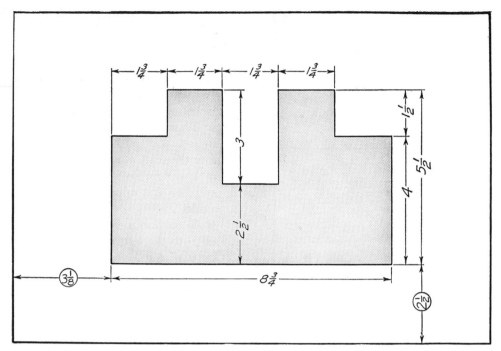

Fig. A-6 Templet. **Prob. A·1.**

the four marks last made (Space 2). Next draw vertical lines through the five vertical marks (Space 3). Then brighten up the border lines and the sheet will appear as in Space 4; it is now ready to be used for a drawing.

GROUP A. USE OF INSTRUMENTS

Problem A·1. The first sheet (Fig. A-6) is a one-view drawing of a *templet.* Complete specifications would include the thickness and kind of material.

In this and the following one-view problems the order of making the drawing is shown in progressive stages. These stages should be followed carefully because they represent the draftsman's procedure in making drawings.

It is necessary for the beginner to learn to draw in good form, and the most important feature in this regard is the order of working. Do not simply follow the explanations as being directions for the particular problem, but try to understand the system and the reasons for it. This system, thoroughly mastered at the start, will apply to all drawings and will develop the two requirements in execution: accuracy and speed.

ORDER OF WORKING (Fig. A-7)
1) Lay out the sheet as described on the preceding page.
2) Measure 3⅛″ from left border line and from this mark measure 8¾″ toward the right.
3) Lay the scale on the paper vertically near (or on) the left edge, make a mark 2½″ up, and from this

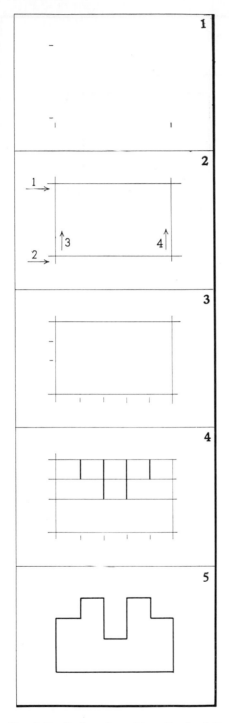

Fig. A-7 Order of working, **Prob. A·1.**

measure 5½″ more. The sheet will appear as in Fig. A-7, Space 1.

4) Draw horizontal lines 1 and 2 with the T-square, and vertical lines 3 and 4 with T-square and triangle (Space 2). Be careful to hold the instruments as illustrated in Fig. 2-4. These four lines block in the figure.

5) Lay the scale along the bottom line of the figure with the measuring edge on the upper side and make marks 1¾″ apart. Then with the scale on line 3, with its measuring edge to the left, measure from the bottom line two successive distances vertically, 2½″ and 1½ (Space 3).

6) Through the two marks draw horizontal lines lightly across the figure.

7) Draw the vertical lines with T-square and triangle by setting the pencil on the marks on the bottom line and starting and stopping the lines on the proper horizontal lines (Space 4).

8) Erase the lines not wanted and brighten the lines of the figure to obtain the finished drawing (Space 5).

9) Write your name, sheet number, and date lightly in the record strip. The record strip (or title block) is to be lettered in later.

10) Trim sheet to finished size.

Problems A·2 and A·3. Alternates with same layout as in Fig. A-6.

Problem A·4. To make a drawing of the *stencil* (Fig. A-10). This drawing gives practice in accurate measuring with the scale and making careful corners with short lines. The construction

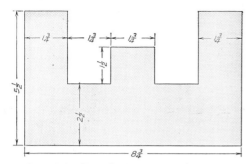

Fig. A-8 Templet No. 2. **Prob. A·2.**

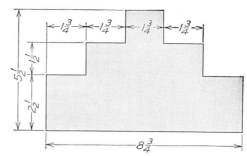

Fig. A-9 Gage. **Prob. A·3.**

lines shown in Fig. A-11 should be drawn very lightly and with a well-sharpened 3H or 4H pencil. All measurements must be made very carefully and accurately.

ORDER OF WORKING (Figs. A-11 and A-11 *continued*)

1) Find the center of the sheet inside the border by laying the T-square blade face down across the opposite corners and drawing short lines

where the diagonals intersect (Fig. A-11, Space 1).

2) Through the center draw a horizontal center line and on it measure and mark off points for the four vertical lines. The drawing will appear as in Space 2.

3) Draw the vertical lines lightly with T-square and triangle. On the first vertical line, at the extreme left, measure and mark off points for all

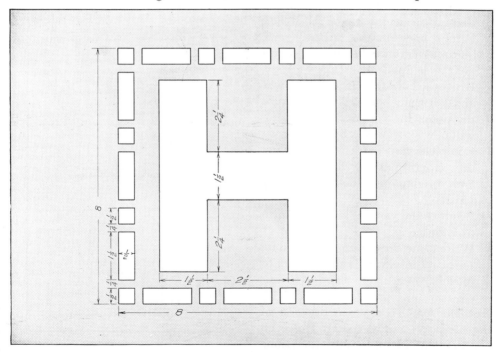

Fig. A-10 Stencil. **Prob. A·4.**

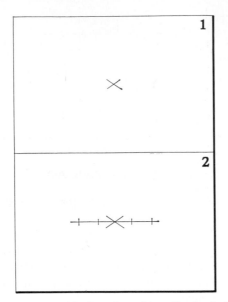

Fig. A-11   Order of working. **Prob. A·4.**

horizontal lines. The drawing will now appear as in Space 3.

4) Draw the horizontal lines as finished lines. Measure points for the stencil border lines on the left side and bottom. The drawing will now appear as in Space 4.

5) Draw the border lines. On the lower and left-hand border lines, measure the points for the ties. The drawing will now appear as in Space 5.

6) Complete the border by drawing the cross lines as finished lines and brightening the other lines (Space 6).

7) Brighten the vertical lines and finish as in Space 7.

8) Write name, sheet number, and date in the record strip. Trim the sheet to finished size.

Problem A·5. To make a drawing of the *tile pattern* (Fig. A-12). This is an alternate problem, using the same measurements as in Fig. A-10 with ad-

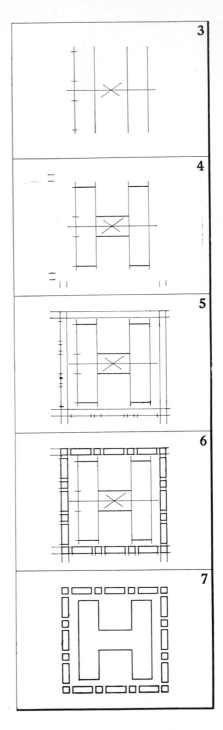

Fig. A-11 (*Continued*)

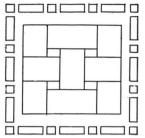

Fig. A-12   Tile pattern. Prob. A·5.

ditional 1½″ measurements for the top and bottom strips and for the middle vertical strip.

Problem A·6. To make a drawing of the *shim* (Fig. A-13). For practice with compasses. Read Art. 2·29. When circles and circle arcs occur on a drawing, the first step is to locate the centers, the second, to mark off the radii, the third, to locate the points of tangency and make sure of smooth joints.

Be sure that the lead in the compasses is carefully sharpened and adjusted with the needle point as shown in Fig. 2-23. Draw intersecting center lines on a separate sheet. Practice handling both the compasses and bow pencil in drawing circles, carefully observing the operations illustrated in Figs. 2-22 and 2-26. The needle point may be placed at the exact crossing of the two center lines by guiding it with the little finger of the left hand, resting the other fingers of the left hand on the paper.

Tangents occur constantly on all machine drawings and must be drawn neatly and quickly. Accuracy in setting the compasses to a required radius should be practiced. Any error is doubled when the diameter is measured.

Note that when two circle arcs are tangent to each other the point of tan-

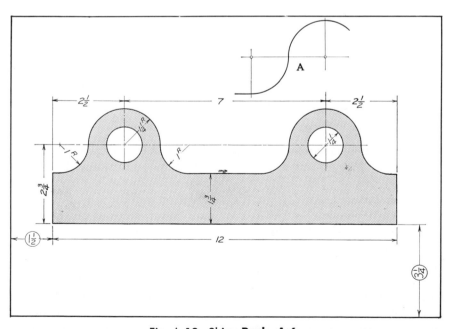

Fig. A-13   Shim. Prob. A·6.

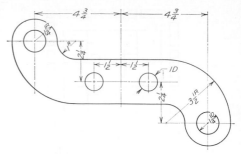

Fig. A-15 Brace. **Prob. A·7.**

two circles, the two semicircles, then the four quarter circles. Be sure to stop at the tangent points (Space 2).

5) Brighten the lines of the figure. Leave the center lines lighter than the outlines, as in Space 3.

6) Write name, sheet number, and date lightly in the record strip, and then trim the sheet.

Problem A·7. Make a drawing of a *brace* (Fig. A-15). Plan a systematic order of working before starting the drawing.

Problem A·8. Make a drawing to show the layout for a *basketball floor* (Fig. A-16). Use a scale of ⅛″ = 1′ (Art. 2·23). Distance A to be at least 3′.

Problem A·9. To draw an *inlaid table top* (Fig. A-17). Draw horizontal and vertical center lines. Plan a systematic order of working. The central inlay may be varied, using one of the suggestions of Fig. A-18 or the student's own original design.

Problem A·10. To make a drawing of the *shearing blank* (Fig. A-19). When a view has inclined lines, it should first be blocked in with square corners. Angles of 15°, 30°, 45°, 60°, and 75° are

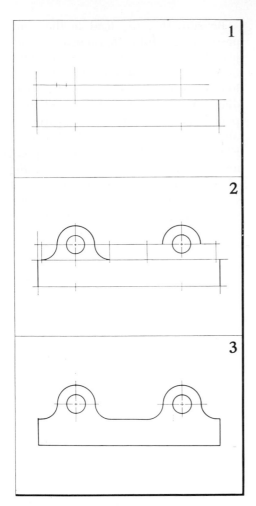

Fig. A-14 Order of working. **Prob. A·6.**

gency must lie on a line joining the centers of the arcs (Fig. A-13 at A).

ORDER OF WORKING (Fig. A-14)

1) Draw the base line 3¼″ from the bottom. On it measure in 1½″ from the left border, then the distances 2½″, 7″, and 2½″ (Space 1).

2) Measure the vertical distances 1¾″ and 2¾″ (Space 1).

3) Draw the horizontal lines, then the vertical lines (Space 1).

4) On the horizontal center line mark points for the radii and draw the

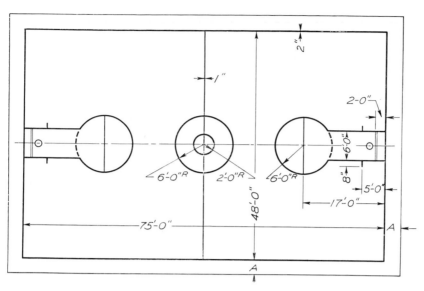

Fig. A-16   Basketball floor. **Prob. A·8.**

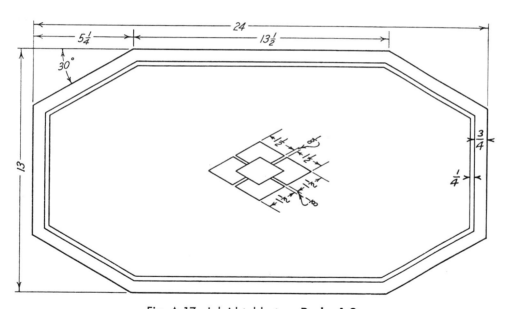

Fig. A-17   Inlaid table top. **Prob. A·9.**

Fig. A-18   Alternate centers for table top.

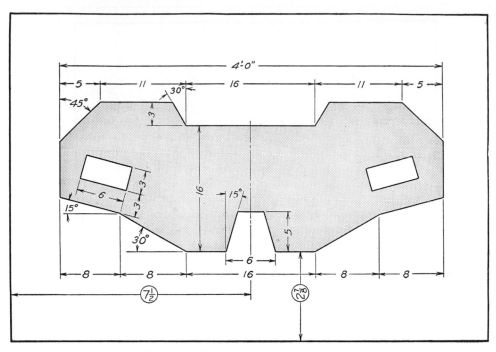

Fig. A-19 Shearing blank. **Prob. A·10.**

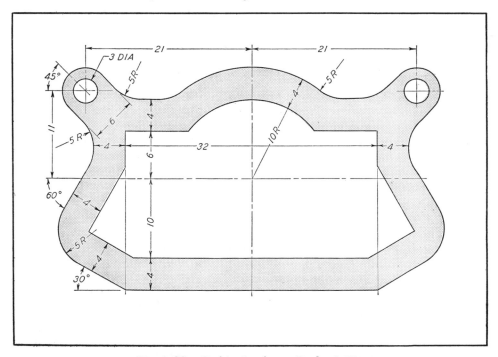

Fig. A-20 Cushioning base. **Prob. A·11.**

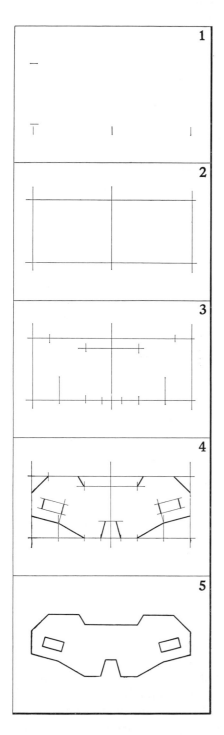

Fig. A-21   Order of working. **Prob. A·10.**

drawn with the triangles after locating one end of the line. See Fig. 2-8.

ORDER OF WORKING (Fig. A-21)

1) Locate vertical center line and measure 2′ on each side (Space 1). Note that this drawing must be made to the scale of 3″ = 1′ (Art. 2·22).
2) Locate vertical distances for top and bottom lines.
3) Draw main blocking-in lines as in Space 2.
4) Make measurements for starting points of inclined lines (Space 3).
5) Draw inclined lines with T-square and triangles (Space 4).
6) Finish as in Space 5.
7) Write name, sheet number, and date in record strip, and trim to size.

Problem A·11. To make a drawing of the *cushioning base* (Fig. A-20). For practice with triangles, compasses, and scale. Centers of arcs and tangent points must be carefully located.

ORDER OF WORKING (Fig. A-22)

1) Through the center of the working space, draw horizontal and vertical center lines. Measure horizontal and vertical distances. This drawing must be made to the scale of 3″ = 1′. Then draw horizontal and vertical lines (Space 1).
2) Draw inclined lines with 45° and 30°–60° triangles. Then draw large arcs and two semicircles with tangents at 45° (Space 2).
3) Locate centers and tangent points for the 5″ radius tangent arcs. To do this, measure 5″ perpendicularly from each tangent line and draw lines parallel to the tangent lines. The intersection of these lines will be the required centers. To find the

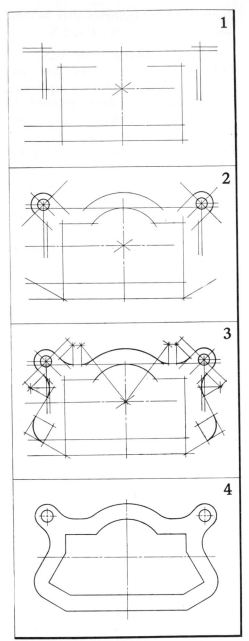

Fig. A-22   Order of working. **Prob. A·11.**

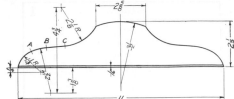

Fig. A-23   T-square head. **Prob. A·12.**

the 5″ arcs tangent to the middle arc, proceed as follows: Increase the radius of the larger arc by 5″ and draw two short arcs cutting lines parallel to and 5″ above the top horizontal tangent line. These points will be the centers. Lines joining these centers with the center of the large arc will locate the points of tangency of the arcs (Space 3).

Draw all the 5″ tangent arcs above the horizontal center line. Locate points of tangency and draw the two 60° tangent lines. Locate centers and draw the 5″ tangent arcs below the center line.

4) Complete the view by drawing the lines for the opening. Brighten the lines and finish (Space 4).

Problem A·12. Make a drawing of a *T-square head* (Fig. A-23). Plan a systematic order of working before starting the drawing. Note tangent points *A*, *B*, and *C*, and that *BC* is a straight line.

24·4 Alternate exercises for use of instruments. The following exercises may be used in place of, or in addition to, Probs. A·1 to A·12. They are to be drawn accurately with thin pencil lines and then brightened as finished pencil drawings, or inked on the paper, or traced.

points of tangency, draw lines from the centers perpendicular to the tangent lines. To find the centers for

Problems A·13 to A·20 are designed to be drawn in one-quarter of the working space of an 11″ × 17″ sheet. Lay out the sheet as in Fig. A-2 and draw horizontal and vertical lines to divide the space into four equal parts as shown in Fig. A-24.

Problem A·13 Fig. A-25. For T-square, triangle, scale, and bow dividers. Draw a 3″ by 5″ rectangle. With the dividers lay off three ¼″ spaces in both directions from each corner. Draw horizontal and vertical lines to complete the *frame*.

Problem A·14 Fig. A-26. For T-square, 45° triangle, scale, and dividers. Draw 3″ by 5″ and 2½″ by 4½″ rectangles. With the dividers, locate points A, B, C, and D, the centers of the sides of the large rectangle. From A, B, C, and D draw 45° lines. Measure ¼″ inside these lines and draw parallel lines to complete the *plate* as shown.

Problem A·15 Fig. A-27. For T-square, 30°–60° triangle, scale, and dividers. Draw 3″ × 5″ and 2½″ × 4½″ rectangles. With the dividers, locate points A and B, the centers of the long sides of the large rectangle. From A and B draw lines at 30° with the horizontal. From C, D, E, and F, draw lines at 60° with the horizontal. Measure ¼″ inside these lines and draw parallel lines to complete the *plate* as shown.

Problem A·16 Fig. A-28. For T-square, both triangles and scale. Draw a 3″ × 5″ rectangle. Locate points A, B,

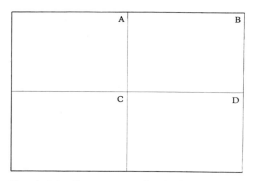

Fig. A-24   Sheet layout for four problems.

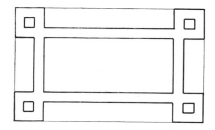

Fig. A-25   Frame. **Prob. A·13.**

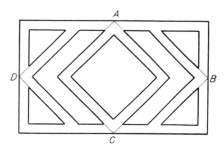

Fig. A-26   Plate. **Prob. A·14.**

Fig. A-27   Plate. **Prob. A·15.**

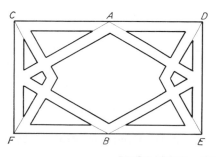

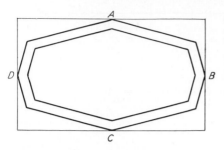

Fig. A-28　Plate. **Prob. A·16.**

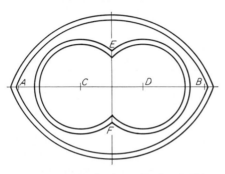

Fig. A-29　Dial plate. **Prob. A·17.**

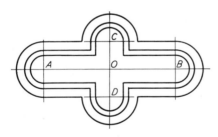

Fig. A-30　Frame. **Prob. A·18.**

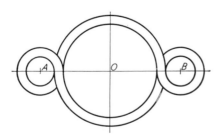

Fig. A-31　Ornament. **Prob. A·19.**

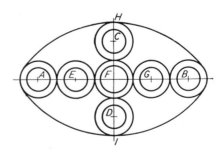

Fig. A-32　Dial plate. **Prob. A·20.**

C, and *D*, the centers of the sides, with the scale. From points *A*, *B*, *C*, and *D* draw lines at 15° with the sides of the rectangle, using combinations of the two triangles. Measure ¼″ inside of each of these lines and complete the *plate* as shown.

Problem A·17 Fig. A-29. For T-square, triangle, scale, dividers, and compasses. Draw line *AB* = 5″ and divide it into three equal parts with the dividers. With centers at *C* and *D*, draw arcs with radii of 1⅛″ and 1¼″. With centers at *E* and *F*, draw arcs with radii of 2¾″ and 2⅞″ to complete the *double dial plate* as shown.

Problem A·18 Fig. A-30. For T-square, triangle, scale, and bow pencil. Draw intersecting lines at right angles. Lay off *AO* = *OB* = 1¾″ and *OC* = *OD* = ¾″ with the scale. With centers at *A*, *B*, *C*, and *D* draw semicircles with radii of ⅜″, ½″, and ¾″. Draw horizontal and vertical tangent lines to complete the *frame* as shown.

Problem A·19 Fig. A-31. For T-square, scale, compasses, and bow pencil. Draw line *AB* = 3¾″. Locate *O*, the mid-point of *AB*. With center at *O*, draw circles with diameters of 2½″ and 3″. With centers at *A* and *B*, draw circles with diameters of ¾″ and 1¼″ to complete the *ornament* as shown.

Problem A·20 Fig. A-32. For T-square, triangle, scale, compasses, and bow pencil. Draw center lines at right angles. Lay off $FC = FD = FG = FE = EA = GB = 1″$. With centers at A, B, C, D, E, F, and G, draw circles with a diameter of 1″. With center at F draw a circle with a diameter of ¾″. With centers at A, B, C, D, E, and G, draw circles with a diameter of ⅝″. With centers at H and I draw tangent arcs with a radius of 3″ to complete *dial plate* as shown.

PROBLEMS FOR USE OF THE SCALES

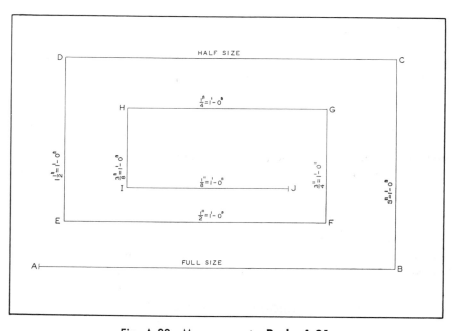

Fig. A-33   Measurements. **Prob. A·21.**

Problem A·21 Fig. A-33. Measure and record the lengths of the lines on the figure in the book at the scales indicated.

Problem A·22. Draw a figure similar to Fig. A-33 (Space 5¼ × 7½). Draw lines at the lengths and to the scales as follows:

$AB = 11⅜″$ at $6″ = 1′-0″$
$BC = 9′-7″$ at $⅜″ = 1′-0″$
$CD = 21′-10″$ at $¼″ = 1′-0″$
$DE = 22′-6″$ at $⅛″ = 1′-0″$
$EF = 3′-2½″$ at $1½″ = 1′-0″$
$FG = 2′-8½″$ at $¾″ = 1′-0″$
$GH = 8′-3″$ at $½″ = 1′-0″$
$HI = 5¾′$ at $3″ = 1′-0″$
$IJ = 3¹¹⁄₁₆″$ full size

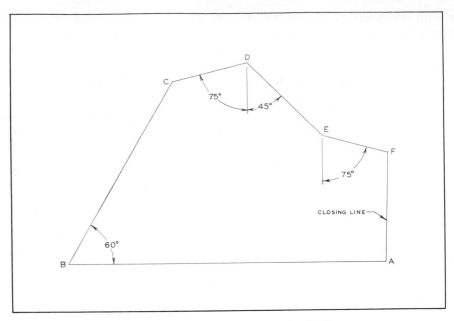

Fig. A-34 Measurements. **Prob. A·23.**

Problem A·23 Fig. A-34. Measure and record the lengths of the lines on the figure in the book. Use civil engineer's scale.
1) For scale of $1'' = 60'-0''$
2) For scale of $1'' = 40'-0''$
3) For scale of $1'' = 30'-0''$
4) For scale of $1'' = 100'-0''$

Problem A·24. Draw a figure similar to Fig. A-34 (Space 5¼ × 7½). Use civil engineer's scale. Draw lines at the angles shown at the lengths as follows for a scale of $1'' = 30'$. Measure closing line to nearest tenth of a foot and note it on your drawing. $AB = 172'$; $BC = 113'$; $CD = 54'$; $DE = 29'$; $EF = 37'$.

GROUP B. LETTERING

24·5 Lettering can best be taught using short practice periods. For such a purpose, inexpensive lettering practice books, ready ruled and with directions, are available. *Book I, Lessons in Lettering*, by French and Turnbull is for vertical letters, and *Book II* is for inclined letters.

The exercises that follow can be done in one-quarter of the working space of a regular sheet (Fig. A-24).

For pencil letters use a long conical point. Rotate the pencil in the fingers after each few strokes to keep the point symmetrical.

For ink letters use a penholder with a cork grip and set the pen well into the holder. Always use drawing ink for lettering. To get clean-cut letters, it is necessary to wipe the pen frequently with a cloth penwiper.

Problems are given for both vertical and inclined letters, but only one kind should be taught beginners.

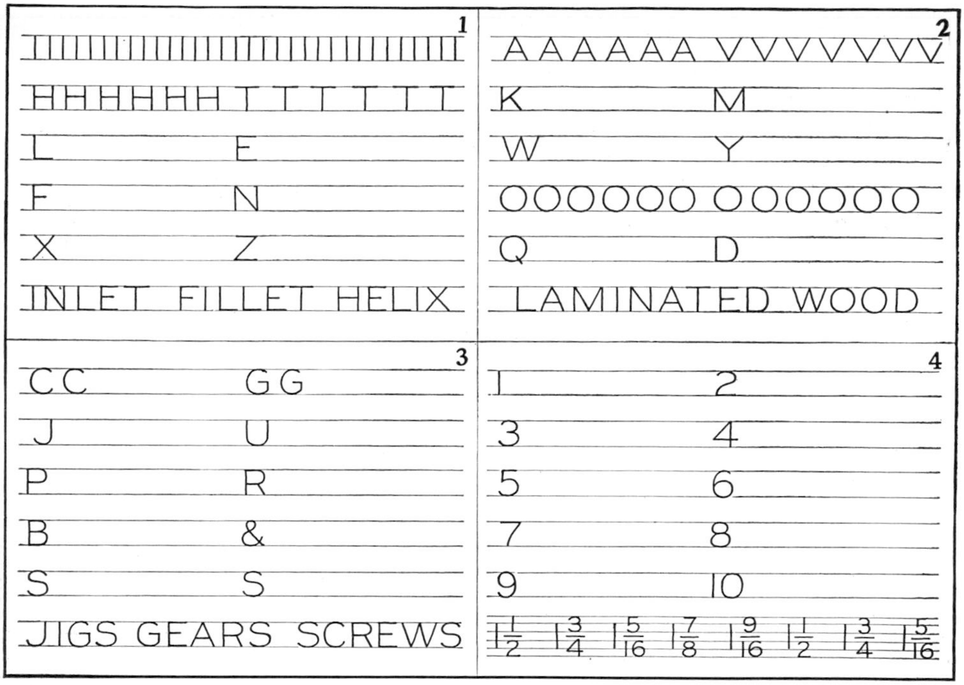

Fig. B-1 content (Above) Probs. B·1 to B·4.

1

IIIIIIIIIIIIIIIIIIIIIIIIIIIIIIII

HHHHHH T T T T T T

L   E

F   N

X   Z

INLET FILLET HELIX

2

A A A A A A V V V V V V V

K   M

W   Y

O O O O O O O O O O O O

Q   D

LAMINATED WOOD

3

C C   G G

J   U

P   R

B   &

S   S

JIGS GEARS SCREWS

4

1   2

3   4

5   6

7   8

9   10

$1\frac{1}{2}$ $1\frac{3}{4}$ $1\frac{5}{16}$ $1\frac{7}{8}$ $1\frac{9}{16}$ $1\frac{1}{2}$ $1\frac{3}{4}$ $1\frac{5}{16}$

Fig. B-1 (Above) **Probs. B·1 to B·4.**   Fig. B-2 (Below) **Probs. B·5 to B·8.**

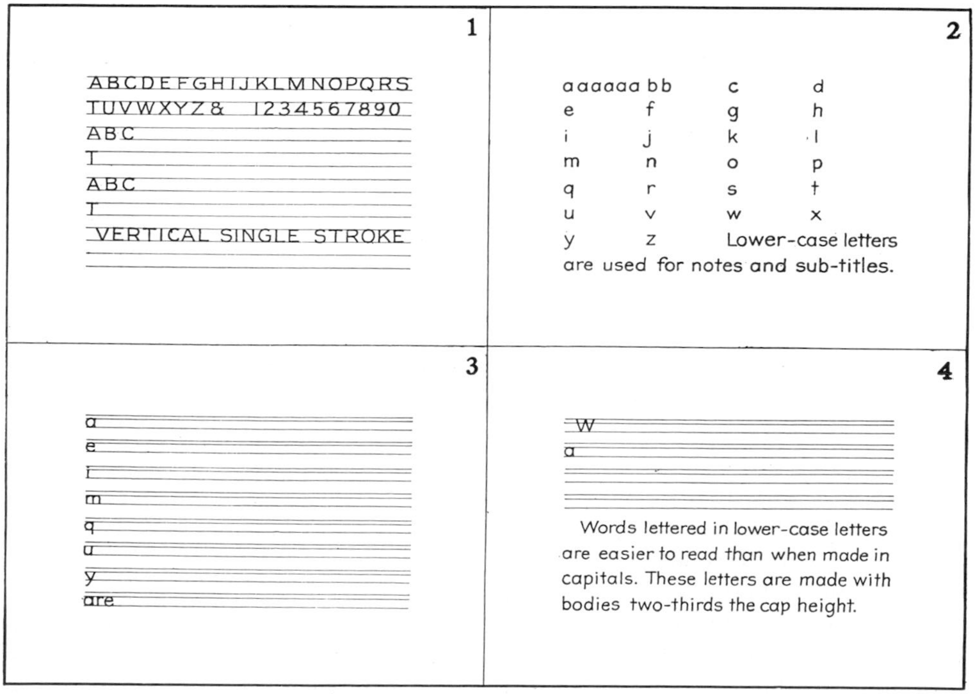

1

ABCDEFGHIJKLMNOPQRS
TUVWXYZ& 1234567890
ABC
I
ABC
I
VERTICAL SINGLE STROKE

2

a a a a a a b b   c   d
e   f   g   h
i   j   k   l
m   n   o   p
q   r   s   t
u   v   w   x
y   z   Lower-case letters
are used for notes and sub-titles.

3

a
e
i
m
q
a
y
are

4

w
a

Words lettered in lower-case letters
are easier to read than when made in
capitals. These letters are made with
bodies two-thirds the cap height.

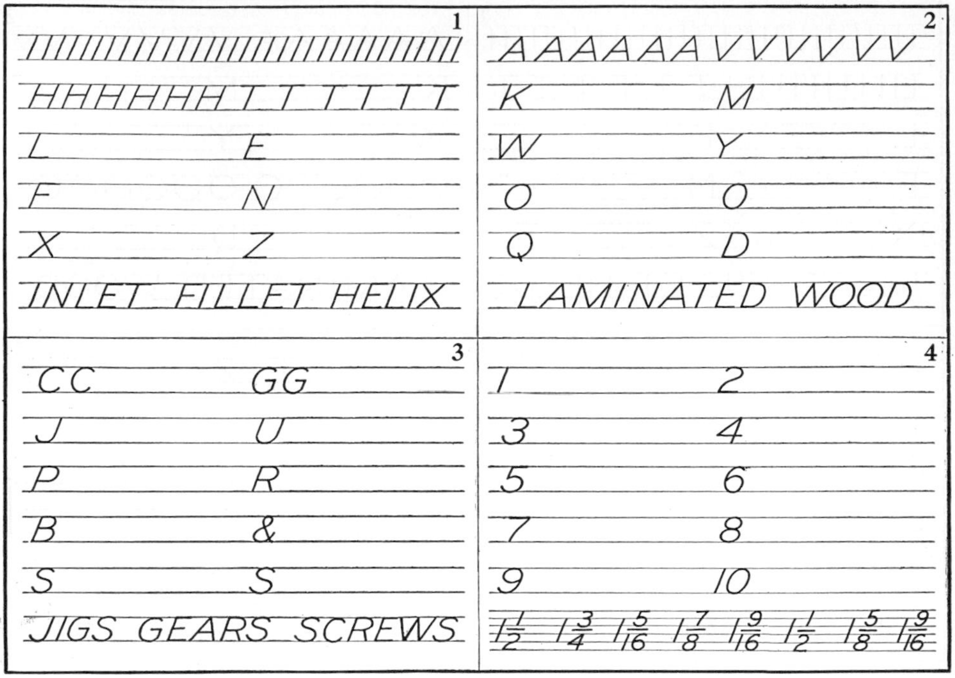

Fig. B-3 **Probs. B·9 to B·12.**

VERTICAL LETTERING

Problems B·1 to B·4 Fig. B-1. Single-stroke vertical capitals in pencil. Layout sheet as in Fig. A-24. Rule guidelines ⅜″ apart, starting ½″ over and 9/16″ down. Letter as indicated in each space, making a careful study of the letters with the order and direction of the strokes as given in Fig. 3-6. Complete each line. Prob. B·1, Space 1. Prob. B·2, Space 2. Prob. B·3, Space 3. Prob. B·4, Space 4 (see Figs. 3-6 and 3-9). Use an F pencil.

Problem B·5 Fig. B-2, Space 1. Rule guidelines 3/16″ apart, starting 1¼″ over and 1 3/16″ down. Make first two lines in pencil. Make next two lines very lightly in pencil and go over them with pen and ink. Use Gillott 404 pen. Make fifth and sixth lines in ink without first

penciling. Seventh line in pencil. Eighth line in ink.

Problem B·6 Fig. B-2, Space 2. Single-stroke vertical lower case in pencil. Rule guidelines as shown in lower left-hand space. Start 1¼″ over and 1 3/16″ down. The bodies of the letters are ⅛″ high. The first space is 1/16″ down, the next ⅛″, and the next 3/16″. Repeat until there are guidelines for eight lines of letters. Complete each line. Study Fig. 3-10.

Problem B·7 Fig. B-2, Space 3. Same as Prob. B·6, except that the lettering is to be done directly in ink.

Problem B·8 Fig. B-2, Space 4. Rule as for Prob. B·6. Letter the sentence first in pencil, then below, directly in ink.

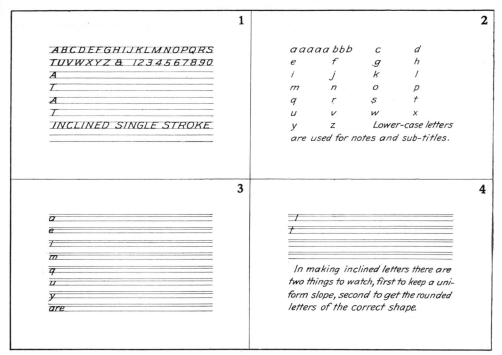

Fig. B-4   Probs. B·13 to B·16.

INCLINED LETTERING

Problems B·9 to B·12 Fig. B-3. Single-stroke inclined capitals in pencil. Lay out sheet as in Fig. A-24. Rule guidelines ⅜" apart, starting ½" over and ⁹⁄₁₆" down. Letter as indicated in each space, making a careful study of the letters with the order and direction of strokes as given in Fig. 3-12. Complete each line. Prob. B·9, Space 1. Prob. B·10, Space 2. Prob. B·11, Space 3. Prob. B·12, Space 4.

Problem B·13 Fig. B-4, Space 1. Rule guidelines ³⁄₁₆" apart, starting 1¼" over and 1³⁄₁₆" down. Make first two lines in pencil. Make next two lines very lightly in pencil and go over them with pen and ink. Use Gillott 404 pen. Make fifth and sixth lines in ink without first pen-

ciling. Seventh line in pencil. Eighth line in ink.

Problem B·14 Fig. B-4, Space 2. Single-stroke inclined lower case in pencil. Rule guidelines as shown in lower left-hand space. Start 1¼" over and 1³⁄₁₆" down. The bodies of the letters are ⅛" high. The first space is ¹⁄₁₆" down, the next ⅛", and the next ³⁄₁₆". Repeat until there are guidelines for eight lines of letters. Complete each line. Study Fig. 3-16.

Problem B·15 Fig. B-4, Space 3. Same as Prob. B·14 except that the lettering is to be done directly in ink.

Problem B·16 Fig. B-4, Space 4. Rule as for Prob. B·14. Letter the sentence first in pencil, then below, directly in ink.

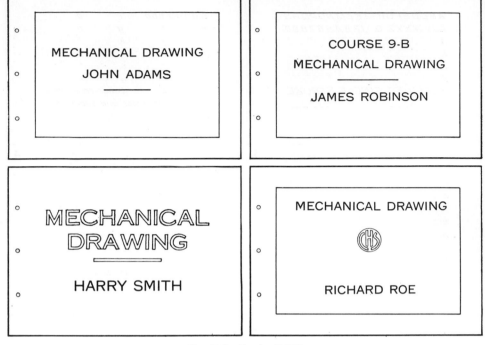

Fig. B-5   Prob. B·17.

Problem B·17. Design a *title page*. Suggestions for composition are shown in Fig. B-5 above.

GROUP C. GEOMETRICAL CONSTRUCTIONS

24·6 The working of a limited number of geometrical exercises is valuable both for the practice in the use of instruments and for the gaining of familiarity with the constructions that occur most frequently in drafting. Such problems must be worked very accurately with a very sharp 3H or 4H pencil and with comparatively light lines. A point should be located by two intersecting lines and the length of a line by two short dashes crossing the given line.

The following Probs. C·1 to C·34 are designed to be drawn in one-quarter of the working space of an 11″ × 17″ sheet. Lay out the sheets as in Fig.

A-24 and draw horizontal and vertical lines to divide the space into four equal parts as shown in Fig. A-24.

Problem C·1 Art. 4·2. Near the center of the space draw a line $3\frac{11}{16}$″ long and bisect it.

Problem C·2 Art. 4·2. Near the center of the space draw a line $3\frac{7}{16}$″ long and bisect it.

Problem C·3 Art. 4·3. Draw a horizontal line $5\frac{1}{2}$″ long and $1\frac{1}{2}$″ above bottom of the space. Erect a perpendicular to the line at a point 1″ to the left of the right-hand end of the line.

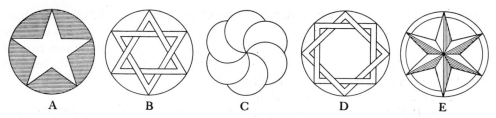

Fig. C-1 Probs. C·28 to C·34.

A   B   C   D   E

Problem C·4 Art. 4·4. Draw a vertical line near the center of the space. Locate a point O, 2″ down from the top of the space and 1″ in from the left side. Erect a perpendicular to the line from point O.

Problem C·5 Art. 4·6. Above the center of the space draw a horizontal line 5¹³⁄₁₆″ long. Divide it into seven equal parts geometrically.

Problem C·6 Art. 4·6. To the left of the center draw a vertical line 3⁷⁄₁₆″ long and divide it into five equal parts geometrically.

Problem C·7 Art. 4·9. Locate a point ¾″ above lower line of space and 1″ from left side. Draw lines joining the middle points of the upper and right-hand sides of the space. Bisect the angle between these lines.

Problem C·8 Art. 4·9. Locate a point ¾″ below the middle of the upper line of the space. Draw lines joining this point with the lower right-hand corner and with the middle of left side of space. Bisect the angle.

Problem C·9 Art. 4·10. Draw a vertical line ¾″ from left edge of space. From a point on this line ¾″ below top of space draw another line making any angle. Copy this angle so that one side is ¾″ from right side of space and vertex is ¾″ from bottom of space.

Problem C·10 Art. 4·10. From the middle of left side of space draw lines to upper and lower right-hand corners. Copy this angle so that one side is horizontal and ½″ above bottom of space.

Problem C·11 Art. 4·11. Draw a horizontal line 4¾″ long and 1″ above bottom of space. On it as a base construct a triangle having sides of 4⅛″ and 3¼″.

Problem C·12 Art. 4·11. Draw a vertical line 2⅞″ long and 1½″ from left side of space. On it construct a triangle having sides of 5⅛″ and 4¾″.

Problem C·13 Art. 4·11. Draw a horizontal line 4½″ long and 1″ above bottom of space. Using this as the longer of two sides, construct a right triangle by the 6–8–10 method.

Problem C·14 Art. 4·12. Draw a regular hexagon 3¾″ across corners.

Problem C·15 Art. 4·13. Draw a regular hexagon 4⅛″ across flats.

Problem C·16 Art. 4·14. Draw a regular pentagon in a circle with a diameter of 3¾″.

Problem C·17 Art. 4·15. Draw a regular octagon in a 3½″ square.

Problem C·18 Art. 4·16. Locate three points as follows: Point A 3¾″ from left edge of space and 4¼″ above bottom of space; B 5¼″ from left edge and 2⅝″ from bottom; C 2″ from left edge and 1¾″ from bottom. Draw a circle through A, B, and C.

Problem C·19 Art. 4·18. Locate a point ½″ from bottom of space and ½″ from left edge. Draw lines from this point to middle of top of space and to lower right-hand corner. Draw an arc tangent to these two lines with a radius of 1½″.

Problem C·20 Art. 4·21. Draw an arc having a radius of 3½″, with its center ¾″ from top of space and 1¾″ from left edge. Find the length of an arc of 60°.

Problem C·21 Art. 4·19. From the left edge of the space draw a horizontal line 1½″ long and 1¼″ below top of space. From right edge draw a horizontal line 1½″ long and 1¼″ above bottom of space. Join these two lines by an ogee curve. Point E to be one-third the distance from B to C (Fig. 4-28).

Problem C·22 Art. 4·22. Draw an equilateral triangle in the center of the space, sides ¾″ long. Draw one turn of an involute of the triangle.

Problem C·23 Art. 4·23. Locate a point 2¾″ below top of space and 2″ from left side of space. With this point as a center draw a circle having a diameter of 3″. Draw an involute of the right half of the circle.

Problem C·24 Art. 4·24. Draw horizontal and vertical lines through the center of the space. Draw one turn of a spiral of Archimedes in a 4″ diameter circle.

Problem C·25 Art. 4·28. Draw an ellipse having a major axis of 4″ and a minor axis of 2½″. Use concentric-circle method.

Problem C·26 Art. 4·27. Draw an ellipse having a major axis of 4″ and a minor axis of 1″. Use trammel method.

Problem C·27 Art. 4·29. Draw an approximate ellipse having a major axis of 4½″ and a minor axis of 3¼″.

Problem C·28. Divide a 4″ circle into 5 equal parts and draw a five-pointed star by connecting opposite points (Fig. C-1 at A).

Problem C·29. In a 4″ circle draw interlaced equilateral triangles (Fig. C-1 at B). The bands are ¼″ wide.

Problem C·30. Draw a 4″ circle. With six equally spaced radii as diameters draw circle arcs as in Fig. C-1 at C.

Problem C·31. Variation of Prob. C·30 using 5, 8, or 12 radii.

Problem C·32. Variation of Prob. C·30 or C·31, adding a concentric-circle arc one-half the radius of first arc.

Problem C·33. In a 4″ circle draw interlaced squares (Fig. C-1 at D), making the bands ¼″ wide.

Problem C·34. With a 30°–60° and 45° triangles together draw the six-pointed star of Fig. C-1 at E. Refer to Fig. 2-8.

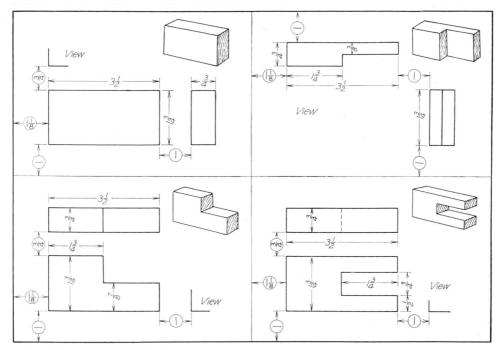

Fig. D-1   Shape description blocks. **Probs. D·1 to D·4.**

GROUP D.   SHAPE DESCRIPTION

24·7 The problems in this group are for practice in representing objects by views in order to gain a thorough understanding of the theory of shape description. Chapters 5, 6, and 7 should be studied carefully first. Views and pictures are given for some of the problems to assist the student in visualizing the object. In others two views are given, from which the student is to work out the third view. In still others pictures are given from which the student is required to determine what views are necessary, to plan and arrange the views in the working space, and then to work out the views.

Problems D·1 to D·4 Fig. D-1. Lay out an 11″ × 17″ sheet, as in Fig. A-2, and divide the working space into four equal parts. In each of the spaces draw three views of the block as shown. A picture of each block is given and two of the three views with dimensions. Complete the three views using full-size scale, and letter the record strip. When the sheet is finished, it will appear as in Fig. D-2. The record strip will contain the title, *Shape Description Blocks;* the scale, Full Size; and the date. See Figs. A-2 and A-3.

Most of the problems that follow may be worked in one-quarter of the regular working space except where otherwise indicated.

Problems D·5 to D·8 Fig. D-3. Draw three complete views of each of the *adjusting pieces.* Do not copy pictures.

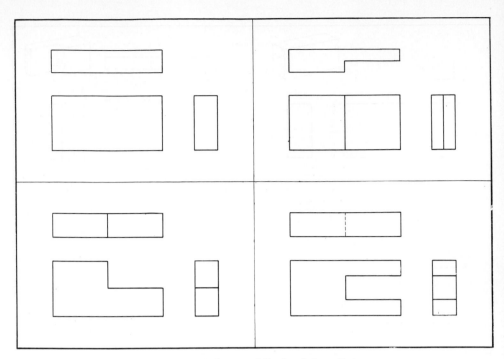

Fig. D-2   Solution of Probs. D·1 to D·4.

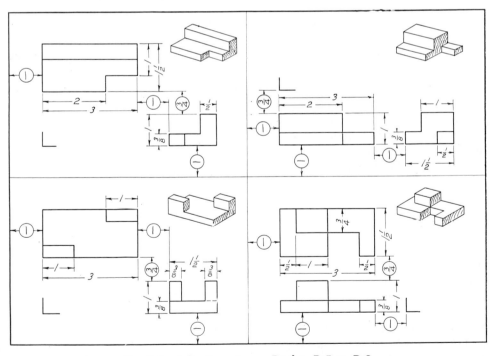

Fig. D-3   Adjusting pieces. **Probs. D·5 to D·8.**

382 MECHANICAL DRAWING

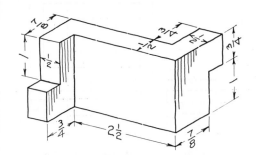

Fig. D-4   Offset spacer. **Prob. D·9.**

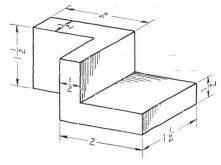

Fig. D-5   Angle spacer. **Prob. D·10.**

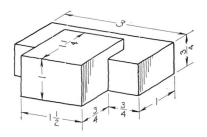

Fig. D-6   Front base. **Prob. D·11.**

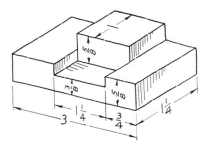

Fig. D-7   Rear base. **Prob. D·12.**

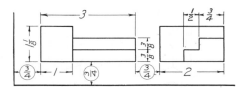

Fig. D-8   End stop. **Prob. D·13.**

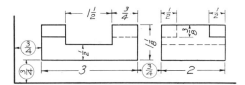

Fig. D-9   Intermediate stop. **Prob. D·14.**

Problem D·9 Fig. D-4. Draw three views of the *offset spacer*.

Problem D·10 Fig. D-5. Draw three views of the *angle spacer*.

Problem D·11 Fig. D-6. Draw three views of the *front base*.

Problem D·12 Fig. D-7. Draw three views of the *rear base*.

Problem D·13 Fig. D-8. Draw three views of the *end stop*.

Problem D·14 Fig. D-9. Draw three views of the *intermediate stop*.

Problem D·15 Fig. D-10. Draw three views of the *guide fork*.

Problem D·16 Fig. D-11. Draw three views of the *locating slide*.

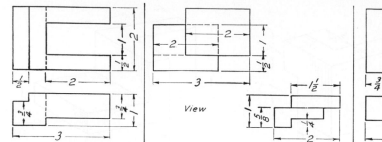

Fig. D-10 Guide fork. **Prob. D·15.**

Fig. D-11 Locating slide. **Prob. D·16.**

Fig. D-12 Guide center. **Prob. D·17.**

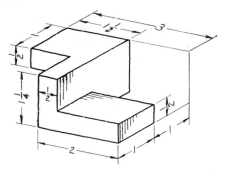

Fig. D-13 Angle stop. **Prob. D·18.**

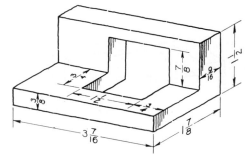

Fig. D-14 Corner lock. **Prob. D·19.**

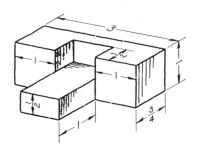

Fig. D-15 End anchor. **Prob. D·20.**

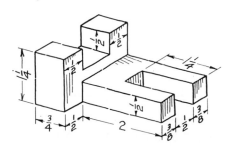

Fig. D-16 Double lock. **Prob. D·21.**

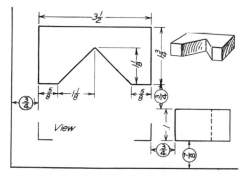

Fig. D-17 V-block. **Prob. D·22.**

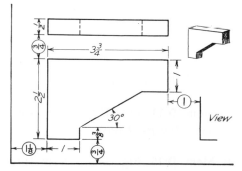

Fig. D-18 Plate bracket. **Prob. D·23.**

384 MECHANICAL DRAWING

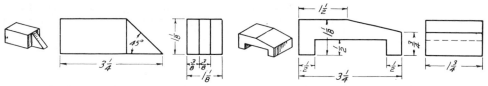

Fig. D-19   Stop. **Prob. D·24.**

Fig. D-20   Crossover. **Prob. D·25.**

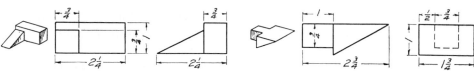

Fig. D-21   Adjusting block. **Prob. D·26.**

Fig. D-22   Plug stop. **Prob. D·27.**

Problem D·17 Fig. D-12. Draw three views of the *guide center*.

Problem D·18 Fig. D-13. Draw three views of the *angle stop*.

Problem D·19 Fig. D-14. Draw three views of the *corner lock*.

Problem D·20 Fig. D-15. Draw three views of the *end anchor*.

Problem D·21 Fig. D-16. Draw three views of the *double lock*.

Problem D·22 Fig. D-17. Draw three views of the *V-block*.

Problem D·23 Fig. D-18. Draw three views of the *plate bracket*.

Problem D·24 Fig. D-19. Draw three views of the *stop*.

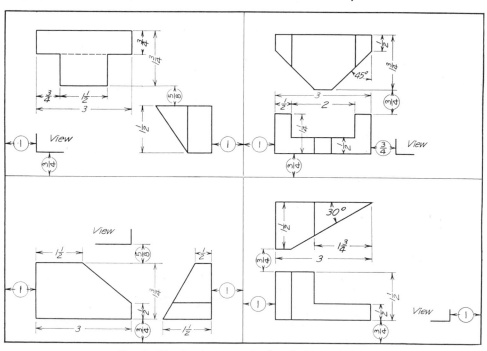

Fig. D-23   Angle stops. **Probs. D·28 to D·31.**

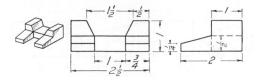

Fig. D-24   Placer. **Prob. D·32.**

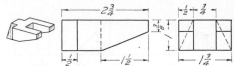

Fig. D-25   Adjustable slide. **Prob. D·33.**

Problem D·25 Fig. D-20. Draw three views of the *crossover*.

Problem D·26 Fig. D-21. Draw three views of the *adjusting block*.

Problem D·27 Fig. D-22. Draw three views of the *plug stop*.

Problems D·28 to D·31 Fig. D-23. Draw three views of each of the *angle stops*.

Problem D·32 Fig. D-24. Draw three views of the *placer*.

Problem D·33 Fig. D-25. Draw three views of the *adjustable slide*.

Problem D·34 Fig. D-26. Draw three views of the *holder*.

Problem D·35 Fig. D-27. Draw three views of the *lock stop*.

Problem D·36 Fig. D-28. Draw three views of the *middle stop*.

Problem D·37 Fig. D-29. Draw three views of the *offset guide*.

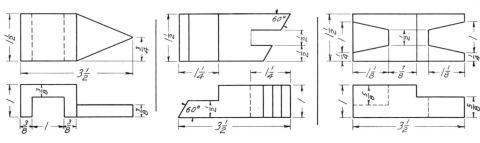

Fig. D-26   Holder.
Prob. D·34.

Fig. D-27   Lock stop.
Prob. D·35.

Fig. D-28   Middle stop.
Prob. D·36.

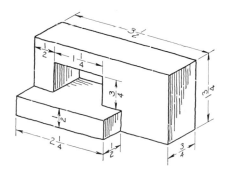

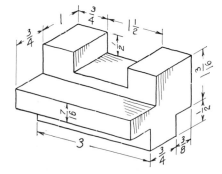

Fig. D-29   Offset guide. **Prob. D·37.**

Fig. D-30   Cross slide. **Prob. D·38.**

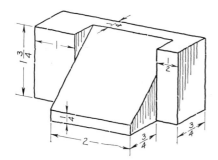

Fig. D-31   End stop. **Prob. D·39.**

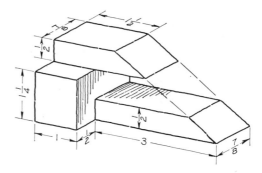

Fig. D-32   Latch. **Prob. D·40.**

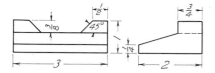

Fig. D-33   Groove support. **Prob. D·41.**

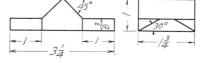

Fig. D-34   V-support. **Prob. D·42.**

Problem D·38 Fig. D-30. Draw three views of the *cross slide.*

Problem D·39 Fig. D-31. Draw three views of the *end stop.*

Problem D·40 Fig. D-32. Draw three views of the *latch.*

Problem D·41 Fig. D-33. Draw three views of the *groove support.*

Problem D·42 Fig. D-34. Draw three views of the *V-support.*

Problem D·43 Fig. D-35. Draw three views of the *bracket.*

Problem D·44 Fig. D-36. Draw three views of the *locator.*

Problem D·45 Fig. D-37. Draw three views of the *V-slide.*

Problem D·46 Fig. D-38. Draw three views of the *Y-guide.*

Problem D·47 Fig. D-39. Draw three views of the *corner lock.*

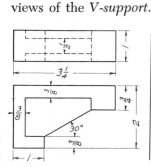

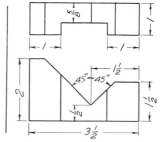

Fig.   D-35   Bracket.   Fig. D-36 Locator. **Prob. D·44.**   Fig.   D-37   V-slide.
Prob. D·43.   **Prob. D·45.**

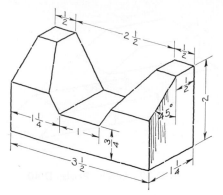

Fig. D-38   Y-guide. **Prob. D·46.**

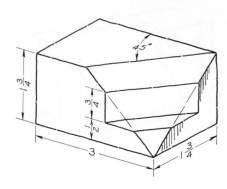

Fig. D-39   Corner lock. **Prob. D·47.**

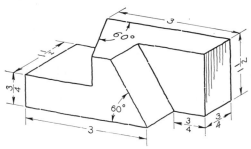

Fig. D-40   Wedge spacer. **Prob. D·48.**

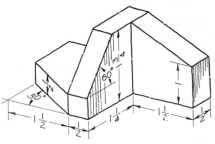

Fig. D-41   Double angle. **Prob. D·49.**

Problem D·48 Fig. D-40. Draw three views of the *wedge spacer.*

Problem D·49 Fig. D-41. Draw three views of the *double angle.*

Problem D·50 Fig. D-42. Draw three views of the *locator.*

Problem D·51 Fig. D-43. Draw three views of the *filler.*

Problem D·52 Fig. D-44. Draw three views of the *wedge.*

Problem D·53 Fig. D-45. Draw three views of the *positioner.*

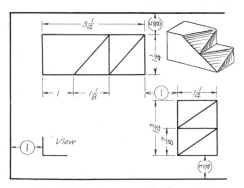

Fig. D-42   Locator. **Prob. D·50.**

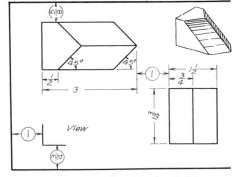

Fig. D-43   Filler. **Prob. D·51.**

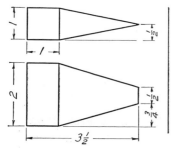

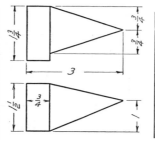

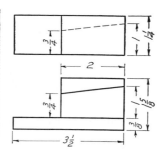

Fig. D-44 Wedge.
Prob. D·52.

Fig. D-45 Positioner.
Prob. D·53.

Fig. D-46 Holder.
Prob. D·54.

Problem D·54 Fig. D-46. Draw three views of the *holder*.

Problem D·55 Fig. D-47. Draw three views of the *latch*.

Problem D·56 Fig. D-48. Draw three views of the *slide*.

Problem D·57 Fig. D-49. Draw three views of the *holder*.

Problem D·58 Fig. D-50. Draw three views of the *pivot*.

Problem D·59 Fig. D-51. Draw three views of the *plate*.

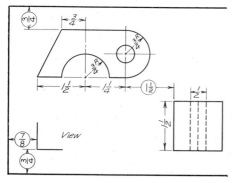

Fig. D-47 Latch. **Prob. D·55.**

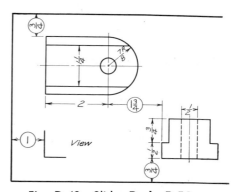

Fig. D-48 Slide. **Prob. D·56.**

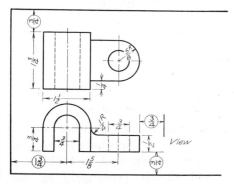

Fig. D-49 Holder. **Prob. D·57.**

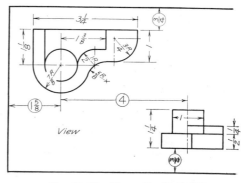

Fig. D-50 Pivot. **Prob. D·58.**

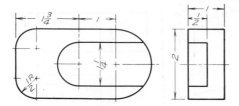

Fig. D-51   Plate. **Prob. D·59.**

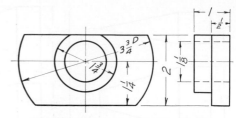

Fig. D-52   Bearing. **Prob. D·60.**

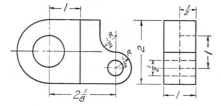

Fig. D-53   Link. **Prob. D·61.**

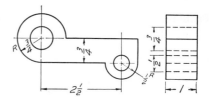

Fig. D-54   Locating plate. **Prob. D·62.**

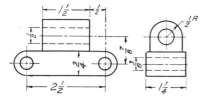

Fig. D-55   Sliding guide. **Prob. D·63.**

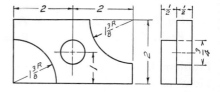

Fig. D-56   Link. **Prob. D·64.**

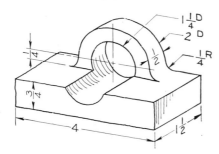

Fig. D-57   Base guide. **Prob. D·65.**

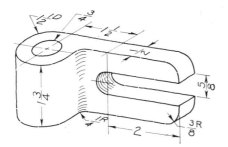

Fig. D-58   Vertical stop. **Prob. D·66.**

Problem D·60 Fig. D-52. Draw three views of the *bearing*.

Problem D·61 Fig. D-53. Draw three views of the *link*.

Problem D·62 Fig. D-54. Draw three views of the *locating plate*.

Problem D·63 Fig. D-55. Draw three views of the *sliding guide*.

Problem D·64 Fig. D-56. Draw three views of the *link*.

Problem D·65 Fig. D-57. Draw three views of the *base guide*.

Problem D·66 Fig. D-58. Draw three views of the *vertical stop*.

Problem D·67 Fig. D-59. A line is missing from one of the views of each of the objects shown at A to R. Make a freehand sketch (enlarged) of the views and supply the missing line.

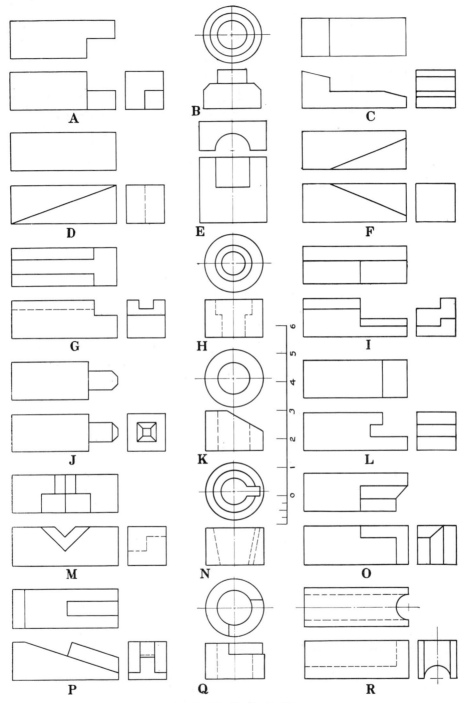

Fig. D-59 **Prob. D·67.**

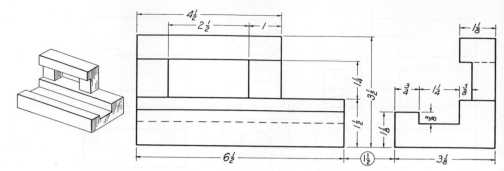

Fig. D-60   Support guide. **Prob. D·68.**

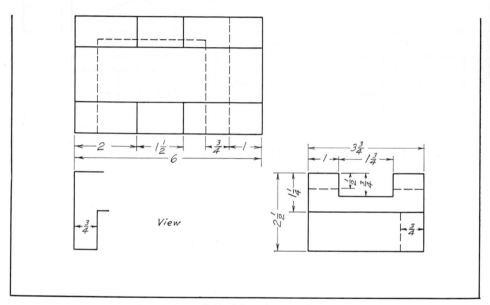

View

Fig. D-61   Slotted bracket. **Prob. D·69.**

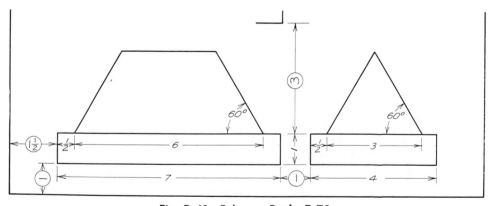

Fig. D-62   Fulcrum. **Prob. D·70.**

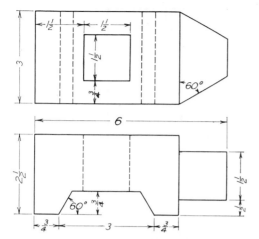

Fig. D-63 Locating support. **Prob. D·71.**

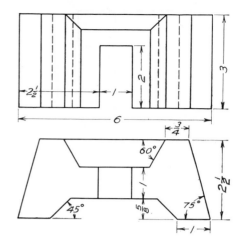

Fig. D-64 Base. **Prob. D·72.**

Problem D·68 Fig. D-60. Draw three views of the *support guide.*

Problem D·69 Fig. D-61. Draw three views of the *slotted bracket.*

Problem D·70 Fig. D-62. Draw three complete views of the *fulcrum.* Find height from the right-hand view.

Problem D·71 Fig. D-63. Draw three views of the *locating support.*

Problem D·72 Fig. D-64. Draw three views of the *base.*

Problem D·73 Fig. D-65. Draw three views of the *dovetail joint.*

Problem D·74 Fig. D-66. Draw three views of the *cast-iron dovetail.* Lay off one-half of 1¾″ on each side of the center line in the top view and draw 60° lines to intersect the ¾″ depth line.

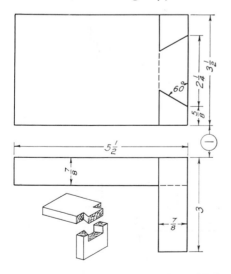

Fig. D-65 Dovetail joint. **Prob. D·73.**

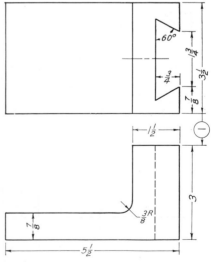

Fig. D-66 Cast-iron dovetail. **Prob. D·74.**

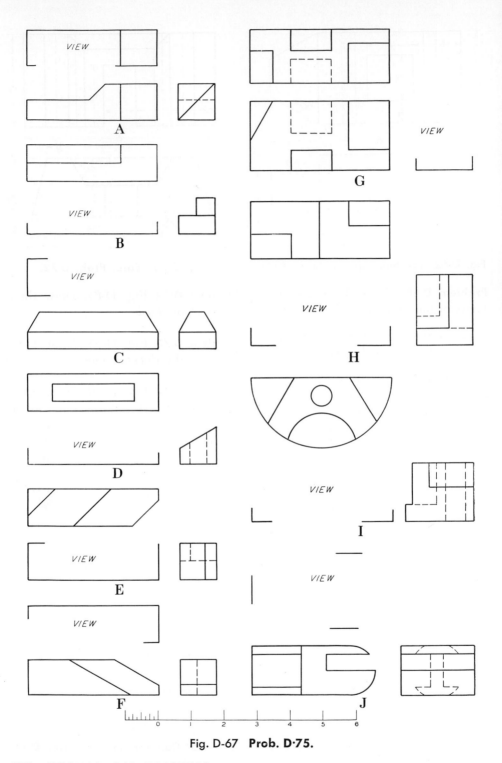

Fig. D-67 **Prob. D·75.**

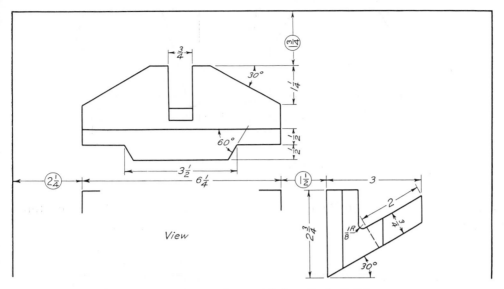

Fig. D-68 Secondary guide lug. **Prob. D·76.**

Problem D·75 Fig. D-67. One view is missing from each of the objects A to J. Make a freehand sketch (enlarged) showing three complete views of each object.

Problem D·76 Fig. D-68. Draw three views of the *secondary guide lug*.

Problem D·77 Fig. D-69. Draw three views of the *separator*.

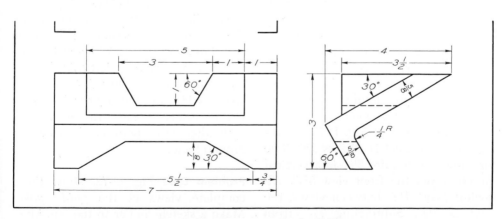

Fig. D-69 Separator. **Prob. D·77.**

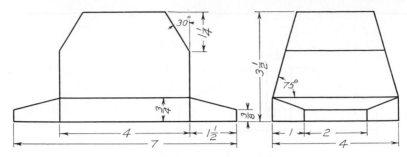

Fig. D-70 Base. **Prob. D·78.**

Problem D·78 Fig. D-70. Draw three views of the *base*.

Problem D·79 Fig. D-71. Draw three views of the *cross slide*.

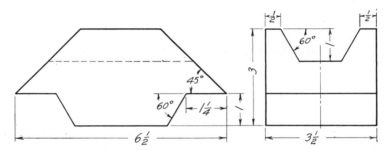

Fig. D-71 Cross slide. **Prob. D·79.**

24·8 Placing views. The location of the views for many of the preceding problems has been given. When drawings are made from objects or for things that have not been made, it is necessary for the draftsman to be able to place the views so that they will go in the space to advantage. This is done by considering the space necessary for each view and comparing the total room required with the size of the sheet.

Note the object of Fig. D-72. Working space on sheet is 10½″ × 15″. The top view will require 2½″ in a vertical direction and the front view 3⅜″. Allowing (say) 1½″ between views, the total is 7⅜″. Subtracting 7⅜″ from 10½″ (the height of the space), we have

left 2⅝″ to be divided between top and bottom. In the layout sketch (Fig. D-72) the base line of the front view has been placed 1⅜″ up, which leaves 1¼″ above the top line of the top view. The sum of the horizontal dimensions of the front and side views is 9¾″. Allowing 1⅞″ between views, there is left 3⅜″ for the two side spaces. In Fig. D-72 the left space is 1¾″ and the right is 1⅝″. It is not necessary to have the spaces exactly alike either between the views or around them.

Problem D·80 Fig. D-72. Draw three complete views of the *guide yoke*. Make a sketch similar to the one illustrated in Fig. D-72 and check the

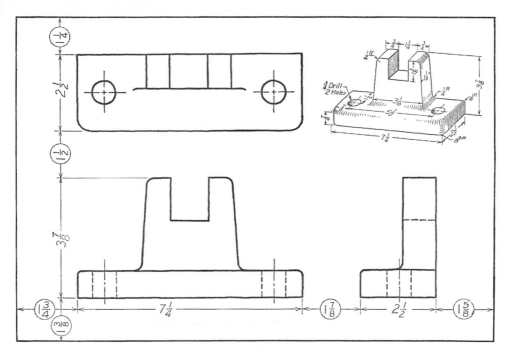

Fig. D-72 Guide yoke. **Prob. D·80.**

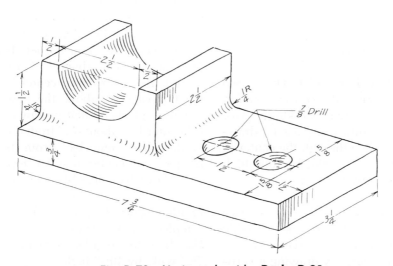

Fig. D-73   Horizontal guide. **Prob. D·81.**

computations for the spacing of the views before beginning the problem.

Problem D·81 Fig. D-73. Draw three views of the *horizontal guide.*

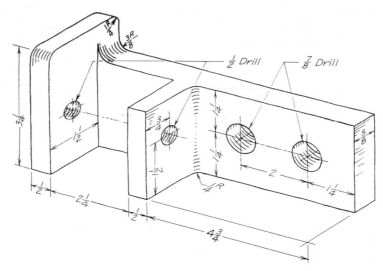

Fig. D-74   Vertical guide. **Prob. D·82.**

Problem D·82 Fig. D-74. Draw three views of the *vertical guide.*

Problem D·83 Fig. D-75. Draw three views of the *side cap.*

Problem D·84 Fig. D-76. Draw two complete views of the *cast-iron collar.* Divide the regular working space (10½″ × 15″) into two parts by drawing a vertical line through the center to provide a space 7½″ wide by 10½″ high in which to draw the views.

Problem D·85 Fig. D-77. Draw two complete views of the *socket.* Divide the regular working space (10½″ × 15″) into two parts by drawing a vertical line through the center to provide a space 7½″ wide by 10½″ high in which to draw the views.

Suggested spacing. For a sheet containing Probs. D·84 and D·85 or D·86

and D·87, the views required for each of these pieces would obviously be a top view and a front view. Draw a vertical center line for the left-hand figure about 3¾″ from the left border. Draw a base line about 1½″ from the bottom and a horizontal center line for the top view 6″ above the base line. For the right-hand figure draw a vertical center line about 3¾″ from the right border, base line 1½″ from bottom border, and center line for top view 5¼″ above base line of front views.

Problem D·86 Fig. D-78. Draw two complete views of the *stud bushing.* Use half the regular working space. 7½″ wide by 10½″ high.

Problem D·87 Fig. D-79. Draw two complete views of the *swivel base.* Use half of the regular working space. 7½″ wide by 10½″ high.

398 MECHANICAL DRAWING

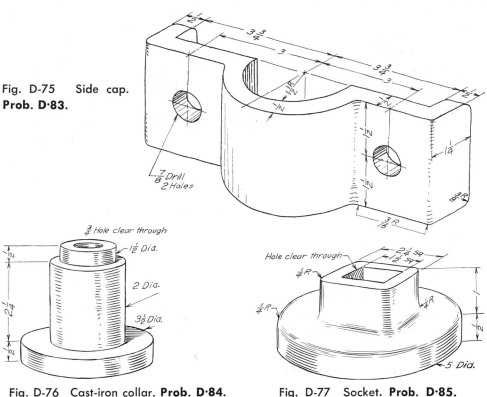

Fig. D-75   Side cap. **Prob. D·83.**

Fig. D-76   Cast-iron collar. **Prob. D·84.**

Fig. D-77   Socket. **Prob. D·85.**

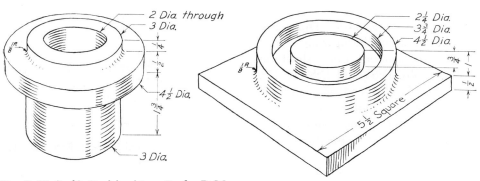

Fig. D-78 (*Left*) Stud bushing. **Prob. D·86.**

Fig. D-79 (*Right*) Swivel base. **Prob. D·87.**

Problem D·88 Fig. D-80. Draw two complete views of the *centering plate.* Four holes are to be drilled and countersunk in the plate for ½″ flat-head cap screws (see Appendix page 535 for dimensions).

Fig. D-80   Centering plate. **Prob. D·88.**

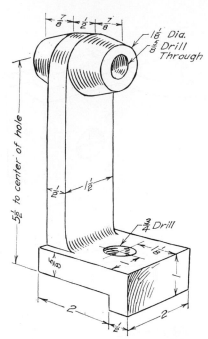

Fig. D-81   Bearing. **Prob. D·89.**

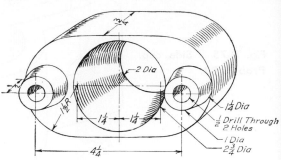

Fig. D-82   Rocker block. **Prob. D·90.**

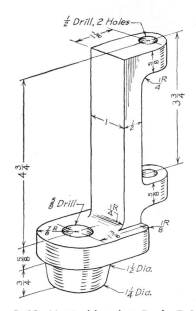

Fig. D-83   Vertical bracket. **Prob. D·91.**

Problem D·89 Fig. D-81. Draw front and side views of the *bearing*.

Suggested spacing. For a sheet containing Probs. D·88 and D·89 or D·90 and D·91, draw a vertical center line for the left-hand figure about 4″ from the left border. Then work out the spacing in a vertical direction on the center line as explained in Art. 24·8 on Placing Views. In a similar manner work out the placing of the views for the right-hand figure in the remaining space.

Problem D·90 Fig. D-82. Draw two complete views of the *rocker block*. The ½″ holes extend through the piece.

Problem D·91 Fig. D-83. Draw three complete views of the *vertical bracket*.

Problem D·92 Fig. D-84. Draw three views of the *dovetail base*.

Problem D·93 Fig. D-85. Draw three views of the *V-block base*.

Problem D·94 Fig. D-86. Draw three views of the *adjustable fork*.

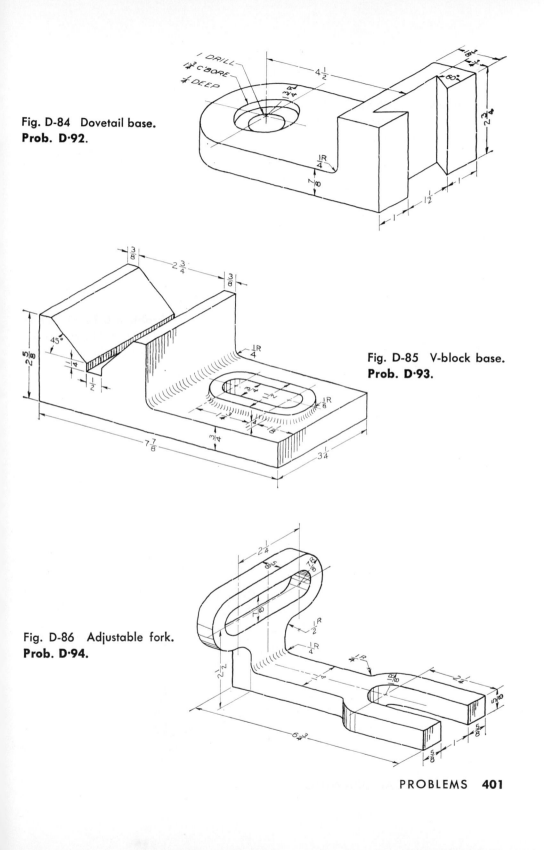

Fig. D-84   Dovetail base.
Prob. D·92.

Fig. D-85   V-block base.
Prob. D·93.

Fig. D-86   Adjustable fork.
Prob. D·94.

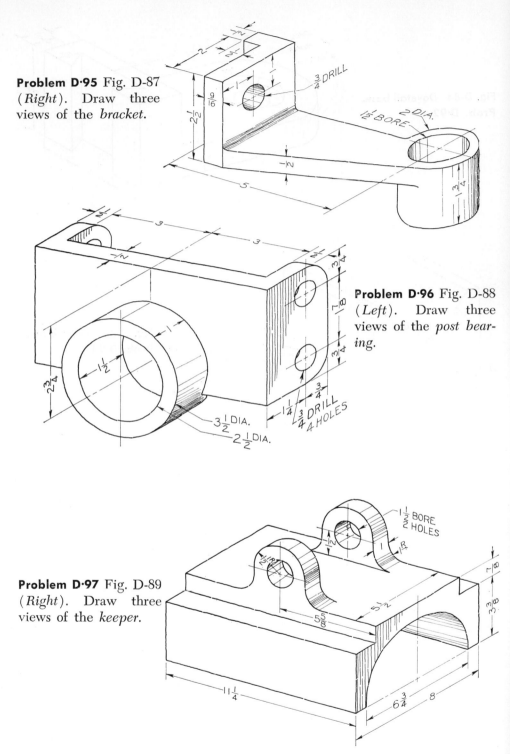

Problem D·95 Fig. D-87 (*Right*). Draw three views of the *bracket*.

Problem D·96 Fig. D-88 (*Left*). Draw three views of the *post bearing*.

Problem D·97 Fig. D-89 (*Right*). Draw three views of the *keeper*.

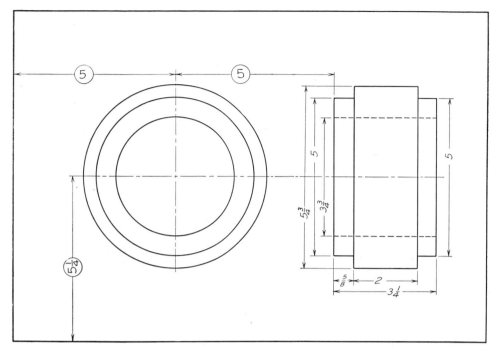

Fig. E-1   Cylindrical spacer. **Prob. E·1.**

24·9 Study carefully Chap. 8. The cut surface is to be indicated by section lining with uniformly spaced thin lines at 45°; about ¹⁄₁₆″ apart.

Problem E·1 Fig. E-1. Make a two-view drawing of the *cylindrical spacer,* the right-hand view to be a full section.

Problem E·2 Fig. E-2. Make a two-view drawing of the *reducing spacer.* The right-hand view, which is given, is to be a full section.

Problem E·3 Fig. E-3. Make a two-view drawing of the *clamping disk.* The right-hand view, which is given, is to be a full section.

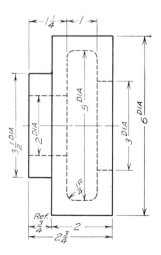

Fig. E-2   Reducing spacer. **Prob. E·2.**

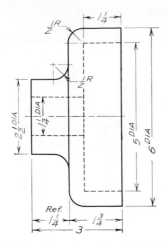

Fig. E-3 Clamping disc. **Prob. E·3.**

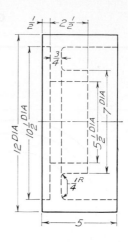

Fig. E-4 Collar. **Prob. E·4.**

Problem E·4 Fig. E-4. Make a two-view drawing of the *collar*. The right-hand view, which is given, is to be a full section.

Problem E·5 Fig. E-5. Make a two-view drawing of the *steam piston*. The left-hand view, which is given, is to be a full section.

Problem E·6 Fig. E-6. Make a two-view drawing of the *water-piston body*. The right-hand view, which is given, is to be a full section.

Problem E·7 Fig. E-7. Make a two-view drawing of the *shaft cap*. The left-hand view, which is given, is to be a full section.

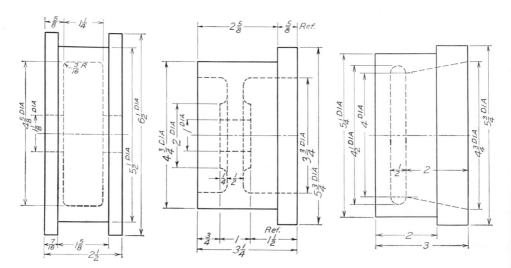

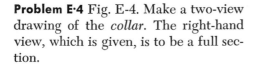

Fig. E-5 Steam piston. **Prob. E·5.**

Fig. E-6 Water-piston body. **Prob. E·6.**

Fig. E-7 Shaft cap. **Prob. E·7.**

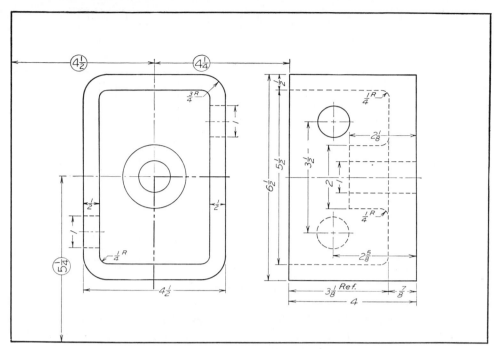

Fig. E-8 Protected bearing. **Prob. E·8.**

Problem E·8 Fig. E-8. Make a two-view drawing of the *protected bearing*, showing the right-hand view as a half section. Read Art. 8·4.

Problem E·9 Fig. E-9. Copy the views (enlarged). Show a view in section on the plane indicated. Use the scale to estimate the dimensions for sketching or for taking off with the dividers if the views are drawn with the instruments.

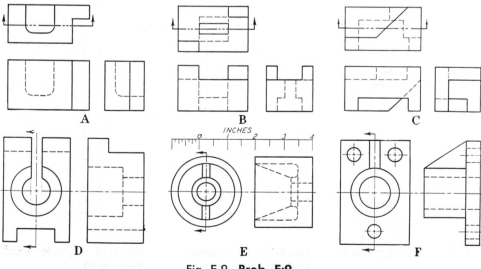

Fig. E-9 **Prob. E·9.**

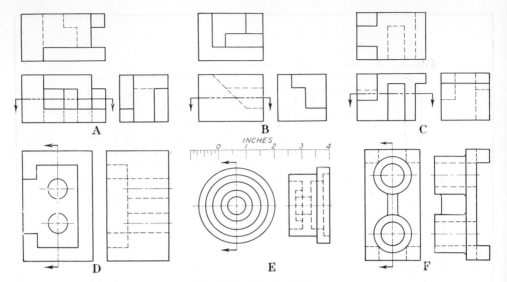

A   B   C

INCHES

D   E   F

Fig. E-10   **Prob. E·10.**

Problem E·10 Fig. E-10. Copy the views freehand (enlarged). Show a view in section on the plane indicated. Use the scale to estimate dimensions for sketching or for taking off with the dividers if the views are drawn with the instruments.

Problem E·11 Fig. E-11. Make a two-view drawing of the *cylinder head*. The left-hand view, which is given, is to be a half section.

Problem E·12 Fig. E-12. Make a two-view drawing of the *cone spacer*. The

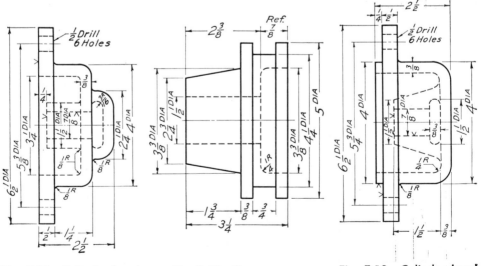

Fig. E-11   Cylinder head.
Prob. E·11.

Fig. E-12   Cone spacer.
Prob. E·12.

Fig. E-13   Cylinder head.
Prob. E·13.

406 MECHANICAL DRAWING

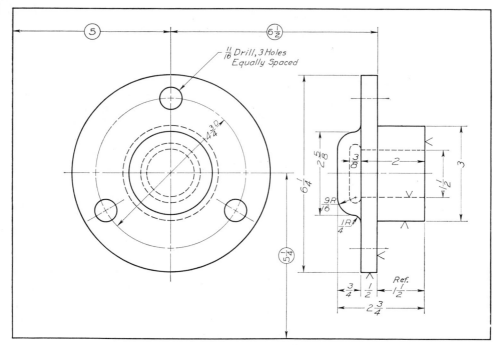

Fig. E-14 End cap. **Prob. E·14.**

right-hand view, which is given, is to be a full section.

Problem E·13 Fig. E-13. Make a two-view drawing of the *cylinder head*. The right-hand view, which is given, is to be a half section.

Problem E·14 Fig. E-14. Make a two-view drawing of the *end cap*, showing the right-hand view in section.

Problem E·15 Fig. E-15. Draw the necessary views of the *flanged latch*. Show a revolved section.

Fig. E-15 Flanged latch. **Prob. E·15.**

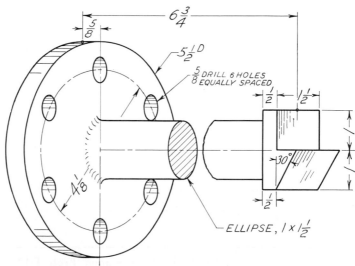

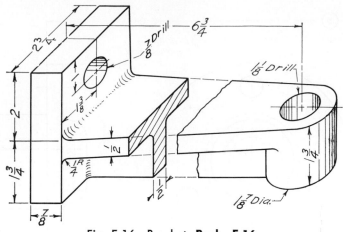

Fig. E-16 Bracket. **Prob. E·16.**

Problem E·16 Fig. E-16. Draw the necessary views of the *bracket*. Show a revolved section.

Problem E·17 Fig. E-17. Make a two-view drawing of the *hood bearing*. Show the right-hand view in section.

Problem E·18 Fig. E-18. Draw three views of the *yoke,* the front view in section. There are two pieces: the yoke and the bushing. Do not copy the picture.

Problem E·19 Fig. E-19. Draw three

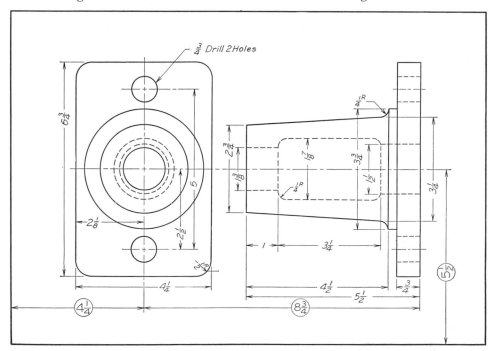

Fig. E-17 Hood bearing. **Prob. E·17.**

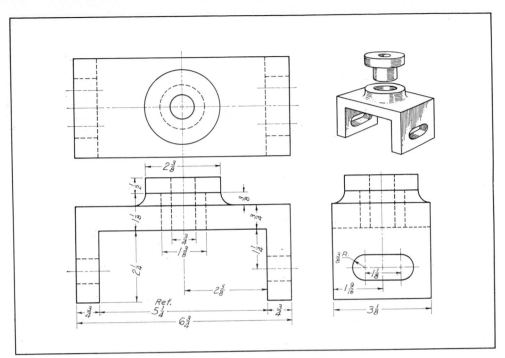

Fig. E-18   Yoke. **Prob. E·18.**

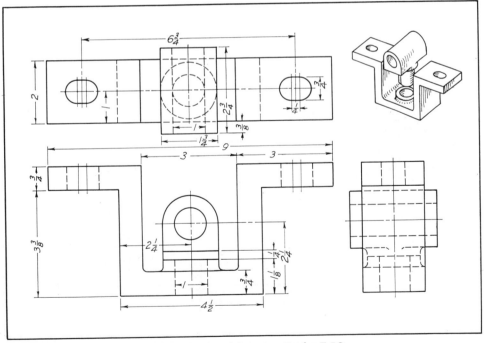

Fig. E-19   Swivel hanger. **Prob. E·19.**

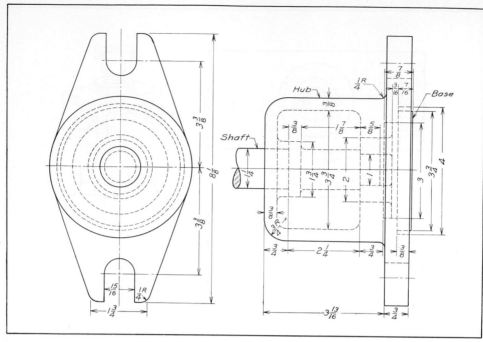

Fig. E-20 Thrust bearing. **Prob. E·20.**

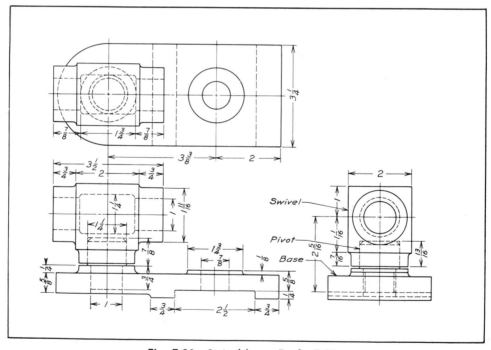

Fig. E-21 Swivel base. **Prob. E·21.**

410 MECHANICAL DRAWING

views of the *swivel hanger,* the right-side view to be a section. There are two pieces: the hanger and the bearing.

Problem E·20 Fig. E-20. Draw three views of the *thrust bearing,* the right-hand view to be a section. There are three parts: the shaft, hub, and base.

Problem E·21 Fig. E-21. Draw three views of the *swivel base.* The front view to be in section.

The problems in this group have all been sectioned lined as if made of cast iron. Occasionally it is desirable, as an aid in reading a drawing, to use one or more of the symbols for other materials, as stated in Art. 11·10. The following exercise is given for practice with symbolic section lining.

Problem E·22 Symbolic section lining. Fig. 11-9. Lay off sixteen $1\frac{1}{2}'' \times 2\frac{1}{2}''$ rectangles equally spaced. In these draw the first 12 and a choice of 4 other symbols shown in Fig. 11-9. Make cast-iron section lines about $\frac{1}{8}''$ apart, and others in proportion. Letter names of materials under the rectangles.

GROUP F. AUXILIARY VIEWS

24·10 Study Chap. 9 on auxiliary views before beginning the problems. In the layouts of the problems the location is given for the center line or reference line, parallel to the slanting surface, on which the auxiliary view is to be constructed. In the case of symmetrical figures the center line corresponds to the horizontal center line of the top view, as in Prob. F·1. For unsymmetrical figures, the reference line is usually taken at the back on the top view as in Prob. F·2. The projection lines from the front view of the object to the auxiliary view are shown in the layouts to aid in starting the problems. If drawn by the student, they should be extremely light so as not to confuse the result. The title for sheets with Probs. F·1 to F·24 is *auxiliary views.*

Problem F·1 Fig. F-1. The figure gives the layout for two problems. Draw the top, front, and the complete auxiliary view of the *rectangular prism* as shown.

Problem F·2 Fig. F-1. Draw the views given and the complete auxiliary view of the *triangular prism.*

Problems F·3 to F·7. Figures F-2 to F-6 are alternate problems similar to Probs. F·1 and F·2. These and many other problems may be changed by using a different angle for the inclined surface, as 30° instead of the 45°.

Problem F·8 Fig. F-7. Use half a regular working space. Make a drawing of the *anchor lug* including a complete auxiliary view. The hole and rounded end need not be shown in the top view.

Problem F·9 Fig. F-8. Use half of a regular working space. Make a drawing of the *inclined bearing* including an aux-
(*Text continued on page 414.*)

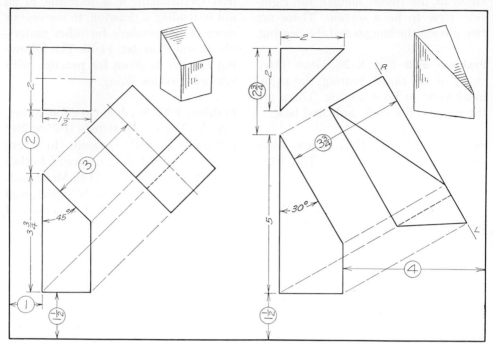

Fig. F-1 Auxiliary views. **Probs. F·1 and F·2.**

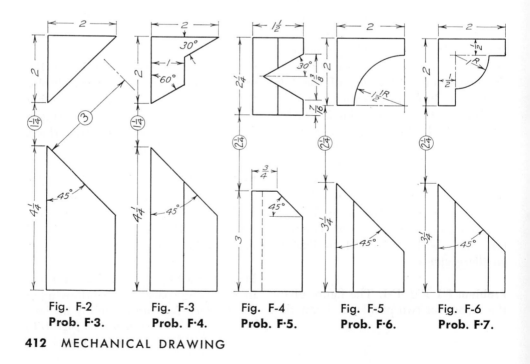

Fig. F-2
Prob. F·3.

Fig. F-3
Prob. F·4.

Fig. F-4
Prob. F·5.

Fig. F-5
Prob. F·6.

Fig. F-6
Prob. F·7.

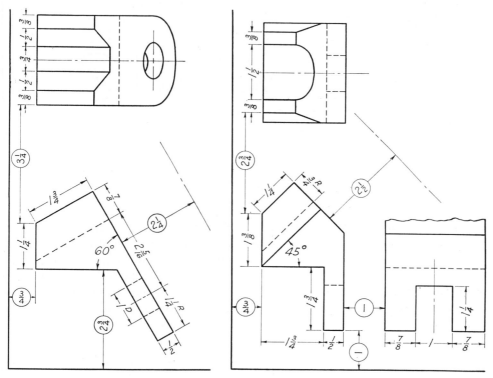

Fig. F-7 Anchor lug. **Prob. F·8.**

Fig. F-8 Inclined bearing. **Prob. F·9.**

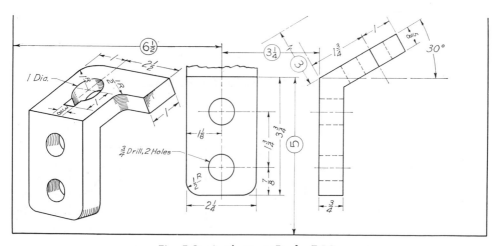

Fig. F-9 Angle stop. **Prob. F·10.**

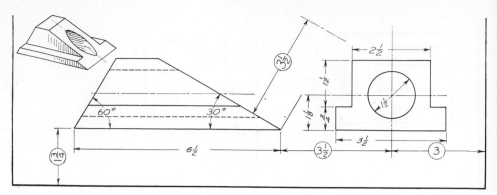

Fig. F-10   Hollow molding. **Prob. F·11.**

iliary view. The top view will not be needed and the right-hand view can be a partial view.

Problem F·10 Fig. F-9. Draw the two views as given and a part auxiliary view for the *angle stop.*

Problem F·11 Fig. F-10. A picture and a layout for a piece of *hollow molding* are shown in the figure. Consider the left-hand view to be the front view. Draw the front and side views as shown. Draw a complete auxiliary view **on** a plane parallel to the cut face. Re-

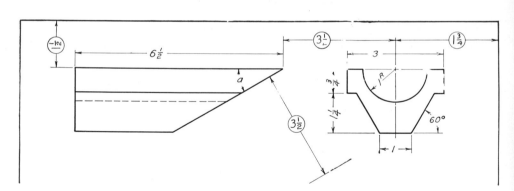

Fig. F-11   Molding. **Prob. F·12.**

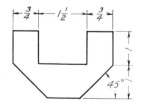

Fig. F-12   **Prob. F·13.**

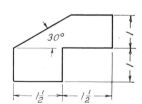

Fig. F-13   **Prob. F·14.**

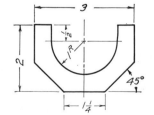

Fig. F-14   **Prob. F·15.**

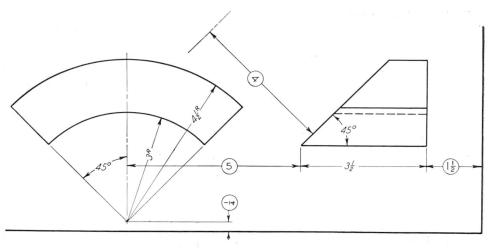

Fig. F-15 Saddle. **Prob. F·16.**

fer to Art. 9·4. Note that this will be a right-auxiliary view made on a plane perpendicular to the vertical plane. See Fig. 9-6 and compare with your solution of this problem. Do not copy the picture.

Problem F·12 Fig. F-11. The views of the piece of *molding* are located from the top of the space. Consider the left-hand view to be the front view. Draw the views as shown and complete aux-

iliary view. Make angle *a* equal to 30° or 45° as directed by the instructor.

Problems F·13 to F·15. Figs. F-12 to F-14. These are alternate problems similar to Prob. F·12. Use layout of Fig. F-11. The right-hand views are shown. Front view is to be 6½″ long and the angle *a* is to be 30° or 45°.

Problem F·16 Fig. F-15. Draw given views and a complete auxiliary view of the *saddle*.

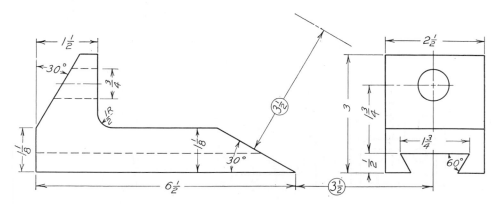

Fig. F-16 Sloping dovetail. **Prob. F·17.**

Fig. F-17 Shaft holder. **Prob. F·18.**

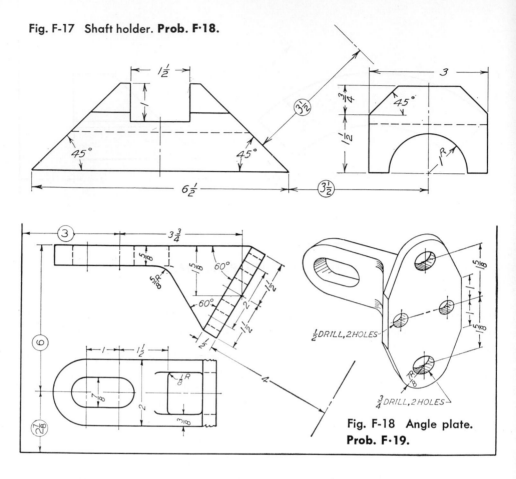

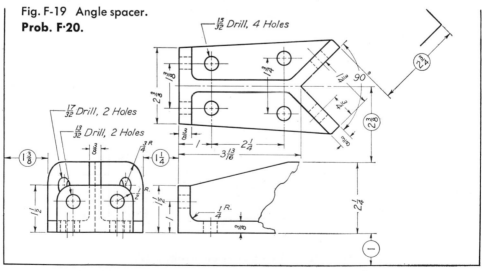

Fig. F-18 Angle plate. **Prob. F·19.**

Fig. F-19 Angle spacer. **Prob. F·20.**

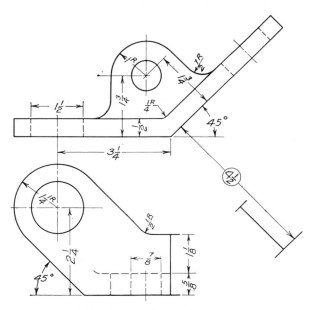

Fig. F-20   Angle rail support. **Prob. F·21.**

Problem F·17 Fig. F-16. Using a layout similar to Fig. F-10, draw the two views given, and from these draw the complete auxiliary view of the *sloping dovetail*.

Problem F·18 Fig. F-17. Draw views given and a complete auxiliary view of the *shaft holder*. Use layout similar to Fig. F-10.

Problem F·19 Fig. F-18. A picture and a layout for an *angle plate* are shown in the figure. Draw the top view and the part front view as shown. Draw a part auxiliary view where indicated on the layout. Note that this is an auxiliary elevation as it is made on a plane perpendicular to the horizontal plane. See Fig. 9-5 and compare with the solution of your problem. Do not copy the picture. Dimension if required by the instructor.

Problem F·20 Fig. F-19. A top view, a left-side view, and an incomplete front view of an *angle spacer* are shown on the layout in the figure. Draw the top view, finish the incomplete front view, and draw the side view. The hidden parts of the holes that show as ellipses in the front and side views need not be drawn. Draw a part auxiliary view where indicated in the upper right-hand part of the space. Art. 9·5. Note that this will be an auxiliary elevation as it is made on a plane perpendicular to the horizontal.

Problem F·21 Fig. F-20. A top view and part front view of an *angle rail support* are shown in the layout in the figure. Draw the top view and the part front view as shown. Draw a part auxiliary view where indicated on the layout. Refer to Art. 9·4. Note that this will be

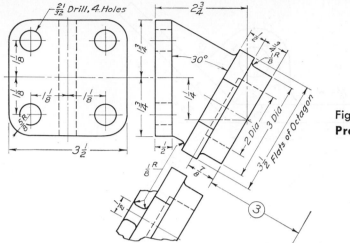

Fig. F-21 Angle cap.
Prob. F·22.

an auxiliary elevation as it is made on a plane perpendicular to the horizontal plane. See Fig. 9-5 and compare with the solution of your problem. Dimension if required by the instructor.

Problem F·22 Fig. F-21. A part front view, a right-side view, and a part auxiliary view of an *angle cap* are shown on the layout in the figure. Draw the views given and another part auxiliary

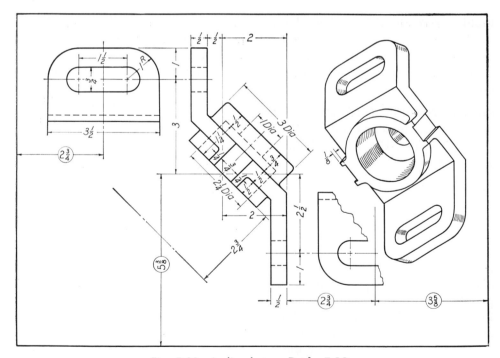

Fig. F-22 Inclined stop. **Prob. F·23.**

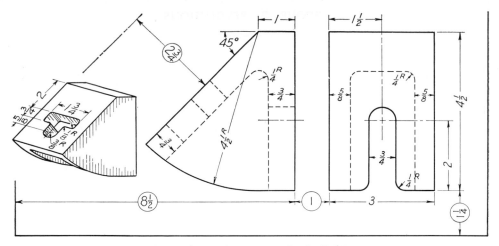

Fig. F-23   Angle support. **Prob. F·24.**

view where indicated on the layout. Refer to Art. 9·4. Note that this last auxiliary view is a rear auxiliary view and that the one shown on the layout is a front auxiliary view. See Fig. 9-7 and compare with the solution of your problem. Dimension if required by the instructor.

Problem F·23 Figure F-22 shows a picture and a layout for an *inclined stop*. The complete view in the middle of the space is the right-side view. Draw

this side view. Draw the part front view shown in the upper left-hand part of the space. Draw a part rear view on both sides of the vertical center line in the lower right-hand part of the space. Draw an auxiliary view of the inclined part. Refer to Art. 9·4. Note that this will be a front auxiliary view.

Problem F·24 Fig. F-23. Draw the two views given and an auxiliary view of the inclined face of the *angle support*.

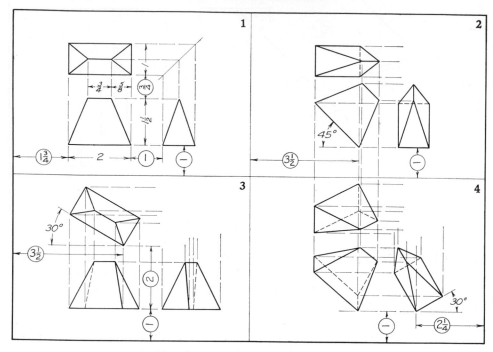

Fig. G-1 Revolutions. **Prob. G·1.**

24·11 Study Arts. 9·7 to 9·13 and understand the rule of revolution as there explained before beginning the problems in this group. The object of including one or two problems in revolution in a course in drawing, when time permits, is to give further training in the relationship of views.

Problem G·1 Fig. G-1. The figure shows the completed problem. It is given for comparison and is not to be copied. Divide the standard sheet into four equal parts. In Space 1 is a three-view drawing of a block in its simplest position. In Space 2 (upper right-hand) the block is shown after being revolved from the position in Space 1, through 45°, about an axis perpendicular to the frontal plane. The front view was

drawn first, copying the front view of Space 1, and the top view obtained by projecting up from the front view and across from the top view in Space 1.

In Space 3 (lower left-hand) the block has been revolved from position one through 30° about an axis perpendicular to the horizontal plane. The top view was drawn first, copied from the top view of Space 1. In Space 4, the block has been tilted forward from position two about an axis perpendicular to the side plane. The side view was drawn first, copied from the side view of Space 2, and the widths of front and top view projected from the front view of Space 2.

One method of obtaining the widths of the side views by mitering from the top view is shown in Fig. G-1.

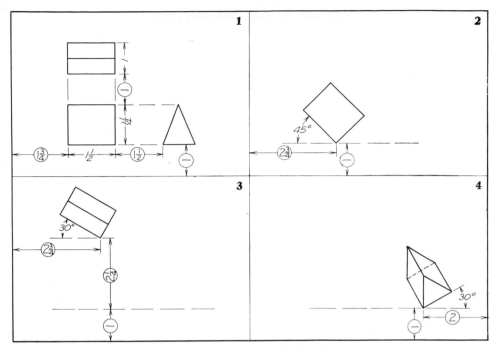

Fig. G-2 Revolutions. **Prob. G·2.**

Problem G·2 Fig. G-2. Revolutions (*above*). Follow the directions for Prob. G·1 and work out the views of the *wedge*.

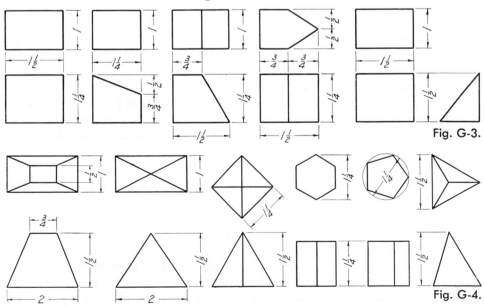

Fig. G-3.

Fig. G-4.

Problems G·3 to G·13 Figs. G-3 and G-4 (*above*). Follow directions for Probs. G·1 and G·2 and work out the required views.

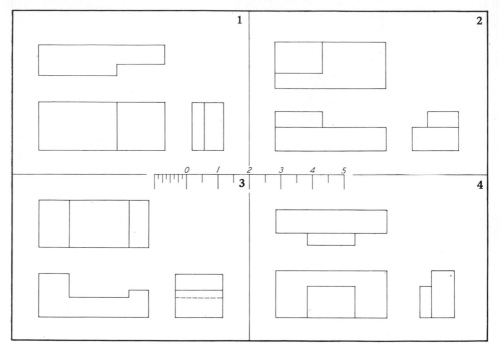

Fig. H-1 Dimensioning studies. **Probs. H·1 to H·4.**

24·12 Size description, or dimensioning, is a very important part of mechanical drawing. Study Chap. 10 carefully and apply the principles described in it to the solutions of the following problems. First draw the complete views for shape description, then put on all dimension lines for size dimensions and for location dimensions. When certain that all dimensions are indicated, fill in the dimensions and add notes where necessary.

Problems H·1 to H·4 Fig. H-1. Lay out an 11″ × 17″ sheet and divide the working space into four parts. The printed scale was full size before the drawing was reduced. Use the dividers to take off the distances from the scale, and draw the views full size. Put on the *size dimensions* as scaled from the views.

Problems H·5 to H·8 Fig. H-2. Draw the views as described for Fig. H-1. Put on the *size dimensions* as scaled from the views.

Problems H·9 to H·12 Fig. H-3. Draw the views as described for Fig. H-1. Put on the *size dimensions* as scaled from the views.

Problems H·13 to H·16 Fig. H-4. Lay out an 11″ × 17″ sheet and divide the working space into four parts. The printed scale was full size before the drawing was reduced. Use the di-

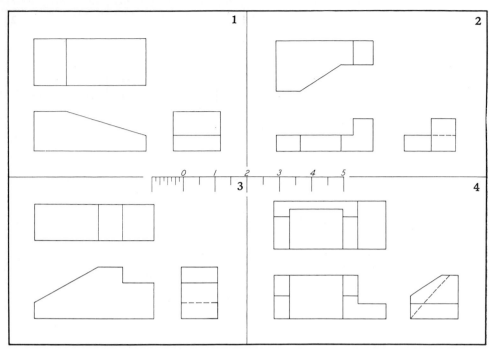

Fig. H-2 Dimensioning studies. **Probs. H·5 to H·8.**

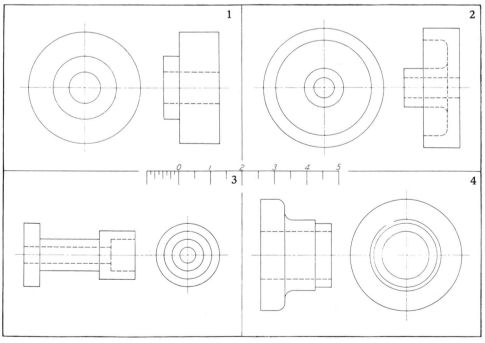

Fig. H-3 Dimensioning studies. **Probs. H·9 to H·12.**

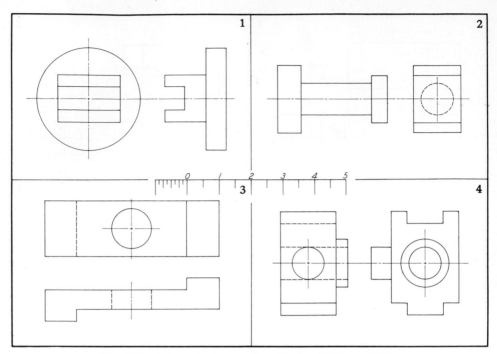

Fig. H-4   Dimensioning studies. **Probs. H·13 to H·16.**

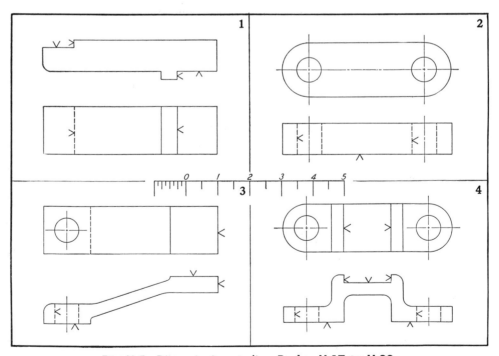

Fig. H-5   Dimensioning studies. **Probs. H·17 to H·20.**

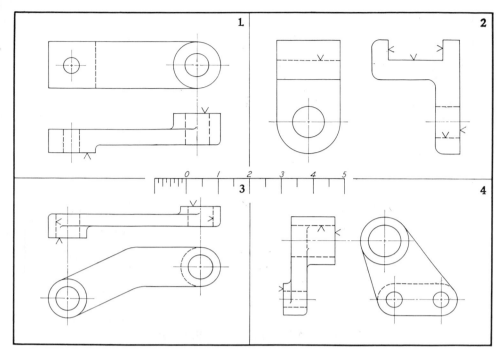

Fig. H-6 Dimensioning studies. **Probs. H·21 to H·24.**

viders to take off the distances from the scale, and draw the views full size. Put on the size dimensions as scaled from the views.

Problems H·17 to H·20 Fig. H-5. Lay out an 11″ × 17″ sheet and divide the working space into four parts. The printed scale was full size before the drawing was reduced. Use the dividers to take off the distances from the scale, and draw the views full size. Put on the location dimensions as scaled from the views.

Problems H·21 to H·24 Fig. H-6. Lay out an 11″ × 17″ sheet and divide the working space into four parts. The printed scale was full size before the drawing was reduced. Use the di-

viders to take off the distances from the scale, and draw the views full size. Put on the location dimensions as scaled from the views.

Problem H·25 Fig. H-7. Make a working drawing of the *adjustable center* with complete dimensions. Locate views to allow for dimensions.

Problem H·26 Fig. H-8. Make working drawings of the *gland* and *bearing* with complete dimensions. The diameter of the hole (1″), hub (1¾″), and flange holes (%₁₆ DRILL) should be added to the gland. For the bearing the distance from underside of base up to center of hole is 2″, length of hole is 1¾″, and diameter is ¾″. Holes in base (⅝ DRILL).

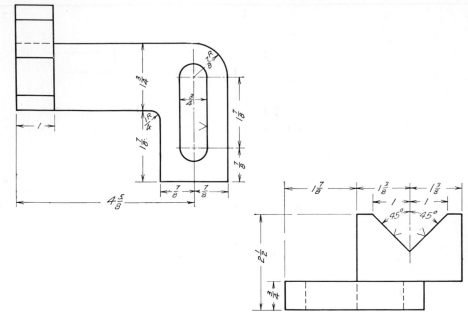

Fig. H-7   Adjustable center. **Prob. H·25.**

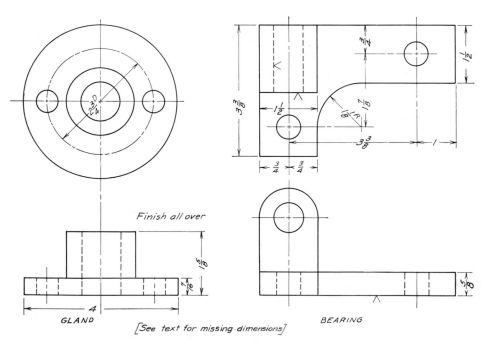

GLAND

Finish all over

[See text for missing dimensions]

BEARING

Fig. H-8   Gland and bearing. **Prob. H·26.**

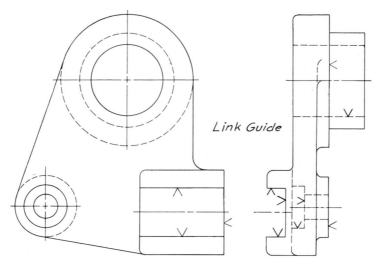

Fig. H-9   Link guide. **Prob. H·27.**

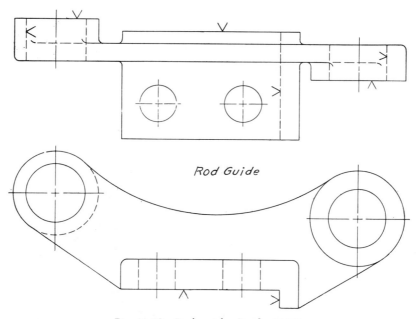

Fig. H-10   Rod guide. **Prob. H·28.**

Problem H·27 Fig. H-9. Copy the views to twice the size in the book. Completely dimension the *link guide*, obtaining the dimensions by scaling your drawing.

Problem H·28 Fig. H-10. Copy the views to twice the size in the book. Completely dimension the *rod guide*, obtaining the dimensions by scaling your drawing.

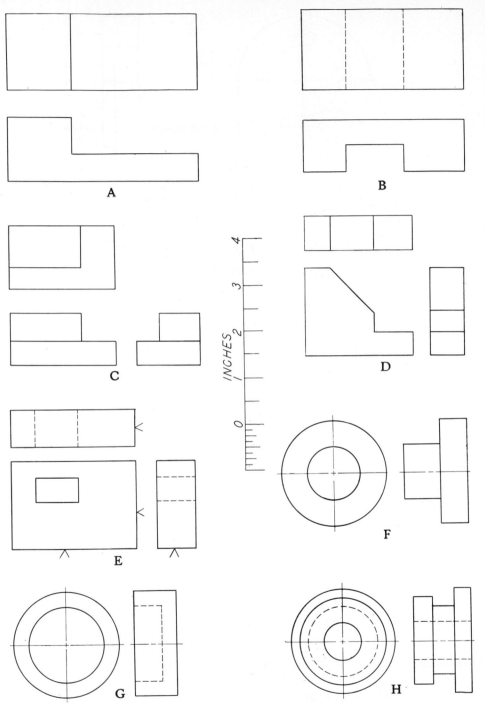

Problem H·29 Fig. H-11 (*above*). Copy the views freehand, enlarged. Add dimensions using S for size dimensions.

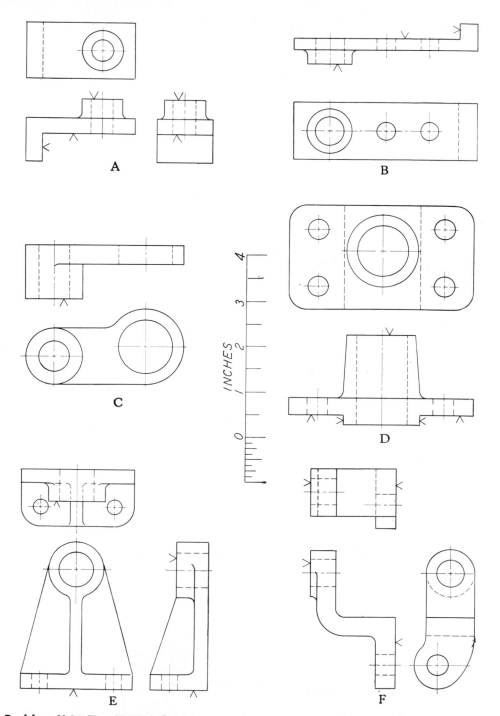

Problem H·30 Fig. H-12 (*above*). Copy the views freehand, enlarged. Add dimensions using S for size dimensions and L for location dimensions.

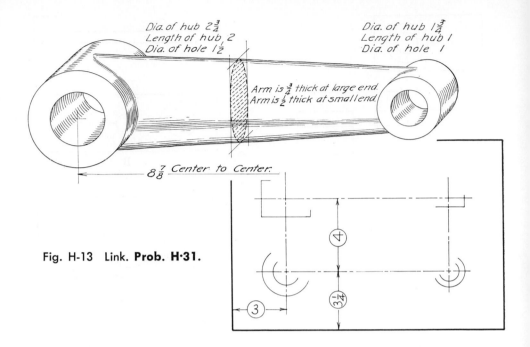

Dia. of hub $2\frac{3}{4}$
Length of hub 2
Dia. of hole $1\frac{1}{2}$

Dia. of hub $1\frac{3}{4}$
Length of hub 1
Dia. of hole 1

Arm is $\frac{3}{4}$ thick at large end.
Arm is $\frac{1}{2}$ thick at small end.

$8\frac{7}{8}$ Center to Center.

Fig. H-13   Link. **Prob. H·31.**

Problem H·31 Fig. H-13. Make a complete working drawing of the *link,* with dimension lines, extension lines, and dimensions correctly placed. Do not

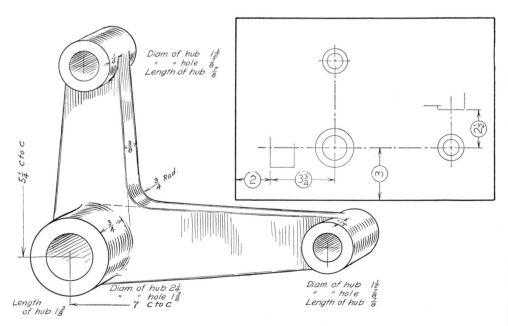

Diam. of hub $1\frac{1}{2}$
" " hole $\frac{7}{8}$
Length of hub $\frac{7}{8}$

$5\frac{1}{4}$ c to c

$\frac{3}{8}$

$\frac{3}{4}$ Rad.

$\frac{3}{4}$

Diam. of hub $2\frac{1}{4}$
" " hole $1\frac{3}{8}$
7 C to C

Length of hub $1\frac{3}{8}$

Diam. of hub $1\frac{1}{2}$
" " hole $\frac{7}{8}$
Length of hub $\frac{7}{8}$

Fig. H-14   Bell crank. **Prob. H·32.**

copy the notes or dimensions as given in the picture. Figure H-13 includes the layout for the problem.

Problem H·32 Fig. H-14. Make a complete working drawing of the *bell crank* with dimensions placed cor-

rectly. Do not copy the notes from the picture. Figure H-14 includes the layout for the problem.

In the layout, note that a complete front view is suggested with a view at the left to show the vertical arm, and a part top view of the horizontal arm.

GROUP I. BOLTS AND SCREWS

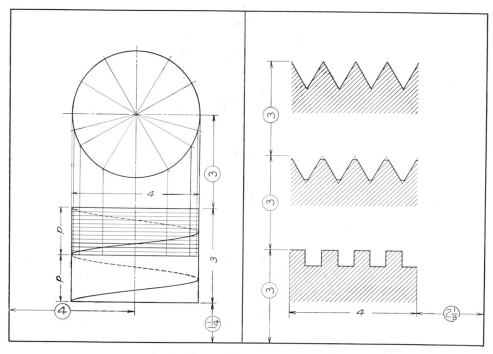

Fig. I-1   Helix and thread forms. **Prob. I·1.**

24·13 It is necessary for a draftsman to know the forms of screw threads and the conventional methods of drawing bolts and screws. Read Chap. 12 carefully before starting the problems in this group. Threads are always understood to be single and right-hand unless otherwise specified. A right-hand thread enters when turned clockwise. A left-hand thread enters when turned counterclockwise and is always marked

LH on a drawing. When the American Standard form and number of threads per inch are used, it is not necessary to specify except by a note. See Appendix for screw-thread information.

Problem I·1 Fig. I-1. In the left half of the sheet construct two complete turns of a right-hand helix whose diameter is 4″ and pitch 1½″ (Art. 10·5). In the right half of the sheet draw, as shown

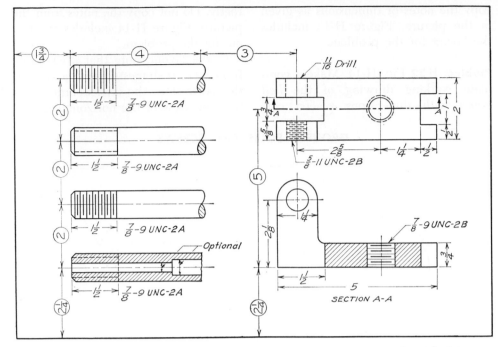

Fig. I-2 Draw the conventional thread representations as specified. **Prob. I·3.**

in the layout, the forms of the V-thread, Unified Standard thread and square thread, each with 1" pitch. Letter the name of each form under the drawing of it.

Sometimes in drawing a helix, a templet is made by laying out the curve on a piece of cardboard, Celluloid, or thin wood and cutting out with a sharp knife.

Problem I·2 An alternate for Prob. I·1. In the left half of the sheet construct two complete turns of a right-hand helix whose diameter is 3" and pitch 2". In the right half draw the forms of the Unified Standard thread, Acme thread, and knuckle thread, each with 1" pitch. Letter the name of each form under the drawing of it.

Problem I·3 Fig. I-2. Draw the conventional thread representations as specified on the layout.

Problem I·4 Fig. I-3. Draw the American Standard bolts and nuts in the positions indicated.

Problem I·5 Fig. I-4. Divide working space into four spaces as shown. In the upper left-hand space draw a stud and American Standard nut. Diameter ⅞"; length 5"; length of thread on each end 1¼". In the upper right-hand space draw an American Standard hexagonal-head cap screw. Diameter ⅞"; length 2¼". In lower left-hand space draw three forms of cap screws, at A, B, and C. Diameter ⁹⁄₁₆"; length 1½". In lower right-hand space draw three setscrews,

432 MECHANICAL DRAWING

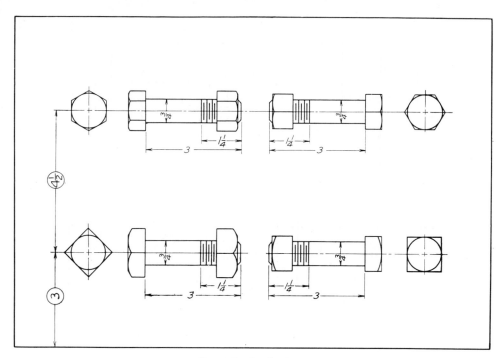

Fig. I-3 **Prob. I·4.**

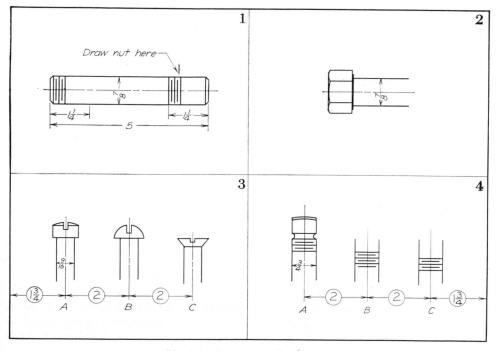

Draw nut here

Fig. I-4 Fastenings. **Prob. I·5.**

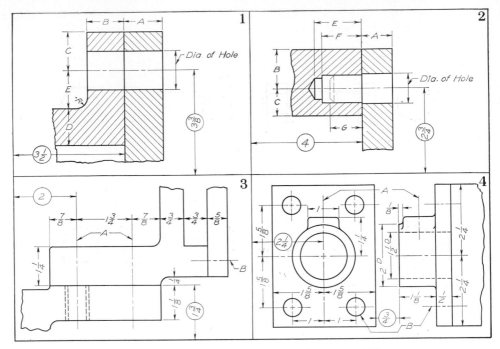

Fig. I-5 Threaded fastenings. **Probs. I·6 to I·19.**

American Standard square head and two headless setscrews. Diameter ¾″; length 1½″. Select points from Appendix, page 537.

Problems I·6 to I·15 Fig. I-5, Space 1. On the center line shown, draw an American Standard bolt and nut for the flange and head plate. Take dimensions from the table in the Appendix, pages 531–532. Place bolthead at the left and show head across flats. Show nut across corners.

Problems I·16 to I·19 Fig. I-5, Space 2. On the center line shown draw a stud with hexagonal or square nut, across flats or corners, as directed by the instructor. Take dimensions from the table in the Appendix, pages 531–532.

Problem I·20 Same as Prob. I·16 but for a tap bolt.

Problem I·21 Same as Prob. I·17 but for a tap bolt.

Problem I·22 Same as Prob. I·18 but for a tap bolt.

Problem I·23 Same as Prob. I·19 but for a tap bolt.

Problem I·24 Fig. I-5, Space 3. On center line at *A*, draw ¾″ fillister-head cap screws. On center line at *B*, draw a ⅜″ flat-head cap screw.

Problem I·25 Fig. I-5, Space 4. At *A* draw a ½″ setscrew (square head or other as directed by instructor). At *B* draw a ⁹⁄₁₆″ hexagon-head cap screw.

Problem	Diam. bolt	Diam. hole	Bolt-head	Nut	A	B	C	D	E	R
1·6	$\frac{5}{8}$	$\frac{11}{16}$	Hex.	Hex.	$\frac{5}{8}$	$\frac{11}{16}$	$\frac{3}{4}$	$\frac{5}{8}$	$\frac{3}{4}$	$\frac{1}{8}$
1·7	$\frac{3}{4}$	$\frac{13}{16}$	Sq.	Hex.	$\frac{3}{4}$	$\frac{13}{16}$	$\frac{7}{8}$	$\frac{3}{4}$	$\frac{7}{8}$	$\frac{3}{16}$
1·8	$\frac{7}{8}$	$\frac{15}{16}$	Hex.	Hex.	$\frac{7}{8}$	1	1	$\frac{7}{8}$	1	$\frac{1}{4}$
1·9	1	$1\frac{1}{8}$	Sq.	Hex.	1	$1\frac{1}{8}$	$1\frac{1}{8}$	1	$1\frac{1}{8}$	$\frac{1}{4}$
1·10	$1\frac{1}{8}$	$1\frac{1}{4}$	Hex.	Hex.	$1\frac{1}{8}$	$1\frac{1}{4}$	$1\frac{1}{4}$	$1\frac{1}{8}$	$1\frac{1}{4}$	$\frac{5}{16}$
1·11	$\frac{5}{8}$	$\frac{11}{16}$	Sq.	Sq.	$\frac{11}{16}$	$\frac{3}{4}$	$\frac{7}{8}$	$\frac{11}{16}$	$\frac{3}{4}$	$\frac{1}{8}$
1·12	$\frac{3}{4}$	$\frac{13}{16}$	Hex.	Sq.	$\frac{13}{16}$	$\frac{7}{8}$	1	$\frac{13}{16}$	$\frac{7}{8}$	$\frac{3}{16}$
1·13	$\frac{7}{8}$	$\frac{15}{16}$	Sq.	Sq.	$\frac{15}{16}$	1	$1\frac{1}{8}$	$\frac{15}{16}$	1	$\frac{1}{4}$
1·14	1	$1\frac{1}{8}$	Hex.	Sq.	$1\frac{1}{16}$	$1\frac{1}{8}$	$1\frac{3}{8}$	$1\frac{1}{16}$	$1\frac{1}{8}$	$\frac{1}{4}$
1·15	$1\frac{1}{8}$	$1\frac{1}{4}$	Sq.	Sq.	$1\frac{3}{16}$	$1\frac{1}{4}$	$1\frac{1}{4}$	$1\frac{3}{16}$	$1\frac{1}{4}$	$\frac{5}{16}$

Problem	Diam. stud	Diam. hole	Nut	A	B	C	E	F	G
1·16	$\frac{3}{4}$	$\frac{13}{16}$	Hex.	$\frac{13}{16}$	$\frac{7}{8}$	$\frac{3}{4}$	$1\frac{3}{4}$	$1\frac{3}{8}$	1
1·17	$\frac{7}{8}$	$\frac{15}{16}$	Sq.	$\frac{15}{16}$	$1\frac{1}{4}$	$\frac{7}{8}$	2	$1\frac{9}{16}$	$1\frac{1}{8}$
1·18	1	$1\frac{1}{8}$	Hex.	$1\frac{1}{8}$	$1\frac{1}{8}$	1	$2\frac{1}{4}$	$1\frac{3}{4}$	$1\frac{1}{4}$
1·19	$1\frac{1}{8}$	$1\frac{1}{4}$	Sq.	$1\frac{1}{4}$	$1\frac{1}{2}$	$1\frac{1}{8}$	$2\frac{3}{4}$	$2\frac{1}{8}$	$1\frac{1}{2}$

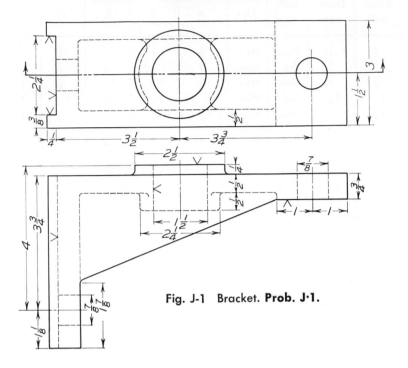

Fig. J-1 Bracket. **Prob. J·1.**

24·14 Study Chaps. 8 and 9 very carefully before starting these problems. Use a definite system. Visualize the shape clearly and locate the views carefully to allow proper placing of dimensions. Use your judgment in selecting a proper scale for the drawing. Complete the views before putting on the dimension lines. Then put in all dimension lines and fill in the dimensions. Add any necessary notes and finally check your drawing.

Some problems in **Groups D, E,** and **F** may be used as working drawings.

Problem J·1 Fig. J-1. Make a working drawing of the *bracket*. Show three views, one in section.

Problem J·2 Fig. J-2. Make a working drawing of the cast-iron *crosshead shoe*.

Problem J·3 Fig. J-3. Make a working drawing of the *double bearing*.

Problem J·4 Fig. J-4. Make a complete working drawing of the *support*. Dimension correctly, supplying missing dimensions. Indicate the surfaces that you assume to be finished. The choice and treatment of views should be considered before starting the drawing. Work out the placing of the views to allow ample room for the dimensions. See Art. 24·8.

Problem J·5 Fig. J-5. Make a working drawing of the *two-part end plate*. Use hexagon-head bolts and nuts.

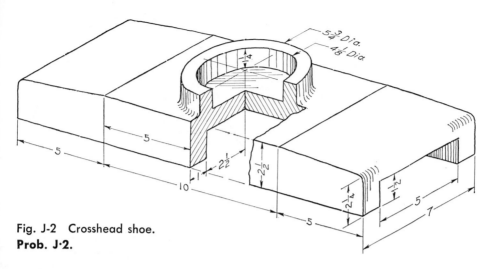

Fig. J-2 Crosshead shoe.
Prob. J·2.

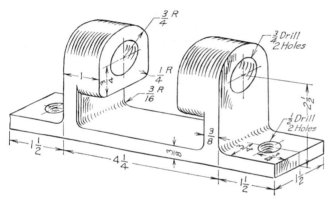

Fig. J-3 Double bearing.
Prob. J·3.

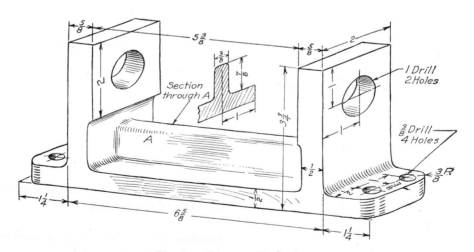

Fig. J-4 Support. **Prob. J·4.**

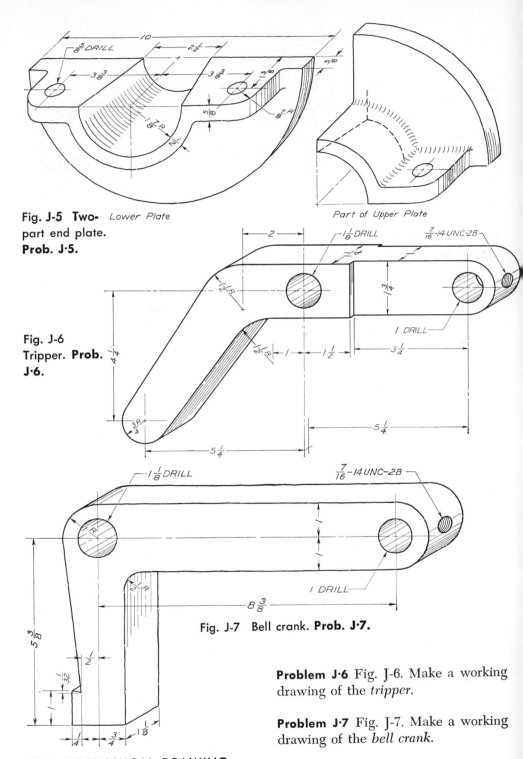

Fig. J-5 Two-part end plate. Prob. J·5. *Lower Plate*

Part of Upper Plate

Fig. J-6 Tripper. Prob. J·6.

Fig. J-7 Bell crank. Prob. J·7.

Problem J·6 Fig. J-6. Make a working drawing of the *tripper*.

Problem J·7 Fig. J-7. Make a working drawing of the *bell crank*.

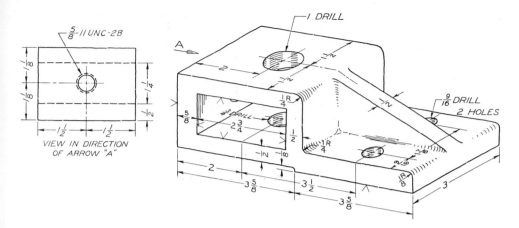

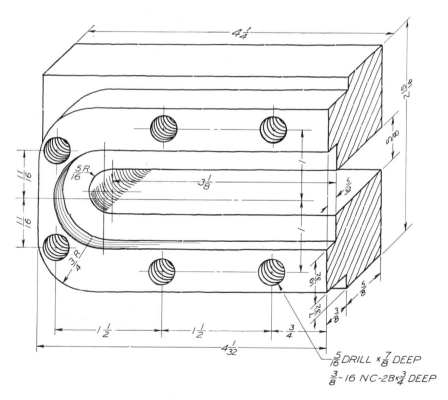

Problem J·8 Fig. J-8 (*above*). Make a working drawing of the cast-iron *adjustable holder*.

Problem J·9 Fig. J-9 (*above*). Make a working drawing of the *fuel-gage block*, one-half of which is shown. Material is machine steel. Finish all over.

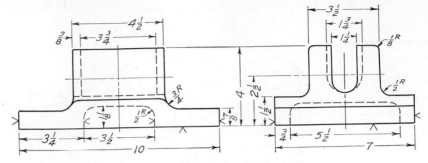

Fig. J-10 Slide valve. Prob. J·10.

Problem J·10 Fig. J-10. Make a three-view working drawing of the *slide valve,* showing the view at the left in Fig. J-10 as a section. Completely dimension the drawing. Material is cast iron. Add notes where necessary and a suitable title.

Problem J·11 Fig. J-11. Make a working drawing for the *top plate for a jig*

shown in the broken view. Material is cast iron.

Problem J·12 Fig. J-12. Make a working drawing of the *pedal lever.* The surfaces indicated by the letter A are tangent to the under surface of the hub.

Problem J·13 Fig. J-13. Make a working drawing of the *link.*

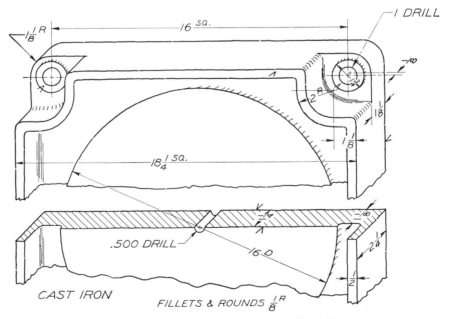

Fig. J-11 Top plate for a jig. Prob. J·11.

440 MECHANICAL DRAWING

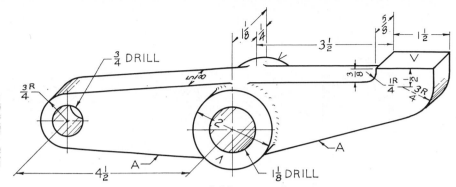

Fig. J-12   Pedal lever. **Prob. J·12.**

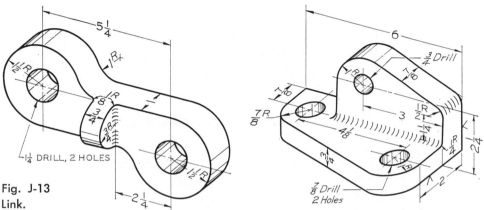

Fig. J-13
Link.
Prob. J·13.

Fig. J-14   Base anchor. **Prob. J·14.**

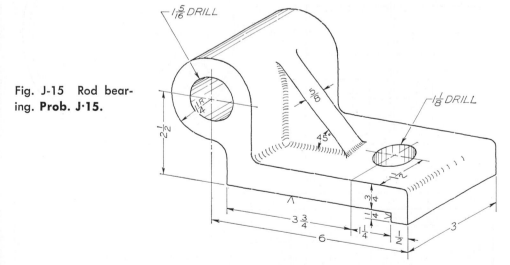

Fig. J-15   Rod bearing. **Prob. J·15.**

Problem J·14 Fig. J-14. Make a working drawing of the *base anchor.*

Problem J·15 Fig. J-15. Make a working drawing of the cast-iron *rod bearing.*

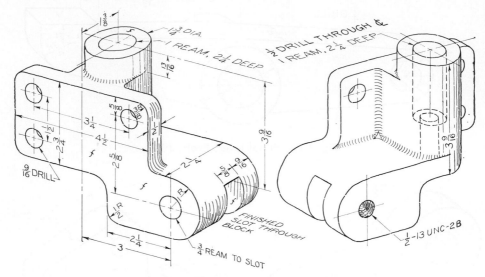

Fig. J-16 Slide-arm bracket. **Prob. J·16.**

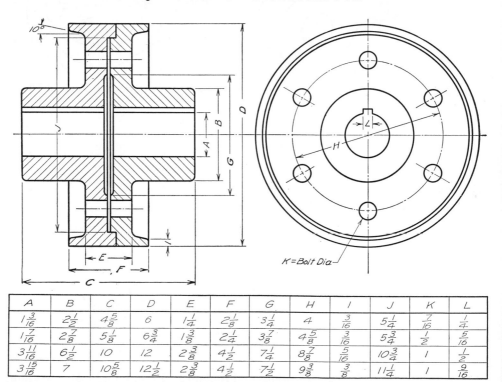

A	B	C	D	E	F	G	H	I	J	K	L
$1\frac{3}{16}$	$2\frac{1}{2}$	$4\frac{5}{8}$	6	$1\frac{1}{4}$	$2\frac{1}{8}$	$3\frac{1}{4}$	4	$\frac{3}{16}$	$5\frac{1}{4}$	$\frac{7}{16}$	$\frac{1}{4}$
$1\frac{7}{16}$	$2\frac{7}{8}$	$5\frac{1}{8}$	$6\frac{3}{4}$	$1\frac{3}{8}$	$2\frac{1}{4}$	$3\frac{7}{8}$	$4\frac{5}{8}$	$\frac{3}{16}$	$5\frac{3}{4}$	$\frac{1}{2}$	$\frac{5}{16}$
$3\frac{11}{16}$	$6\frac{1}{2}$	10	12	$2\frac{3}{8}$	$4\frac{1}{2}$	$7\frac{1}{4}$	$8\frac{7}{8}$	$\frac{5}{16}$	$10\frac{3}{4}$	1	$\frac{1}{2}$
$3\frac{15}{16}$	7	$10\frac{5}{8}$	$12\frac{1}{2}$	$2\frac{3}{8}$	$4\frac{1}{2}$	$7\frac{1}{2}$	$9\frac{3}{8}$	$\frac{3}{8}$	$11\frac{1}{4}$	1	$\frac{9}{16}$

Fig. J-17 Flange coupling. **Prob. J·17.**

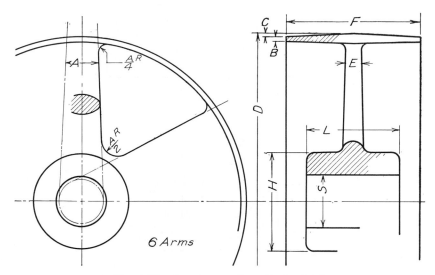

Fig. J-18   Cast-iron pulley. **Prob. J·18.**

Size	D	F	S	H	L	B	C	A	E
x	8	$3\frac{1}{4}$	$1\frac{1}{4}$	$2\frac{3}{8}$	$2\frac{1}{2}$	$\frac{1}{8}$	$\frac{1}{32}$	$\frac{3}{4}$	$\frac{7}{16}$
y	16	$6\frac{1}{2}$	2	$3\frac{1}{4}$	4	$\frac{3}{16}$	$\frac{1}{16}$	$1\frac{1}{8}$	$\frac{9}{16}$
z	30	$8\frac{1}{2}$	$2\frac{3}{4}$	$4\frac{1}{2}$	$5\frac{1}{2}$	$\frac{1}{4}$	$\frac{3}{32}$	$1\frac{1}{2}$	$1\frac{3}{16}$

Problem J·16 Fig. J-16. Make a working drawing of the *slide-arm bracket*. Semisteel casting.

Problem J·17 Fig. J-17. Make a complete working drawing of one of the sizes of *flange coupling*. Choose a suitable scale. Show the bolts and key in position. The missing dimensions are to be supplied by the student.

Problem J·18 Fig. J-18. Make a complete working drawing of a *cast-iron pulley*, with one view in section. Taper of arms about ½″ per foot. For dimensions see accompanying table.

Problem J·19 Fig. J-19. Make a complete working drawing of a *babbitted bearing*, with front and side views as half sections. Missing dimensions to be supplied by the student. For dimensions see accompanying table.

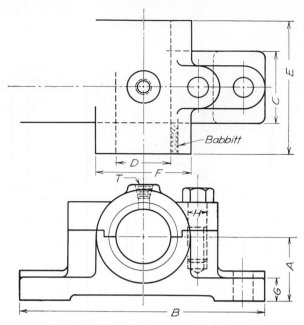

Fig. J-19   Babbitted bearing. **Prob. J·19.**

Size	D	A	B	C	E	F	G	H	T
w	1	$1\frac{1}{4}$	$4\frac{3}{4}$	$1\frac{3}{8}$	$2\frac{1}{2}$	$1\frac{3}{4}$	$\frac{1}{2}$	$\frac{3}{8}$	$\frac{1}{8}$ pipe
x	$1\frac{1}{2}$	$1\frac{3}{4}$	$6\frac{3}{4}$	2	$3\frac{3}{4}$	$2\frac{5}{8}$	$\frac{5}{8}$	$\frac{1}{2}$	$\frac{1}{8}$ pipe
y	2	$2\frac{1}{4}$	$8\frac{3}{4}$	$2\frac{1}{2}$	5	$3\frac{1}{2}$	$\frac{3}{4}$	$\frac{1}{2}$	$\frac{1}{4}$ pipe
z	$2\frac{1}{2}$	$2\frac{3}{4}$	$10\frac{3}{4}$	$3\frac{1}{8}$	$6\frac{1}{4}$	$4\frac{3}{8}$	$\frac{7}{8}$	$\frac{5}{8}$	$\frac{1}{4}$ pipe

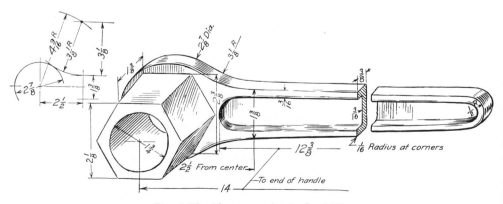

Fig. J-20   Plug wrench. **Prob. J·20.**

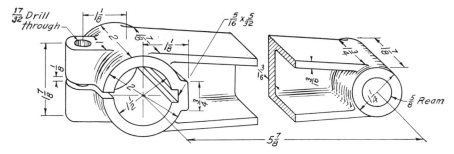

Fig. J-21   Lever. Prob. J·21.

Problem J·20 Fig. J-20. Make a completely dimensioned two-view working drawing of the *plug wrench*. Show a revolved section through the handle. Consider the choice of views, scale, and placing of views before starting the drawing.

Problem J·21 Fig. J-21. Make a two-view working drawing of the *lever* with all necessary dimensions. Use your judgment regarding finished surfaces.

Problem J·22 Fig. J-22. Make a working drawing showing the proper views of the *upper and lower clamps*. One-half of the lower clamp is shown in the figure. Draw the whole clamp. Consider the choice of views, scale, and placing of views before starting the drawing.

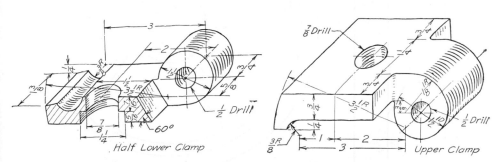

Fig. J-22   Upper and lower clamps. Prob. J·22.

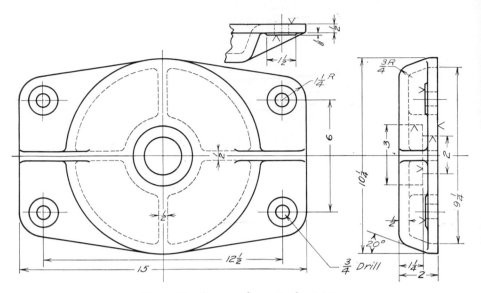

Fig. J-23   Center plate. **Prob. J·23.**

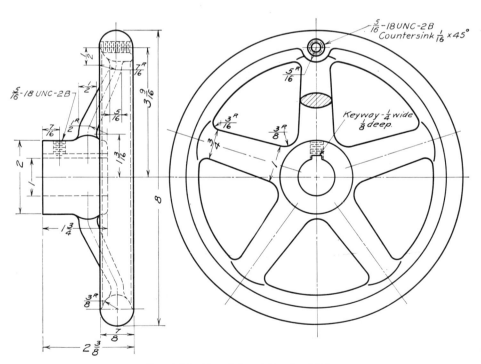

Fig. J-24   Handwheel. **Prob. J·24.**

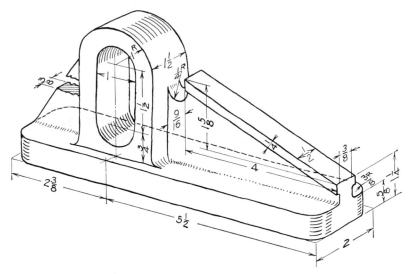

Fig. J-25 Adjusting slide. **Prob. J·25.**

Problem J·23 Fig. J-23. Make a three-view working drawing of the *center plate*, one view to be a section. Consider choice of scale and arrangement of views before starting the drawing. Add a suitable title.

Problem J·24 Fig. J-24. Make a two-view working drawing of the *hand-wheel* showing the left view as a section. Read Art. 11·10 regarding arms in section. Consider choice of scale and arrangement of views before starting the drawing. Add a suitable title.

Problem J·25 Fig. J-25. Make a working drawing of the *adjusting slide*. Consider the choice of views and the scale. Work out the spacing of the views to allow ample room for dimensions and notes. Indicate the surfaces that you assume to be finished. Add a suitable title.

Problem J·26 Fig. J-26. Make a two-view working drawing of the *pulley bracket*.

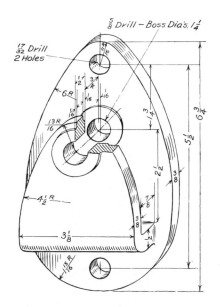

Fig. J-26 Pulley bracket. **Prob. J·26.**

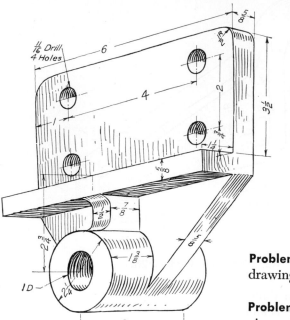

Fig. J-27 Bracket bearing.
Prob. J·27.

Problem J·27 Fig. J-27. Make a working drawing of the *bracket bearing*.

Problem J·28 Fig. J-28. Make a three-view working drawing, completely dimensioned, of the *bearing holder*. Consider the choice of views, scale, and placing of views before starting the drawing.

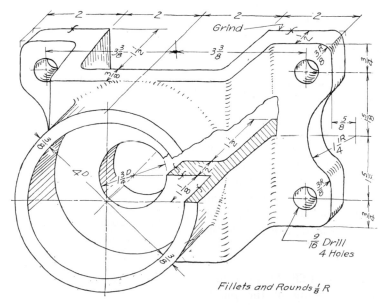

Fillets and Rounds $\frac{1}{8}$ R

Fig. J-28 Bearing holder. **Prob. J·28.**

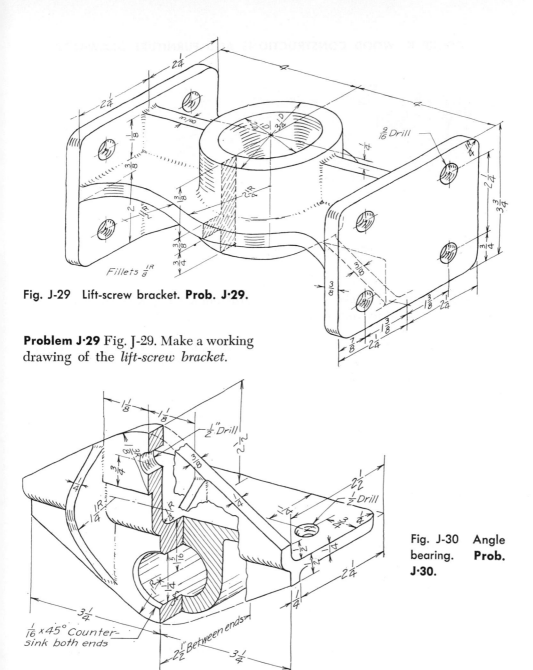

Fig. J-29 Lift-screw bracket. **Prob. J·29.**

Problem J·29 Fig. J-29. Make a working drawing of the *lift-screw bracket.*

Fig. J-30 Angle bearing. **Prob. J·30.**

Problem J·30 Fig. J-30. Make a working drawing of the *angle bearing*. This object is symmetrical, but in the picture a part is broken away to show the interior. Consider choice of views, treatment of views, and scale. Work out the spacing of the views to allow ample room for dimensions and notes. Indicate the surfaces you assume to be finished. Add a suitable title.

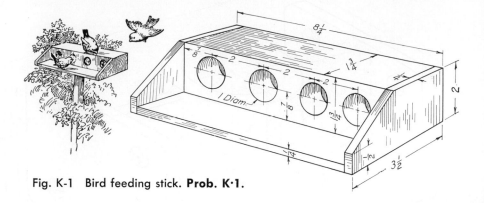

Fig. K-1   Bird feeding stick. **Prob. K·1.**

Problem K·1 Fig. K-1. Make a working drawing of the *bird feeding stick*.

Problem K·2 Fig. K-2. Make a working drawing of the *martin house*. Consider the choice and treatment of views and choice of scale. Material is ⅜″ white pine. Supply details and dimensions not shown in the pictures.

Problem K·3 Fig. K-3. Make a working drawing of the *radio shelf*. Select views and scale.

Problem K·4 Fig. K-4. Make a working drawing of the *bench hook*.

Problem K·5 Fig. K-5. Make a working drawing of the *waste basket*. It is 12″ square at the top, 10″ square at bottom, 16″ high. Sides of hardboard or similar material.

Problem K·6 Fig. K-6. Make a working drawing of the *nail box*.

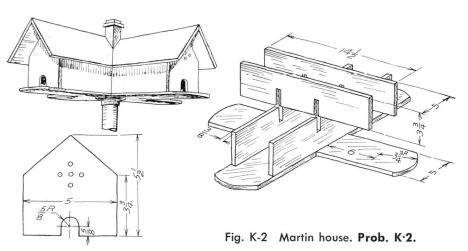

Fig. K-2   Martin house. **Prob. K·2.**

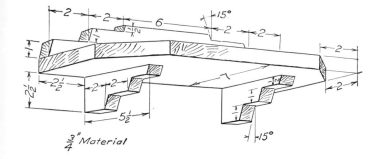

Fig. K-3 Radio shelf.
Prob. K·3.

$\frac{3}{4}$" Material

Fig. K-4 (*Above*) Bench hook. **Prob. K·4.**

Fig. K-5 (*Right*) Waste basket. **Prob. K·5.**

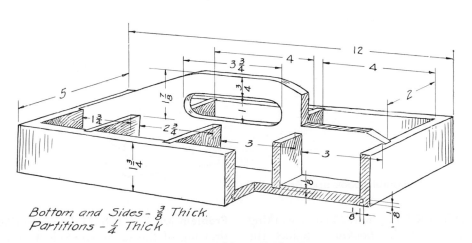

Bottom and Sides - $\frac{3}{8}$ Thick.
Partitions - $\frac{1}{4}$ Thick

Fig. K-6 Nail box. **Prob. K·6.**

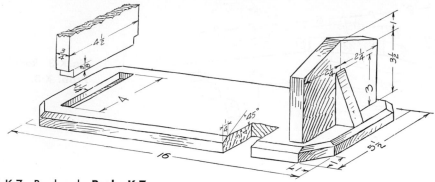

Fig. K-7 Bookrack. **Prob. K·7.**

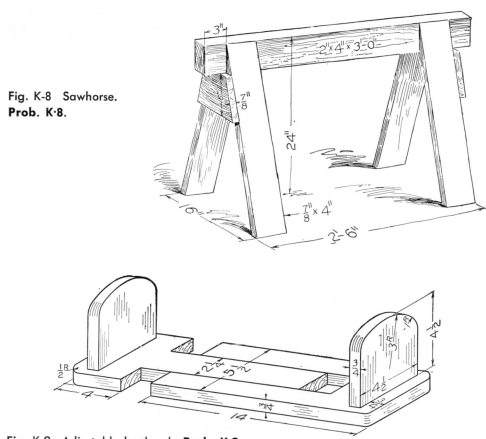

Fig. K-8 Sawhorse.
Prob. K·8.

Fig. K-9 Adjustable bookrack. **Prob. K·9.**

Problem K·7 Fig. K-7. Make a working drawing of the *bookrack*. Select the views and scale.

Problem K·8 Fig. K-8. Make a working drawing of the *sawhorse*. Select views and scale.

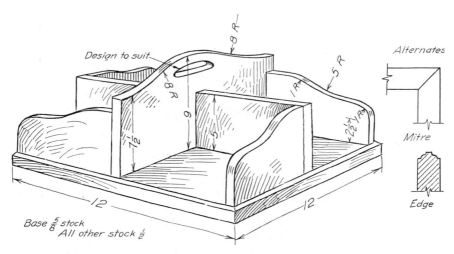

Fig. K-10   Four-compartment bookrack. **Prob. K·10.**

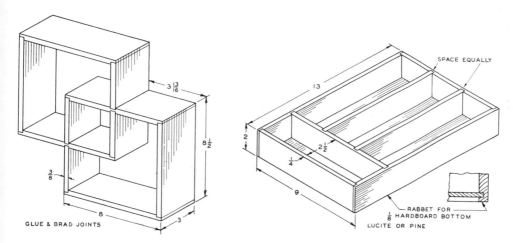

Fig. K-11   Shadow box. **Prob. K·11.**

Fig. K-12   Silverware box. **Prob. K·12.**

Problem K·9 Fig. K-9. Make a working drawing of the *adjustable bookrack*. Select views and scale.

Problem K·10 Fig. K-10. Make a working drawing of the *four-compartment bookrack*. Select views and scale.

Problem K·11 Fig. K-11. Make a working drawing of the *shadow box*. Construction to be as shown.

Problem K·12 Fig. K-12. Make a working drawing of the *silverware box*. Construction as shown.

PROBLEMS   **453**

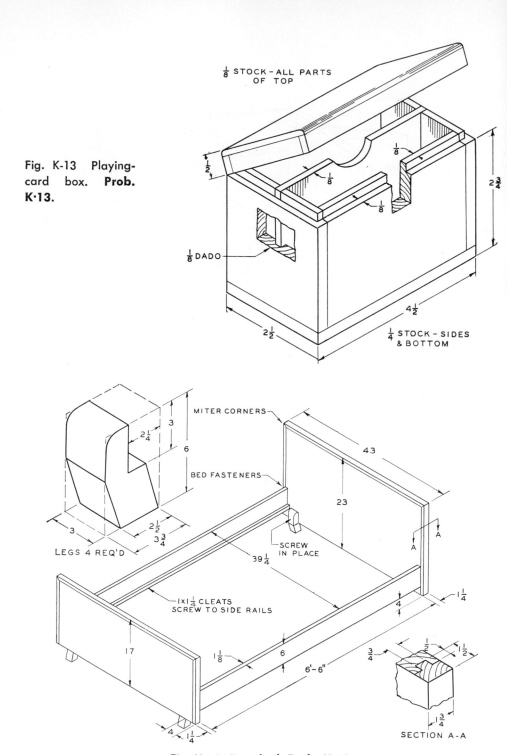

Fig. K-13 Playing-card box. **Prob. K·13.**

$\frac{1}{8}$ STOCK – ALL PARTS OF TOP

$\frac{1}{2}$

$\frac{1}{8}$

$\frac{1}{8}$

$\frac{1}{8}$

$2\frac{3}{4}$

$\frac{1}{8}$ DADO

$2\frac{1}{2}$

$4\frac{1}{2}$

$\frac{1}{4}$ STOCK – SIDES & BOTTOM

MITER CORNERS

3

$2\frac{1}{4}$

6

BED FASTENERS

43

23

3

$2\frac{1}{2}$

$3\frac{3}{4}$

LEGS 4 REQ'D

SCREW IN PLACE

$39\frac{1}{4}$

A

A

1x1$\frac{1}{4}$ CLEATS SCREW TO SIDE RAILS

4

$1\frac{1}{4}$

17

$1\frac{1}{8}$

6

$\frac{3}{4}$

$\frac{1}{2}$

$1\frac{1}{2}$

$6'-6''$

$1\frac{3}{4}$

4

$1\frac{1}{4}$

SECTION A-A

Fig. K-14 Twin bed. **Prob. K·14.**

454 MECHANICAL DRAWING

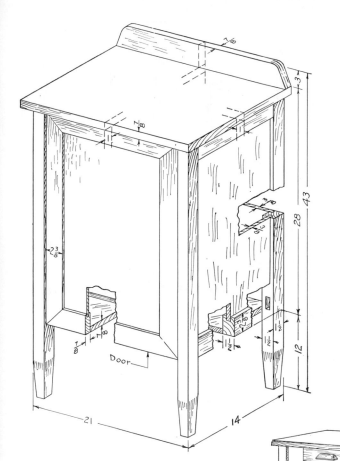

Fig. K-15 (*Left*) Music cabinet. **Prob. K·15.**

Door

Fig. K-16 (*Below*) Typewriter table. **Prob. K·16.**

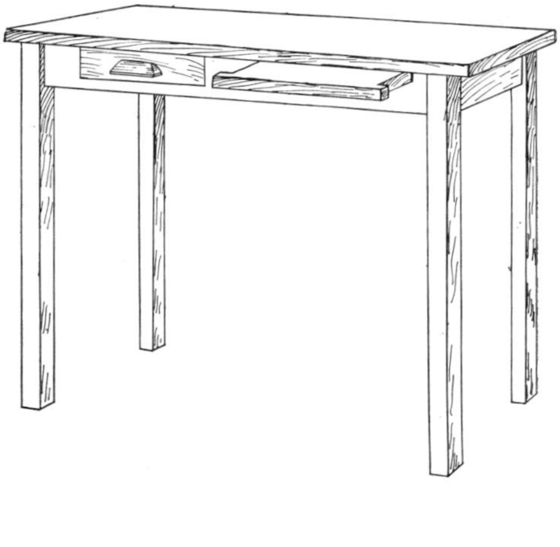

Problem K·13 Fig. K-13. Make a working drawing of the *playing-card box.* Box may be made of wood or plastic.

Problem K·14 Fig. K-14. Make a working drawing of the *twin bed.* Side rails connected to the head and foot boards with bed fasteners (Broadhead Garrett No. 10 or similar).

Problem K·15 Fig. K-15. Make a working drawing of the *music cabinet.* Supply missing details and hardware.

Problem K·16 Fig. K-16. Make a working drawing of the *typewriter table.* Legs, 1¼″ square; top, 18″ × 32″ × ¼″; height, 20″; apron, 4″. Supply details and dimensions not shown.

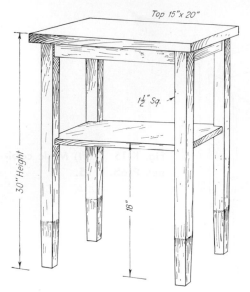

Fig. K-17　Telephone stand. **Prob. K·17.**

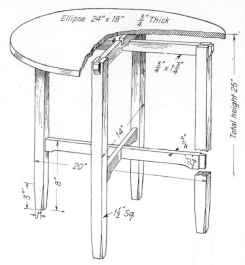

Fig. K-18　Tea table. **Prob. K·18.**

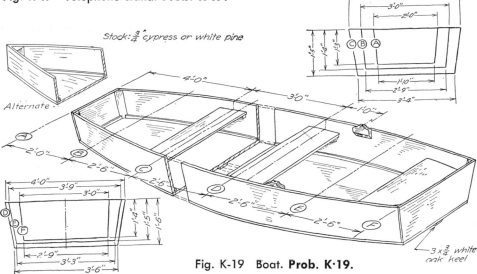

Fig. K-19　Boat. **Prob. K·19.**

Problem K·17 Fig. K-17. Make a working drawing of the *telephone stand*. Supply details and dimensions not shown.

Problem K·18 Fig. K-18. Make an assembly working drawing, with extra part views if necessary, for the *tea table*. Supply missing dimensions.

Problem K·19 Fig. K-19. Make detail and assembly drawings for the *boat*. The shape is defined by the inside dimensions of the bow, sections, and stern, *A, B, C, D, E, F*. These shapes may be drawn separate or "stacked." The widths of the seats from bow to stern are 1'–0", 1'–3", and 1'–3". Select views and scale. Use two standard sheets.

456　MECHANICAL DRAWING

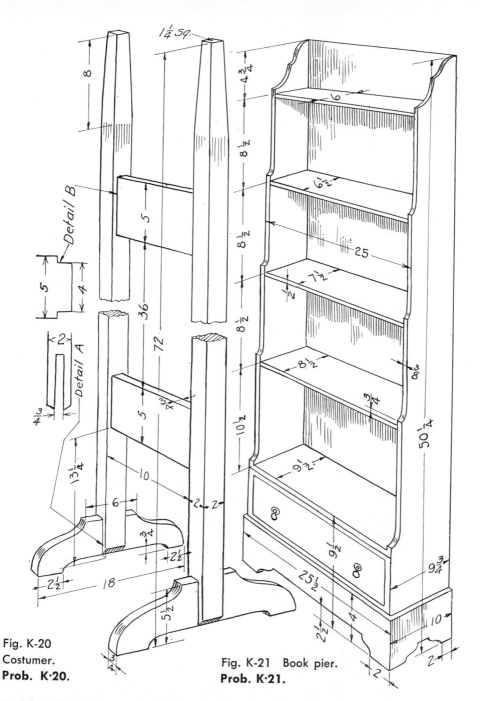

Fig. K-20
Costumer.
Prob. K·20.

Fig. K-21 Book pier.
Prob. K·21.

Problem K·20 Fig. K-20. Make an assembly working drawing, with extra part views if necessary, for the *costumer*.

Problem K·21 Fig. K-21. Make an assembly working drawing of the *book pier*. Design the construction of the drawer.

PROBLEMS **457**

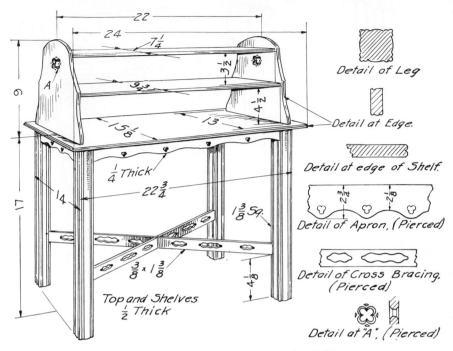

Detail of Leg

Detail at Edge.

Detail at edge of Shelf.

Detail of Apron, (Pierced)

**Detail of Cross Bracing,
(Pierced)**

Detail at "A", (Pierced)

¼ Thick

Top and Shelves
½ Thick

Fig. K-22   Magazine table. **Prob. K·22.**

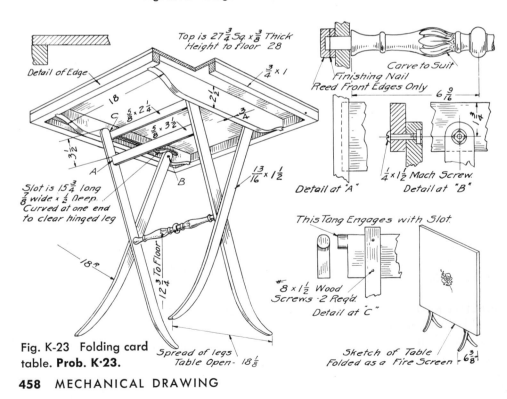

Top is 27¾ Sq.× ⅜ Thick
Height to floor 28

Detail of Edge

Carve to Suit

Finishing Nail
Reed Front Edges Only

Detail at "A"

Detail at "B"

¼ × 1½ Mach Screw.

Slot is 15¾ long
⅞ wide × ½ Deep.
Curved at one end
to clear hinged leg

Spread of legs
Table Open- 18⅛

This Tang Engages with Slot.

#8 × 1½ Wood
Screws -2 Req'd.

Detail at "C"

Sketch of Table
Folded as a Fire Screen

Fig. K-23   Folding card
table. **Prob. K·23.**

Problem K·22 Fig. K-22. Make a working drawing of the *magazine table*. See top of page 458.

Problem K·23 Fig. K-23. Draw assembly and detail drawings for the *folding card table*. See bottom of page 458.

GROUP L. ASSEMBLY AND DETAIL DRAWINGS

Fig. L-1 Pilot hub. **Prob. L·1.**

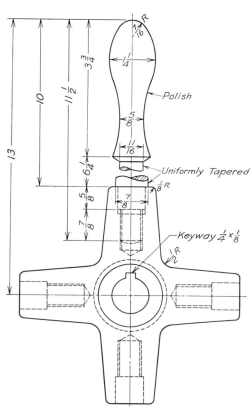

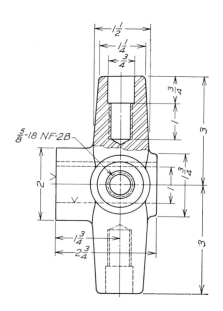

24·15 Before starting these problems, study the views given and see just what is required in each case. See how many pieces are to be represented and the best method of showing them. It will be necessary to use judgment to arrange for the spacing of the views for detail drawings of several pieces. Each piece should be completely dimensioned and should be named.

Assembly drawings may have different treatments according to the purpose to be served. They may have no dimensions; they may have dimensions necessary for assembling or erection, for operation, and so forth; or they may have all dimensions. If not stated in the problem, consult your instructor.

The chapters on size description, technique of the finished drawing, bolts and screws, and mechanical drafting should be used for study and reference in connection with these assembly and detail drawings.

Problem L·1 Fig. L-1. Make detail drawings for the *pilot hub* showing each piece fully dimensioned.

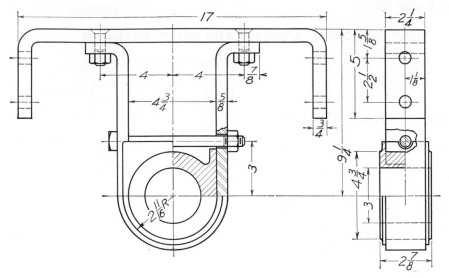

Fig. L-2 Hung bearing. **Prob. L·2.**

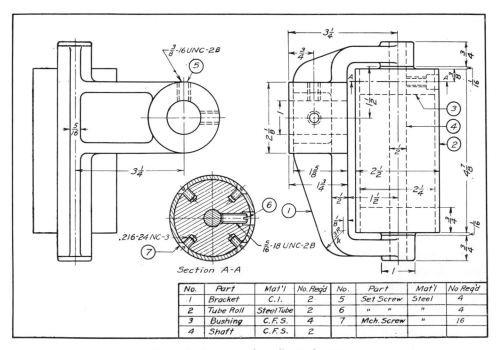

No.	Part	Mat'l	No. Req'd	No.	Part	Mat'l	No Req'd
1	Bracket	C.I.	2	5	Set Screw	Steel	4
2	Tube Roll	Steel Tube	2	6	"	"	4
3	Bushing	C.F.S.	4	7	Mch. Screw	"	16
4	Shaft	C.F.S.	2				

Fig. L-3 Pivot-guide roll. **Prob. L·3.**

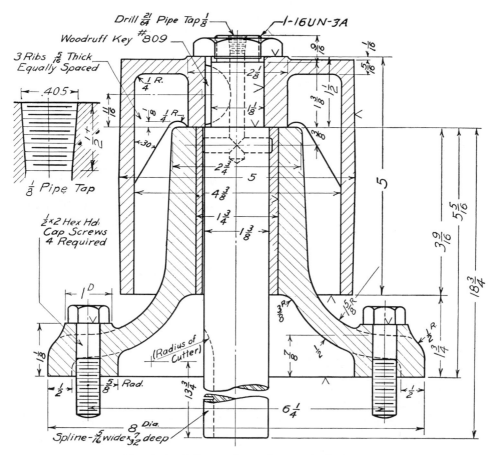

Fig. L-4 Pulley-and-stand unit. **Prob. L·4.**

Problem L·2 Fig. L-2. Make detail working drawings of the *hung bearing* showing each piece fully dimensioned. All bolts are ⅝″ in diameter.

Problem L·3 Fig. L-3. Make detail drawings of the *pivot-guide roll.*

Problem L·4 Fig. L-4. Make working detail drawings of base, pulley, bushing, and shaft with bill of material for complete *pulley-and-stand unit.* Full size, three sheets. If necessary, the top view may be a half plan.

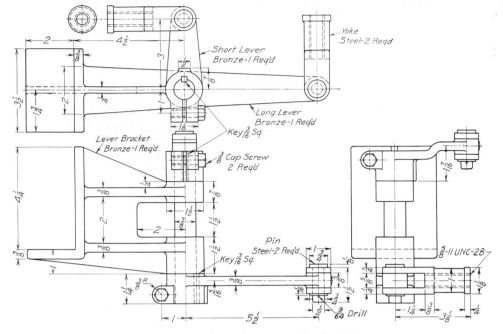

Fig. L-5   Bell-crank reverse. **Prob. L·5.**

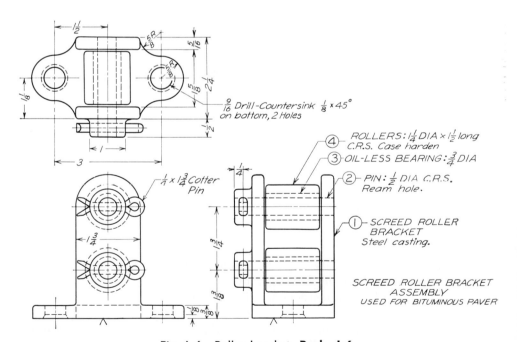

Fig. L-6   Roller bracket. **Prob. L·6.**

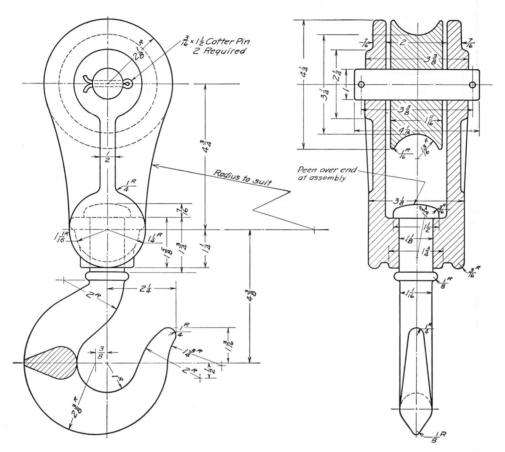

Fig. L-7 Crane hook. **Prob. L·7.**

Problem L·5 Fig. L-5. Make detail drawings of the *bell-crank reverse.*

Problem L·6 Fig. L-6. Make detail drawings of the *roller bracket.*

Problem L·7 Fig. L-7. Make detail drawings of the *crane hook.*

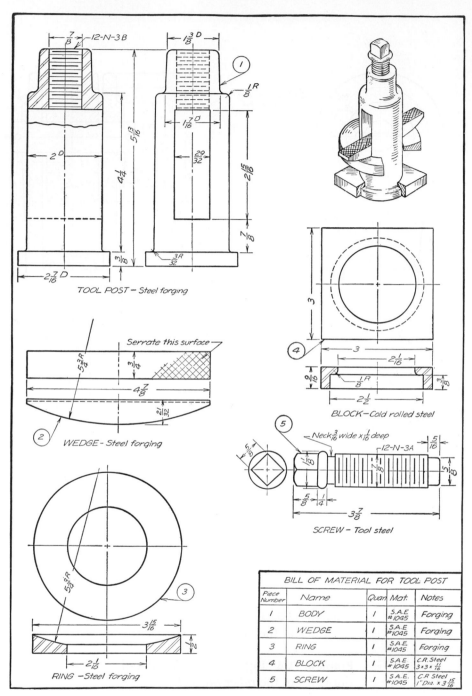

TOOL POST – Steel forging

WEDGE – Steel forging

BLOCK – Cold rolled steel

SCREW – Tool steel

RING – Steel forging

Piece Number	Name	Quan.	Mat.	Notes
1	BODY	1	S.A.E. #1045	Forging
2	WEDGE	1	S.A.E. #1045	Forging
3	RING	1	S.A.E. #1045	Forging
4	BLOCK	1	S.A.E. #1045	C.R.Steel 3×3×$\frac{11}{16}$
5	SCREW	1	S.A.E. #1045	C.R Steel 1″ Dia. × 3$\frac{15}{16}$

BILL OF MATERIAL FOR TOOL POST

Fig. L-8 Tool post. **Prob. L·8.**

Problem L·8 Fig. L-8. Make a two-view assembly drawing of the *tool post*.

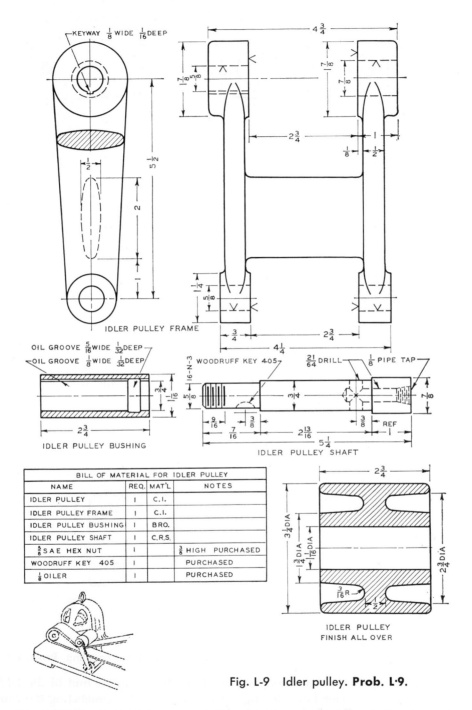

KEYWAY $\frac{1}{8}$ WIDE $\frac{1}{16}$ DEEP

IDLER PULLEY FRAME

OIL GROOVE $\frac{5}{16}$ WIDE $\frac{1}{32}$ DEEP

OIL GROOVE $\frac{1}{8}$ WIDE $\frac{1}{32}$ DEEP

IDLER PULLEY BUSHING

WOODRUFF KEY 405 $\frac{21}{64}$ DRILL $\frac{1}{8}$ PIPE TAP

16-N-3

IDLER PULLEY SHAFT

BILL OF MATERIAL FOR IDLER PULLEY			
NAME	REQ.	MAT'L	NOTES
IDLER PULLEY	I	C.I.	
IDLER PULLEY FRAME	I	C.I.	
IDLER PULLEY BUSHING	I	BRO.	
IDLER PULLEY SHAFT	I	C.R.S.	
$\frac{5}{8}$ SAE HEX NUT	I		$\frac{3}{8}$ HIGH PURCHASED
WOODRUFF KEY 405	I		PURCHASED
$\frac{1}{8}$ OILER	I		PURCHASED

IDLER PULLEY
FINISH ALL OVER

Fig. L-9   Idler pulley. **Prob. L·9.**

Problem L·9 Fig. L-9. Make an assembly drawing of the *idler pulley*, two views, full size, showing pulley, bushing, and upper end of frame in section.

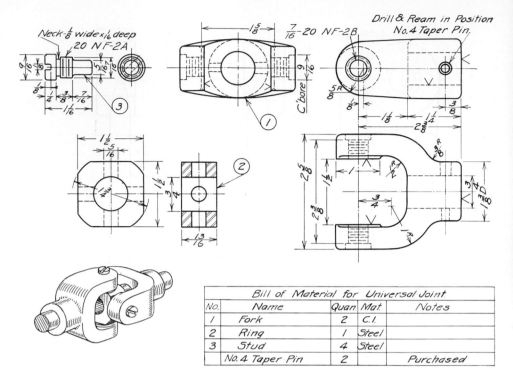

No.	Name	Quan.	Mat.	Notes
	Bill of Material for Universal Joint			
1	Fork	2	C.I.	
2	Ring	1	Steel	
3	Stud	4	Steel	
	No. 4 Taper Pin	2		Purchased

Problem L·10 Fig. L-10 (*Above*). Make a two-view assembly drawing of the *universal joint* in section.

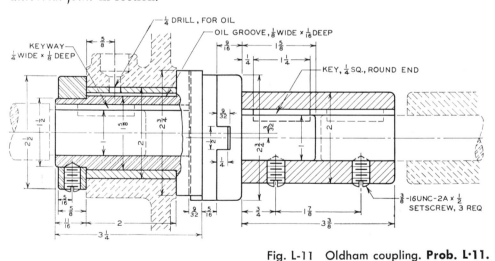

Fig. L-11 Oldham coupling. **Prob. L·11.**

Problem L·11 Fig. L-11. Make working detail drawings of clutches, driving and driven; clutch cross, muff coupling, collar, bushing, and key with bill of material for complete unit of the *Oldham coupling* (for connecting the ends of two rotating shafts, not in accurate alignment). Full size. Two sheets.

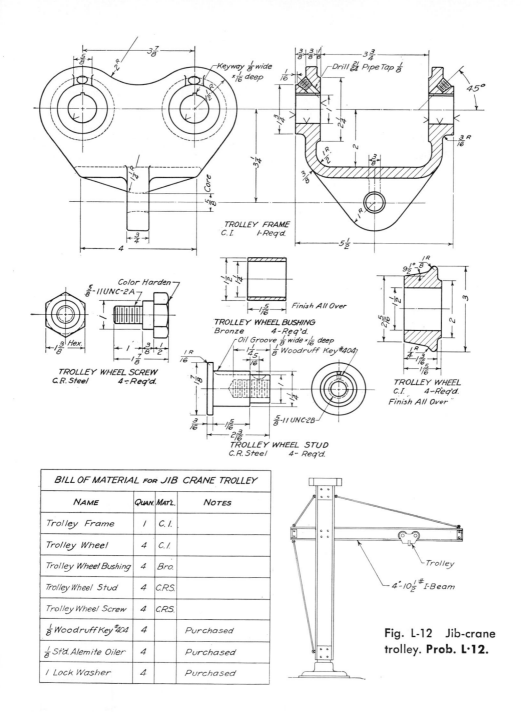

TROLLEY FRAME
C.I.   1-Req'd.

Keyway $\frac{1}{8}$ wide $\times \frac{1}{16}$ deep

Drill $\frac{21}{64}$ Pipe Tap $\frac{1}{8}$

Color Harden

$\frac{5}{8}$-11UNC-2A

TROLLEY WHEEL SCREW
C.R. Steel   4-Req'd.

TROLLEY WHEEL BUSHING
Bronze   4-Req'd.

Finish All Over

Oil Groove $\frac{1}{8}$ wide $\times \frac{1}{16}$ deep

$\frac{1}{8}$ Woodruff Key #404

$\frac{5}{8}$-11 UNC-2B

TROLLEY WHEEL STUD
C.R. Steel   4-Req'd.

TROLLEY WHEEL
C.I.   4-Req'd.
Finish All Over

BILL OF MATERIAL for JIB CRANE TROLLEY			
NAME	QUAN.	MAT'L.	NOTES
Trolley Frame	1	C.I.	
Trolley Wheel	4	C.I.	
Trolley Wheel Bushing	4	Bro.	
Trolley Wheel Stud	4	C.R.S.	
Trolley Wheel Screw	4	C.R.S.	
$\frac{1}{8}$ Woodruff Key #404	4		Purchased
$\frac{1}{8}$ Std. Alemite Oiler	4		Purchased
1 Lock Washer	4		Purchased

Trolley

4"-10$\frac{1}{2}$# I-Beam

Fig. L-12   Jib-crane trolley. Prob. L·12.

Problem L·12 Fig. L-12. Make an assembly drawing of the *jib-crane trolley*. Draw one view in section. The I-beam may be indicated if desired, obtaining dimensions from a structural-steel handbook.

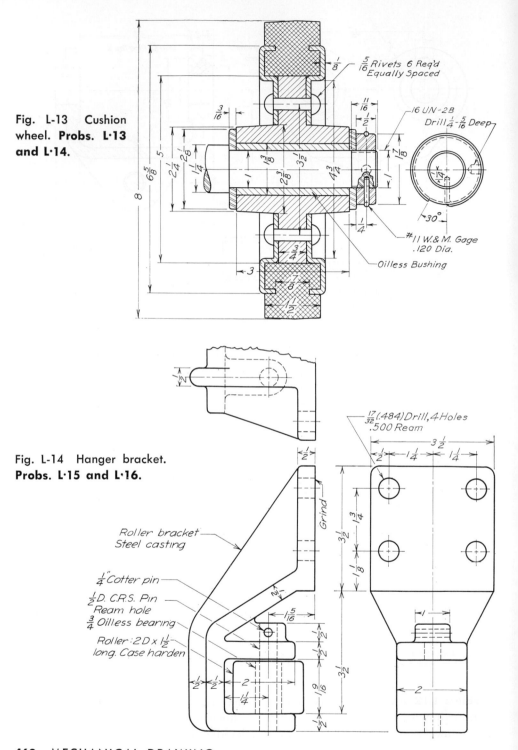

Fig. L-13 Cushion wheel. **Probs. L·13 and L·14.**

$\frac{5}{16}$ Rivets 6 Req'd Equally Spaced

16 UN-2B
Drill $\frac{1}{4}-\frac{5}{16}$ Deep

#11 W.& M. Gage .120 Dia.

Oilless Bushing

Fig. L-14 Hanger bracket. **Probs. L·15 and L·16.**

$\frac{17}{32}$(.484) Drill, 4 Holes .500 Ream

Grind

Roller bracket Steel casting

$\frac{1}{4}$" Cotter pin

$\frac{1}{2}$ D. C.R.S. Pin Ream hole

$\frac{3}{4}$ Oilless bearing

Roller: 2 D x $1\frac{1}{2}$ long. Case harden

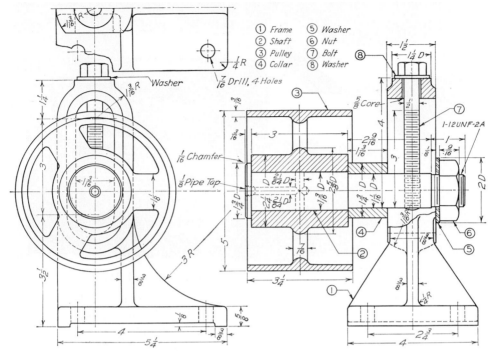

Fig. L-15 Belt tightener. Probs. L·17 and L·18.

Problem L·13 Fig. L-13. Make a front view and section of the *cushion wheel*, full size. This type of wheel is used on warehouse or platform trucks to reduce noise and vibration.

Problem L·14 Fig. L-13. Make a complete set of detail drawings, full size, with bill of material, for the *cushion wheel*. Three sheets will be needed. Rivets are purchased and, therefore, would not be detailed but would be specified in the bill of material.

Problem L·15 Fig. L-14. Make a complete assembly drawing of the *hanger bracket*. Place the vertical distances of the figure parallel to the long dimension of the sheet. Supply the missing details.

Problem L·16 Fig. L-14. Make a complete set of detail drawings with bill of material for the *hanger bracket*. Supply missing details.

Problem L·17 Fig. L-15. Make an assembly drawing of the *belt tightener*. Show three exterior views.

Problem L·18 Fig. L-15. Make a complete set of detail drawings for the *belt tightener*.

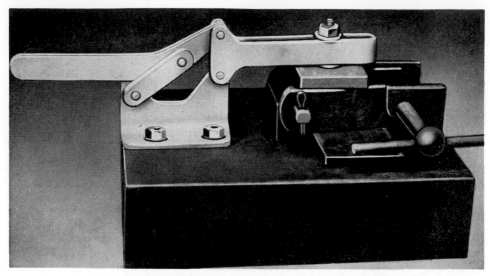

Fig. L-16 Toggle-action clamp. **Probs. L·19 to L·21.**

Problems L·19 to L·21 Fig. L-16 and L-17. The Model KP-186 toggle-action clamp, shown in Figs. L-16 and L-17, is one of a large variety of clamping fixtures made by Knu-Vise Incorporated, Detroit, Mich. Note the U-shaped toggle bar used to hold work in place. It may be used without the spindle to clamp the work directly. The handle is pivoted on the link and, when raised, releases the toggle bar. The link and toggle bar are also pivoted on the base. Dimensions not given are to be worked out as the parts are drawn.

This low-model clamp allows free overhead movement of operating tools in drilling, routing, or end-mill operations. The parts are made of steel, and all parts except the toggle bar are heat-treated. The entire clamp is cadmium-plated. Weight is 19 oz.

Part 1. Base—RH, made of SAE #1020, CRS (Society of Automotive Engineers, No. 1020, cold-rolled steel), thickness #9 (0.1494) USS, GA. (US Standard Gage). Pierce 2 holes 0.238 $^{+0.003}_{-0.000}$ diameter, ream 0.250 $^{+0.001}_{-0.000}$. Distance between centers B and C is 2.470. Spotweld RH and LH bases together at places marked X.

Part 2. Base—RH, same as Part 1 but left hand.

Part 3. Toggle bar, made of SAE #1020, CRS, thickness #11 (0.1196) USS, GA. Pierce 4 holes 0.187 $^{+0.001}_{-0.000}$ diameter.

Part 4. Handle—RH made of SAE #1020, CRS, thickness #9 (0.1494) USS, GA. Pierce 2 holes 0.238 $^{+0.003}_{-0.000}$ diameter, ream 0.250 $^{+0.001}_{-0.000}$. Spotweld RH and LH handles together at places marked X.

Part 5. Handle—LH, same as Part 4 but left hand.

Part 6. Link, made of SAE #1020, CRS, thickness #11 (0.1196) USS, GA. Pierce 2 holes 0.187 $^{+0.001}_{-0.000}$.

Distance between centers C and D is 1.625 $^{+0.001}_{-0.001}$.

Part 7. Shoulder rivet, made of SAE #X-1112, screw stock, cyanide harden. Four required. See enlarged view on Fig. L-17.

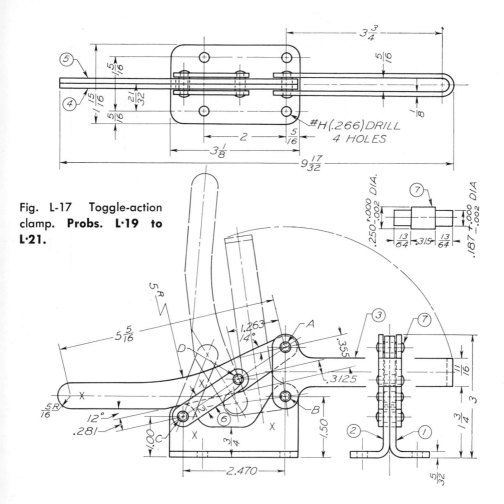

Fig. L-17 Toggle-action clamp. **Probs. L·19 to L·21.**

Problem L·19 Figs. L-16 and L-17. Make a set of detail working drawings for the parts of the Model KP-186 *toggle-action clamp.*

Problem L·20 Figs. L-16 and L-17. Prepare a complete parts list for the Model KP-186 *toggle-action clamp.*

Problem L·21 Figs. L-16 and L-17. Make an assembly drawing of the Model KP-186 *toggle-action clamp.* Work out the open position carefully and draw it in with the proper lines for showing an alternate position. A con-

venient method is to make tracings of parts with accurate center distances, place them in the desired position, and punch the centers with a needle point. The parts can then be drawn.

Problems L·22 to L·24 Fig. L-18. A jig is a device used to hold a machine part (called the *work* or *production*) while it is being machined, or produced, so that all the parts will be alike within specified limits of accuracy. Note the production shown in the upper left-hand corner of the figure (Fig. L-18).

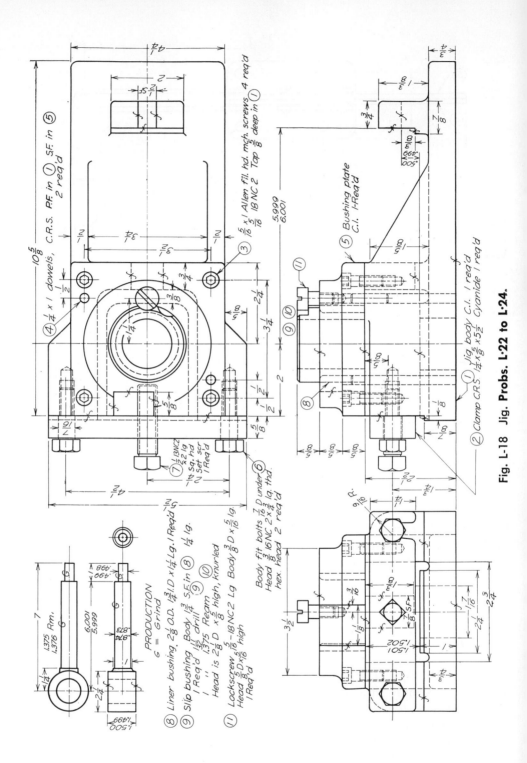

Fig. L-18 Jig. **Probs. L-22 to L-24.**

Problem L·22 Fig. L-18. Make a detail working drawing of the *jig body*.

Problem L·23 Fig. L-18. Make a complete set of detail drawings for the *jig* with bill of material. Use as many sheets as necessary or use larger sheets.

Problem L·24 Fig. L-18. Make a complete assembly drawing of the *jig*, three views. Give only such dimensions as are necessary for putting the parts together and using the jig.

GROUP M. PIPING DRAWINGS

24·16 Information about pipe, fittings, and so forth, is given in the published standards of the American Standards Association, 29 West 39th Street, New York 17. Obtain dimensions of pipe fittings from the above standards or from a handbook or a piping catalogue. Study Arts. 13·18 to 13·21.

Problem M·1 Lay out a standard sheet (Fig. A-2). Use the representations of Fig. 13-23. In the upper left-hand corner of the sheet draw a ½″ cross, full size. Plug the upper and left-hand outlets with square-head and countersunk plugs, respectively. In the right outlet place a 4″ nipple followed in order by the following fittings: standard ½″ screw union, ½″ nipple, ½″ street elbow, ½″ to ⅜″ reducing coupling, ⅜″ nipple, ⅜″ 45° branch, ⅜″ nipple in angle outlet of branch, 45° elbow ⅜″ pipe, ½″ to ⅜″ reducing bushing, ½″ standard elbow, and ½″ nipple. This last nipple should screw into the lower outlet of the cross thus closing the system. The run outlet of the branch should be plugged.

Problem M·2 In the upper left-hand corner of the sheet draw, full size, a ½″ standard tee with the run outlets horizontal. Place a countersunk plug in the left-hand outlet. Starting at the right-hand outlet, draw the following fittings in the order mentioned below, the last nipple fitting in the bottom outlet of the tee: nipple, globe valve, nipple, elbow, nipple, 45°—½″ × ½″ × ⅜″ branch, ⅜″ nipple, 45° elbow, nipple, R & L coupling, nipple, ½″ to ⅜″ reducing bushing, ½″ screwed union, street elbow, nipple, coupling, and nipple. Place a nipple and cap in the run outlet of the branch. Use the representations of Fig. 13-23.

Problem M·3 Draw two horizontal center lines 6¾″ apart and between them a third 3″ from the lower one. Draw two vertical center lines 10″ apart. On these center lines draw the following pipe fittings, full size, making two closed systems interconnected: ½″ standard tee, square-head plug, ½″ to ⅜″ reducing coupling, ⅜″ standard coupling, ⅜″ R & L coupling, ⅜″ angle valve, ⅜″— 45° branch, ½″ to ⅜″ reducing bushing, ½″ street elbow, ½″ gate valve, ½″ screwed union, ½″ elbow, ½″ × ½″ × ⅜″ tee, ⅜″ cross, ⅜″ countersunk plug, ⅜″ cap, and ⅜″—45° elbow. Use nipples to suit. Use the representations of Fig. 13-25.

Problems M·4 to M·6 Same as Probs. M·1 to M·3 respectively, but use single-line conventions (see Fig. 13-28).

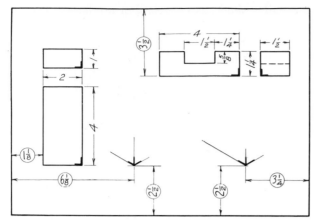

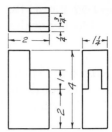

Fig. N-2 Anchor block.
Prob. N·3.

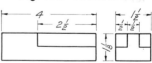

Fig. N-1 Isometric drawing. Notched block.
Probs. N·1 and N·2.

Fig. N-3 Locator.
Prob. N·4.

GROUP N. PICTORIAL DRAWING

24·17 Study Chap. 14 carefully before beginning the problems. Use regular sheet with 10½″ ×15″ working space.

The two starting positions for the isometric axes are shown in Figs. 14-5 and 14-6. Remember that all measurements must be taken parallel to the axes.

Problem N·1 Fig. N-1. Draw the two orthographic views. Construct the *isometric drawing*, using the axes in the second position as indicated.

Problem N·2 Fig. N-1. Draw the two

orthographic views and an isometric drawing of the *notched block.*

Problem N·3 Fig. N-2. Draw the two orthographic views and an isometric drawing of the *anchor block.* Alternate for Prob. N·1.

Problem N·4 Fig. N-3. Draw the two orthographic views and an isometric drawing of the *locator.* Alternate for Prob. N·2.

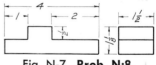

Fig. N-7 **Prob. N·8.**

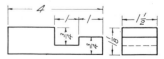

Fig. N-8 (*Above*) **Prob. N·9.**
Fig. N-9 (*Below*) **Prob. N·10.**

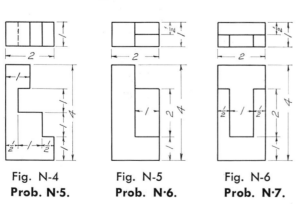

Fig. N-4   Fig. N-5   Fig. N-6
Prob. N·5.   **Prob. N·6.**   **Prob. N·7.**

474 MECHANICAL DRAWING

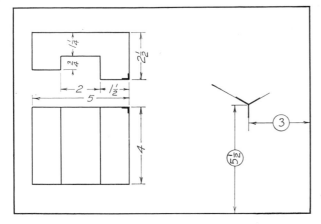

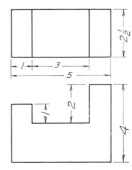

Fig. N-11   **Prob. N·12.**

Fig. N-10   Guide.   **Prob. N·11.**

Problems N·5, N·6, and N·7 Figs. N-4, N-5, and N-6. Alternates for Prob. N·1.

Problems N·8, N·9, and N·10 Figs. N-7, N-8, and N-9. Alternates for Prob. N·2.

Problem N·11 Fig. N-10. Draw the views given and an isometric drawing of the *guide* using the axes in the position indicated.

Problems N·12, N·13, N·14, N·15, and N·16 Figs. N-11, N-12, N-13, N-14, and N-15. Alternate problems for Prob. N·11.

Problem N·17 Fig. N-16. Draw the orthographic views given and an isometric drawing of the *tenoned block.*

Problem N·18 Fig. N-16. Draw the orthographic views given and an isometric drawing of the *mortised block.*

Problem N·19 Fig. N-17. Alternate for Prob. N·17.

Problem N·20 Fig. N-18. Alternate for Prob. N·18.

Problem N·21 Fig. N-19. Alternate for Prob. N·17.

Problem N·22 Fig. N-20. Alternate for Prob. N·18.

Problem N·23 Fig. N-21. Alternate for Prob. N·17 or N·18.

Problem N·24 Fig. N-22. Draw the or-

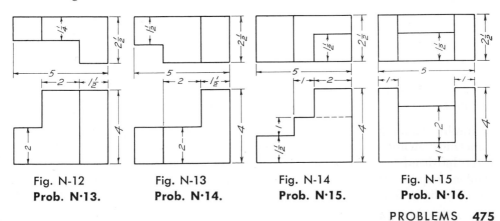

Fig. N-12
Prob. N·13.

Fig. N-13
Prob. N·14.

Fig. N-14
Prob. N·15.

Fig. N-15
Prob. N·16.

PROBLEMS   **475**

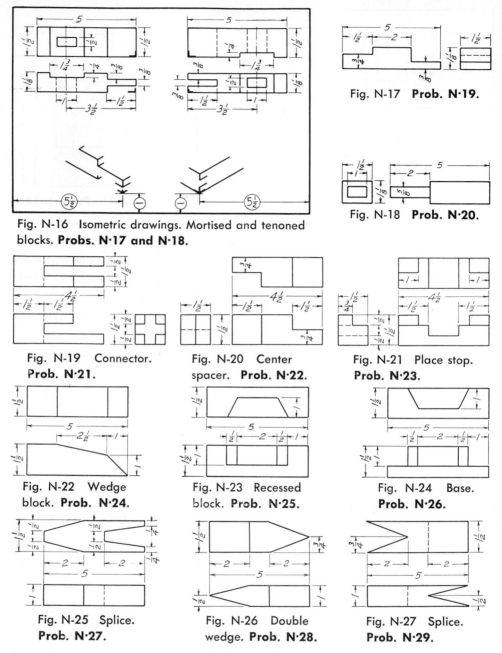

Fig. N-16 Isometric drawings. Mortised and tenoned blocks. **Probs. N·17 and N·18.**

Fig. N-17 **Prob. N·19.**

Fig. N-18 **Prob. N·20.**

Fig. N-19 Connector. **Prob. N·21.**

Fig. N-20 Center spacer. **Prob. N·22.**

Fig. N-21 Place stop. **Prob. N·23.**

Fig. N-22 Wedge block. **Prob. N·24.**

Fig. N-23 Recessed block. **Prob. N·25.**

Fig. N-24 Base. **Prob. N·26.**

Fig. N-25 Splice. **Prob. N·27.**

Fig. N-26 Double wedge. **Prob. N·28.**

Fig. N-27 Splice. **Prob. N·29.**

thographic views given and make an isometric drawing of the *wedge block* in the left-hand half of the sheet. This problem requires the locating of non-isometric lines. Read Art. 14·5 and ob-

serve the construction in Fig. 14-7 before starting this problem. The layout of Fig. N-16 may be used. The construction lines should be drawn very lightly and either to the left or the right

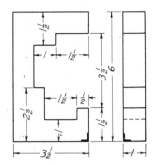

Fig. N-28 Notched block. **Prob. N·30.**

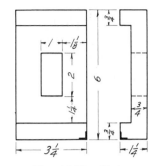

Fig. N-29 Plate. **Prob. N·31.**

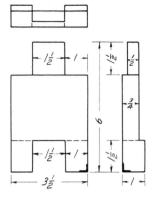

Fig. N-30 Lock joint. **Prob. N·32.**

on the drawing and are not to be erased until they have been inspected by the instructor. The final lines of the isometric drawing should be brightened with a sharp pencil.

Problem N·25 Fig. N-23. Draw the orthographic views and make an isometric drawing of the *recessed block* in the right-hand half of the sheet. The same procedure should be followed as in Prob. N·24.

Problem N·26 Fig. N-24. Alternate for Prob. N·25.

Problem N·27 Fig. N-25. Alternate for Prob. N·24 or N·25.

Problem N·28 Fig. N-26. Alternate for Prob. N·24 or N·25.

Problem N·29 Fig. N-27. Alternate for Prob. N·24 or N·25.

Problem N·30 Fig. N-28. Make an isometric drawing of the *notched block*. Start with the corner indicated by the heavy lines. Locate at the left as on the layout of Fig. N-31.

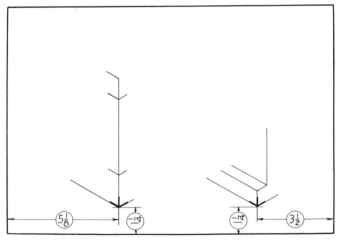

Fig. N-31 Layout for Probs. N·30 to N·36.

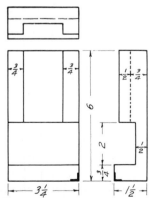

Fig. N-32 Rabbited stop. **Prob. N·33.**

PROBLEMS **477**

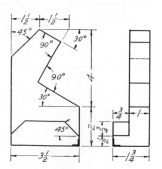

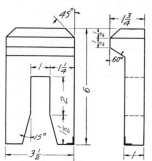

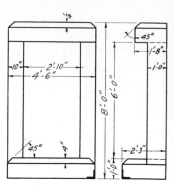

Fig. N-33 Notched slide. **Prob. N·34.**

Fig. N-34 Slotted stop. **Prob. N·35.**

Fig. N-35 Frame. **Prob. N·36.**

Problem N·31 Fig. N-29. Make an isometric drawing of the *plate*. Locate at the right as on the layout of Fig. N-31.

Problem N·32 Fig. N-30. Alternate for Prob. N·30 or N·31.

Problem N·33 Fig. N-32. Alternate for Prob. N·30 or N·31.

Problem N·34 Fig. N-33. Make an iso- metric drawing of the *notched slide* using layout of Fig. N-31.

Problem N·35 Fig. N-34. Make an isometric drawing of the *slotted stop* using the layout of Fig. N-31.

Problem N·36 Fig. N-35. Make an isometric drawing of the *frame* using the layout of Fig. N-31. Use scale of 3″ = 1′–0″.

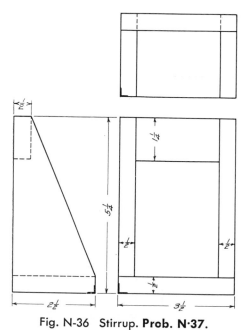

Fig. N-36 Stirrup. **Prob. N·37.**

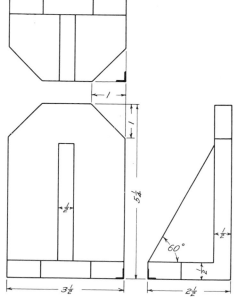

Fig. N-37 Brace. **Prob. N·38.**

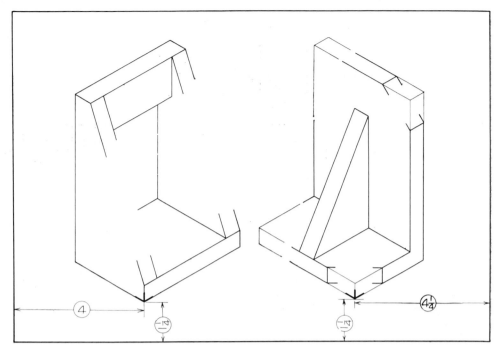

Fig. N-38   Layout for Probs. N·37 and N·38.

Problem N·37 Fig. N-36. Make an isometric drawing of the *stirrup*. The drawing is started on the layout of Fig. N-38. Note the heavy lines for the starting corner.

Problem N·38 Fig. N-37. Make an isometric drawing of the *brace*. The drawing is started on the layout of Fig. N-38. Note the 60° angle and read Art. 14·5.

Problems N·39 and N·40 Figs. N-39 and N-40. Make isometric drawings. Use layout of Fig. N-38.

Problems N·41 and N·42 Fig. N-41. Make isometric drawing of a 3″ cube with isometric circle on each face (Art. 14·6) and of a cylinder resting on a square plate.

Problem N·43 Fig. N-42. Draw the

three views given and an isometric drawing of the *hung bearing*. Most of the construction is indicated on the layout. Make the drawing as though all corners were square and then construct the curves as described in Art. 14·6.

Problem N·44 Fig. N-43. Draw the three views given and then make an isometric drawing of the *bracket*. Some of the construction is indicated on the layout. Make the drawing as though the corners were square and then construct the curves. Read Art. 14·6. (An alternate for Prob. N·43.)

Problem N·45 Fig. N-44. Draw the three views given and then make an isometric drawing of the *lug*. Make the drawing as though the corners were square and then construct the curves. Read Art. 14·6.

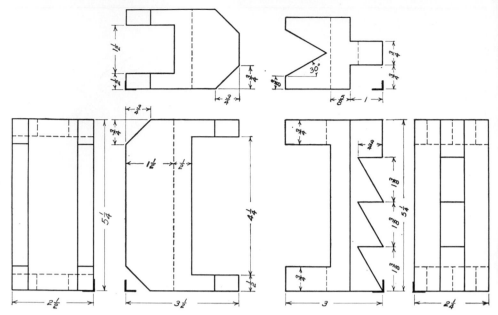

Fig. N-39 Cross slide. **Prob. N·39.**

Fig. N-40 Ratchet. **Prob. N·40.**

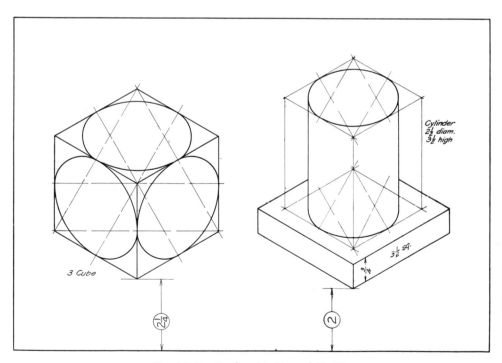

3 Cube

Cylinder
2½ diam.
3½ high

3½ SQ.

Fig. N-41 **Probs. N·41 and N·42.**

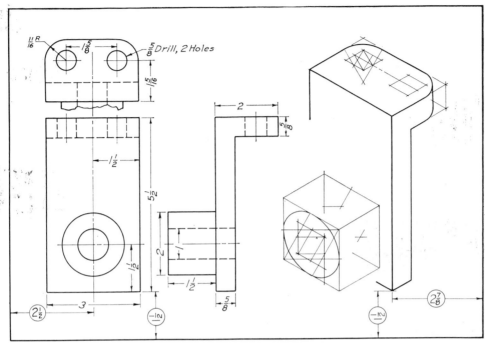

Fig. N-42   Hung bearing. **Prob. N·43.**

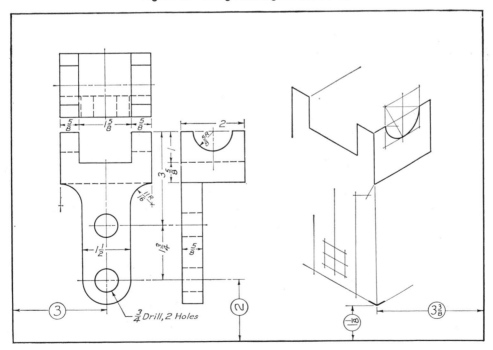

Fig. N-43   Bracket. **Prob. N·44.**

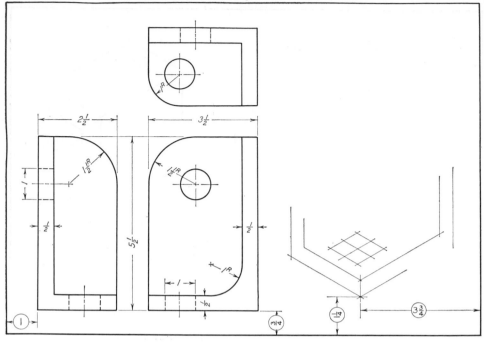

Fig. N-44 Lug. **Prob. N·45.**

24·18 Isometric sections. The next four problems are sectional views on isometric drawings. As referred to in Art. 14·8, these are often useful in showing interior construction. The cutting planes must be isometric planes, that is, parallel to the faces of the isometric cube. Section lining is done with the 60° triangle. In making a full section, as for Probs. N·46 and N·49, draw the cut surface first, then add the part of the object behind it. For a half section, as called for in Probs. N·47 and N·48, it is usually best to draw the full isometric view, very lightly, first, then cut out the front quarter by two isometric planes as indicated in the layouts (Figs. N-47 and N-51) and as shown in Figs. 14-10 and 14-11.

Problem N·46 Fig. N-45. Make an iso-metric drawing in section of the *post socket*. Layout of Fig. N-47.

Problem N·47 Fig. N-46. Make an iso-metric drawing in half section of the *box step*. Layout of Fig. N-47.

Problem N·48 Fig. N-48. Isometric drawing in half section. Layout of Fig. N-47 or N-51.

Problem N·49 Fig. N-49. Isometric sec-tion. Layout of Fig. N-51.

Problem N·50 Fig. N-50. Isometric half section. Layout of Fig. N-51.

Problem N·51 Fig. N-52. Isometric half section. Layout of Fig. N-51.

Problem N·52 Fig. N-53. Draw views

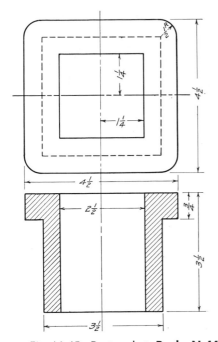

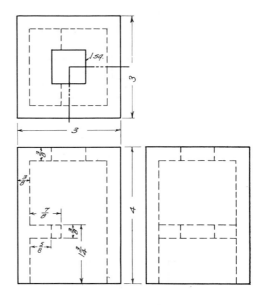

Fig. N-45   Post socket. **Prob. N·46.**

Fig. N-46   Box step. **Prob. N·47.**

given and make an isometric drawing of the *tablet*. Reversed axes, Art. 14·11.

drawing of the *bracket*. Reversed axes. Layout of Fig. N-53.

Problem N·53 Fig. N-54. Draw the views given and make an isometric

Problem N·54 Fig. N-55. Draw the views given and make an isometric

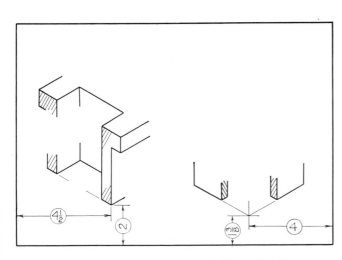

Fig. N-47   Layout for Probs. N·46 and N·47.

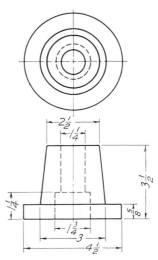

Fig. N-48   Cone bearing. **Prob. N·48.**

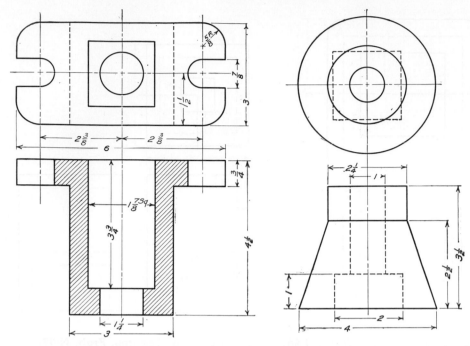

Fig. N-49   Post support. **Prob. N·49.**

Fig. N-50   Foundation washer. **Prob. N·50.**

drawing of the *bracket*. Reversed axes. Layout of Fig. N-53.

Problem N·55 Fig. N-56. Draw the views given and make an isometric

drawing of the *bracket*. Reversed axes. Layout of Fig. N-53. Note the construction for the ogee curve.

Problem N·56 Fig. N-57. Draw the

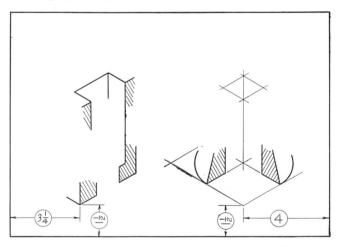

Fig. N-51   Layout for Probs. N·49 and N·50.

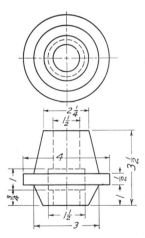

Fig. N-52   Centering cone. **Prob. N·51.**

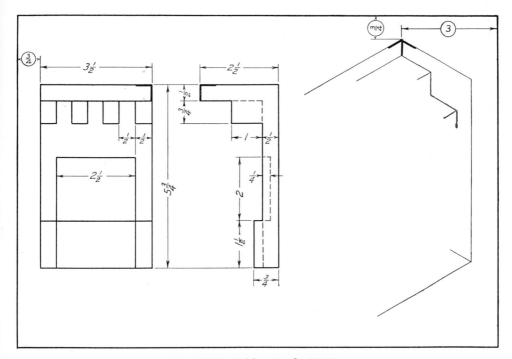

Fig. N-53 Tablet. **Prob. N·52.**

views given and make an isometric drawing of the *extension bar*. Long axis horizontal Art. 14·12.

Problem N·57 Fig. N-58. Make an isometric drawing of the *spacing bar*. Long axis horizontal.

Problem N·58 Fig. N-59. Make an isometric drawing of the *special rod*. Long axis horizontal.

Problem N·59 Fig. N-60. Make an oblique drawing of the *angle support*. Layout of Fig. N-63.

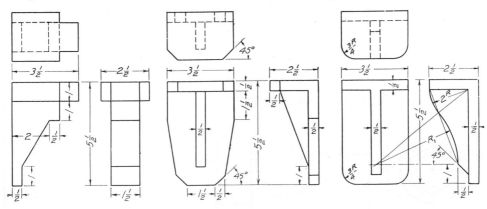

Fig. N-54 Bracket.
Prob. N·53.

Fig. N-55 Bracket.
Prob. N·54.

Fig. N-56 Bracket.
Prob. N·55.

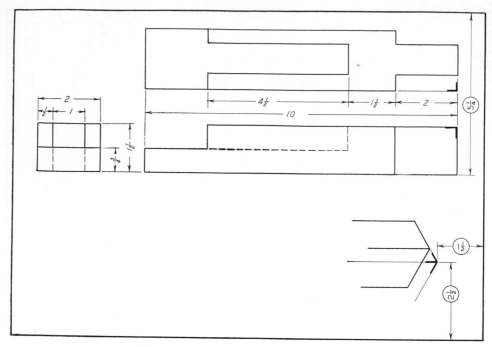

Fig. N-57 Extension bar. **Prob. N·56.**

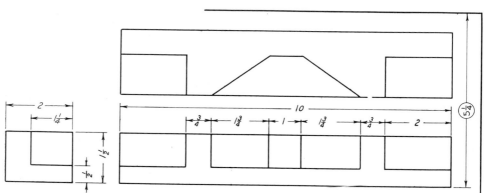

Fig. N-58 Spacing bar. **Prob. N·57.**

Fig. N·59 Special rod. **Prob. N·58.**

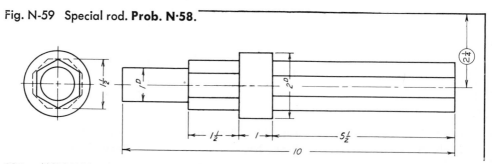

486 MECHANICAL DRAWING

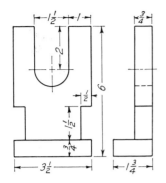

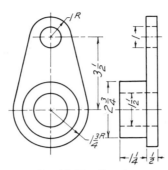

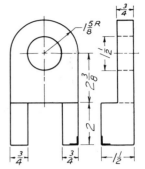

Fig. N-60   Angle   support.
Prob. N·59.

Fig. N-61   Crank.
Prob. N·60.

Fig. N-62   Forked   guide.
Prob. N·61.

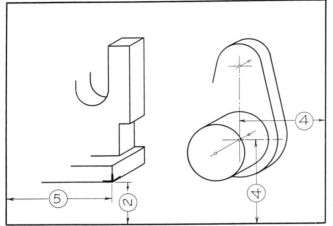

Fig. N-63   Layout for Probs. N·60 and N·61.

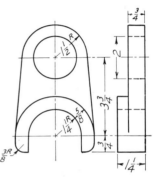

Fig.   N-64   Guide   link.
Prob. N·62.

Problem N·60 Fig. N-61. Make an oblique drawing of the *crank*. Layout of Fig. N-63.

Problem N·61 Fig. N-62. Make an oblique drawing of the *forked guide*. Layout of Fig. N-63.

Problem N·62 Fig. N-64. Make an oblique drawing of the *guide link*. Layout of Fig. N-63.

Problem N·63 Fig. N-65. Make an oblique drawing of the *slotted sector*. This drawing can be made in one-half of a sheet divided by a vertical line

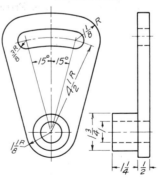

Fig. N-65   Slotted sector. **Prob. N·63.**

through the center. Use an axis of 30° or 45° to the right or the left as directed by the instructor.

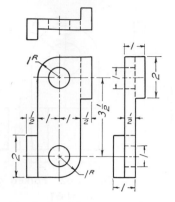

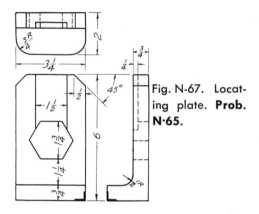

Fig. N-66 Double stop. **Prob. N·64.**

Fig. N-67. Locating plate. **Prob. N·65.**

Fig. N-68 (*Below*) Clock case. **Prob. N·66.**

Problem N·64 Fig. N-66. Make an oblique drawing of the *double stop*. One-half of regular space. Axis 30° or 45° to the right or the left as directed by instructor.

Problem N·65 Fig. N-67. Make an oblique drawing of the *locating plate*. One-half of regular space. Axis 30° or 45° to the right or the left as directed by instructor.

Problem N·66 Fig. N-68. Make an oblique drawing of the *clock case*. Use an axis of 30° to the right.

24·19 Pictorial sketching is important for the study of reading drawings and blueprints. The following 24 problems are designed for practice.

Problems N·67 to N·74 Fig. N-69. Problems for pictorial sketching.

Problems N·75 to N·82 Fig. N-70. Problems for pictorial sketching.

Problems N·83 to N·90 Fig. N-71. Problems for pictorial sketching.

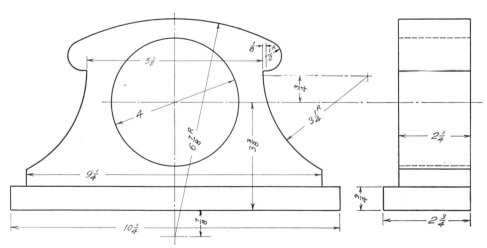

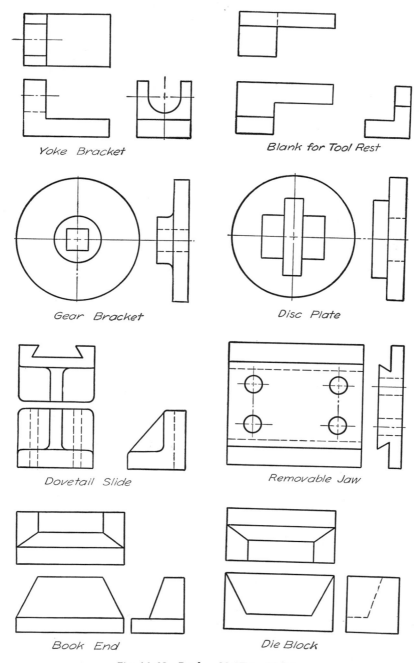

Yoke Bracket

Blank for Tool Rest

Gear Bracket

Disc Plate

Dovetail Slide

Removable Jaw

Book End

Die Block

Fig. N-69 **Probs. N·67 to N·74.**

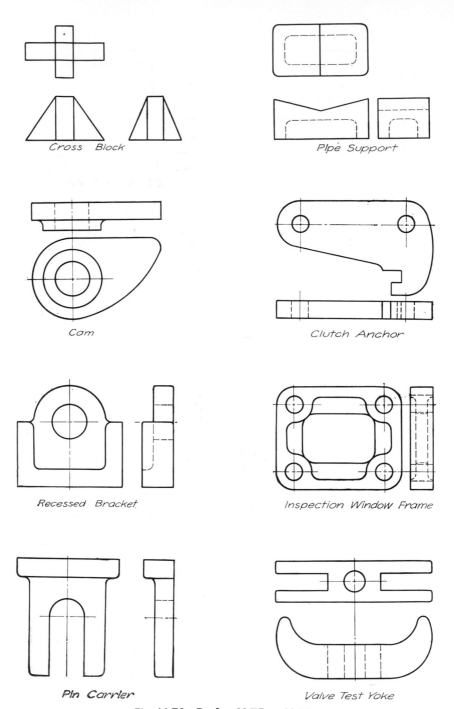

Cross Block

Pipe Support

Cam

Clutch Anchor

Recessed Bracket

Inspection Window Frame

Pin Carrier

Valve Test Yoke

Fig. N-70 **Probs. N·75 to N·82.**

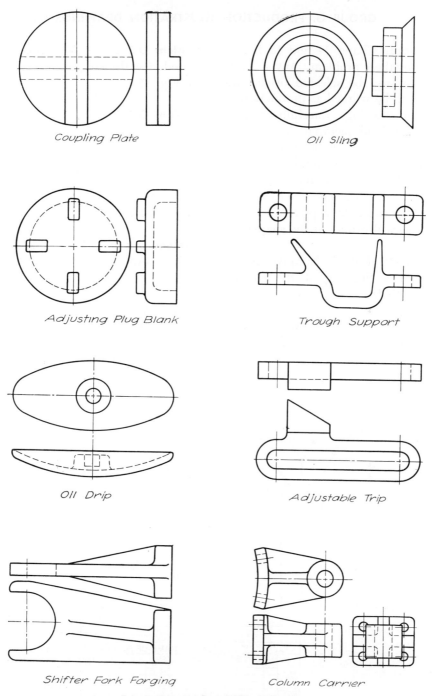

Coupling Plate

Oil Sling

Adjusting Plug Blank

Trough Support

Oil Drip

Adjustable Trip

Shifter Fork Forging

Column Carrier

Fig. N-71 **Probs. N·83 to N·90.**

24·20 Study Chaps. 14 and 15 before beginning these problems. Any suitable problems may be selected by the instructor to be worked as production-illustration drawings. Carefully proportioned freehand pictorial drawings in isometric, oblique, or perspective may be used depending upon the most effective result. A few problems may be drawn with instruments. The amount of rendering should be kept down to the least that will bring out the shapes.

Problem O·1 Fig. N-36. Make an exploded-view drawing of the *stirrup*. See Fig. 15-4.

Problem O·2 Fig. N-37. Make an exploded-view drawing of the *brace*. See Fig. 15-4.

Problem O·3 Fig. N-39. Make an exploded-view drawing of the *cross slide*. See Fig. 15-4.

Problem O·4 Fig. N-42. Make an exploded-view drawing of the *hung bearing*. See Fig. 15-4.

Problem O·5 Fig. D-81. Make an exploded-view drawing of the *bearing*. See Fig. 15-4.

Problem O·6 Fig. K-4. Make an exploded-view drawing of the *bench hook*.

Problem O·7 Fig. K-6. Make a production drawing of the *nail box*.

Fig. P-1   Tube assembly. **Prob. P·7.**

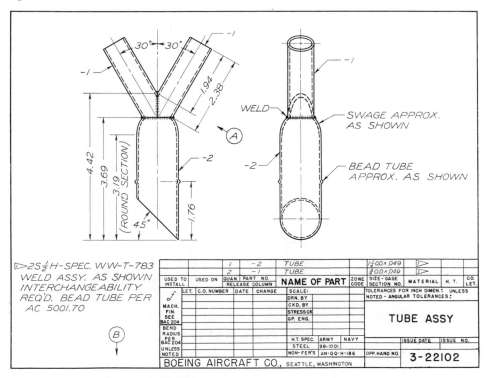

Problem O·8 Fig. K-7. Make a production drawing of the *book rack*.

Problem O·9 Fig. J-19. Make a production drawing of the *babbitted bearing*.

Problem O·10 Fig. L-2. Make an exploded-view drawing of the *hung bearing*.

Problem O·11 Fig. L-14. Make an exploded-view drawing of the *hanger bracket*.

Problem O·12 Fig. L-3. Make an exploded-view drawing of the *pivot-guide roll*.

Problem O·13 Fig. L-8. Make an exploded-view drawing of the *tool post*.

Problem O·14 Fig. L-9. Make an exploded-view drawing of the *idler pulley*.

Problem O·15 Fig. L-4. Make an exploded-view drawing of the *pulley-and-stand unit*.

Problem O·16 Fig. L-15. Make an exploded-view drawing of the *belt tightener*.

GROUP P. AIRCRAFT DRAWINGS

24·21 Study Chap. 16 before beginning these problems. It will be helpful to have some special books on hand for reference and additional problems where more study of aircraft drawings is desired.[1]

Problem P·1 Fig. 16-16. Make a drawing of the *fitting*.

Problem P·2 Fig. 16-8. Make a drawing of the *fitting*.

[1] The following books are recommended for reference purposes: *A Manual of Aircraft Drafting* by Carl L. Svensen, D. Van Nostrand Company, Inc., Princeton, N.J. *Aircraft Layout and Detail Design* by N. H. Anderson, 2d ed., McGraw-Hill Book Company, Inc., New York. *A Simple Guide to Blueprint Reading: With Applications to Aircraft* by William Wright, McGraw-Hill Book Company, Inc., New York.

Students will also find the following books of help although the books themselves are not on drafting: *Aircraft Basic Science, Aircraft Maintenance and Repairs,* and *Aircraft Power Plants* by Northrop Aeronautical Institute; *Jet Aircraft Power Systems* by J. V. Casamassa, McGraw-Hill Book Company, Inc., New York.

Problem P·3 Fig. 16-5. Make a forging blank drawing of the *roller arm*.

Problem P·4 Fig. 16-6. Make a forging machining drawing of the *roller arm*.

Problem P·5 Fig. 16-7. Make a forging drawing of the *fitting*.

Problem P·6 Fig. 16-14. Make a tabulated drawing of the *plunger assembly*.

Problem P·7 Fig. P-1. Make a drawing of the *tube assembly*.

Problem P·8 Fig. 16-15. Make a drawing of the *brace assembly*.

Problem P·9 Fig. 16-4. Make a casting drawing of the *bracket*.

Problem P·10 Fig. 16-17. Make a drawing of the *stabilizer frame*.

Problem P·11 Fig. P-2. Make a drawing of the *flap hinge*.

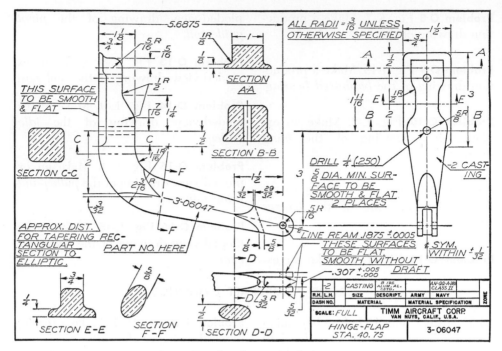

Fig. P-2   Flap hinge. **Prob. P·11.**

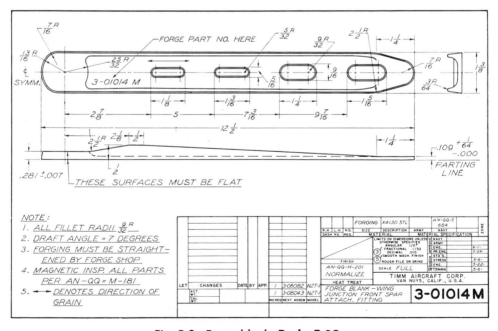

Fig. P-3   Forge blank. **Prob. P·12.**

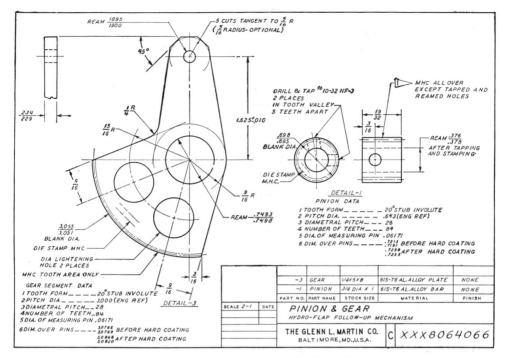

Fig. P-4 Pinion and gear. **Prob. P·13.**

Problem P·12 Fig. P-3. Make a drawing of the *forge blank*.

Problem P·13 Fig. P-4. Make a drawing of the *pinion and gear*.

Problem P·14 Fig. P-5. Make a drawing showing the necessary view and notes for the **LEVER—COCKPIT AIR-VALVE CONTROL**. Note that the letter *B* is to be used for the center-to-center dimen-

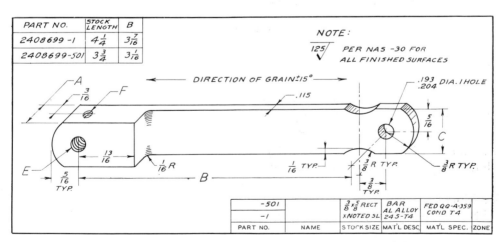

Fig. P-5 Lever. *(Douglas Aircraft Company, Inc.)* **Prob. P·14.**

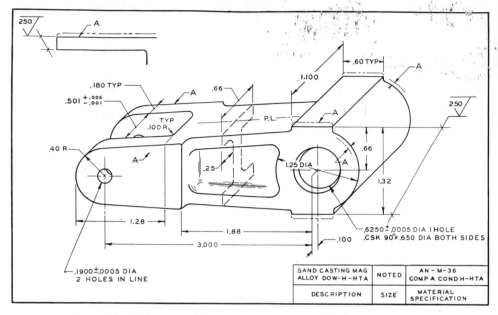

Fig. P-6 Arm. (Northrup Aircraft, Inc.) Prob. P·15.

sion since the drawing is for two parts as set out in the tabulation in the upper left-hand corner. Replace the letter *A* with the words **STOCK SIZE**. Replace the letter *C* with the words **STOCK SIZE**. Replace the letter *E* with the note: $^{0.2113}_{0.2173}$ **DIA THRU, CSK 90° × ¼, THD ¼—28NF—3 per AN–S–126.** Replace the letter *F* with the note: $^{0.1042}_{0.1145}$ **DIA**

depth ⁵⁄₁₆, **CSK 90° × ⅛, THD 6—32NC —3 per AN–S–126.**

Problem P·15 Fig. P-6. Make a drawing showing the necessary views and notes for the **ARM—BRAKE-VALVE ACT. LOWER.** Indicate the parting line (PL). Indicate an allowance at *A* to be removed for surface roughness.

GROUP Q. WELDING DRAWINGS

24·22 Study Chap. 17 before beginning these problems.

Problem Q·1 Fig. 17-4. Make a drawing showing the *basic types of joints.*

Problem Q·2 Fig. 17-5. Make a drawing showing the *grooved joints* illustrated.

Problem Q·3 Fig. 17-2. Make a drawing of the casting for the *sheave housing.*

Problem Q·4 Make a welding drawing

for the *sheave housing* of Fig. 17-3 and compare your drawing with Fig. 17-3.

Problem Q·5 Fig. N-36. Make a complete welding drawing for the *stirrup.* Show three views with welding symbols.

Problem Q·6 Fig. N-37. Make a complete welding drawing of the *brace.* Show three views with symbols.

Problem Q·7 Fig. N-42. Make a complete welding drawing of the *hung bearing*. Show three views with welding symbols.

Problem Q·8 Fig. D-81. Make a complete welding drawing with welding symbols for the *bearing* to replace the casting shown. Use ⅜″ steel for all except the hubs.

Problem Q·9 Fig. F-18. Same as Prob. Q·8 for the *angle plate*.

Problem Q·10 Fig. J-28. Make a welding drawing for the *bearing holder*. Use welded steel and show the welding symbols.

Problem Q·11 Fig. J-27. Make a complete welding drawing for the *bracket bearing* to replace the casting shown. Use ½″ steel except for the hub.

Problem Q·12 Fig. 17-14. Make a welding drawing of the structural detail.

GROUP R. ELECTRICAL DRAWING PROBLEMS

24·23 Study Chap. 18 before beginning the problems in this group.

Problem R·1 Fig. 18-2. Draw symbols as selected by the instructor. Make about two or more times as large as shown in the book.

Problems R·2 to R·13 Figs. 18-6 to 18-17. Make a drawing of a circuit similar to the figure. Draw about three times the size shown in the book.

Problem R·2 Fig. 18-6.

Problem R·3 Fig. 18-7.

Problem R·4 Fig. 18-8.

Problem R·5 Fig. 18-9.

Problem R·6 Fig. 18-10.

Problem R·7 Fig. 18-11.

Problem R·8 Fig. 18-12.

Problem R·9 Fig. 18-13.

Problem R·10 Fig. 18-14.

Problem R·11 Fig. 18-15.

Problem R·12 Fig. 18-16.

Problem R·13 Fig. 18-17.

Problem R·14 Fig. R-1. Draw the diagram. Show the proper symbols. Push button at A_1 to operate bell at B_1 and push button at A_2 to operate bell at B_2. This is a return, or answer, call system.

Problem R·15 Fig. R-2. Draw the diagram. Show the proper symbols. Three

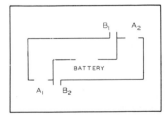

Fig. R-1 **Prob. R·14.**

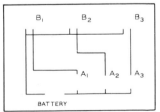

Fig. R-2 **Prob. R·15.**

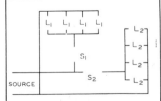

Fig. R-3 **Prob. R·16.**

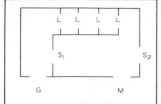

Fig. R-4 **Prob. R·17.**

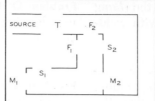

Fig. R-5 **Prob. R·18.**

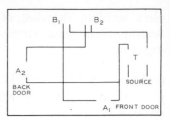

Fig. R-6 **Prob. R·19.**

bells are to be operated separately from the battery: bell B_1 by push-button A_1, bell B_2 by push-button A_2, and bell B_3 by push-button A_3.

Problem R·16 Fig. R-3. Draw the diagram. Show the proper symbols. Current is supplied from an outside source. Lamps at L_1 are operated by a fused switch at S_1. Lamps at L_2 are operated by a fused switch at S_2.

Problem R·17 Fig. R-4. Draw the diagram. Show the proper symbols. Generator at G, motor at M, lamps at L, fused switches at S_1 and S_2.

Problem R·18 Fig. R-5. Draw the diagram. Show the proper symbols. Transformer at T, motors at M_1 and M_2,

switches at S_1 and S_2, circuit breakers at F_1 and F_2.

Problem R·19 Fig. R-6. Draw the diagram. Show the proper symbols. Transformer at T, push button at A_1 at front door operates bell at B_1, push button at A_2 at back door operates buzzer at B_2.

Problem R·20 Fig. 18-18. Make a drawing of the single-phase starter diagram. Make about three or four times the size shown in the book. Use 11″ × 17″ sheet with long dimension vertical.

Problem R·21 Fig. 18-19. Make a drawing of the diagram. Draw about three times the size shown in the book.

Problem R·22 Fig. 18-24. Draw symbols

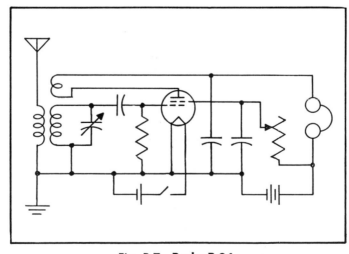

Fig. R-7 **Prob. R·24.**

as selected by the instructor. Make the symbols about twice the size shown in the book.

Problem R·23 Fig. 18-1. Make a drawing of the simple radio circuit. Make about two or three times the size shown in the book. Do not copy the picture.

Problem R·24 Fig. R-7. Make a drawing of the circuit for the simple regenerative radio. Make two or three times the size shown in the book.

Problem R·25 Fig. R-8. Draw a schematic diagram for the plate circuit. See Fig. 18-1 before starting this problem. Also Figs. 18-2 and 18-24 for symbols. In Fig. R-8: A = A battery; B = B battery; C = input posts; D = output posts for meter, earphones, or other load; E = rheostat; F = 1H4G tube.

Problem R·26 Fig. R-9. Draw a schematic diagram for the radio set using the loading-coil tuner. See Figs. 18-1, 18-2, and 18-24. In Fig. R-9: A = A battery, 1½ volts; B = B battery, 22½ volts;

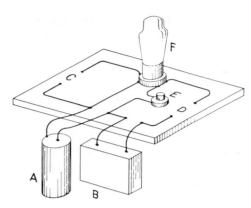

Fig. R-8 (Adapted from "Understanding Radio" by H. M. Watson, H. E. Welch, G. S. Eby, McGraw-Hill Book Company, Inc.) **Prob. R·25.**

D = output; E = grid leak resistor, ½ to 3 megohms; F = 1H4G tube; G = ground; H = antenna; C = loading-coil tuner.

Problem R·27 Fig. 18-27. Make a drawing of the schematic diagram shown. Make two or more times the size shown.

Problem R·28 Fig. 18-28. Make a drawing of the schematic diagram shown. Make two or more times the size shown.

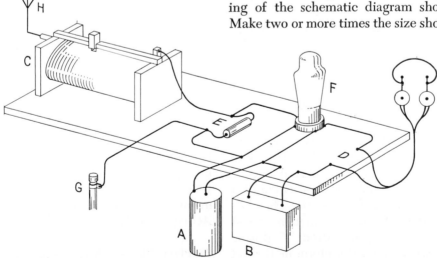

Fig. R-9 (Adapted from "Understanding Radio" by H. M. Watson, H. E. Welch, G. S. Eby, McGraw-Hill Book Company, Inc.) **Prob. R·26.**

Problem R·29 Fig. 18-29. Make a drawing of the schematic diagram shown. Make two or more times the size shown in the book.

Problem R·30 Fig. 18-26. Make a drawing of the schematic diagram shown. Make three or four times the size shown in the book.

GROUP S. CAM AND GEAR DRAWINGS[1]

24·24 Study Chap. 19 carefully before starting the problems in this group. It will be necessary to make some calculations to obtain dimensions for the gear drawings. Formulas are given in Art. 19·10. The formulas used, the given values, the calculations, and the figured values should be neatly lettered on the drawing or on a separate sheet as directed by the instructor.

Accuracy and neatness are necessary to obtain satisfactory drawings in this group. The pencil must be kept sharp and the lines fine and light. When the desired result has been obtained, the drawing should be brightened, using a sharp pencil of the proper grade to make the views stand out.

Problem S·1 Lay out a sheet as in Fig. A-24. In each space draw a rectangle 5″ long and 2¾″ high. Refer to Fig. 19-10. In Space A draw a diagram for uniform rising motion; in Space B, for modified uniform falling motion; in Space C, for harmonic rising motion; in Space D, for gravity falling motion.

Problem S·2 Draw a displacement diagram. Refer to Fig. 19-9 at B and to Fig. 19-10. Draw a horizontal line 9″ long, representing the base circle of a cam. Motion as follows: rise 1¾″ during 100° with harmonic motion, at rest (dwell) during 40°, drop ⅞″ during 100° with modified uniform motion, at

[1] For helpful references when working these problems, see the Bibliography page 550.

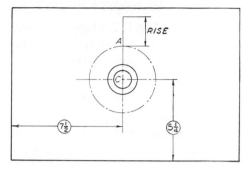

Fig. S-1   Layout for Probs. S·1 to S·4.

rest during 30°, drop ⅞″ during 90° with harmonic motion. Complete and letter the diagram. See Fig. 19-9 at B.

Problem S·3 Fig. S-1. Design a *plate cam* with point contact (see Fig. 19-6 at B). Motion as follows: rise 1½″ with uniform motion during one-half revolution, drop 1½″ with uniform motion during one-fourth revolution, at rest during the remaining one-fourth revolution. Distance *AC* equals 2¼″.

Problem S·4 Fig. S-1. Design a *plate cam* with point contact (See Fig. 19-6 at B). Motion as follows: rise 2″ with uniform motion during one-third revolution, at rest during one-sixth revolution, drop 2″ uniformly during one-fourth revolution, at rest during remaining one-fourth revolution. Distance *AC* equals 1¾″.

Problem S·5 Fig. S-1. Design a *plate cam* with roller. Motion as follows: rise 2″ with uniform motion during 180°,

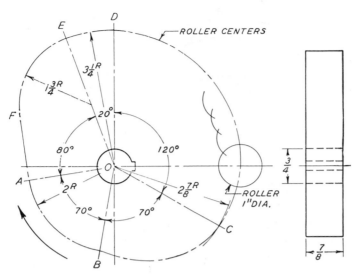

Fig. S-2   **Prob. S·7.**

drop 1″, remain at rest during 75°, drop 1″ with uniform motion during remaining 105°. Diameter of roller ⅞″. Distance *AC* equals 2¼″.

Problem S·6 Fig. S-1. Design a *plate cam* with roller. Motion as follows: rise 1¾″ with harmonic motion during 120°, at rest during 60°, drop 1¾″ with modified uniform motion during 120°, at rest during remaining 60°. Diameter of roller ⅞″. Distance *AC* equals 2½″. Draw a displacement diagram first.

Problem S·7 Fig. S-2. Make a drawing for a *plate cam* for the conditions given in the figure. Lay off the angles and draw radial lines from *O*. Draw the path of the roll centers. From *E* to *D*, dwell, radius 3¼″. From *D* to *C*, drop from 4¼″ to 2⅞″ uniform motion. From *C* to *B*, drop from 2⅞″ to 2″, with harmonic motion. From *B* to *A*, dwell, radius 2″. From *A* to *F*, straight line. From *F* to *E*, radius of 1¾″ as shown. Draw cam face using 1″ diameter roller

in sufficient number of positions to determine the outline. Keyway ¼″ × ⅛″.

Problem S·8 Fig. S-3. Draw a *box (grooved) cam* for the conditions given in the figure. Lay off the angles. Draw the path of the roll centers. From *A* to *B*, rise from 2½″ to 3½″, with modified uniform motion. From *B* to *C*, dwell, radius 3½″. From *C* to *D*, drop from 3½″ to 2½″ with harmonic motion. From *D* to *A*, dwell, radius 2½″. Draw groove using roller with 1″ diameter in sufficient number of positions to fix outlines for the groove. Complete the cam drawing. Keyway ¼″ × ⅛″.

Problem S·9 Fig. 19-11. Make a drawing of the *face cam* shown in the figure.

Problem S·10 Fig. 19-12. Make a drawing of the *barrel (cylindrical) cam* shown in the figure.

Problem S·11 Fig. S-4. Refer to Figs. 19-19 and 19-20. Draw *two gear teeth*

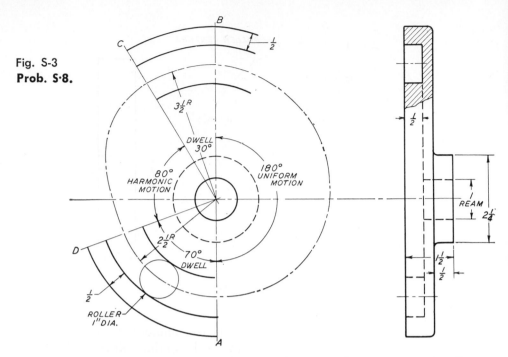

Fig. S-3
Prob. S·8.

B
$\frac{1}{2}$

C

$3\frac{1}{2}R$

DWELL
30°

80°
HARMONIC
MOTION

180°
UNIFORM
MOTION

REAM
$2\frac{1}{4}$

$2\frac{1}{2}R$

70°
DWELL

D

$\frac{1}{2}$

$\frac{1}{2}$

$\frac{1}{2}$

$\frac{1}{2}$

$\frac{1}{2}$

ROLLER
1" DIA.

A

in contact on the line of centers AB (at point C). Gear with center at A has 20 teeth. Pinion with center at B has 14 teeth. Diametral pitch is 1¼. Draw the line of centers. Calculate the radii of the gear and pinion. Lay off the angle of pressure using 15° for convenience. Draw the pitch circles, addendum and dedendum circles. Draw the base circles. Compute and lay off the circular thickness of a tooth (one-half the circular pitch) from C for the gear

and pinion. Starting at point C, construct an involute from the base circles to the addendum circle. Refer to Fig. 4-32 for involute. Draw the fillets. Brighten the two resulting gear teeth. Put on notes or information that the instructor may require. Use civil engineer's scale for decimal dimensions.

Problem S·12 Make a working drawing for a *cut spur gear* similar to Fig. 19-21

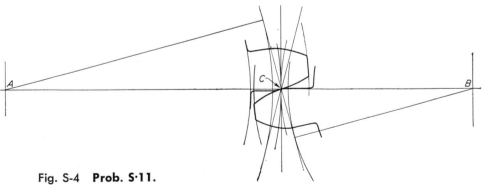

A   B

C

Fig. S-4   **Prob. S·11.**

but with 72 teeth and 12 diametral pitch.

Problem S·13 Make a working drawing for a *cut spur gear:* diametral pitch 6, pitch diameter 8", width of face 1⅝", diameter of shaft or bore 1⅞", and length of hub 2".

Problem S·14 Make a working drawing for a *cut spur gear and a pinion.* Outside diameter of gear is 6½", width of face 1¼", and length of hub 1½". Pitch diameter of pinion is 1½" and number of teeth 12. Other dimensions to be worked up as views are drawn.

GROUP T. DEVELOPMENTS AND INTERSECTIONS

24·25 Study Chap. 20 before starting these problems: Arts. 20·1 to 20·15 for development problems and Arts. 20·16 to 20·23 for developments.

Problem T·1 Fig. T-1. Develop the lateral surface of the *truncated prism* using the layout given. Read Art. 20·3. Use regular sheet, Fig. A-2.

Problems T·2 to T·8 Figs. T-2 to T-8. Develop the lateral surface of the prism. Use layout of Fig. T-1.

Problems T·9 to T·13 Figs. T-9 to T-13. Develop the lateral surface of the cylinder. Read Art. 20·5. Use layout of Fig. T-9, full sheet.

Problem T·14 Fig. T-14. Develop the

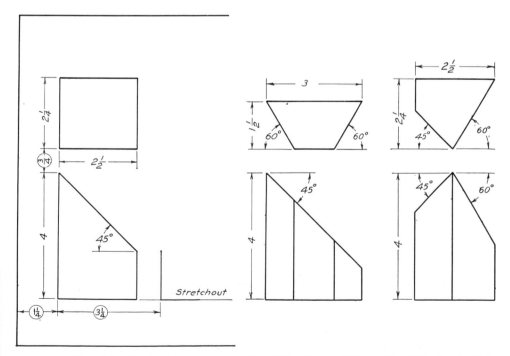

Fig. T-1 **Prob. T·1.**   Fig. T-2 **Prob. T·2.**   Fig. T-3 **Prob. T·3.**

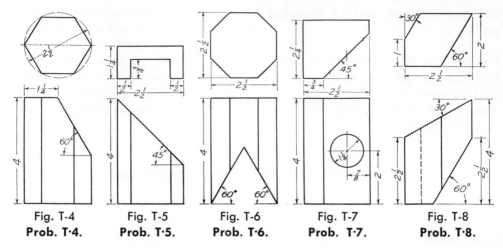

Fig. T-4	Fig. T-5	Fig. T-6	Fig. T-7	Fig. T-8
Prob. T·4.	**Prob. T·5.**	**Prob. T·6.**	**Prob. T·7.**	**Prob. T·8.**

three-piece elbow. Refer to Arts. 20·6 and 20·7. Use a full sheet. Space views and the pattern carefully.

Problems T·15 and T·16 Figs. T-15 and T-16. Develop the lateral surface. Use a layout similar to Fig. T-9.

Problems T·17 and T·18 Figs. T-17 and T-18. Develop the lateral surface. First revolve the edge *04* until its true length shows in the front view at *TL*. Start the development with edge in the position shown to the right of the front view in the layout of Fig. T-17.

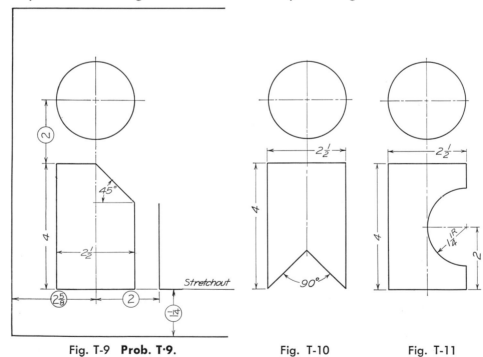

Fig. T-9 **Prob. T·9.**	Fig. T-10	Fig. T-11
	Prob. T·10.	**Prob. T·11.**

504 MECHANICAL DRAWING

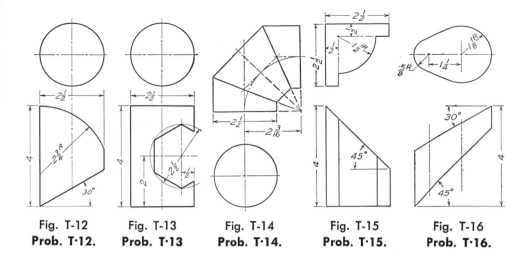

Fig. T-12	Fig. T-13	Fig. T-14	Fig. T-15	Fig. T-16
Prob. T·12.	**Prob. T·13**	**Prob. T·14.**	**Prob. T·15.**	**Prob. T·16.**

Problems T·19 to T·21 Figs. T-19 to T-21. Develop the surface.

Problems T·22 to T·24 Figs. T-22 to T-24. Develop the lateral surface.

Problems T·25 to T·27 Figs. T-25 to T-27. Develop the conical surface.

Problem T·28 Fig. T-28. Draw patterns for the *funnel*.

Problem T·29 Fig. T-29. Draw patterns for the *scoop*.

Problem T·30 Fig. T-30. Draw patterns for the *candlestick*.

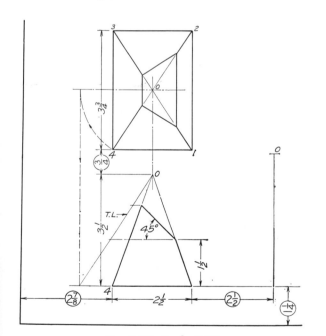

Fig. T-17 **Prob. T·17.**

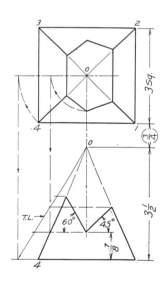

Fig. T-18 **Prob. T·18.**

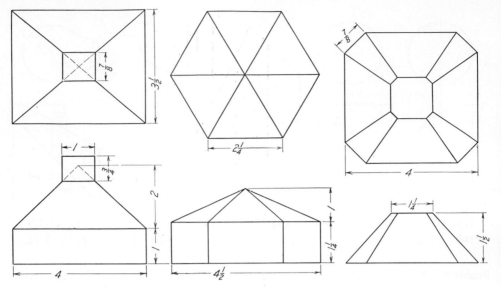

Fig. T-19   **Prob. T-19.**   Fig. T-20   **Prob. T-20.**   Fig. T-21   **Prob. T-21.**

Problem T·31 Fig. T-31. Draw patterns for the *half-pint measure*.

Problem T·32 Fig. T-32. Draw a pattern for the *offset funnel*. See Arts. 20·10 and 20·15 for the general method of solution.

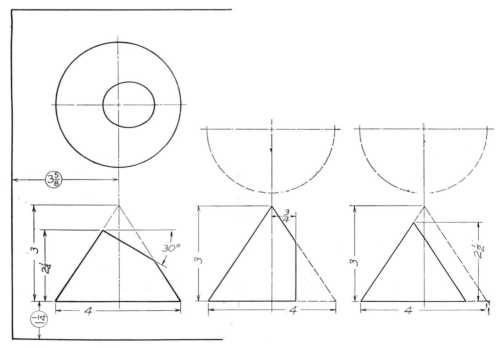

Fig. T-22   **Prob. T·22.**   Fig. T-23   **Prob. T·23.**   Fig. T-24   **Prob. T·24.**

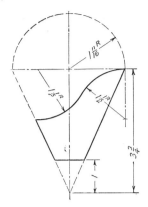

Fig. T-25 **Prob. T·25.**

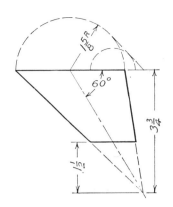

Fig. T-26 **Prob. T·26.**

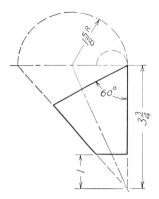

Fig. T-27 **Prob. T·27.**

Problem T·33 Fig. T-33. Make a working drawing with patterns for the *bird house.*

Problem T·34 Fig. T-34. Draw the orthographic views and the pattern for the *conductor head.* Use a scale that will be suitable for a standard-size sheet. Note that the profile is defined by the outline on the squared paper. Each square represents 1″.

Problem T·35 Fig. T-35. Draw the views and the pattern for the *jewel box.*

Problem T·36 Fig. T-36. Draw the views and the pattern for the *ridge roll.*

Problem T·37 Fig. T-37. Draw a pattern for the *bed-lamp shade.* Use a scale that will be suitable for a standard-size sheet.

24·26 Study Arts. 20·16 to 20·21 on intersections before starting the following problems. First observe the kinds of surfaces and the relative positions. Then see where the limiting planes are needed. Find where the lines cut and

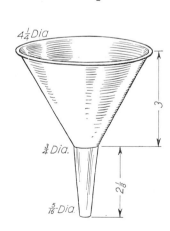

Fig. T-28 Funnel.
Prob. T·28.

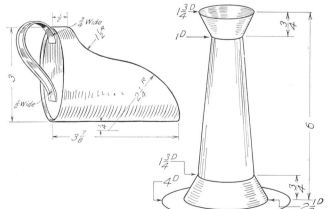

Fig. T-29 Scoop.
Prob. T·29.

Fig. T-30 Candlestick.
Prob. T·30.

PROBLEMS **507**

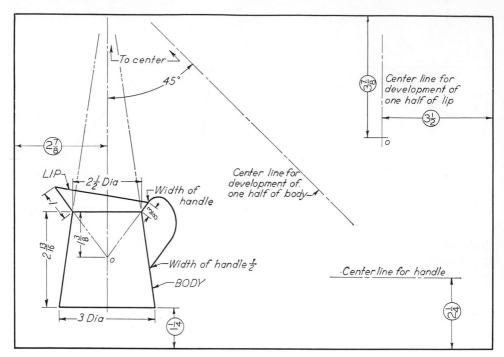

Fig. T-31 Pattern for half-pint measure. **Prob. T·31.**

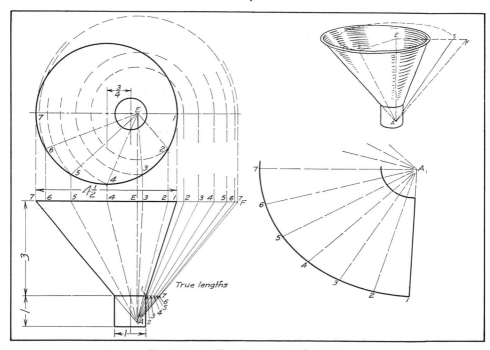

Fig. T-32 Offset funnel. **Prob. T·32.**

508 MECHANICAL DRAWING

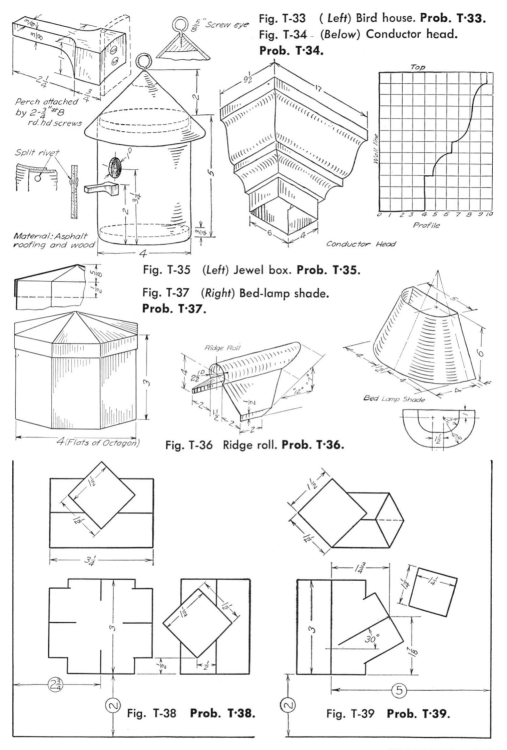

Fig. T-33 (*Left*) Bird house. **Prob. T·33.**
Fig. T-34 – (*Below*) Conductor head. **Prob. T·34.**

Perch attached by 2-¾"#8 rd. hd screws

Split rivet

Material: Asphalt roofing and wood

⅝" Screw eye

Wall line

Top

Profile

Conductor Head

Fig. T-35 (*Left*) Jewel box. **Prob. T·35.**

Fig. T-37 (*Right*) Bed-lamp shade. **Prob. T·37.**

4 (Flats of Octagon)

Ridge Roll

Fig. T-36 Ridge roll. **Prob. T·36.**

Bed Lamp Shade

Fig. T-38 **Prob. T·38.**

30°

Fig. T-39 **Prob. T·39.**

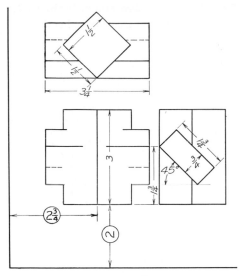

Fig. T-40   **Prob. T·40.**

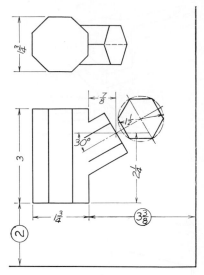

Fig. T-41   **Prob. T·41.**

locate the points on the lines of inter-section, that is, where the lines cut from both surfaces by the same plate cross each other.

Problem T·38 Fig. T-38. Find the line of intersection between the two prisms (Art. 20·17).

Problem T·39 Fig. T-39. Find the line of intersection between the two prisms (Art. 20·17).

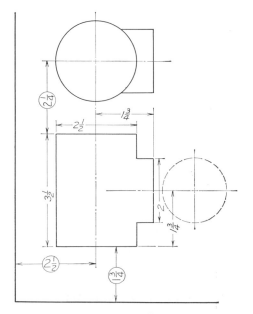

Fig. T-42   **Prob. T·42.**

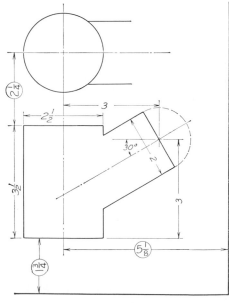

Fig. T-43   **Prob. T·43.**

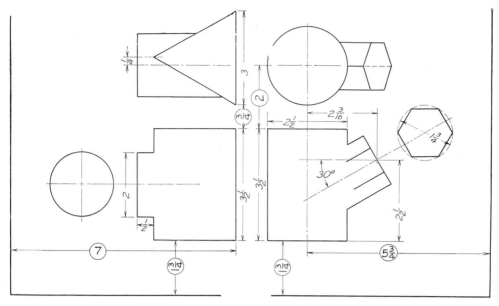

Fig. T-44 **Prob. T·44.**   Fig. T-45 **Prob. T·45.**

Problem T·40 Fig. T-40. Find the line of intersection between the two prisms (Art. 20·17).

Problem T·41 Fig. T-41. Find the line of intersection between the two prisms.

Problem T·42 Fig. T-42. Find the line of intersection between the two cylinders. (Art. 20·18).

Problem T·43 Fig. T-43. Find the line of intersection between the two cylinders.

Problem T·44 Fig. T-44. Find the line of intersection between the triangular prism and the cylinder (Art. 20·19).

Problem T·45 Fig. T-45. Find the line of intersection between the hexagonal prism and the cylinder.

Problem T·46 Fig. T-46. Find the line of intersection between the hexagonal prism and the cylinder.

Fig. T-46 **Prob. T·46.**

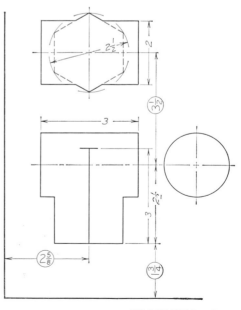

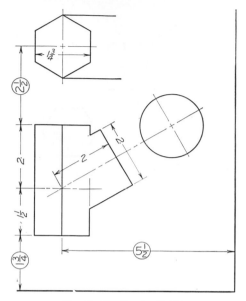

Fig. T-47   **Prob. T·47.**

Problem T·47 Fig. T-47. Find the line of intersection between the hexagonal prism and the cylinder.

Problem T·48 Fig. T-48. Find the line of intersection and develop the lateral surface of the cylinder.

Problem T·49 Fig T-49. Find the line of intersection and develop the vertical surface.

Problems T·50 and T·51 Figs. T-50 and T-51. Find the line of intersection and develop the pyramid.

Problem T·52 Fig. T-52. Find the line of intersection and develop the cone.

Problem T·53 Fig. T-53. Find the line of intersection and develop the pyramid.

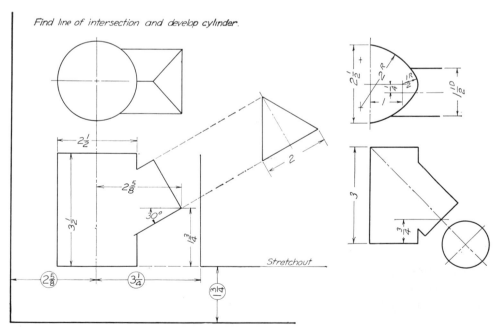

Find line of intersection and develop cylinder.

Stretchout

Fig. T-48   **Prob. T·48.**

Fig. T-49   **Prob. T·49.**

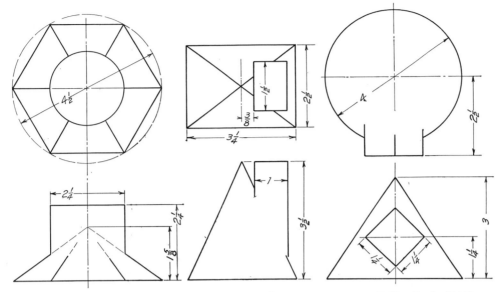

Fig. T-50 **Prob. T·50.**   Fig. T-51 **Prob. T·51.**   Fig. T-52 **Prob. T·52.**

Problem T·54 Fig. T-54. Find the line of intersection and develop the cone.

Problem T·55 Fig. T-55. Find the line of intersection and develop the pyramid.

Problem T·56 Fig. T-56. Develop the

surface of the *transition piece* (Art. 20·15).

Problems T·57 to T·60 Figs. T-57 to T-60. Develop the surface of the transition piece. Study Art. 20·15 carefully. Any of the intersection problems may be used for development by solving one problem on a sheet.

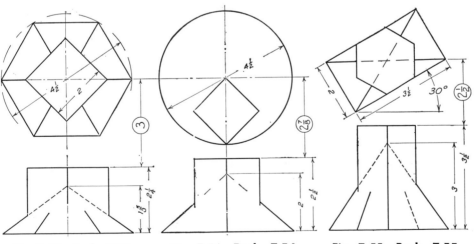

Fig. T-53 **Prob. T·53.**   Fig. T-54 **Prob. T·54.**   Fig. T-55 **Prob. T·55.**

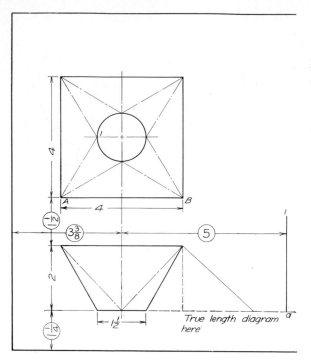

True length diagram here

Fig. T-56   **Prob. T·56.**

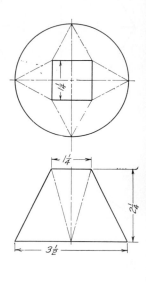

Fig. T-57   **Prob. T·57.**

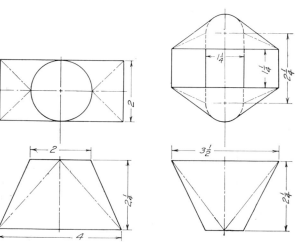

Fig. T-58   **Prob. T·58.**

Fig. T-59   **Prob. T·59.**

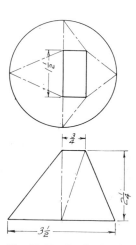

Fig. T-60   **Prob. T·60.**

514   MECHANICAL DRAWING

GROUP U. ARCHITECTURAL LETTERING AND DRAWING

24·27 Architectural lettering. Study Arts. 21·2 and 21·3 before starting these lettering exercises. It will be helpful to have some special books on lettering at hand for reference such as *The Art of Lettering* by Carl L. Svensen.

Problems U·1 to U·4 Fig. U-1. Single-stroke Old Roman capitals in pencil. Lay out sheet and divide into four parts. Rule guidelines ⅜″ apart starting ½″ over and 9/16″ down. Letter as indicated in each of the four spaces making a careful study of each of the letters (refer to Fig. 21-4). Complete each line by repeating the letters. On the last line of Space 1 letter: FIX LINTEL "HZ". On the last line of Space 2 letter: LAMINATED WOOD. On the last line of Space 3 letter: BRIDGE SPACE RULE. On the last line of Space 4 put the date—month, day, and year.

Problem U·5 Fig. U-2, Space 1. Single-stroke Roman capitals, Fig. 21-4. Start 1½″ over and ⅝″ down. The first space is ¼″ down, the next 3/16″. Repeat until there are guidelines for nine lines of ¼″ high letters. Make the first three lines in pencil. Repeat the same copy on the next three lines very lightly in pencil and go over them in ink. Use a Hunt 512 or Esterbrook 802 pen. Repeat same copy on last three lines directly in ink.

Problem U·6 Fig. U-2, Space 2. Single-stroke lower-case letters, Fig. 21-4. Start 1½″ over and ⅝″ down. The bodies of the letters are ⅛″ high (one-

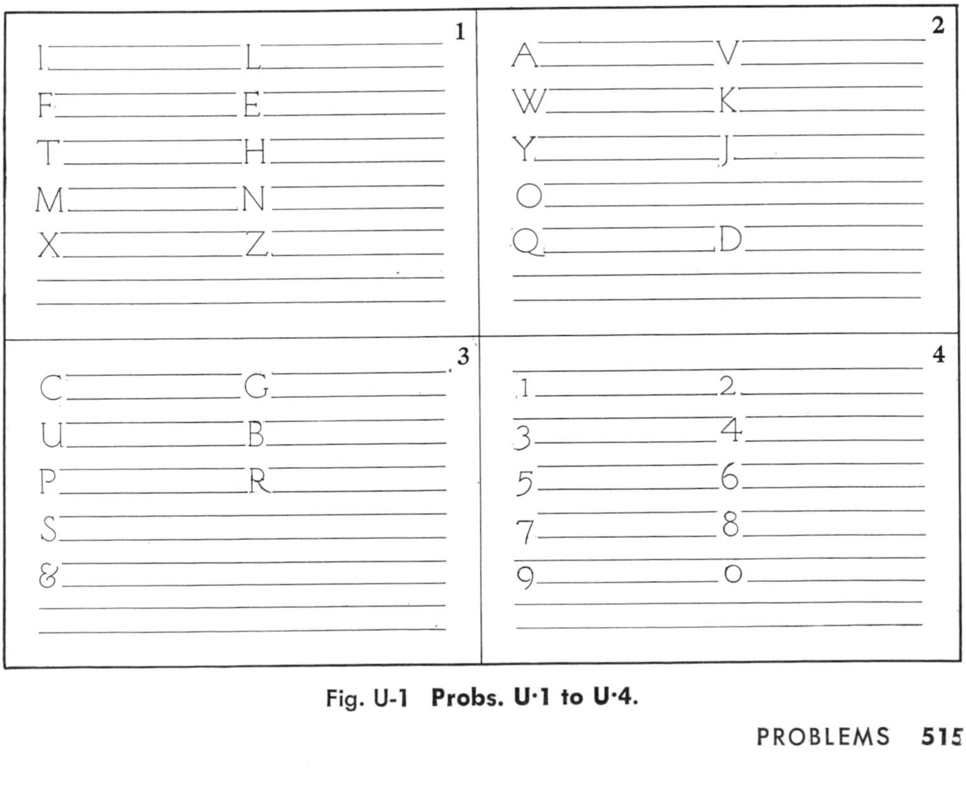

Fig. U-1 Probs. U·1 to U·4.

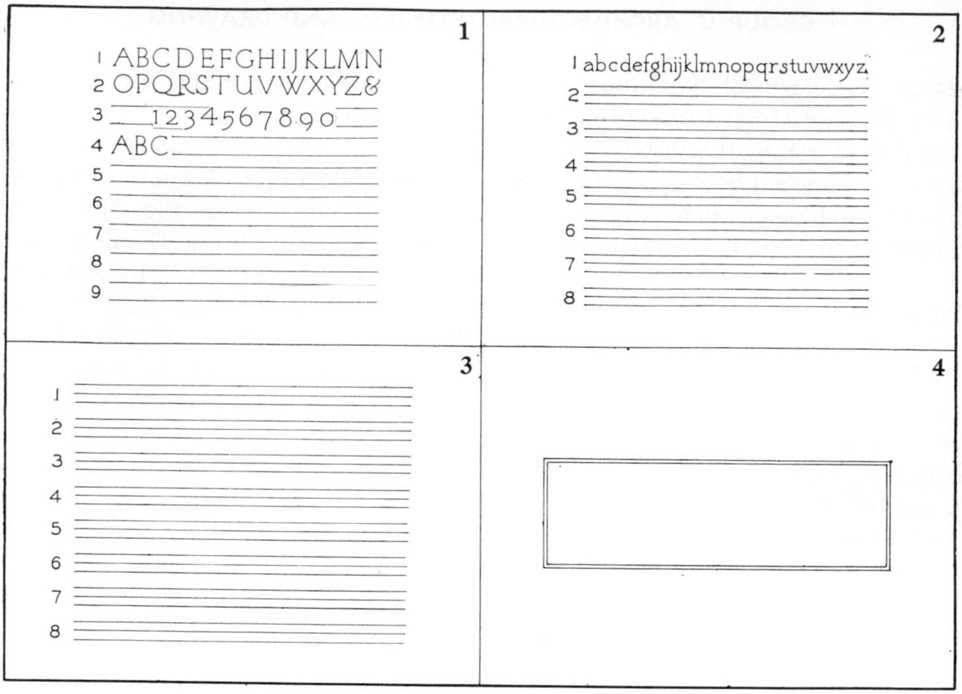

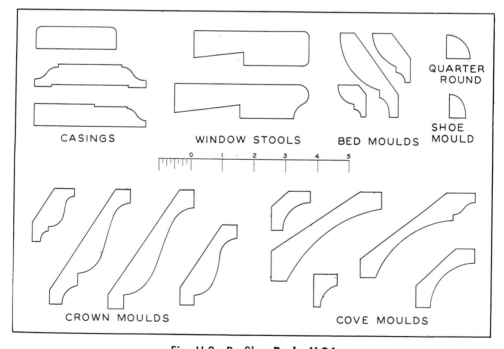

1

1 ABCDEFGHIJKLMN
2 OPQRSTUVWXYZ&
3 ___1234567890___
4 ABC_____
5 _____
6 _____
7 _____
8 _____
9 _____

2

1 abcdefghijklmnopqrstuvwxyz
2 _____
3 _____
4 _____
5 _____
6 _____
7 _____
8 _____

3

1 _____
2 _____
3 _____
4 _____
5 _____
6 _____
7 _____
8 _____

4

Fig. U-2 **Probs. U·5 to U·8**

CASINGS

WINDOW STOOLS

BED MOULDS

QUARTER ROUND

SHOE MOULD

0 1 2 3 4 5

CROWN MOULDS

COVE MOULDS

Fig. U-3 Profiles. **Prob. U·24.**

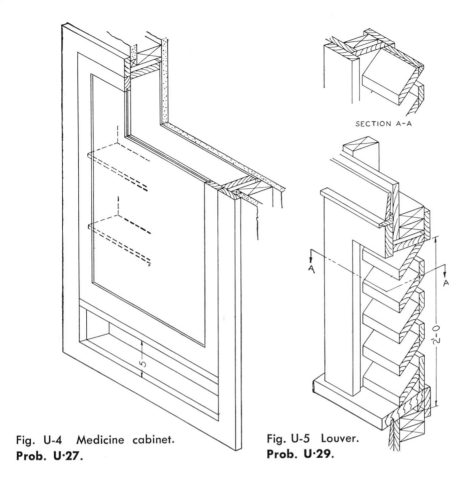

SECTION A-A

Fig. U-4 Medicine cabinet.
Prob. U·27.

Fig. U-5 Louver.
Prob. U·29.

half the cap height). The first space is
⅛″, the second space is ⅛″, and the
third space ¼″. Repeat until there are
guidelines as shown. Make the alphabet in pencil on the first two lines. Repeat lightly in pencil on the next two
lines and go over them in ink. Use a
ball-point pen. Repeat on the next two
lines in ink without first penciling. Letter your name in caps and lower case
on line 7, in pencil. Repeat on line 8
directly in ink.

Problem U·7 Fig. U-2, Space 3. Rule
guidelines as directed for Prob. U·6 except start 1″ over. Letter the sentence

shown on Prob. B·8 (except change
two-thirds in last line to *one-half*) first
in pencil on the first four lines, then repeat on the last four lines directly in
ink.

Problem U·8 Fig. U-2, Space 4. In the
middle of the space lay out a rectangle
5″ wide and 1½″ high. Letter a title
similar to the one shown in Fig. 21-6.

Problem U·9 Using the Roman alphabet
shown in Fig. 21-3, design a *title page*
similar to one of those shown in Fig.
B-5. Use architectural drawing instead
of mechanical drawing.

24·28 The reading and making of house plans are important parts of mechanical drawing. Several houses under construction should be visited at different stages of completion and compared with the working drawings. Study Chap. 21 carefully, especially the set of plans in Figs. 21-56 to 21-60 before starting the problems in this group.

Problem U·10 Fig. 21-26. Turn the sheet with the long dimension vertical. Make an isometric drawing showing *balloon framing*. Select a suitable scale. Studs and floor joists to be spaced 16″ center to center. Use 2″ × 4″ studs and 2″ × 8″ floor joists.

Problem U·11 Fig. 21-25. Turn the sheet with the long dimension vertical. Make an isometric drawing showing *western framing*. Select a suitable scale. Studs and floor joists to be spaced 16″ center to center. Use 2″ × 4″ studs and 2″ × 8″ floor joists.

Problem U·12 Figs. 21-28 and 21-30. In the left-hand half of the sheet make a drawing showing a *box sill for wood siding*. In the right-hand half of the sheet make a drawing showing a *box sill for brick veneer*.

Problem U·13 Same as Prob. U·12 but for the sills shown in Figs. 21-29 and 21-31.

Problem U·14 Same as Prob. U·12 but for the sills shown in Figs. 21-32 and 21-33.

Problem U·15 Fig. 21-34. Make a draw-

ing showing *diagonal sheathing*. Select a suitable scale to show the construction clearly.

Problem U·16 Fig. 21-35. Make a drawing showing *horizontal sheathing*. Select a suitable scale to show the construction clearly.

Problem U·17 Figs. 21-38 and 21-39. Make a drawing to show two of the *cornices* illustrated, one in the left-hand half of the sheet and the other in the right-hand half. Select a scale to show the construction clearly.

Problem U·18 Draw a *stair layout* similar to the plan and elevations of Fig. 21-40 for a floor to floor height of 9′–4″.

Problem U·19 Refer to Fig. 21-42. Turn the sheet with the long dimension vertical. Make a drawing of a *window with the sash in place* showing the framing. Draw an elevation, a vertical section at one side, and a horizontal section below.

Problem U·20 Refer to Fig. 21-43 and draw detail sections for a *double hung window* in a brick veneer wall.

Problem U·21 Same as Prob. U·20 but for a *masonry wall*. Refer to Fig. 21-43.

Problem U·22 Fig. 21-45. Make drawings of the *two doors* shown. Place them side by side.

Problem U·23 Refer to Fig. 21-46. Turn the sheet with the long dimension vertical and make a drawing for *door fram-*

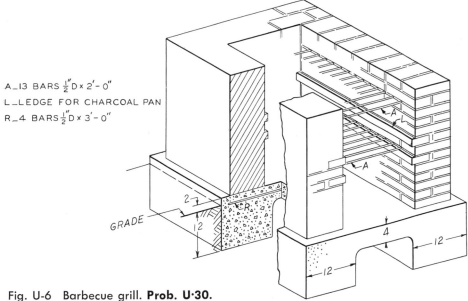

A — I3 BARS $\frac{1}{2}$"D × 2'-0"

L — LEDGE FOR CHARCOAL PAN

R — 4 BARS $\frac{1}{2}$"D × 3'-0"

GRADE

Fig. U-6   Barbecue grill. **Prob. U·30.**

ing details. Show an elevation, a vertical section at one side and a horizontal section below.

Problem U·24 Fig. U-3. Draw full size profiles (sections) of the *trim and moldings* shown. Obtain dimensions from the scale (11" × 17" sheet).

Problem U·25 Make a drawing of a typical *wall section* similar to that shown on Fig. 21-59 but for a brick-veneer wall and box cornice. Turn sheet with long dimension vertical.

Problem U·26 Make a drawing of a typical *wall section* similar to that shown on Fig. 21-59 but for a stucco wall and cornice with exposed rafters. Turn sheet with long dimension vertical.

Problem U·27 Fig. U-4. Make a working drawing of a *medicine cabinet* including the framing. Inside of closed part to

be 1'–9" wide and 2'–4" high. Show a front elevation and a vertical section. Back of cabinet may be ⅛" Presdwood.

Problem U·28 Same as Prob. U-27 but without the open space. Assume a suitable size.

Problem U·29 Fig. U-5. Make a working drawing of a *louver* to go between studs that are 16" on centers. Show framing and give necessary dimensions. Select suitable scale and views.

Problem U·30 Fig. U-6. Make a working drawing of the *barbecue grill.*

Problems U·31 to U·33 Figs U-7 to U-9. Draw plan and elevations for one of the *garages.* Size to be specified by the instructor. Refer to current descriptive circulars for over-all dimensions of automobiles.

Problems U·34 to U·41 Figs. U-17 to

Fig. U-7 **Prob. U·31.**

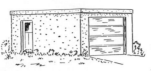
Fig. U-8 **Prob. U·32.**

Fig. U-9 **Prob. U·33.**

U-24. Select one of the suggested plans. Make a *kitchen* plan showing the size and location of both movable and built-in features. Refer to catalogues and trade literature for necessary information.

Problems U·42 to U·49 Figs. U-17 to U-24. Select one of the suggested plans. Make a *bathroom* plan showing the sizes and location of plumbing fixtures. Refer to manufacturer's catalogues for sizes and styles of fixtures.

Problem U·50 Fig. U-10. Draw a floor plan, foundation plan, and elevations for the *club house*. No basement. Piers to be placed inside of the foundation where needed to support a central lengthwise girder.

Problem U·51 Figs. 21-56 to 21-60. Make a set of plans for the *house* illustrated in Fig. 21-54. Draw all four elevations and cabinet details if required by the instructor.

Problems U·52 to U·57 Figs. U-11 to U-16. Make drawings for one of the suggested houses as directed by your instructor: (1) Basement plan, (2) floor plan or plans, (3) elevations—four, and

MEETING ROOM 18'-0"x24'-0"

Fig. U-10 Club house. **Prob. U·50.**

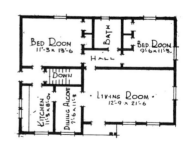

BED ROOM 11'-3 x 13'-6 BATH BED ROOM 9'-6x11'-3

HALL

DOWN

KITCHEN 11'-5 x 8'-0

DINING ALCOVE 7'-6 x 11'-3

LIVING ROOM 12'-9 x 21'-6

Fig. U-11 **Prob. U·52.**

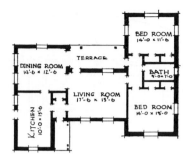

Fig. U-12   **Prob. U·53.**

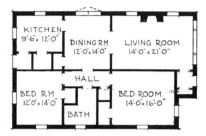

Fig. U-13   **Prob. U·54.**

BEACH HOUSE

Fig. U-14   **Prob. U·55.**

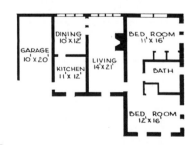

Fig. U-15   **Prob. U·56.**

(4) details. In some sections of the country the basement may be omitted. In such cases draw a foundation plan instead of a basement plan. Piers or a slab foundation may be used in some cases.

Fig. U-16   **Prob. U·57.**

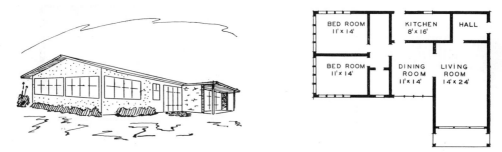

Fig. U-17   **Probs. U·34, U·42, U·58.**

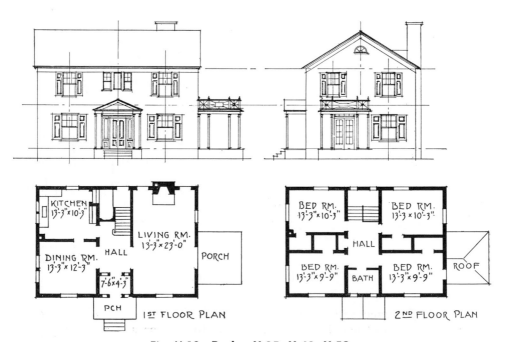

Fig. U-18   **Probs. U·35, U·43, U·59.**

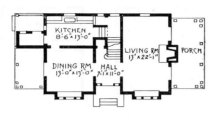

Fig. U-19 **Probs. U·36, U·44, U·60.**

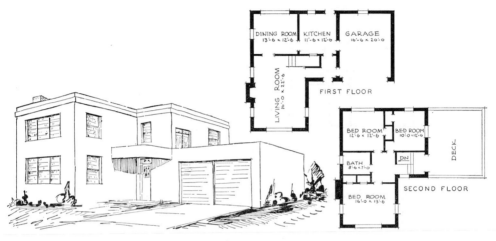

Fig. U-20 **Probs. U·37, U·45, U·61.**

Problems U·58 to U·65 Figs. U-17 to U-24. Select one of the sketch plans and make *architectural working drawings* as specified by the instructor.

1) Basement plan
2) First-floor plan
3) Second-floor plan
4) Front elevation
5) Right-side elevation
6) Left-side elevation
7) Rear elevation
8) Details

Problems U·66 to U·70 Figs. 21-9 to 21-13. Make *floor plans* to suit the exterior of one of the houses illustrated as specified by the instructor.

Fig. U-21 **Probs. U·38, U·46, U·62.**

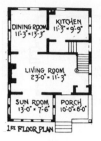

Fig. U-22   **Probs. U·39, U·47, U·63.**

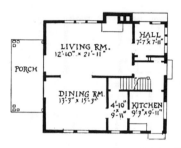

Fig. U-23   **Probs. U·40, U·48, U·64.**

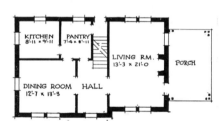

Fig. U-24   **Probs. U·41, U·49, U·65.**

Problems U·71 to U·78 Figs. U-25 to U-32. Make *floor plans* to suit the exterior of one of the houses illustrated as specified by the instructor.

Problem U·79 Fig. 21-44. Make a drawing of the *casement window details*. Select a suitable scale and size of sheet.

Problem U·80 Fig. 21-47. Make a draw-

ing of the *entrance details*. Select a suitable scale and size of sheet.

Problem U·81 Figs. 21-1 and 21-2. Make a set of plans for the house illustrated as specified by the instructor.

Other problems may be assigned from Figs. 21-15 to 21-22 and 21-61 to 21-80 or other illustrations in Chap. 21 as desired by the instructor.

Fig. U-25 **Prob. U·71.**

Fig. U-26 **Prob. U·72.**

Fig. U-27 **Prob. U·73.**

Fig. U-28 **Prob. U·74.**

Fig. U-29 **Prob. U·75.**

Fig. U-30 (*Structural Clay Products Institute design*) **Prob. U·76.**

Fig. U-31 **Prob. U·77.**

Fig. U-32 **Prob. U·78.**

GROUP V. STRUCTURAL DRAWINGS

24·29 Study Chap. 22 before starting these problems.

Problem V·1 Fig. 22-5. Make a drawing of the structural-steel shapes shown.

Problem V·2 Fig. 22-6. Make a drawing showing the rivet symbols. Rearrange to make a good appearing sheet.

Problem V·3 Fig. 22-8. Make a drawing of the structural-steel detail shown.

Consult a structural-steel handbook. Scale: ¾″ = 1′–0″.

Problem V·4 Fig. 22-7. Make a structural drawing of the truss shown. Consult a structural-steel handbook. Scales: ¾″ = 1′–0″ and 1½″ = 1′–0″.

Problem V·5 Fig. 22-9. Make a drawing of the reinforced-concrete detail shown. Scale: 1½″ = 1′–0″.

GROUP W. MAP DRAWINGS

24·30 Study Chap. 23 before starting these problems.

Problem W·1 Fig. 23-1. Make a plat of a survey as shown.

Problem W·2 Fig. 23-2. Make a city map as shown or a part of your own town or city. Use dividers to transfer and enlarge the figure.

Problem W·3 Fig. 23-3. Make a contour drawing as shown. Use dividers to

transfer and enlarge the figure.

Problem W·4 Fig. 23-3. Make a contour drawing similar to the figure but show the profile closer to the front.

Problem W·5 Fig. 23-4. Make a contour map as shown. Use dividers to transfer and enlarge the figure.

Problem W·6 Fig. 23-5. Draw the conventional symbols and letter them as indicated. Make rectangles 2″ × 1¾″.

Appendix

American Standards

A few standards are listed below that are useful for reference when making working drawings. A complete list of American Standards, with prices, is published by the American Standards Association, 70 East 45th Street, New York 17, N.Y.

Acme Screw Threads	B1.5–1952
Buttress Screw Threads	B1.9–1953
Graphical Electrical Symbols for Architectural Plans	Y32.9–1943
Graphical Symbols for Electrical Diagrams	Y32.2–1954
Graphical Symbols for Heating, Ventilating, and Air Conditioning	Z32.2.4–1949
Graphical Symbols for Pipe Fittings, Valves, and Piping	Z32.2.3–1949
Graphical Symbols for Plumbing	Y32.4–1955
Graphical Symbols for Welding	Z32.2.1–1949
Hexagon Head Cap Screws, Slotted Head Cap Screws, Square Head Set Screws, Slotted Headless Set Screws	B18.6.2–1956
Pipe Threads	B2.1–1945
Slotted and Recessed Head Screws	B18.6.1–1956
Socket Head Cap Screws and Socket Set Screws	B18.3–1954
Square and Hexagon Bolts and Nuts	B18.2–1955
Stub Acme Screw Threads	B1.8–1952
Unified and American Screw Threads for Screws, Bolts, Nuts, and Other Threaded Parts	B1.1–1949
Woodruff Keys, Keyslots, and Cutters	B17f–1930
American Drafting Standards Manual	
Section 1. Size and Format	Y14.1–1957
Section 2. Line Conventions, Sectioning, and Lettering	Y14.2–1957
Section 3. Projections	Y14.3–1957
Section 4. Pictorial Drawing	Y14.4–1957
Section 5. Dimensioning and Notes	Y14.5–1957
Section 6. Screw Threads	Y14.6–1957
Section 7. Gears, Splines, and Serrations	Y14.7
Section 8. Castings	Y14.8
Section 9. Forging	Y14.9
Section 10. Metal Stamping	Y14.10
Section 11. Plastics	Y14.11
Section 12. Die Castings	Y14.12
Section 13. Springs, Helical and Flat	Y14.13

Sections 7 to 17 are in preparation.

Table 1. Decimal Equivalents of Common Fractions

$\frac{1}{64}$	0.015625	$\frac{17}{64}$	0.265625	$\frac{33}{64}$	0.515625	$\frac{49}{64}$	0.765625
$\frac{1}{32}$	0.03125	$\frac{9}{32}$	0.28125	$\frac{17}{32}$	0.53125	$\frac{25}{32}$	0.78125
$\frac{3}{64}$	0.046875	$\frac{19}{64}$	0.296875	$\frac{35}{64}$	0.546875	$\frac{51}{64}$	0.796875
$\frac{1}{16}$	0.0625	$\frac{5}{16}$	0.3125	$\frac{9}{16}$	0.5625	$\frac{13}{16}$	0.8125
$\frac{5}{64}$	0.078125	$\frac{21}{64}$	0.328125	$\frac{37}{64}$	0.578125	$\frac{53}{64}$	0.828125
$\frac{3}{32}$	0.09375	$\frac{11}{32}$	0.34375	$\frac{19}{32}$	0.59375	$\frac{27}{32}$	0.84375
$\frac{7}{64}$	0.109375	$\frac{23}{64}$	0.359375	$\frac{39}{64}$	0.609375	$\frac{55}{64}$	0.859375
$\frac{1}{8}$	0.1250	$\frac{3}{8}$	0.3750	$\frac{5}{8}$	0.6250	$\frac{7}{8}$	0.8750
$\frac{9}{64}$	0.140625	$\frac{25}{64}$	0.390625	$\frac{41}{64}$	0.640625	$\frac{57}{64}$	0.890625
$\frac{5}{32}$	0.15625	$\frac{13}{32}$	0.40625	$\frac{21}{32}$	0.65625	$\frac{29}{32}$	0.90625
$\frac{11}{64}$	0.171875	$\frac{27}{64}$	0.421875	$\frac{43}{64}$	0.671875	$\frac{59}{64}$	0.921875
$\frac{3}{16}$	0.1875	$\frac{7}{16}$	0.4375	$\frac{11}{16}$	0.6875	$\frac{15}{16}$	0.9375
$\frac{13}{64}$	0.203125	$\frac{29}{64}$	0.453125	$\frac{45}{64}$	0.703125	$\frac{61}{64}$	0.953125
$\frac{7}{32}$	0.21875	$\frac{15}{32}$	0.46875	$\frac{23}{32}$	0.71875	$\frac{31}{32}$	0.96875
$\frac{15}{64}$	0.234375	$\frac{31}{64}$	0.484375	$\frac{47}{64}$	0.734375	$\frac{63}{64}$	0.984375
$\frac{1}{4}$	0.2500	$\frac{1}{2}$	0.5000	$\frac{3}{4}$	0.7500	1	1.0000

Table 2. Unified and American Thread Series

With Minor Diameters for Tap-drill Sizes

Diameter	Threads per inch Coarse NC	Fine NF	Tap-drill sizes Coarse NC	Fine NF	Diameter	Threads per inch Coarse NC	Fine NF	Tap-drill sizes Coarse NC	Fine NF
$\frac{1}{4}$	20	28	0.1959	0.2113	$1\frac{3}{8}$	6	12	1.1946	1.2848
$\frac{5}{16}$	18	24	0.2524	0.2674	$1\frac{1}{2}$	6	12	1.3196	1.4098
$\frac{3}{8}$	16	24	0.3073	0.3299	$1\frac{3}{4}$	5	..	1.5335	
$\frac{7}{16}$	14	20	0.3602	0.3834	2	$4\frac{1}{2}$	..	1.7594	
$\frac{1}{2}$*	13	..	0.4167		$2\frac{1}{4}$	$4\frac{1}{2}$	..	2.0094	
$\frac{1}{2}$	12	20	0.4098	0.4459					
$\frac{9}{16}$	12	18	0.4723	0.5024	$2\frac{1}{2}$	4	..	2.2294	
$\frac{5}{8}$	11	18	0.5266	0.5649	$2\frac{3}{4}$	4	..	2.4794	
$\frac{3}{4}$	10	16	0.6417	0.6823	3	4	..	2.7294	
$\frac{7}{8}$	9	14	0.7547	0.7977	$3\frac{1}{4}$	4	..	2.9794	
1	8	12	0.8647	0.9098	$3\frac{1}{2}$	4	..	3.2294	
$1\frac{1}{8}$	7	12	0.9704	1.0348	$3\frac{3}{4}$	4	..	3.4794	
$1\frac{1}{4}$	7	12	1.0954	1.1598	4	4	..	3.7294	

* Not Unified.

Source: Extracted from American Standard *Unified and American Screw Threads for Screws, Bolts, Nuts, and Other Threaded Parts* (ASA B1.1–1949), with the permission of the publisher, The American Society of Mechanical Engineers.

Table 3. American Standard Regular Hexagon Bolts

Diameter	Flats	Height			Diameter	Flats	Height		
		Unfinished	Semi-finished	Finished			Unfinished	Semi-finished	Finished
$\frac{1}{4}$	$\frac{7}{16}$	$\frac{11}{64}$	$\frac{5}{32}$	$\frac{5}{32}$	$1\frac{3}{8}$	$2\frac{1}{16}$	$\frac{29}{32}$	$\frac{27}{32}$	$\frac{27}{32}$
$\frac{5}{16}$	$\frac{1}{2}$	$\frac{7}{32}$	$\frac{13}{64}$	$\frac{13}{64}$	$1\frac{1}{2}$	$2\frac{1}{4}$	1	$\frac{15}{16}$	$\frac{15}{16}$
$\frac{3}{8}$	$\frac{9}{16}$	$\frac{1}{4}$	$\frac{15}{64}$	$\frac{15}{64}$	$1\frac{3}{4}$	$2\frac{5}{8}$	$1\frac{5}{32}$	$1\frac{3}{32}$	$1\frac{3}{32}$
$\frac{7}{16}$	$\frac{5}{8}$	$\frac{19}{64}$	$\frac{9}{32}$	$\frac{9}{32}$	2	3	$1\frac{11}{32}$	$1\frac{7}{32}$	$1\frac{7}{32}$
$\frac{1}{2}$	$\frac{3}{4}$	$\frac{11}{32}$	$\frac{5}{16}$	$\frac{5}{16}$	$2\frac{1}{4}$	$3\frac{3}{8}$	$1\frac{1}{2}$	$1\frac{3}{8}$	$1\frac{3}{8}$
$\frac{9}{16}$	$\frac{13}{16}$	....	....	$\frac{23}{64}$	$2\frac{1}{2}$	$3\frac{3}{4}$	$1\frac{21}{32}$	$1\frac{17}{32}$	$1\frac{17}{32}$
$\frac{5}{8}$	$\frac{15}{16}$	$\frac{27}{64}$	$\frac{25}{64}$	$\frac{25}{64}$	$2\frac{3}{4}$	$4\frac{1}{8}$	$1\frac{13}{16}$	$1\frac{11}{16}$	$1\frac{11}{16}$
$\frac{3}{4}$	$1\frac{1}{8}$	$\frac{1}{2}$	$\frac{15}{32}$	$\frac{15}{32}$	3	$4\frac{1}{2}$	2	$1\frac{7}{8}$	$1\frac{7}{8}$
$\frac{7}{8}$	$1\frac{5}{16}$	$\frac{37}{64}$	$\frac{35}{64}$	$\frac{35}{64}$	$3\frac{1}{4}$	$4\frac{7}{8}$	$2\frac{3}{16}$	2	
1	$1\frac{1}{2}$	$\frac{43}{64}$	$\frac{39}{64}$	$\frac{39}{64}$	$3\frac{1}{2}$	$5\frac{1}{4}$	$2\frac{5}{16}$	$2\frac{1}{8}$	
$1\frac{1}{8}$	$1\frac{11}{16}$	$\frac{3}{4}$	$\frac{11}{16}$	$\frac{11}{16}$	$3\frac{3}{4}$	$5\frac{5}{8}$	$2\frac{1}{2}$	$2\frac{5}{16}$	
$1\frac{1}{4}$	$1\frac{7}{8}$	$\frac{27}{32}$	$\frac{25}{32}$	$\frac{25}{32}$	4	6	$2\frac{11}{16}$	$2\frac{1}{2}$	

Source: Extracted from American Standard *Square and Hexagon Bolts and Nuts* (ASA B18.2–1955), with the permission of the publisher, The American Society of Mechanical Engineers.

Table 4. American Standard Regular Square Bolts and Nuts

Diameter	Bolthead		Nut		Diameter	Bolthead		Nut	
	Flats	Height of head	Flats	Thickness of nut		Flats	Height of head	Flats	Thickness of nut
$\frac{1}{4}$	$\frac{3}{8}$	$\frac{11}{64}$	$\frac{7}{16}$	$\frac{7}{32}$	$\frac{7}{8}$	$1\frac{5}{16}$	$\frac{19}{32}$	$1\frac{5}{16}$	$\frac{49}{64}$
$\frac{5}{16}$	$\frac{1}{2}$	$\frac{13}{64}$	$\frac{9}{16}$	$\frac{17}{64}$	1	$1\frac{1}{2}$	$\frac{21}{32}$	$1\frac{1}{2}$	$\frac{7}{8}$
$\frac{3}{8}$	$\frac{9}{16}$	$\frac{1}{4}$	$\frac{5}{8}$	$\frac{21}{64}$	$1\frac{1}{8}$	$1\frac{11}{16}$	$\frac{3}{4}$	$1\frac{11}{16}$	1
$\frac{7}{16}$	$\frac{5}{8}$	$\frac{19}{64}$	$\frac{3}{4}$	$\frac{3}{8}$	$1\frac{1}{4}$	$1\frac{7}{8}$	$\frac{27}{32}$	$1\frac{7}{8}$	$1\frac{3}{32}$
$\frac{1}{2}$	$\frac{3}{4}$	$\frac{21}{64}$	$\frac{13}{16}$	$\frac{7}{16}$	$1\frac{3}{8}$	$2\frac{1}{16}$	$\frac{29}{32}$	$2\frac{1}{16}$	$1\frac{13}{64}$
$\frac{5}{8}$	$\frac{15}{16}$	$\frac{27}{64}$	1	$\frac{35}{64}$	$1\frac{1}{2}$	$2\frac{1}{4}$	1	$2\frac{1}{4}$	$1\frac{5}{16}$
$\frac{3}{4}$	$1\frac{1}{8}$	$\frac{1}{2}$	$1\frac{1}{8}$	$\frac{21}{32}$	$1\frac{5}{8}$	$2\frac{7}{16}$	$1\frac{3}{32}$		

Source: Extracted from American Standard *Square and Hexagon Bolts and Nuts* (ASA B18.2–1955), with the permission of the publisher, The American Society of Mechanical Engineers.

Table 5. American Standard Regular Hexagonal Nuts

Diameter	Unfinished		Semifinished		Finished	
	Flats	Thickness	Flats	Thickness	Flats	Thickness
$\frac{1}{4}$	$\frac{7}{16}$	$\frac{7}{32}$	$\frac{7}{16}$	$\frac{13}{64}$	$\frac{7}{16}$	$\frac{7}{32}$
$\frac{5}{16}$	$\frac{9}{16}$	$\frac{17}{64}$	$\frac{9}{16}$	$\frac{1}{4}$	$\frac{1}{2}$	$\frac{17}{64}$
$\frac{3}{8}$	$\frac{5}{8}$	$\frac{21}{64}$	$\frac{5}{8}$	$\frac{5}{16}$	$\frac{9}{16}$	$\frac{21}{64}$
$\frac{7}{16}$	$\frac{3}{4}$	$\frac{3}{8}$	$\frac{3}{4}$	$\frac{23}{64}$	$\frac{11}{16}$	$\frac{3}{8}$
$\frac{1}{2}$	$\frac{13}{16}$	$\frac{7}{16}$	$\frac{13}{16}$	$\frac{27}{64}$	$\frac{3}{4}$	$\frac{7}{16}$
$\frac{9}{16}$	$\frac{7}{8}$	$\frac{1}{2}$	$\frac{7}{8}$	$\frac{31}{64}$	$\frac{7}{8}$	$\frac{31}{64}$
$\frac{5}{8}$	1	$\frac{35}{64}$	1	$\frac{17}{32}$	$\frac{15}{16}$	$\frac{35}{64}$
$\frac{3}{4}$	$1\frac{1}{8}$	$\frac{21}{32}$	$1\frac{1}{8}$	$\frac{41}{64}$	$1\frac{1}{8}$	$\frac{41}{64}$
$\frac{7}{8}$	$1\frac{5}{16}$	$\frac{49}{64}$	$1\frac{5}{16}$	$\frac{3}{4}$	$1\frac{5}{16}$	$\frac{3}{4}$
1	$1\frac{1}{2}$	$\frac{7}{8}$	$1\frac{1}{2}$	$\frac{55}{64}$	$1\frac{1}{2}$	$\frac{55}{64}$
$1\frac{1}{8}$	$1\frac{11}{16}$	1	$1\frac{11}{16}$	$\frac{31}{32}$	$1\frac{11}{16}$	$\frac{31}{32}$
$1\frac{1}{4}$	$1\frac{7}{8}$	$1\frac{3}{32}$	$1\frac{7}{8}$	$1\frac{1}{16}$	$1\frac{7}{8}$	$1\frac{1}{16}$
$1\frac{3}{8}$	$2\frac{1}{16}$	$1\frac{13}{64}$	$2\frac{1}{16}$	$1\frac{11}{64}$	$2\frac{1}{16}$	$1\frac{11}{64}$
$1\frac{1}{2}$	$2\frac{1}{4}$	$1\frac{5}{16}$	$2\frac{1}{4}$	$1\frac{9}{32}$	$2\frac{1}{4}$	$1\frac{9}{32}$
$1\frac{5}{8}$	...	...	$2\frac{7}{16}$	$1\frac{25}{64}$		
$1\frac{3}{4}$	...	...	$2\frac{5}{8}$	$1\frac{1}{2}$	$2\frac{5}{8}$	$1\frac{1}{2}$
$1\frac{7}{8}$	...	...	$2\frac{13}{16}$	$1\frac{39}{64}$		
2	...	...	3	$1\frac{23}{32}$	3	$1\frac{23}{32}$
$2\frac{1}{4}$	...	...	$3\frac{3}{8}$	$1\frac{59}{64}$	$3\frac{3}{8}$	$1\frac{59}{64}$
$2\frac{1}{2}$	...	...	$3\frac{3}{4}$	$2\frac{9}{64}$	$3\frac{3}{4}$	$2\frac{9}{64}$
$2\frac{3}{4}$	...	...	$4\frac{1}{8}$	$2\frac{23}{64}$	$4\frac{1}{8}$	$2\frac{23}{64}$
3	...	...	$4\frac{1}{2}$	$2\frac{37}{64}$	$4\frac{1}{2}$	$2\frac{37}{64}$

Source: Extracted from American Standard *Square and Hexagon Bolts and Nuts* (ASA B18.2–1955), with the permission of the publisher, The American Society of Mechanical Engineers.

Table 6. American Standard Heavy Hexagon Bolts

Diameter	Flats: Unfinished semifinished finished	Height of head: Unfinished	Height of head: Semifinished finished	Diameter	Flats: Unfinished semifinished finished	Height of head: Unfinished	Height of head: Semifinished
$\frac{1}{2}$	$\frac{7}{8}$	$\frac{7}{16}$	$\frac{13}{32}$	$1\frac{5}{8}$	$2\frac{9}{16}$	$1\frac{9}{32}$	$1\frac{7}{32}$
$\frac{5}{8}$	$1\frac{1}{16}$	$\frac{17}{32}$	$\frac{1}{2}$	$1\frac{3}{4}$	$2\frac{3}{4}$	$1\frac{3}{8}$	$1\frac{5}{16}$
$\frac{3}{4}$	$1\frac{1}{4}$	$\frac{5}{8}$	$\frac{19}{32}$	$1\frac{7}{8}$	$2\frac{15}{16}$	$1\frac{15}{32}$	$1\frac{13}{32}$
$\frac{7}{8}$	$1\frac{7}{16}$	$\frac{23}{32}$	$\frac{11}{16}$	2	$3\frac{1}{8}$	$1\frac{9}{16}$	$1\frac{7}{16}$
1	$1\frac{5}{8}$	$\frac{13}{16}$	$\frac{3}{4}$	$2\frac{1}{4}$	$3\frac{1}{2}$	$1\frac{3}{4}$	$1\frac{5}{8}$
$1\frac{1}{8}$	$1\frac{13}{16}$	$\frac{29}{32}$	$\frac{27}{32}$	$2\frac{1}{2}$	$3\frac{7}{8}$	$1\frac{15}{16}$	$1\frac{13}{16}$
$1\frac{1}{4}$	2	1	$\frac{15}{16}$	$2\frac{3}{4}$	$4\frac{1}{4}$	$2\frac{1}{8}$	2
$1\frac{3}{8}$	$2\frac{3}{16}$	$1\frac{3}{32}$	$1\frac{3}{32}$	3	$4\frac{5}{8}$	$2\frac{5}{16}$	$2\frac{3}{16}$
$1\frac{1}{2}$	$2\frac{3}{8}$	$1\frac{3}{16}$	$1\frac{1}{8}$				

Note: $1\frac{5}{8}$, $1\frac{7}{8}$ not in unfinished or semifinished bolts.

Source: Extracted from American Standard Square and Hexagon Bolts and Nuts (ASA B18.2–1955), with the permission of the publisher, The American Society of Mechanical Engineers.

Table 7. American Standard Hexagon-head Cap Screws

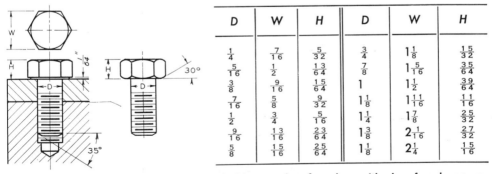

D	W	H	D	W	H
$\frac{1}{4}$	$\frac{7}{16}$	$\frac{5}{32}$	$\frac{3}{4}$	$1\frac{1}{8}$	$\frac{15}{32}$
$\frac{5}{16}$	$\frac{1}{2}$	$\frac{13}{64}$	$\frac{7}{8}$	$1\frac{5}{16}$	$\frac{35}{64}$
$\frac{3}{8}$	$\frac{9}{16}$	$\frac{15}{64}$	1	$1\frac{1}{2}$	$\frac{39}{64}$
$\frac{7}{16}$	$\frac{5}{8}$	$\frac{9}{32}$	$1\frac{1}{8}$	$1\frac{11}{16}$	$\frac{11}{16}$
$\frac{1}{2}$	$\frac{3}{4}$	$\frac{5}{16}$	$1\frac{1}{4}$	$1\frac{7}{8}$	$\frac{25}{32}$
$\frac{9}{16}$	$\frac{13}{16}$	$\frac{23}{64}$	$1\frac{3}{8}$	$2\frac{1}{16}$	$\frac{27}{32}$
$\frac{5}{8}$	$\frac{15}{16}$	$\frac{25}{64}$	$1\frac{1}{2}$	$2\frac{1}{4}$	$\frac{15}{16}$

Note: Bearing surfaces shall be flat and either washer faced or with chamfered corners. Minimum thread length shall be twice the diameter plus $\frac{1}{4}$ in. for lengths up to and including 6 in.; twice the diameter plus $\frac{1}{2}$ in. for lengths over 6 in. Extracted from American Standard Hexagon Head Cap Screws, Slotted Head Cap Screws, Square Head Set Screws, Slotted Headless Set Screws (ASA B18.6.2–1956), with the permission of the publisher, The American Society of Mechanical Engineers.

Table 8. American Standard Heavy Nuts—Square and Hexagon

Diameter	Flats: Unfinished semi-finished square and hexagon	Thickness of nut: Unfinished square and hexagon	Thickness of nut: Semi-finished hexagon	Diameter	Flats: Unfinished semi-finished square and hexagon	Thickness of nut: Unfinished square and hexagon	Thickness of nut: Semi-finished hexagon
$\frac{1}{4}$	$\frac{1}{2}$	$\frac{1}{4}$	$\frac{15}{64}$	$1\frac{1}{2}$	$2\frac{3}{8}$	$1\frac{1}{2}$	$1\frac{15}{32}$
$\frac{5}{16}$	$\frac{9}{16}$	$\frac{5}{16}$	$\frac{19}{64}$	$1\frac{5}{8}$	$2\frac{9}{16}$	....	$1\frac{19}{32}$
$\frac{3}{8}$	$\frac{11}{16}$	$\frac{3}{8}$	$\frac{23}{64}$	$1\frac{3}{4}$	$2\frac{3}{4}$	$1\frac{3}{4}$	$1\frac{23}{32}$
$\frac{7}{16}$	$\frac{3}{4}$	$\frac{7}{16}$	$\frac{27}{64}$	$1\frac{7}{8}$	$2\frac{15}{16}$	....	$1\frac{27}{32}$
$\frac{1}{2}$	$\frac{7}{8}$	$\frac{1}{2}$	$\frac{31}{64}$	2	$3\frac{1}{8}$	2	$1\frac{31}{32}$
$\frac{9}{16}$	$\frac{15}{16}$	....	$\frac{35}{64}$	$2\frac{1}{4}$	$3\frac{1}{2}$	$2\frac{1}{4}$	$2\frac{13}{64}$
$\frac{5}{8}$	$1\frac{1}{16}$	$\frac{5}{8}$	$\frac{39}{64}$	$2\frac{1}{2}$	$3\frac{7}{8}$	$2\frac{1}{2}$	$2\frac{29}{64}$
$\frac{3}{4}$	$1\frac{1}{4}$	$\frac{3}{4}$	$\frac{47}{64}$	$2\frac{3}{4}$	$4\frac{1}{4}$	$2\frac{3}{4}$	$2\frac{45}{64}$
$\frac{7}{8}$	$1\frac{7}{16}$	$\frac{7}{8}$	$\frac{55}{64}$	3	$4\frac{5}{8}$	3	$2\frac{61}{64}$
1	$1\frac{5}{8}$	1	$\frac{63}{64}$	$3\frac{1}{4}$	5	$3\frac{1}{4}$	$3\frac{3}{16}$
$1\frac{1}{8}$	$1\frac{13}{16}$	$1\frac{1}{8}$	$1\frac{7}{64}$	$3\frac{1}{2}$	$5\frac{3}{8}$	$3\frac{1}{2}$	$3\frac{7}{16}$
$1\frac{1}{4}$	2	$1\frac{1}{4}$	$1\frac{7}{32}$	$3\frac{3}{4}$	$5\frac{3}{4}$	$3\frac{3}{4}$	$3\frac{11}{16}$
$1\frac{3}{8}$	$2\frac{3}{16}$	$1\frac{3}{8}$	$1\frac{11}{32}$	4	$6\frac{1}{8}$	4	$3\frac{15}{16}$

Note: $\frac{9}{16}$, $1\frac{5}{8}$, $1\frac{7}{8}$ not in unfinished nuts.

Source: Extracted from American Standard *Square and Hexagon Bolts and Nuts* (ASA B18.2–1955), with the permission of the publisher, The American Society of Mechanical Engineers.

Table 9. American Standard Slotted-head Cap Screws

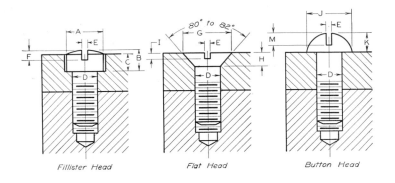

Nominal diameter D	A max.	B max.	C max.	E max.	F max.	G max.	H aver-age	I max.	J max.	K max.	M max.
$\frac{1}{4}$	0.375	0.216	0.172	0.075	0.097	0.500	0.140	0.068	0.437	0.191	0.117
$\frac{5}{16}$	0.437	0.253	0.203	0.084	0.115	0.625	0.177	0.086	0.562	0.245	0.151
$\frac{3}{8}$	0.562	0.314	0.250	0.094	0.142	0.750	0.210	0.103	0.625	0.273	0.168
$\frac{7}{16}$	0.625	0.368	0.297	0.094	0.168	0.812	0.210	0.103	0.750	0.328	0.202
$\frac{1}{2}$	0.750	0.413	0.328	0.106	0.193	0.875	0.210	0.103	0.812	0.354	0.218
$\frac{9}{16}$	0.812	0.467	0.375	0.118	0.213	1.000	0.244	0.120	0.937	0.409	0.252
$\frac{5}{8}$	0.875	0.521	0.422	0.133	0.239	1.125	0.281	0.137	1.000	0.437	0.270
$\frac{3}{4}$	1.000	0.612	0.500	0.149	0.283	1.375	0.352	0.171	1.250	0.546	0.338
$\frac{7}{8}$	1.125	0.720	0.594	0.167	0.334	1.625	0.423	0.206			
1	1.312	0.803	0.656	0.188	0.371	1.875	0.494	0.240			
$1\frac{1}{8}$	....	....	....	0.196	....	2.062	0.529	0.257			
$1\frac{1}{4}$	....	....	....	0.211	....	2.312	0.600	0.291			
$1\frac{3}{8}$	....	....	....	0.226	....	2.562	0.665	0.326			
$1\frac{1}{2}$	....	....	....	0.258	....	2.812	0.742	0.360			

Source: Extracted from American Standard *Hexagon Head Cap Screws, Slotted Head Cap Screws, Square Head Set Screws, Slotted Headless Set Screws* (ASA B18.6.2–1956), with the permission of the publisher, The American Society of Mechanical Engineers.

Table 10. American Standard Machine Screws

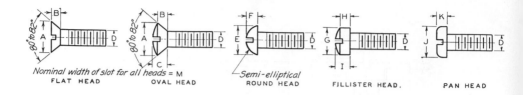

Nominal width of slot for all heads = M

FLAT HEAD   OVAL HEAD   Semi-elliptical ROUND HEAD   FILLISTER HEAD.   PAN HEAD

Maximum Dimensions

Nominal	Max.	A	B	C	E	F	G	H	I	J	K	M
0	0.060	0.119	0.035	0.056	0.113	0.053	0.096	0.045	0.059	....	....	0.023
1	0.073	0.146	0.043	0.068	0.138	0.061	0.118	0.053	0.071	....	....	0.026
2	0.086	0.172	0.051	0.080	0.162	0.069	0.140	0.062	0.083	0.167	0.053	0.031
3	0.099	0.199	0.059	0.092	0.187	0.078	0.161	0.070	0.095	0.193	0.060	0.035
4	0.112	0.225	0.067	0.104	0.211	0.086	0.183	0.079	0.107	0.219	0.068	0.039
5	0.125	0.252	0.075	0.116	0.236	0.095	0.205	0.088	0.120	0.245	0.075	0.043
6	0.138	0.279	0.083	0.128	0.260	0.103	0.226	0.096	0.132	0.270	0.082	0.048
8	0.164	0.332	0.100	0.152	0.309	0.120	0.270	0.113	0.156	0.322	0.096	0.054
10	0.190	0.385	0.116	0.176	0.359	0.137	0.313	0.130	0.180	0.373	0.110	0.060
12	0.216	0.438	0.132	0.200	0.408	0.153	0.357	0.148	0.205	0.425	0.125	0.067
$\frac{1}{4}$	0.250	0.507	0.153	0.232	0.472	0.175	0.414	0.170	0.237	0.492	0.144	0.075
$\frac{5}{16}$	0.3125	0.635	0.191	0.290	0.590	0.216	0.518	0.211	0.295	0.615	0.178	0.084
$\frac{3}{8}$	0.375	0.762	0.230	0.347	0.708	0.256	0.622	0.253	0.355	0.740	0.212	0.094
$\frac{7}{16}$	0.4375	0.812	0.223	0.345	0.750	0.328	0.625	0.265	0.368	....	....	0.094
$\frac{1}{2}$	0.500	0.875	0.223	0.354	0.813	0.355	0.750	0.297	0.412	....	....	0.106
$\frac{9}{16}$	0.5625	1.000	0.260	0.410	0.938	0.410	0.812	0.336	0.466	....	....	0.118
$\frac{5}{8}$	0.625	1.125	0.298	0.467	1.000	0.438	0.875	0.375	0.521	....	....	0.133
$\frac{3}{4}$	0.750	1.375	0.372	0.578	1.250	0.547	1.000	0.441	0.612	....	....	0.149

Source: Extracted from American Standard *Slotted and Recessed Head Screws* (ASA B18.6–1947), with the permission of the publisher, The American Society of Mechanical Engineers.

Table 11. American Standard Square-head Setscrews and Points

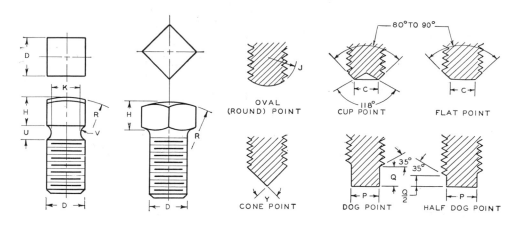

OVAL (ROUND) POINT · CUP POINT · FLAT POINT · CONE POINT · DOG POINT · HALF DOG POINT

D	H nom.	R nom.	K max.	U min.	V max.	C nom.	J nom.	P max.	Q
10 (0.190)	$\frac{9}{64}$	$\frac{15}{32}$	0.145	0.083	0.027	$\frac{3}{32}$	0.141	0.127	0.090
12 (0.216)	$\frac{5}{32}$	$\frac{35}{64}$	0.162	0.091	0.029	$\frac{7}{64}$	0.156	0.144	0.110
$\frac{1}{4}$	$\frac{3}{16}$	$\frac{5}{8}$	0.185	0.100	0.032	$\frac{1}{8}$	0.188	0.156	0.125
$\frac{5}{16}$	$\frac{15}{64}$	$\frac{25}{32}$	0.240	0.111	0.036	$\frac{11}{64}$	0.234	0.203	0.156
$\frac{3}{8}$	$\frac{9}{32}$	$\frac{15}{16}$	0.294	0.125	0.041	$\frac{13}{64}$	0.281	0.250	0.188
$\frac{7}{16}$	$\frac{21}{64}$	$1\frac{3}{32}$	0.345	0.143	0.046	$\frac{15}{64}$	0.328	0.297	0.219
$\frac{1}{2}$	$\frac{3}{8}$	$1\frac{1}{4}$	0.400	0.154	0.050	$\frac{9}{32}$	0.375	0.344	0.250
$\frac{9}{16}$	$\frac{27}{64}$	$1\frac{13}{32}$	0.454	0.167	0.054	$\frac{5}{16}$	0.422	0.391	0.281
$\frac{5}{8}$	$\frac{15}{32}$	$1\frac{9}{16}$	0.507	0.182	0.059	$\frac{23}{64}$	0.469	0.469	0.313
$\frac{3}{4}$	$\frac{9}{16}$	$1\frac{7}{8}$	0.620	0.200	0.065	$\frac{7}{16}$	0.563	0.563	0.375
$\frac{7}{8}$	$\frac{21}{32}$	$2\frac{3}{16}$	0.731	0.222	0.072	$\frac{33}{64}$	0.656	0.656	0.438
1	$\frac{3}{4}$	$2\frac{1}{2}$	0.838	0.250	0.081	$\frac{19}{32}$	0.750	0.750	0.500
$1\frac{1}{8}$	$\frac{27}{32}$	$2\frac{13}{16}$	0.939	0.283	0.092	$\frac{43}{64}$	0.844	0.844	0.562
$1\frac{1}{4}$	$\frac{15}{16}$	$3\frac{1}{8}$	1.064	0.283	0.092	$\frac{3}{4}$	0.938	0.938	0.625
$1\frac{3}{8}$	$1\frac{1}{32}$	$3\frac{7}{16}$	1.159	0.333	0.109	$\frac{53}{64}$	1.031	1.031	0.688
$1\frac{1}{2}$	$1\frac{1}{8}$	$3\frac{3}{4}$	1.284	0.333	0.109	$\frac{29}{32}$	1.125	1.125	0.750

Note: Threads may be coarse-, fine-, or 8-thread series, class 2A. Coarse thread normally used on $\frac{1}{4}$ in. and larger. When length equals nominal diameter or less $Y = 118°$. When length exceeds nominal diameter $Y = 90°$.

Source: Extracted from American Standard *Hexagon Head Cap Screws, Slotted Head Cap Screws, Square Head Setscrews, Slotted Headless Setscrews* (ASA B18.6.2–1956), with the permission of the publisher, The American Society of Mechanical Engineers.

Table 12. American Standard Slotted-head Wood Screws

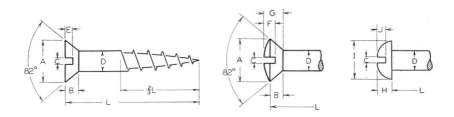

Maximum Dimensions

Nominal size	D	A	B	C	E	F	G	H	I	J	Number threads per inch
0	0.060	0.119	0.035	0.023	0.015	0.030	0.056	0.053	0.113	0.039	32
1	0.073	0.146	0.043	0.026	0.019	0.038	0.068	0.061	0.138	0.044	28
2	0.086	0.172	0.051	0.031	0.023	0.045	0.080	0.069	0.162	0.048	26
3	0.099	0.199	0.059	0.035	0.027	0.052	0.092	0.078	0.187	0.053	24
4	0.112	0.225	0.067	0.039	0.030	0.059	0.104	0.086	0.211	0.058	22
5	0.125	0.252	0.075	0.043	0.034	0.067	0.116	0.095	0.236	0.063	20
6	0.138	0.279	0.083	0.048	0.038	0.074	0.128	0.103	0.260	0.068	18
7	0.151	0.305	0.091	0.048	0.041	0.081	0.140	0.111	0.285	0.072	16
8	0.164	0.332	0.100	0.054	0.045	0.088	0.152	0.120	0.309	0.077	15
9	0.177	0.358	0.108	0.054	0.049	0.095	0.164	0.128	0.334	0.082	14
10	0.190	0.385	0.116	0.060	0.053	0.103	0.176	0.137	0.359	0.087	13
12	0.216	0.438	0.132	0.067	0.060	0.117	0.200	0.153	0.408	0.096	11
14	0.242	0.491	0.148	0.075	0.068	0.132	0.224	0.170	0.457	0.106	10
16	0.268	0.544	0.164	0.075	0.075	0.146	0.248	0.187	0.506	0.115	9
18	0.294	0.597	0.180	0.084	0.083	0.160	0.272	0.204	0.555	0.125	8
20	0.320	0.650	0.196	0.084	0.090	0.175	0.296	0.220	0.604	0.134	8
24	0.372	0.756	0.228	0.094	0.105	0.204	0.344	0.254	0.702	0.154	7

Source: Extracted from American Standard *Slotted and Recessed Head Screws, Machine, Cap, Wood, Tapping, and Slotted Headless Types* (ASA B18.6.1–1956), with the permission of the publisher, The American Society of Mechanical Engineers.

Table 13. American Standard Plain Washers

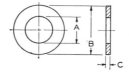

Inside diameter A	Outside diameter B	Thickness, C Gage	Thickness, C Nom.	Inside diameter A	Outside diameter B	Thickness, C Gage	Thickness, C Nom.	Inside diameter A	Outside diameter B	Thickness, C Gage	Thickness, C Nom.
$\frac{5}{64}$	$\frac{3}{16}$	25	0.020	$\frac{7}{16}$	$\frac{7}{8}$	14	0.083	$\frac{15}{16}$	$3\frac{3}{8}$	7	0.180
$\frac{3}{32}$	$\frac{7}{32}$	25	0.020	$\frac{7}{16}$	1	14	0.083	$1\frac{1}{16}$	2	10	0.134
$\frac{3}{32}$	$\frac{1}{4}$	25	0.020	$\frac{7}{16}$	$1\frac{3}{8}$	14	0.083	$1\frac{1}{16}$	$2\frac{1}{4}$	8	0.165
$\frac{1}{8}$	$\frac{1}{4}$	24	0.022	$\frac{15}{32}$	$\frac{59}{64}$	16	0.065	$1\frac{1}{16}$	$2\frac{1}{2}$	8	0.165
$\frac{1}{8}$	$\frac{5}{16}$	21	0.032	$\frac{1}{2}$	$1\frac{1}{8}$	14	0.083	$1\frac{1}{16}$	$3\frac{3}{8}$	4	0.238
$\frac{5}{32}$	$\frac{5}{16}$	20	0.035	$\frac{1}{2}$	$1\frac{1}{4}$	14	0.083	$1\frac{3}{16}$	$2\frac{1}{2}$	8	0.165
$\frac{5}{32}$	$\frac{3}{8}$	18	0.049	$\frac{1}{2}$	$1\frac{5}{8}$	14	0.083	$1\frac{1}{4}$	$2\frac{3}{4}$	8	0.165
$\frac{11}{64}$	$\frac{13}{32}$	18	0.049	$\frac{17}{32}$	$1\frac{1}{16}$	13	0.095	$1\frac{5}{16}$	$2\frac{3}{4}$	8	0.165
$\frac{3}{16}$	$\frac{3}{8}$	18	0.049	$\frac{9}{16}$	$1\frac{1}{4}$	12	0.109	$1\frac{3}{8}$	3	8	0.165
$\frac{3}{16}$	$\frac{7}{16}$	18	0.049	$\frac{9}{16}$	$1\frac{3}{8}$	12	0.109	$1\frac{7}{16}$	3	7	0.180
$\frac{13}{64}$	$\frac{15}{32}$	18	0.049	$\frac{9}{16}$	$1\frac{7}{8}$	12	0.109	$1\frac{1}{2}$	$3\frac{1}{4}$	7	0.180
$\frac{7}{32}$	$\frac{7}{16}$	18	0.049	$\frac{19}{32}$	$1\frac{3}{16}$	13	0.095	$1\frac{9}{16}$	$3\frac{1}{4}$	7	0.180
$\frac{7}{32}$	$\frac{1}{2}$	18	0.049	$\frac{5}{8}$	$1\frac{3}{8}$	12	0.109	$1\frac{5}{8}$	$3\frac{1}{2}$	7	0.180
$\frac{15}{64}$	$\frac{17}{32}$	18	0.049	$\frac{5}{8}$	$1\frac{1}{2}$	12	0.109	$1\frac{11}{16}$	$3\frac{1}{2}$	7	0.180
$\frac{1}{4}$	$\frac{1}{2}$	18	0.049	$\frac{5}{8}$	$2\frac{1}{8}$	10	0.134	$1\frac{3}{4}$	$3\frac{3}{4}$	7	0.180
$\frac{1}{4}$*	$\frac{9}{16}$	18	0.049	$\frac{21}{32}$	$1\frac{5}{16}$	13	0.095	$1\frac{13}{16}$	$3\frac{3}{4}$	7	0.180
$\frac{1}{4}$*	$\frac{9}{16}$	16	0.065	$\frac{11}{16}$	$1\frac{1}{2}$	10	0.134	$1\frac{7}{8}$	4	7	0.180
$\frac{17}{64}$	$\frac{5}{8}$	18	0.049	$\frac{11}{16}$	$1\frac{3}{4}$	10	0.134	$1\frac{15}{16}$	4	7	0.180
$\frac{9}{32}$	$\frac{5}{8}$	16	0.065	$\frac{11}{16}$	$2\frac{3}{8}$	8	0.165	2	$4\frac{1}{4}$	7	0.180
$\frac{5}{16}$	$\frac{3}{4}$	16	0.065	$\frac{13}{16}$	$1\frac{1}{2}$	10	0.134	$2\frac{1}{16}$	$4\frac{1}{4}$	7	0.180
$\frac{5}{16}$	$\frac{7}{8}$	16	0.065	$\frac{13}{16}$	$1\frac{3}{4}$	9	0.148	$2\frac{1}{8}$	$4\frac{1}{2}$	7	0.180
$\frac{11}{32}$	$\frac{11}{16}$	16	0.065	$\frac{13}{16}$	2	9	0.148	$2\frac{3}{8}$	$4\frac{3}{4}$	5	0.220
$\frac{3}{8}$	$\frac{3}{4}$	16	0.065	$\frac{13}{16}$	$2\frac{7}{8}$	8	0.165	$2\frac{5}{8}$	5	4	0.238
$\frac{3}{8}$	$\frac{7}{8}$	14	0.083	$\frac{15}{16}$	$1\frac{3}{4}$	10	0.134	$2\frac{7}{8}$	$5\frac{1}{4}$	3	0.259
$\frac{3}{8}$	$1\frac{1}{8}$	16	0.065	$\frac{15}{16}$	2	8	0.165	$3\frac{1}{8}$	$5\frac{1}{2}$	2	0.284
$\frac{13}{32}$	$\frac{13}{16}$	16	0.065	$\frac{15}{16}$	$2\frac{1}{4}$	8	0.165				

Source: Nominal thicknesses of washers are Birmingham gage sizes. Extracted from American Standard *Plain Washers* (ASA B27.2–1953), with the permission of the publisher, The American Society of Mechanical Engineers.

Table 14. American Standard Lock Washers

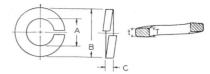

Nominal size	A min.	Light		Medium		Heavy		Extra heavy	
		B max.	$\frac{T+t}{2}$	B max.	$\frac{T+t}{2}$	B max.	$\frac{T+t}{2}$	B max.	$\frac{T+t}{2}$
0.086(No. 2)	0.088	0.165	0.015	0.175	0.020	0.185	0.025	0.211	0.027
0.099(No. 3)	0.102	0.188	0.020	0.198	0.025	0.212	0.031	0.242	0.034
0.112(No. 4)	0.115	0.202	0.020	0.212	0.025	0.226	0.031	0.256	0.034
0.125(No. 5)	0.128	0.225	0.025	0.239	0.031	0.255	0.040	0.303	0.045
0.138(No. 6)	0.141	0.239	0.025	0.253	0.031	0.269	0.040	0.317	0.045
0.164(No. 8)	0.168	0.280	0.031	0.296	0.040	0.310	0.047	0.378	0.057
0.190(No. 10)	0.194	0.323	0.040	0.337	0.047	0.353	0.056	0.437	0.068
0.216(No. 12)	0.221	0.364	0.047	0.380	0.056	0.394	0.063	0.500	0.080
$\frac{1}{4}$	0.255	0.489	0.047	0.493	0.062	0.495	0.077	0.539	0.084
$\frac{5}{16}$	0.319	0.575	0.056	0.591	0.078	0.601	0.097	0.627	0.108
$\frac{3}{8}$	0.382	0.678	0.070	0.688	0.094	0.696	0.115	0.746	0.123
$\frac{7}{16}$	0.446	0.780	0.085	0.784	0.109	0.792	0.133	0.844	0.143
$\frac{1}{2}$	0.509	0.877	0.099	0.879	0.125	0.889	0.151	0.945	0.162
$\frac{9}{16}$	0.573	0.975	0.113	0.979	0.141	0.989	0.170	1.049	0.182
$\frac{5}{8}$	0.636	1.082	0.126	1.086	0.156	1.100	0.189	1.164	0.202
$\frac{11}{16}$	0.700	1.178	0.138	1.184	0.172	1.200	0.207	1.266	0.221
$\frac{3}{4}$	0.763	1.277	0.153	1.279	0.188	1.299	0.226	1.369	0.241
$\frac{13}{16}$	0.827	1.375	0.168	1.377	0.203	1.401	0.246	1.473	0.261
$\frac{7}{8}$	0.890	1.470	0.179	1.474	0.219	1.504	0.266	1.586	0.285
$\frac{15}{16}$	0.954	1.562	0.191	1.570	0.234	1.604	0.284	1.698	0.308
1	1.017	1.656	0.202	1.672	0.250	1.716	0.306	1.810	0.330
$1\frac{1}{16}$	1.081	1.746	0.213	1.768	0.266	1.820	0.326	1.922	0.352
$1\frac{1}{8}$	1.144	1.837	0.224	1.865	0.281	1.921	0.345	2.031	0.375
$1\frac{3}{16}$	1.208	1.923	0.234	1.963	0.297	2.021	0.364	2.137	0.396
$1\frac{1}{4}$	1.271	2.012	0.244	2.058	0.312	2.126	0.384	2.244	0.417
$1\frac{5}{16}$	1.335	2.098	0.254	2.156	0.328	2.226	0.403	2.350	0.438
$1\frac{3}{8}$	1.398	2.183	0.264	2.253	0.344	2.325	0.422	2.453	0.458
$1\frac{7}{16}$	1.462	2.269	0.273	2.349	0.359	2.421	0.440	2.555	0.478
$1\frac{1}{2}$	1.525	2.352	0.282	2.446	0.375	2.518	0.458	2.654	0.496

Source: Extracted from American Standard Lock Washers (ASA B27.1–1950), with the permission of the publisher, The American Society of Mechanical Engineers.

Table 15. American Standard Taper Pins and Cotter Pins

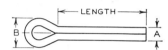

TAPER PINS *Maximum length for which standard reamers are available. Taper ¼ in. per ft.

Size No.	0000000	000000	00000	0000	000	00	0
Size (large end)	0.0625	0.0780	0.0940	0.1090	0.1250	0.1410	0.1560
Maximum length*	0.625	0.750	1.000	1.000	1.000	1.250	1.250
Size No.	1	2	3	4	5	6	7
Size (large end)	0.1720	0.1930	0.2190	0.2500	0.2890	0.3410	0.4090
Maximum length*	1.250	1.500	1.750	2.000	2.250	3.000	3.750
Size No.	8	9	10	11	12	13	14
Size (large end)	0.4920	0.5910	0.7060	0.8600	1.032	1.241	1.523
Maximum length*	4.500	5.250	6.000	(Special sizes. Special lengths.)			

COTTER PINS Design of head may vary but outside diameters should be adhered to.

A nominal	B min.	Hole sizes recommended	A nominal	B min.	Hole sizes recommended	A nominal	B min.	Hole sizes recommended
0.031	$\frac{1}{16}$	$\frac{3}{64}$	0.125	$\frac{1}{4}$	$\frac{9}{64}$	0.312	$\frac{5}{8}$	$\frac{5}{16}$
0.047	$\frac{3}{32}$	$\frac{1}{16}$	0.141	$\frac{9}{32}$	$\frac{5}{32}$	0.375	$\frac{3}{4}$	$\frac{3}{8}$
0.062	$\frac{1}{8}$	$\frac{5}{64}$	0.156	$\frac{5}{16}$	$\frac{11}{64}$	0.438	$\frac{7}{8}$	$\frac{7}{16}$
0.078	$\frac{5}{32}$	$\frac{3}{32}$	0.188	$\frac{3}{8}$	$\frac{13}{64}$	0.500	1	$\frac{1}{2}$
0.094	$\frac{3}{16}$	$\frac{7}{64}$	0.219	$\frac{7}{16}$	$\frac{15}{64}$	0.625	$1\frac{1}{4}$	$\frac{5}{8}$
0.109	$\frac{7}{32}$	$\frac{1}{8}$	0.250	$\frac{1}{2}$	$\frac{17}{64}$	0.750	$1\frac{1}{2}$	$\frac{3}{4}$

Source: Extracted from American Standard *Machine Pins* (ASA B5.20–1958), with the permission of the publisher, The American Society of Mechanical Engineers.

Table 16. American Standard Square- and Flat-stock Keys and Shaft Diameters

Diameter of shaft D inclusive	Square keys W	Flat keys W × H	Diameter of shaft D inclusive	Square keys W	Flat keys W × H
$\frac{1}{2}-\frac{9}{16}$	$\frac{1}{8}$	$\frac{1}{8} \times \frac{3}{32}$	$2\frac{5}{16}-2\frac{3}{4}$	$\frac{5}{8}$	$\frac{5}{8} \times \frac{7}{16}$
$\frac{5}{8}-\frac{7}{8}$	$\frac{3}{16}$	$\frac{3}{16} \times \frac{1}{8}$	$2\frac{7}{8}-3\frac{1}{4}$	$\frac{3}{4}$	$\frac{3}{4} \times \frac{1}{2}$
$\frac{15}{16}-1\frac{1}{4}$	$\frac{1}{4}$	$\frac{1}{4} \times \frac{3}{16}$	$3\frac{3}{8}-3\frac{3}{4}$	$\frac{7}{8}$	$\frac{7}{8} \times \frac{5}{8}$
$1\frac{5}{16}-1\frac{3}{8}$	$\frac{5}{16}$	$\frac{5}{16} \times \frac{1}{4}$	$3\frac{7}{8}-4\frac{1}{2}$	1	$1 \times \frac{3}{4}$
$1\frac{7}{16}-1\frac{3}{4}$	$\frac{3}{8}$	$\frac{3}{8} \times \frac{1}{4}$	$4\frac{3}{4}-5\frac{1}{2}$	$1\frac{1}{4}$	$1\frac{1}{4} \times \frac{7}{8}$
$1\frac{13}{16}-2\frac{1}{4}$	$\frac{1}{2}$	$\frac{1}{2} \times \frac{3}{8}$	$5\frac{3}{4}-6$	$1\frac{1}{2}$	$1\frac{1}{2} \times 1$

Source: Extracted from American Standard *Shafting and Stock Keys* (ASA B17.1–1943), with the permission of the publisher, The American Society of Mechanical Engineers.

Table 17. Woodruff Keys Dimensions in Inches

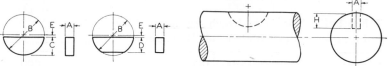

Key No.	Nominal			Maximum		
	A	B	E	C	D	H
204	$\frac{1}{16}$	$\frac{1}{2}$	$\frac{3}{64}$	0.203	0.194	0.1718
304	$\frac{3}{32}$	$\frac{1}{2}$	$\frac{3}{64}$	0.203	0.194	0.1561
305	$\frac{3}{32}$	$\frac{5}{8}$	$\frac{1}{16}$	0.250	0.240	0.2031
404	$\frac{1}{8}$	$\frac{1}{2}$	$\frac{3}{64}$	0.203	0.194	0.1405
405	$\frac{1}{8}$	$\frac{5}{8}$	$\frac{1}{16}$	0.250	0.240	0.1875
406	$\frac{1}{8}$	$\frac{3}{4}$	$\frac{1}{16}$	0.313	0.303	0.2505
505	$\frac{5}{32}$	$\frac{5}{8}$	$\frac{1}{16}$	0.250	0.240	0.1719
506	$\frac{5}{32}$	$\frac{3}{4}$	$\frac{1}{16}$	0.313	0.303	0.2349
507	$\frac{5}{32}$	$\frac{7}{8}$	$\frac{1}{16}$	0.375	0.365	0.2969
606	$\frac{3}{16}$	$\frac{3}{4}$	$\frac{1}{16}$	0.313	0.303	0.2193
607	$\frac{3}{16}$	$\frac{7}{8}$	$\frac{1}{16}$	0.375	0.365	0.2813
608	$\frac{3}{16}$	1	$\frac{1}{16}$	0.438	0.428	0.3443
609	$\frac{3}{16}$	$1\frac{1}{8}$	$\frac{5}{64}$	0.484	0.475	0.3903
807	$\frac{1}{4}$	$\frac{7}{8}$	$\frac{1}{16}$	0.375	0.365	0.2500
808	$\frac{1}{4}$	1	$\frac{1}{16}$	0.438	0.428	0.3130
809	$\frac{1}{4}$	$1\frac{1}{8}$	$\frac{5}{64}$	0.484	0.475	0.3590
810	$\frac{1}{4}$	$1\frac{1}{4}$	$\frac{5}{64}$	0.547	0.537	0.4220
811	$\frac{1}{4}$	$1\frac{3}{8}$	$\frac{3}{32}$	0.594	0.584	0.4690
812	$\frac{1}{4}$	$1\frac{1}{2}$	$\frac{7}{64}$	0.641	0.631	0.5160
1008	$\frac{5}{16}$	1	$\frac{1}{16}$	0.438	0.428	0.2818
1009	$\frac{5}{16}$	$1\frac{1}{8}$	$\frac{5}{64}$	0.484	0.475	0.3278
1010	$\frac{5}{16}$	$1\frac{1}{4}$	$\frac{5}{16}$	0.547	0.537	0.3908
1011	$\frac{5}{16}$	$1\frac{3}{8}$	$\frac{3}{32}$	0.594	0.584	0.4378
1012	$\frac{5}{16}$	$1\frac{1}{2}$	$\frac{7}{64}$	0.641	0.631	0.4848
1210	$\frac{3}{8}$	$1\frac{1}{4}$	$\frac{5}{64}$	0.547	0.537	0.3595
1211	$\frac{3}{8}$	$1\frac{3}{8}$	$\frac{3}{32}$	0.594	0.584	0.4060
1212	$\frac{3}{8}$	$1\frac{1}{2}$	$\frac{7}{64}$	0.641	0.631	0.4535

Note: Nominal dimensions are indicated by the key number in which the last two digits give the diameter (B) in eighths and the ones in front of them give the width (A) in thirty-seconds. For example, No. 809 means $B = \frac{9}{8}$ or $1\frac{1}{8}$ and $A = \frac{8}{32}$ or $\frac{1}{4}$.

Source: Extracted from American Standard *Woodruff Keys, Keyslots and Cutters* (ASA B17f–1930), with the permission of the publisher, The American Society of Mechanical Engineers.

Table 18. Wire and Sheet-metal Gages

Dimensions in Decimal Parts of an Inch

No. of wire gage	American, or Brown & Sharpe	Birmingham, or Stubs wire	Washburn & Moen or American Steel & Wire Co.	W. & M. steel music wire	New American S. & W. Co. music wire gage	Imperial wire gage	U.S. Standard gage for sheet amd plate iron and steel
00000000	....	....	....	0.0083			
0000000	....	....	....	0.0087			
000000	....	....	....	0.0095	0.004	0.464	0.46875
00000	....	....	....	0.010	0.005	0.432	0.4375
0000	0.460	0.454	0.3938	0.011	0.006	0.400	0.40625
000	0.40964	0.425	0.3625	0.012	0.007	0.372	0.375
00	0.3648	0.380	0.3310	0.0133	0.008	0.348	0.34375
0	0.32486	0.340	0.3065	0.0144	0.009	0.324	0.3125
1	0.2893	0.300	0.2830	0.0156	0.010	0.300	0.28125
2	0.25763	0.284	0.2625	0.0166	0.011	0.276	0.265625
3	0.22942	0.259	0.2437	0.0178	0.012	0.252	0.250
4	0.20431	0.238	0.2253	0.0188	0.013	0.232	0.234375
5	0.18194	0.220	0.2070	0.0202	0.014	0.212	0.21875
6	0.16202	0.203	0.1920	0.0215	0.016	0.192	0.203125
7	0.14428	0.180	0.1770	0.023	0.018	0.176	0.1875
8	0.12849	0.165	0.1620	0.0243	0.020	0.160	0.171875
9	0.11443	0.148	0.1483	0.0256	0.022	0.144	0.15625
10	0.10189	0.134	0.1350	0.027	0.024	0.128	0.140625
11	0.090742	0.120	0.1205	0.0284	0.026	0.116	0.125
12	0.080808	0.109	0.1055	0.0296	0.029	0.104	0.109375
13	0.071961	0.095	0.0915	0.0314	0.031	0.092	0.09375
14	0.064084	0.083	0.0800	0.0326	0.033	0.080	0.078125
15	0.057068	0.072	0.0720	0.0345	0.035	0.072	0.0703125
16	0.05082	0.065	0.0625	0.036	0.037	0.064	0.0625
17	0.045257	0.058	0.0540	0.0377	0.039	0.056	0.05625
18	0.040303	0.049	0.0475	0.0395	0.041	0.048	0.050
19	0.03589	0.042	0.0410	0.0414	0.043	0.040	0.04375
20	0.031961	0.035	0.0348	0.0434	0.045	0.036	0.0375
21	0.028462	0.032	0.03175	0.046	0.047	0.032	0.034375
22	0.025347	0.028	0.0286	0.0483	0.049	0.028	0.03125
23	0.022571	0.025	0.0258	0.051	0.051	0.024	0.028125
24	0.0201	0.022	0.0230	0.055	0.055	0.022	0.025
25	0.0179	0.020	0.0204	0.0586	0.059	0.020	0.021875
26	0.01594	0.018	0.0181	0.0626	0.063	0.018	0.01875
27	0.014195	0.016	0.0173	0.0658	0.067	0.0164	0.0171875
28	0.012641	0.014	0.0162	0.072	0.071	0.0149	0.015625
29	0.011257	0.013	0.0150	0.076	0.075	0.0136	0.0140625
30	0.010025	0.012	0.0140	0.080	0.080	0.0124	0.0125
31	0.008928	0.010	0.0132	....	0.085	0.0116	0.0109375
32	0.00795	0.009	0.0128	....	0.090	0.0108	0.01015625
33	0.00708	0.008	0.0118	....	0.095	0.0100	0.009375
34	0.006304	0.007	0.0104	....	....	0.0092	0.00859375
35	0.005614	0.005	0.0095	....	....	0.0084	0.0078125
36	0.005	0.004	0.0090	....	....	0.0076	0.00703125
37	0.004453	....	....	....	....	0.0068	0.006640625
38	0.003965	....	....	....	....	0.0060	0.00625
39	0.003531	....	....	....	....	0.0052	
40	0.003144	....	....	....	....	0.0048	

Table 19. American Standard Welded and Seamless Steel Pipe

Nominal pipe size	Out-side diam.	Nominal wall thickness			Threads per inch	Nominal pipe size	Out-side diam.	Nominal wall thickness			Threads per inch
		Stand-ard wall	Extra strong wall	Double extra strong wall				Stand-ard wall	Extra strong wall	Double extra strong wall	
$\frac{1}{8}$	0.405	0.068	0.095	....	27	4	4.500	0.237	0.337	0.674	8
$\frac{1}{4}$	0.540	0.088	0.119	....	18	5	5.563	0.258	0.375	0.750	8
$\frac{3}{8}$	0.675	0.091	0.126	....	18	6	6.625	0.280	0.432	0.864	8
$\frac{1}{2}$	0.840	0.109	0.147	0.294	14	8	8.625	0.322	0.500	0.875	8
$\frac{3}{4}$	1.050	0.113	0.154	0.308	14	10	10.750	0.365	0.500	....	8
1	1.315	0.133	0.179	0.358	$11\frac{1}{2}$	12	12.750	0.375	0.500	....	8
$1\frac{1}{4}$	1.660	0.140	0.191	0.382	$11\frac{1}{2}$	14	14.000	0.375	0.500	....	8
$1\frac{1}{2}$	1.900	0.145	0.200	0.400	$11\frac{1}{2}$	16	16.000	0.375	0.500	....	8
2	2.375	0.154	0.218	0.436	$11\frac{1}{2}$	18	18.000	0.375	0.500	....	8
$2\frac{1}{2}$	2.875	0.203	0.276	0.552	8	20	20.000	0.375	0.500	....	8
3	3.500	0.216	0.300	0.600	8	24	24.000	0.375	0.500	....	8
$3\frac{1}{2}$	4.000	0.226	0.318	....	8						

Note: To find the inside diameter subtract twice the wall thickness from the outside diameter. Schedule numbers have been set up for wall thicknesses for pipe and the American Standard should be consulted for complete information. Standard wall thicknesses are for Schedule 40 up to and including nominal size 10. Extra strong walls are Schedule 80 up to and including size 8, and Schedule 60 for size 10.

Source: Extracted from American Standard *Wrought-steel and Wrought-iron Pipe* (ASA B36.10–1950) and American Standard *Pipe Threads* (taper threads) (ASA B2.1–1945), with the permission of the publisher, The American Society of Mechanical Engineers.

Table 20. Steel-wire Nails
American Steel & Wire Company Gage

Size	Length	Common wire nails and brads		Casing nails		Finishing nails	
		Gage, diam.	No. to pound	Gage, diam.	No. to pound	Gage, diam.	No. to pound
2d	1	15	876	$15\frac{1}{2}$	1010	$16\frac{1}{2}$	1351
3d	$1\frac{1}{4}$	14	568	$14\frac{1}{2}$	635	$15\frac{1}{2}$	807
4d	$1\frac{1}{2}$	$12\frac{1}{2}$	316	14	473	15	584
5d	$1\frac{3}{4}$	$12\frac{1}{2}$	271	14	406	15	500
6d	2	$11\frac{1}{2}$	181	$12\frac{1}{2}$	236	13	309
7d	$2\frac{1}{4}$	$11\frac{1}{2}$	161	$12\frac{1}{2}$	210	13	238
8d	$2\frac{1}{2}$	$10\frac{1}{4}$	106	$11\frac{1}{2}$	145	$12\frac{1}{2}$	189
9d	$2\frac{3}{4}$	$10\frac{1}{4}$	96	$11\frac{1}{2}$	132	$12\frac{1}{2}$	172
10d	3	9	69	$10\frac{1}{2}$	94	$11\frac{1}{2}$	121
12d	$3\frac{1}{4}$	9	64	$10\frac{1}{2}$	87	$11\frac{1}{2}$	113
16d	$3\frac{1}{2}$	8	49	10	71	11	90
20d	4	6	31	9	52	10	62
30d	$4\frac{1}{2}$	5	24	9	46		
40d	5	4	18	8	35		
50d	$5\frac{1}{2}$	3	14				
60d	6	2	11				

Table 21. American Standard Large Rivets

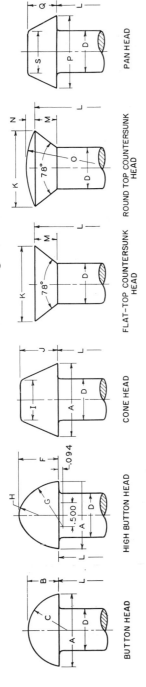

BUTTON HEAD

HIGH BUTTON HEAD

CONE HEAD

FLAT-TOP COUNTERSUNK HEAD

ROUND TOP COUNTERSUNK HEAD

PAN HEAD

Manufactured Shapes

D nominal	A basic	B basic (min.)	C	E basic	F basic	G	H	I basic	J basic (min.)	K basic	M basic (min.)	N	O	P basic	Q basic (min.)	S basic
$\frac{1}{2}$	0.875	0.375	0.443	0.781	0.500	0.656	0.094	0.469	0.438	0.905	0.250	0.095	1.125	0.800	0.381	0.500
$\frac{5}{8}$	1.094	0.469	0.553	0.969	0.594	0.750	0.188	0.586	0.547	1.131	0.312	0.119	1.405	1.000	0.469	0.625
$\frac{3}{4}$	1.312	0.562	0.664	1.156	0.688	0.844	0.282	0.703	0.656	1.358	0.375	0.142	1.688	1.200	0.556	0.750
$\frac{7}{8}$	1.531	0.656	0.775	1.344	0.781	0.937	0.375	0.820	0.766	1.584	0.438	0.166	1.969	1.400	0.643	0.875
1	1.750	0.750	0.885	1.531	0.875	1.031	0.469	0.938	0.875	1.810	0.500	0.190	2.250	1.600	0.731	1.000
$1\frac{1}{8}$	1.969	0.844	0.996	1.719	0.969	1.125	0.563	1.055	0.984	2.036	0.562	0.214	2.531	1.800	0.835	1.125
$1\frac{1}{4}$	2.188	0.938	1.107	1.906	1.062	1.218	0.656	1.172	1.094	2.262	0.625	0.238	2.812	2.000	0.922	1.250
$1\frac{3}{8}$	2.406	1.031	1.217	2.094	1.156	1.312	0.750	1.290	1.203	2.489	0.688	0.261	3.094	2.200	1.009	1.375
$1\frac{1}{2}$	2.625	1.125	1.328	2.281	1.250	1.406	0.844	1.406	1.312	2.715	0.750	0.285	3.375	2.400	1.113	1.500
$1\frac{5}{8}$	2.844	1.219	1.439	2.469	1.344	1.500	0.938	1.524	1.422	2.941	0.812	0.309	3.656	2.600	1.201	1.625
$1\frac{3}{4}$	3.062	1.312	1.549	2.656	1.438	1.594	1.032	1.641	1.531	3.168	0.875	0.332	3.938	2.800	1.288	1.750

Source: Extracted from American Standard *Large Rivets* (ASA B18.4–1950), with the permission of the publisher, The American Society of Mechanical Engineers,

Table 22. Geometrical Shapes

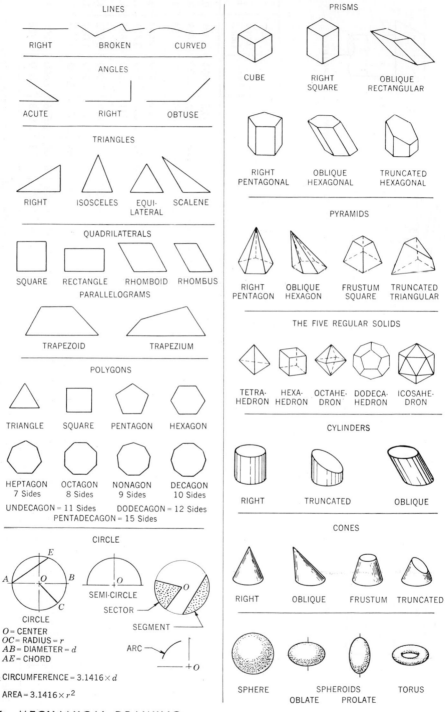

LINES

RIGHT   BROKEN   CURVED

ANGLES

ACUTE   RIGHT   OBTUSE

TRIANGLES

RIGHT   ISOSCELES   EQUI-LATERAL   SCALENE

QUADRILATERALS

SQUARE   RECTANGLE   RHOMBOID   RHOMBUS

PARALLELOGRAMS

TRAPEZOID   TRAPEZIUM

POLYGONS

TRIANGLE   SQUARE   PENTAGON   HEXAGON

HEPTAGON 7 Sides   OCTAGON 8 Sides   NONAGON 9 Sides   DECAGON 10 Sides

UNDECAGON = 11 Sides   DODECAGON = 12 Sides
PENTADECAGON = 15 Sides

CIRCLE

O = CENTER
OC = RADIUS = r
AB = DIAMETER = d
AE = CHORD

CIRCLE   SEMI-CIRCLE   SECTOR   SEGMENT   ARC

CIRCUMFERENCE = $3.1416 \times d$

AREA = $3.1416 \times r^2$

PRISMS

CUBE   RIGHT SQUARE   OBLIQUE RECTANGULAR

RIGHT PENTAGONAL   OBLIQUE HEXAGONAL   TRUNCATED HEXAGONAL

PYRAMIDS

RIGHT PENTAGON   OBLIQUE HEXAGON   FRUSTUM SQUARE   TRUNCATED TRIANGULAR

THE FIVE REGULAR SOLIDS

TETRA-HEDRON   HEXA-HEDRON   OCTAHE-DRON   DODECA-HEDRON   ICOSAHE-DRON

CYLINDERS

RIGHT   TRUNCATED   OBLIQUE

CONES

RIGHT   OBLIQUE   FRUSTUM   TRUNCATED

SPHERE   SPHEROIDS OBLATE   PROLATE   TORUS

Glossary of Shop Terms[1]

(v) = Verb (n) = Noun

anneal (v) To heat slowly to a critical temperature and gradually cool. Used to soften and to remove internal stresses.

babbitt or babbitt metal (n) An antifriction bearing metal, invented by Isaac Babbitt. Composed of antimony, tin, and copper.

bearing (n) Any part that bears up or supports another part. In particular the support for a revolving shaft.

bevel (n) A surface slanted to another surface. Called a *miter* when the angle is 45°.

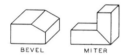

BEVEL   MITER

bore (v) To enlarge or to finish a hole by means of a cutting tool called a *boring bar*, used in a boring mill or lathe.

boss (n) A raised surface of circular outline as used on a casting or forging.

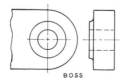

BOSS

[1] Terms defined and illustrated within the text are not included in this list. Such terms may be found by referring to the Index.

brass (n) An alloy of copper and zinc or copper with zinc and lead.

broach (v) To machine and change the form of holes or outside surfaces to a desired shape, generally other than round. (n) A tool with a series of chisel edges used to broach.

bronzes (n) Alloys of copper and tin in varying proportions, mostly copper. Sometimes other metals, such as zinc, are added.

bushing (n) A hollow cylindrical sleeve used as a bearing or as a guide for drills or other tools. See oilless bushing in Fig. L-13.

cam (n) A machine part mounted on a revolving shaft used for changing rotary motion into an alternating back and forth motion. See Chap. 19.

caseharden (carbonize or carburize) (v) To heat-treat steel to harden the surface by causing it to absorb carbon by quenching in an oil or lead bath.

casting (n) A part formed by pouring molten metal into a hollow form (mold) of the desired shape and allowing it to harden.

chamfer (v) To bevel an edge. (n) An edge which has been beveled.

CHAMFER

core (v) To form the hollow part of a casting by means of a part made of sand and shaped like the hollow part (called a *core*) and placed in the mold (see Casting). The core is broken up and removed after the casting is cool.

counterbore (*v*) To enlarge an end of a hole to a desired depth and of cylindrical form. Such an enlargement is called a *counterbore*.

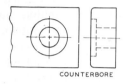

COUNTERBORE

countersink (*v*) To form a conical space at the end of a hole.

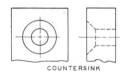

COUNTERSINK

crown (*n*) The contour of the face of a belt pulley, rounded or angular, used to keep the belt in place. The belt tends to climb to the highest place.

CROWN

die (*n*) A hardened metal block of a shape to form a desired shape by cutting or pressing. Also, a tool used to cut external screw threads.

die casting (*n*) A casting made of molten alloy (or plastic composition) by pouring it into a metal mold or die, generally forced under pressure. Die castings are smooth and accurate.

die stamping (*n*) A piece which has been formed or cut from sheet material, generally sheet metal.

drill (*v*) To make a cylindrical hole using a revolving tool with cutting edges, called a drill, generally a twist drill.

drop forging (*n*) A piece formed between dies while hot, using pressure or a drop hammer.

face (*v*) To machine (finish) a flat surface on a lathe with the surface perpendicular to the axis of rotation.

file (*v*) To smooth, finish, or shape with a file.

fillet (*n*) The rounded-in corner between two surfaces.

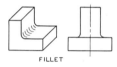

FILLET

flange (*n*) A rim extension as at the end of a pipe or similar construction.

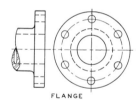

FLANGE

forge (*v*) To give the desired shape or form to hot metal by hammering or pressure.

galvanize (*v*) To give a coating by means of a bath of zinc or zinc and lead.

grind (*v*) To use an abrasive wheel to polish or to finish a surface.

key (*n*) A piece used to fasten a hub to a shaft or for a similar purpose. See Fig. 12-35.

keyway or **keyseat** (*n*) A groove or slot in a shaft or hub into which a key is placed.

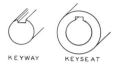

KEYWAY KEYSEAT

knurl (*v*) To form a series of regular dents to roughen a cylindrical surface so that it can be held or turned by hand.

lug (*n*) An "ear" forming a part of and extending from a part.

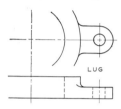

LUG

malleable casting (*n*) A casting which has been toughened by annealing it.

mill (*v*) To machine a part on a milling machine, using a rotating toothed cutter.

neck (*v*) To cut a groove around a cylindrical part, generally at a change in diameter.

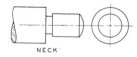

NECK

peen (*v*) To stretch or head over material with the peen or ball end of a machinist's hammer.

punch (*v*) To pierce thin metal by pressing a tool of the desired shape through it.

ream (*v*) To make a hole the exact size by finishing with a rotating fluted cutting tool.

round (*n*) The rounded-over corner of two surfaces.

ROUND

shim (*n*) A thin plate of metal used between two surfaces to adjust the distance between them.

spot-face (*v*) To finish a circular spot slightly below a rough surface on a casting to provide a smooth flat seat for a bolthead or other fastening.

steel casting (*n*) A part made of cast iron to which scrap steel has been added when melted.

tap (*v*) To cut threads in a hole with a threading tool called a tap. (*n*) A hardened screw, fluted to provide cutting edges.

temper (*v*) To reduce the brittleness in hardened steel by heating in various ways, as in a bath of oil, salt, sand, or lead, to a specified temperature and then cooling.

template or **templet** (*n*) A flat form or pattern of full size used to lay out a shape and to locate holes or other features.

turn (*v*) To machine a piece on a lathe by rotating the piece against a cutting tool (as when forming a cylindrical surface, and so forth).

upset (*v*) To make an enlarged section or shoulder on a rod, bar, or similar piece while forging.

weld (*v*) To join pieces of metal, which have been heated to a fusing temperature, by pressing or hammering them together. See Chap. 17.

Bibliography

For a more extended explanation of some of the special applications of mechanical drawing and for information on related subject matter, the following books can be referred to:

Aeronautical Drafting

Aircraft Designers' Data Book by Leslie E. Neville, McGraw-Hill Book Company, Inc., New York.

Aircraft Drafting by H. H. Katz, The Macmillan Company, New York.

Aircraft Layout and Detail Design by Newton H. Anderson, 2d ed., McGraw-Hill Book Company, Inc., New York.

A Manual of Aircraft Drafting by Carl L. Svensen, D. Van Nostrand Company, Inc., Princeton, N.J.

Architectural Drawing

Architectural Drafting by C. L. Svensen and E. G. Shelton, D. Van Nostrand Company, Inc., Princeton, N.J.

Architectural Drawing by W. B. Field, McGraw-Hill Book Company, Inc., New York.

Architectural Drawing by S. W. Morgan, McGraw-Hill Book Company, Inc., New York.

Architectural Drawing for the Building Trades by J. E. Kennedy and J. P. McGrail, McGraw-Hill Book Company, Inc., New York.

Carpentry for the Building Trades by E. A. Lair, 2d ed., McGraw-Hill Book Company, Inc., New York.

Don Graf's Data Sheets, 2d ed., Reinhold Publishing Corporation, New York.

Cams and Gears

Cams, Elementary and Advanced by F. Der Furman, John Wiley & Sons, Inc., New York.

Practical Gear Design by D. W. Dudley, McGraw-Hill Book Company, Inc., New York.

Treatise on Commercial Gear Cutting, Fellows Gear Shaper Company, Springfield, Vt.

Electrical and Electronics Drafting

Drafting for Electronics by L. F. B. Carini, McGraw-Hill Book Company, Inc., New York.

Electrical Drafting by D. W. Van Gieson, McGraw-Hill Book Company, Inc., New York.

Electrical Drafting and Design by C. C. Bishop, 3d ed., McGraw-Hill Book Company, Inc., New York.

Handbooks and Manuals

Although only a few are listed here, there are a large number of handbooks and manuals that, if available for the student, are useful for reference.

Architects' and Builders' Handbook by F. E. Kidder and H. Parker, 18th ed., John Wiley & Sons, Inc., New York.

Machinery's Handbook by Erik Oberg and F. D. Jones, 15th ed., The Industrial Press, New York.

The Machinists' and Draftsmen's Handbook by A. M. Wagener and H. R. Arthur, D. Van Nostrand Company, Inc., Princeton, N.J.

The New American Machinists' Handbook edited by Rupert Le Grand, McGraw-Hill Book Company, Inc., New York.

Steel Construction, 5th ed., American Institute of Steel Construction, Inc., New York.

Handbooks and manuals of Bethlehem Steel Company, U.S. Steel Company, Aluminum Company of America, Reynolds Metals Company, Portland Cement Association, Society of Automotive Engineers, and American Society of Tool Engineers.

Illustration, Perspective, and Sketching

Freehand Drafting for Technical Sketching by A. E. Zipprich, 3d ed., D. Van Nostrand Company, Inc., Princeton, N.J.

Industrial Production Illustration by R. P. Hoelscher, C. H. Springer, and R. F. Pohle, 2d ed., McGraw-Hill Book Company, Inc., New York.

Perspective by B. J. Lubschez, 4th ed., D. Van Nostrand Company, Inc., Princeton, N.J.

Practical Perspective Drawing by P. J. Lawson, McGraw-Hill Book Company, Inc., New York.

Production Illustration by John Treacy, John Wiley & Sons, Inc., New York.

Technical Sketching and Visualization for Engineers by H. H. Katz, The Macmillan Company, New York.

Lettering

An Alphabet Source Book by Oscar Ogg, Dover Publications, Inc., New York.

The Art of Lettering by Carl L. Svensen, 2d ed., D. Van Nostrand Company, Inc., Princeton, N.J.

Learning to Letter by Paul Carlyle, Guy Oring, and Herbert S. Richland, McGraw-Hill Book Company, Inc., New York.

Lessons in Lettering, Books I and II, by Thomas E. French and William D. Turnbull, 3d ed., McGraw-Hill Book Company, Inc., New York.

Map Drawing

Cartography by Charles H. Deetz, U.S. Government Printing Office, Washington, D.C.

Elements of Topographic Drawing by R. C. Sloane and J. M. Montz, 2d ed., McGraw-Hill Book Company, Inc., New York.

Mechanical Drawing Problem Workbooks

Problems in Mechanical Drawing, First Course and Second Course, by A. S. Levens and A. E. Edstrom, McGraw-Hill Book Company, Inc., New York.

Sheet-metal Drafting

Industrial Sheet Metal Drawing by J. H. Paull, D. Van Nostrand Company, Inc., Princeton, N.J.

Sheet-metal Pattern Drafting and Shop Problems by J. S. Daugherty, Chas. A. Bennett Company, Inc., Peoria, Ill.

Sheet Metal Shop Practice by Leroy Fowler Bruce, American Technical Society, Chicago.

Shop Processes

Engineering Tools and Processes by H. C. Hesse, D. Van Nostrand Company, Inc., Princeton, N.J.

Foundry Work by R. E. Wendt, 4th ed., McGraw-Hill Book Company, Inc., New York.

Manufacturing Processes by M. L. Begeman, 3d ed., John Wiley & Sons, Inc., New York.

Metal Processing by O. W. Boston, 2d ed., John Wiley & Sons, Inc., New York

Shop Theory, Henry Ford Trade School, 4th ed. revised by Fred Nicholson, McGraw-Hill Book Company, Inc., New York.

Structural Drawing

Manual of Standard Practice for Detailing Reinforced Concrete Structures, American Concrete Institute, Detroit.

Structural Drafting by C. T. Bishop, John Wiley & Sons, Inc., New York.

Textbook of Structural Shop Drafting, vols. 1–3, American Institute of Steel Construction, Inc., New York.

Welding

Procedure Handbook of Arc Welding Design and Practice, Lincoln Electric Company, Cleveland.

Simple Blueprint Reading with Particular Reference to Welding, Lincoln Electric Company, Cleveland.

Welding Encyclopedia by T. B. Jefferson, 13th ed., McGraw-Hill Book Company, Inc., New York.

Welding Engineering by B. E. Rossi, McGraw-Hill Book Company, Inc., New York.

Catalogues of Drawing Instruments

To obtain catalogues of drawing instruments, you may write to any of the following companies:

Theo. Alteneder & Sons, Philadelphia, Pa.

Chas. Bruning Company, Inc., Chicago, Ill.

Eugene Dietzgen Company, Chicago, Ill.

B. K. Elliott Company, Pittsburgh, Pa.

Gramercy Import Company, Inc., New York, N.Y.

Keuffel & Esser Company, Hoboken, N.J.

A. Lietz Company, San Francisco, Calif.

The Frederick Post Company, Chicago, Ill.

U.S. Blue Print Paper Company, Chicago, Ill.

Universal Drafting Machine Corporation, Cleveland, Ohio.

V. & E. Manufacturing Company, P. O. Box 950M, Pasadena 20, Calif.

F. Weber Company, Philadelphia, Pa.

List of Visual Aids

The films listed below and on the following pages can be used to visualize and supplement much of the material in this book. For the convenience of users, they have been grouped by chapters, but many of them can be appropriately used in the study of other topics. Both motion pictures and filmstrips are included, the character of each being identified by the self-explanatory abbreviations "MP" and "FS." Immediately following this identification is the name of the primary distributor of the film. Abbreviations used for these names are identified in the list of sources at the end of the bibliography. In many instances, the films can be borrowed or rented from local or state 16mm film libraries. A nationwide list of these local sources is given in *A Directory of 3,300 16mm Film Libraries,* available from the Superintendent of Documents, U.S. Government Printing Office, Washington 25, D.C. Unless otherwise indicated, the motion pictures are 16mm sound black-and-white films and the filmstrips are 35mm black-and-white and silent. The length of motion pictures is given in minutes (min), of filmstrips in frames (fr).

While this bibliography is fairly complete, film users should examine the latest annual editions and supplements of *Educational Film Guide* and *Filmstrip Guide,* published by the H. W. Wilson Company, New York. The *Guides,* standard reference books, are available in most school, college, and public libraries.

Of special importance to this textbook are the following films (8 motion pictures with 7 follow-up filmstrips; and 6 separate filmstrips —3 in color) designed and produced by the Text-Film Department of McGraw-Hill Book Company to correlate with the text material: *Language of Drawing; Shape Description, Parts 1 and 2; Shop Procedures; Sections; Auxiliary Views, Parts 1 and 2; Size Description; Scales: Flat and Triangular; Compasses and Bow Instruments; Freehand Lettering and Figures for Working Drawings; Isometric Drawing; Developments;* and *Intersections.* Each film is described under the chapter with which it is correlated.

Also of importance are these films (10 motion pictures and 9 follow-up filmstrips) correlated with French and Vierck's *Engineering Drawing: According to Plan: Introduction to Engineering Drawing; Orthographic Projection; Auxiliary Views: Single Auxiliaries; Auxiliary Views: Double Auxiliaries, Sections and Conventions; Drawings and the Shop; Selection of Dimensions; Pictorial Sketching; Simple Developments; Oblique Cones and Transitional Developments.* Each of these films, also produced by the Text-Film Department of McGraw-Hill Book Company, is described under the most appropriate chapter heading.

Chapter 1. The Language of Drawing

According to Plan: Introduction to Engineering Drawing (MP McGraw 9min). Demonstrates the need for engineering drawing and its importance as a language or means of communication for the coordinated work of the many people involved in modern production.

The Draftsman (MP VGF 11min). Reviews the skills required of a draftsman, the kinds of drafting from freehand sketches to finished drawings, and the vocational opportunities for draftsmen.

Drawings and the Shop (MP McGraw 15min). Explains the relationships between drawings and various production operations in shop and factory. (Follow-up filmstrip, 43 frames.)

Language of Drawing (MP McGraw 10min). Explains the importance and uses of mechanical drawing, the common language of the building world.

Chapter 2. Learning to Draw

Compasses and Bow Instruments (FS McGraw). The various uses of compasses and bow instruments are described and demonstrated. Covers in detail the proper sharpening and installation of the lead; setting the radius; the technique of drawing circles; and the use of the instruments to divide lines and transfer distances.

Drafting Tips (MP PSU 28min). Explains the care and use of drafting equipment, proper sheet layout, the use of an alphabet of lines, and the procedure of developing a drawing from beginning to end.

Scales: Flat and Triangular (FS McGraw). Explains the wide range of scales and scale graduations designed for the use of mechanical engineers, architects, and civil engineers.

Chapter 3. Lettering

Engineering Letters (MP Purdue 16min). Demonstrates the making of the entire alphabet, the ampersand, and numerals for inclined capital letters. Time for practice of each character is allowed during the film.

Freehand Lettering and Figures for Working Drawings (FS McGraw). Discusses and demonstrates how to learn to letter by grouping vertical and inclined letters of similar proportion and form for study and practice.

Lower Case Letters (MP Purdue 15min). Demonstrates the making of the entire alphabet for inclined lower-case letters. Time for practice of each character is allowed during the film.

Technical Lettering (FS series Handy). Five filmstrips with the following titles: *Single-stroke Gothic—Introduction; Vertical Capitals IHT LEF AVW; Vertical Capitals MN YZXK4 OQCG; Vertical Capitals 069 83S DUJ PRB; Vertical Capitals 725& and Spacing.*

Chapter 4. Geometrical Constructions

Applied Geometry (MP Purdue 17min silent). Explains nine different geometric constructions from that of constructing a hexagon when the distance across corners is known to drawing an arc tangent to two circles.

Descriptive Geometry: Finding the Line of Intersection between Two Solids (MP USN/UWF 22min). Methods of determining intersecting lines of a cylinder and a cone by passing planes through the objects on an orthographic drawing.

Intersection of Surfaces (MP Purdue 10min silent). Explains by means of models

and drawings the principles for finding the lines of intersection between intersecting surfaces; discusses the problems of finding the intersection between two prisms, two cylinders, and cylinder and cone.

Oblique Cones and Transitional Developments (MP McGraw 11min). Uses animated drawings to show the development of an oblique cone, a transition connecting a circular opening, and a transition connecting two curved openings. Demonstrates the use of true-length diagrams and triangulation. (Follow-up filmstrip, 40 frames.)

Practical Geometry (MP series KB). Seventeen films, 10 to 12 minutes each, with the following definitive titles: *Angles; Angles and Arcs in Circles; Areas; Chords and Tangents of Circles; The Circle; Congruent Figures; Indirect Measurement; Lines and Angles; Locus; Polygons; Practical Geometry; Properties of Triangles; Pythagorean Theorem; Quadrilaterals; Ratio and Proportion; Rectilinear Coordinates; Similar Triangles.*

Simple Developments (MP McGraw 11min). Shows the development of a hexagonal prism, truncated cylinder, right rectangular pyramid, oblique pyramid, right circular cone, and truncated right circular cone. (Follow-up filmstrip, 40 frames.)

Use of T-square and Triangles (MP Purdue 22min silent). Explains the basic principles of using the T-square and triangles and demonstrates the drawing of several kinds of lines and angles.

Chapter 5. Theory of Shape Description

Multi-view Drawing (MP Purdue 27min silent). Demonstrates the way to represent an object by means of three orthographic views.

Orthographic Projection (MP McGraw 18min). Explains by animation the purpose and method of preparing front, side, and top views of an object. (Follow-up filmstrip, 40 frames.)

Shape Description (MP Purdue 25min). Demonstrates the relationship between an object itself, its pictorial representation, and its representation by three orthographic views.

Shape Description, Part 1 (MP McGraw 11min). Describes orthographic projection, utilizing a combination of animated diagrams and photography of specially prepared models to provide unusual three-dimensional effects. (Follow-up filmstrip, 33 frames.)

Shape Description, Part 2 (MP McGraw 8min). Demonstrates the step-by-step procedure for constructing a drawing using orthographic projection. (Follow-up filmstrip, 32 frames.)

Chapter 6. Sketching

Pictorial Sketching (MP McGraw 11min). Covers the basic principles of pictorial sketching which engineers should know. Describes the axometric, oblique, and perspective methods and explains where and how to use each method. (Follow-up filmstrip, 40 frames.)

Chapter 7. Reading and Making Drawings

Blueprint Reading (MP series USOE/UWF). Five motion pictures and correlated filmstrips explaining the importance of reading a blueprint drawing correctly. Titles and running times are: *Visualizing an Object* (9min); *Reading a Three-view Drawing* (10min); *Principal Dimensions, Reference Surfaces, and Tolerances* (12min); *Sectional Views and Projections, Finish Marks* (15min); *Reading a Drawing of a Valve Bonnet* (20min).

Shop Procedures (MP McGraw 17min). Shows how finished drawings are used in machine-shop work and demonstrates the operation of various basic machine tools. (Follow-up filmstrip, 41 frames.)

Chapter 8. Sections

Sectional Views (MP Purdue 22min silent). Illustrates the principles of sectioning—full section, half section, and offset section.

Sectional Views and Projections, Finish Marks (MP USOE/UWF 15min). Dimension, center, cross-section, and object lines; projection of a sectional view; uses of finish marks; and meanings of standard cross-section lines. (Follow-up filmstrip, 29 frames.)

Sections (MP McGraw 10min). Explains the need for sectional views formed by imaginary cutting away of part of the object, thereby revealing interior details. Describes various symbols used in sectioning. (Follow-up filmstrip, 32 frames.)

Sections and Conventions (MP McGraw 15min). Explains the meaning of sectioning; describes the various types of sections and the meaning of symbols used in sectioning. (Follow-up filmstrip, 44 frames.)

Chapter 9. Auxiliary Views and Revolutions

Auxiliary Views (MP Purdue 18min silent). Illustrates principles of auxiliary views and shows the construction of auxiliary views for straight and curved line figures.

Auxiliary Views, Part 1 (MP McGraw 11min). Explains the need for auxiliary views, defines auxiliary projection, and demonstrates the construction of an auxiliary elevation (Follow-up filmstrip, 32 frames.)

Auxiliary Views, Part 2 (MP McGraw 10min). Reviews the principles of auxiliary views treated in Part 1; describes in detail three types of single auxiliaries—auxiliary elevations, right and left auxiliaries, and front and rear auxiliaries. (Follow-up filmstrip, 34 frames.)

Auxiliary Views: Single Auxiliaries (MP McGraw 23min). Reviews the principles of orthographic projection, shows the conditions requiring projection of a slanting surface on a plane parallel to but not one of the principal planes, and thus defines auxiliary projection. (Follow-up filmstrip, 38 frames.)

Auxiliary Views: Double Auxiliaries (MP McGraw 13min). Reviews orthographic projection; shows why a single auxiliary does not give an accurate picture of an oblique face; and describes the theory of the double auxiliary or oblique view, using the visualization effects of combined animated drawings and models. (Follow-up filmstrip, 26 frames.)

Chapter 10. Principles of Size Description

Selection of Dimensions (MP McGraw 18min). Explains the principles governing the choice of dimensions. Gives the meaning of and techniques for applying such marks as dimension lines, arrowheads, extension lines, leaders, and finish marks. (Follow-up filmstrip, 48 frames.)

Size Description (MP McGraw 13min). Emphasizes the importance of uniformity in dimensioning. Shows the method for describing complex drawings by breaking them down into simple geometric parts for dimensioning. (Follow-up filmstrip, 33 frames.)

Chapter 11. Technique of the Finished Drawing

Ink Work and Tracing (MP Purdue 34min silent). Demonstrates the various steps in making tracings on tracing cloth.

Chapter 12. Screws, Bolts, and Other Fastenings

Screw Threads (MP Purdue 24min). Defines important terms associated with screw threads, shows the construction of national and square threads, and explains the meaning of each line of a drawing.

Chapter 13. Mechanical Drafting

Shop Procedures (MP McGraw 17min and FS). Shows how drawings are used in every stage of shop production and operation of basic machines. Points out that draftsman and shop worker must share the common knowledge of mechanical drawing. Filmstrip summarizes film and presents questions for review and discussion.

Chapter 14. Pictorial Drawing

Isometric Drawing (Color FS McGraw). A presentation of the theory of isometric projection and its application to isometric drawing. Covers the construction of the principal axes and the completion of the figures.

Perspective Drawing (MP UCLA 8min). With a cube used as a basic form, describes the one-point, two-point, and three-point perspective techniques. Also, demonstrates the meaning of horizon line and picture plane.

Pictorial Drawing (MP Purdue 22min silent). Demonstrates principles of isometric drawing by means of models and shows the construction of objects with isometric and nonisometric lines and with circles.

Chapters 16 to 19 and 21 to 22

Many films portraying industrial processes and skills show how operators depend upon blueprints and visualize drawings used in machine-shop work, sheet metal, and so forth. Film users should examine particularly the training films of the U.S. Office of Education.

Chapter 20. Sheet-metal Drafting

Developments (Color FS McGraw). Begins with a development or pattern of an object's surfaces, both flat and curved, laid out in a plane. Demonstrates the development of many solids.

Intersections (Color FS McGraw). Demonstrates basic principles by presenting a series of problems in each of which the lines of intersection of two objects is determined.

Chapter 23. Map Drafting

Charts (MP USN/UWF 18min). Explains the meaning, advantages, and limitations of Mercator, gnomonic, and Lambert conformal projections.

Introduction to Map Projection (MP UWF 18min). Demonstrates various types of map projection and discusses the advantages and disadvantages of each projection.

Multiplex Mapping, Part 1 (MP USA 26min color). Describes the multiplex method of producing accurate topographical maps from aerial photographs. Primarily for technical use.

Multiplex Mapping, Part 2 (MP USA 40min color). Explains the process of converting three-dimensional aerial photographs into topographical maps.

Negative Scribing (MP USGS 24min color). Shows the procedures of preparing negatives for map reproduction by hand scribing, including sheet coating, guide copy preparation, and close-ups of the various scribing operations and instruments.

SOURCES OF FILMS LISTED

Beseler—Charles Beseler Company, 219 South 18th St., East Orange, N.J.

Handy—Jam Handy Organization, 2821 East Grand Blvd., Detroit, Mich.

KB—Knowledge Builders, Floral Park, N.Y.

McGraw—McGraw-Hill Book Company, Inc., Text-Film Dept., 330 West 42d St., New York 36, N.Y.

PSU—Pennsylvania State University, University Park, Pa.

Purdue—Purdue University, Lafayette, Ind.

UCLA—University of California at Los Angeles, Los Angeles 24, Calif.

USA—U.S. Department of the Army, Washington 25, D.C.

USGS—U.S. Geological Survey, Map Information Office, Washington 25, D.C.

USN—U.S. Department of the Navy, Washington 25, D.C. (Films distributed by United World Films, Inc.)

USOE—U.S. Office of Education, Washington 25, D.C. (Films distributed by United World Films, Inc.)

UWF—United World Films, Inc., 1445 Park Ave., New York 29, N.Y.

VGF—Vocational Guidance Films, 215 East 3d St., Des Moines 9, Iowa.

Index

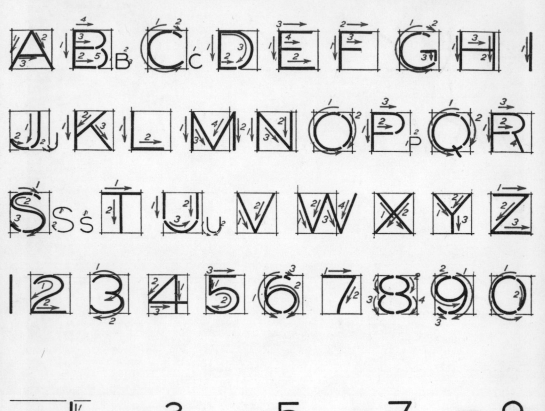

1½   2¾   3⁵⁄₁₆   4⁷⁄₈   5⁹⁄₁₆

a or a b c d e f g or g h i j k l m

n o p q r s t u v w x y or y z